# OIL IN THE MIDDLE EAST

# OIL IN THE MIDDLE EAST

## ITS DISCOVERY AND DEVELOPMENT

STEPHEN HEMSLEY LONGRIGG

**THIRD EDITION**

*O tempora recordationis dignissima.*

FULCHER OF CHARTRES

*Issued under the auspices of the*
*Royal Institute of International Affairs*

OXFORD UNIVERSITY PRESS
LONDON   NEW YORK   TORONTO

1968

*Oxford University Press, Ely House, London W.1*

GLASGOW  NEW YORK  TORONTO  MELBOURNE  WELLINGTON
CAPE TOWN  SALISBURY  IBADAN  NAIROBI  LUSAKA  ADDIS ABABA
BOMBAY  CALCUTTA  MADRAS  KARACHI  LAHORE  DACCA
KUALA LUMPUR  HONG KONG  TOKYO

| | |
|---|---|
| *First edition* | *1954* |
| *Second edition* | *1961* |
| *Third edition* | *1968* |

REPRINTED BY LITHOGRAPHY IN GREAT BRITAIN
BY JARROLD AND SONS LTD, NORWICH

# PREFACE TO THE THIRD EDITION

THE first edition of this work, published in 1954, brought the narrative of Middle Eastern oil discovery and development from its obscure beginnings early in this century to the middle of 1953; the second edition prolonged the story as far as the summer of 1960. This, the third edition, is intended to add a further six years to the record by describing developments up to the autumn of 1966. This task has involved the writing of six new chapters numbered XX to XXV, to record progress in each of the concerned territories, and the substitution of a new Chapter XXVI for the former Chapter XX as a general survey and appreciation of the position reached. Changes have been made in the appendixes, maps, and index.

I realize, as well as any reader will do, that the attempt to cover my subject with adequate fullness and clarity while remaining non-technical cannot be wholly satisfactory, and that the specialists in every relevant branch of science and technology, if they turn these pages, will be discontented if not scornful. But an attempt to give all the experts the material which they rightly expect would have demanded a quite different sort of treatment—and a quite different author. I hope nevertheless that the narrative as it is will be found (as, I am told, the previous editions have been found) sufficiently interesting and instructive to enough oil-interested persons and/or students of the Middle East, and to a few of the less frivolous members of the general public, to justify the considerable labour for which it has called. It deals, at least, with a rapid and remarkable industrial development in a highly important and sensitive region of the world, and can perhaps aspire to throw a little light upon some significant aspects of this.

For certain inconsistencies of treatment and scale which may be detected, and even of transliteration, as between popular and correct forms, I can only express regret. The addition, also, to the main body of the book (pp. 1–261) of two fairly bulky subsequent instalments, each covering a six-year period of much and varied activity (pp. 262–348 and 349–475), must have destroyed any elegance of form and balance which the work might have possessed, while the photographic method of reproduction of all except the now-added portion renders any extensive alteration of former pages impracticable.

Middle Eastern oil has by now, late in 1966, offered a subject to many students and writers, whose published works form part of the materials I have consulted; but I have found more copious and valuable sources of information—in addition to my own many years of service in the Middle East, and in the industry—in the published and sometimes the unpublished reports of operating companies: in specialized articles, lectures or essays by authorities with first-hand knowledge: in innumerable conversations with friends and colleagues in a variety of oil companies; in the Press, and in particular in the specialized periodical literature of the industry in Great Britain and America, notably the *Oil and Gas Journal*, the *Petroleum Press Service*, the annual *Bulletins of the American Association of Petroleum Geologists*, the *Petroleum Times*, *World Petroleum*, the *Petroleum Intelligence Weekly*, the *Middle East Economic Survey* (Beirut), and others. I have enjoyed, in the course of my researches, an extraordinary degree of personal kindness and co-operation, for which I am most grateful—and some who may read these words will realize, I hope, that I mean *them*.

S. H. L.

*November 1966*

# CONTENTS

# NOTES ON SOME ABBREVIATIONS
# AND QUANTITIES

*(Where these abbreviations are those of the names of composite companies,
see Appendix V.)*

| | |
|---|---|
| A.D.M.A. | Abu Dhabi Marine Areas Ltd. |
| A.D.P.C. | Abu Dhabi Petroleum Co. Ltd. |
| A.E.O. | Anglo-Egyptian Oilfields Ltd. |
| A.G.I.P. | Azienda Generale Italiana Petroli. |
| A.I.O.C. | Anglo-Iranian Oil Co. Ltd. |
| Aminoil | American Independent Oil Co. |
| Amoseas | American Overseas Petroleum Ltd. |
| A.P.I. | American Petroleum Institute. |
| A.P.O.C. | Anglo-Persian Oil Co. Ltd. |
| Aramco | Arabian American Oil Co. |
| A.T.A.S. | Anadolu Tasfiyehanesi A.S. (Anatolian Refining Co.). |
| Auxirap | Société Auxiliaire de la Régie Autonome des Pétroles. |
| Bapco | Bahrain Petroleum Co. Ltd. |
| bbl | barrels. |
| b/d | barrels per day. |
| B.O.D. | British Oil Development Ltd. (The initials were the registered name.) |
| B.P. | British Petroleum Co. Ltd., the, or one of its affiliates or associates. |
| B.P.C. | Basrah Petroleum Co. Ltd. |
| B.R.P. | Bureau de Recherches de Pétrole (incorporated in 1966 in Entreprise de Recherches et d'Activités Pétrolières (E.R.A.P.)). |
| Caltex | California-Texas Oil Corporation. |
| Casoc | California Arabian Standard Oil Co. |
| C.F.P. | Compagnie Française des Pétroles. |
| C.O.P.E. | Compagnie Orientale des Pétroles d'Egypte. |
| D.M.A. | Dubai Marine Areas Ltd. |
| D.O.P.C.O. | Dashtestan Offshore Petroleum Co. |
| E.G.P.C. | Egyptian General Petroleum Corporation. |
| E.N.I. | Ente Nazionale Idrocarburi. |
| G.O.R.A. | ('Iraq) Government Oil Refineries Administration. |
| G.P.A. | General Petroleum Authority (of U.A.R.). |
| I.E.O.C. | International Egyptian Oil Co. |
| I.M.I.N.O.C.O. | Iranian Marine International Oil Co. |
| I.N.O.C. | 'Iraq National Oil Co. |
| I.O.C. | Iranian Oil Co. |
| I.P.A.C. | Iran Pan American Oil Co. |
| I.P.C. | 'Iraq Petroleum Co. Ltd. |
| I.P.R.A.S. | Istanbul Petrol Rafinerisi, A.S. (Istanbul Petroleum Refinery Co.). |

xi

| | |
|---|---|
| I.R.C.A.N. | Iranian-Canadian Oil Co. |
| Iricon | Iricon Agency Ltd. |
| I.R.O.P.C.O. | Iranian Offshore Petroleum Co. |
| K.N.P.C. | Kuwait National Petroleum Co. |
| K.O.C. | (1) Khanaqin Oil Co. Ltd.⎫ according to context. |
| | (2) Kuwait Oil Co. Ltd.  ⎭ |
| L.A.P.C.O. | Lavan Petroleum Co. |
| l.p.g. | Liquefied petroleum gas. |
| Medreco | Mediterranean Refining Co. |
| M.E.P.C. | Middle East Pipelines Ltd. |
| M.P.C. | Mosul Petroleum Co. Ltd. |
| M.T.A. | [Turkish] Mining Research Institute. |
| N.E.D.C. | Near East Development Corporation. |
| N.I.O.C. | National Iranian Oil Co. |
| N.Z. | Neutral Zone (Kuwaiti-Sa'udi). |
| O.P.E.C. | Organization of Petroleum Exporting Countries. |
| P.C.L. | Petroleum Concessions Ltd. |
| P.D.(—) | Petroleum Development (—) Ltd. |
| P.E.G.U.P.C.O. | Persian Gulf Petroleum Co. |
| Petromin | [Sa'udi] General Petroleum and Mining Organization. |
| Q.P.C. | Qatar Petroleum Co. Ltd. |
| R.A.P. | Régie Autonome des Pétroles. |
| S.I.R.I.P. | Société Iran-Italienne des Pétroles. |
| Sofiran | Société Française des Pétroles d'Iran. |
| S.P.C. | Syria Petroleum Co. Ltd. |
| Tapline | Trans-Arabian Pipeline Co. |
| T.P.A.O. | Turkiye Petrolleri Anonim Ortakligi (Turkish Petroleum Corporation). |
| t/y | tons per year. |
| U.A.R. | United Arab Republic (1958–61, Egypt with Syria; from March 1961, Egypt alone). |

*Note:* Tons in the text are long tons of 2,240 lb. unless stated to be metric tons, which are ·12 bbl or 36 lb. less. A barrel is 35 imperial gal. or 42 U.S. gal. With an average crude, there are 7·42 bbl per long ton or 7·3 bbl per metric ton.

## CHAPTER I

# THE BEGINNING

## I. OIL FORMATION

THE presence in western Asia of rich petroleum deposits is due to a coincidence of favourable factors, operating throughout scores or hundreds of millions of years. The reconstruction of these factors and the assessment of each: the collection of a great body of information on the successive changes on land and sea in that region, and the accompanying earth movements: the tracing of the development of life-forms, the study of rock structures and sequences: the ascertainment of the half-mysterious processes by which petroleum itself came into existence —these achievements, which still contain their unknown and perhaps unknowable phases, have called for the contributions of geologist, meteorologist, astronomer, biologist, and chemist. The results whereby the regional history of the earth can now in outline be written, in the Middle East as elsewhere, form a remarkable monument to patient, penetrating, and co-ordinated research.

At no time since land and sea came into existence has there been pause in that oft-repeated cycle of events which, throughout the geological systems, has created the form and body of the modern world. Disturbed at times and in places by volcanic action or by faulting or subsidence, the slow but inexorable upward and downward movements of this or that region of the earth's crust have alternately submerged the lands of what today is western Asia below sea level or elevated them far above it. And these lands themselves, by a distinguishable type of earth movement, have at various periods been stretched or over-weighted so as to form basins or depressions, have been laterally compressed or uplifted from below so as to form mountain ranges. Isthmuses have joined the separate continents, only to sink again beneath the sea or to broaden out into wide territories. The oceans by similar movement have been at times deepened, at times broken into shallow isolated lakes, at times left dry; the sea itself has at times been lowered or raised by polar freezing in an ice age or by thawing at its close. Concurrently with these cyclically-repeated continent-building or mountain-building movements the processes of denudation of the land-surface have ceaselessly continued, lowering and possibly demolishing mountain and plateau by the age-long action of rain and snow, wind and glacier, and chemical decomposition. Immense quantities of matter, first loosened and then washed or blown from the land, have been deposited by rivers in their estuaries and in the nearer seas, there to form sediments which by compression beneath the cumulative overburden become rock-masses. The texture and the mineral or chemical qualities of these rocks reflect the nature of the denuded mainland; in the course of their deposition under the sea they are sifted or sorted into the conglomerate and coarse sandstones dropped nearest to the shore, the fine sandstones and shelly or coral limestones in shallow water off-shore, and the fine-grained clay and shale left in deeper water farther out.

Yet again, in sea-areas beyond reach of land-derived detritus, calcium carbonate, calcium sulphate, sodium chloride, and other minerals are deposited from solution in sea-water, to form limestone, gypsum, salt, etc. These various deposits may grade laterally and vertically one into another, as conditions change. The age of exposed rocks can be established by their own qualities and by their fossil content; it has, therefore, been possible for geologists to reconstruct much of the sequences of these normal processes as they have occurred in the Middle East, and to sketch the rise, the fall, and the extent of long-vanished lands and to identify the earliest mountain-building. Among the major land-masses, it is apparent, there have been differences in the degree of their stability; and, as elsewhere, solid nuclear areas of the most ancient rocks have influenced the continental framework. Such areas, never submerged unless along their fringes, have been at all ages the source of original sediment and have played their part also in restricting the lines or zones of surrounding earth-movement. Such an area is that of the 'Arabian Shield', an eastern continuation of the great Shield centred in northern Africa. Other regions have proved scarcely less resistant by reason of the rock-types of which they are formed, or of their own firm basing in the earth's crust; such are the compressed 'Median Masses' of central Persia and central Anatolia, which were compressed in early times and have resisted the later folding which deformed adjacent zones. Other areas, marked today by mountain ranges or by sedimentary basins, have proved less resistant and by their compliant reaction to earth-movement have offered sites first for the formation and then for the storage of petroleum.

Ages before the mountain system of modern Asia had been formed, and before the division of land and sea had taken a shape recognizable today, the conditions of the region had ordained that the first steps could occur towards the formation there of oil in immense quantities. During Palæozoic times the Pre-Cambrian continental mass, which occupied the present site of western Asia, began to subside beneath the shallow epicontinental seas which ebbed and flowed round residual land-areas, fragments of which are still seen in parts of the Hijaz and Somaliland, central Iran, and Anatolia. The sea slowly gained upon the land, the phases of subsidence upon those of uplift, until the shallow basins of western Asia linked up to form part of the great Tethyan Ocean in Mesozoic and Tertiary times. The Tethys teemed with marine life, a proportion of which, thanks to special qualities in its molecular structure and the nature of the sea-bottom and to some power of chemical adaptation, was to prove capable of re-creation into oil. Vast quantities of such organisms lived, died, and sank to the bottom off-shore of the land-masses of the period and were there safely covered by the deposit above them of deep land-scoured sediments, able to protect them from oxidation and from destruction by sea-scavengers.

Thus the three first essentials of oil-formation were present: seas with shallow in-shore reaches full of plankton and other animal and vegetable marine life, coasts offering zones of security, and the deep, regular accumulation of fine-grained sediments washed seaward by the familiar and ceaseless processes of land denudation. Where these processes occur without interruption for long ages in an area of sinking sea-floor and of sediments actively deposited, conditions are at their most favourable for oil-formation; and they were found conspicuously—more notably, indeed, than anywhere else in the world—in that area of western Asia which was one day to become southern Anatolia, western Persia, 'Iraq, eastern Arabia, and the Persian Gulf. In this wide area a deep and persistent geosyncline had formed which was sinking and refilling throughout the Mesozoic period.

Such sedimentation amongst and over the mass of marine organic matter is normally followed in succeeding ages by the compaction of the deposited silt and mud into rock, and by the squeezing out of some or most of that rock's seawater content; and thereafter by stages of the transformation of the enclosed plankton into tiny but innumerable globules of liquid or gaseous petroleum by chemical action, by the action of anærobic bacteria, and by suitable pressures and temperatures maintained for long ages. This process of oil-making seems in the Middle East to have occurred principally in Mesozoic times, and possibly earlier than that, in the Permian period, and certainly later, in the Tertiary; but the reservoir-rocks in which oil is now found give no certain clue to those of its original formation. On the contrary, the processes of oil creation, it would seem, were followed or perhaps were accompanied by the gradual movement of the oil, under pressure of gravity or water-drive or its own newly-formed gases, from the fine-grained strata, where it came into being, to new homes in more porous, coarser-grained adjacent sediments of sandstone or limestone; and thereafter by its collection, from a state of diffusion over wide regions of rock, into smaller areas of relative, and finally of compact, concentration.

The Middle Eastern geographic features of our own times, and the changes of land level and stratification and mountain-building which produced them, are chiefly the products of movements in Tertiary times; that is, within the era stretching from some 75 million years ago until recent times. During this period, which was one of alternating submergence and emergence over much of the area, heavy deposition on top of earlier strata occurred in the sunken basin areas. It occurred also, to a lesser extent, wherever a shallow sea for a time transgressed the adjacent land-mass or washed over the fringes of the Arabian Shield or penetrated to the hard, flat heart of Persia and Turkey. During these ages were formed limestone rocks in which, thanks to easy access thereto from the source-rocks or the rocks of primary accumulation, and thanks also to its own hospitable cracks, joints and porous zones, much of the oil of Persia and 'Iraq is now to be found stored and safely capped by impermeable marl, shale, salt, or anhydrite. The great mountain-building movements of the middle and later Tertiary period, which straddled Anatolia, threw up the Armenian and Elburz ranges, lifted the Zagros from the heart of the sediment-filled Persian Gulf geosyncline, and folded the already elevated Oman ranges, were, perhaps, the successors of previous uplifts long since denuded, but recorded by irregularities in the deeper strata. It formed, in world structure, part of the great Alpine-Himalayan system. These movements, the result of profound pressure on an unstable area between the more rigid blocks, led to the loss by exposure and erosion of any oil deposits which might have lain in the higher parts of the now intensely folded uplift; Zagros is the graveyard of dead oilfields; but at the same time, by the parallel wave-like folding of the strata into troughs and ridges or anticlines which it created in the more gently deformed foothills, the movement made possible the accumulation of oil by density-segregation in arched-up segments of the reservoir strata, these segments or reservoirs being of exceptional amplitude and simplicity and capable of holding the oil and its attendant or absorbed gases concentrated from wide areas of original occurrence.

The deep rift-system west of the Arabian block, separating it from the greater block of Africa, began in the same Tertiary age to assume its present form; the sediments of that age were here laid, in the Levant and north-eastern Egypt, on the broken or buckled rift of the ancient Shield.

The history of later Tertiary times, until our own age—the 'recent' age of the last two or three million years—is one of the continued subsistence and the continued replenishment by sediments of the great syncline which the Zagros uplift had in part displaced and restricted: of continued folding on the same ranges: of local and irregular folding of, and a regional uplift around, the group of internal basins in the Turkish and Persian 'Median Masses': and finally of the emergence of shore-lines more and more approaching those of the Mediterranean, Persian, and Arabian seas today.

As the Middle East, fashioned by geological time, emerged into the period of that last afterthought of world-history, the appearance of man, it showed itself to have been dominated by three main factors. These were the Arabian Shield, the Persian Gulf geosyncline, and the system of mountain-folding to the north and east of these, with its enclosed 'Median Masses' of Persia and Turkey. The territories thus conditioned must, it is clear, be far from equal in their possibility of containing oil deposits. These could not exist in igneous rock or on the ancient crystalline shield of Arabia; nor was there, even in all sedimentary areas, an equal likelihood of oil wealth. There can be no oilfield where folding or breakage has been too violent to permit an oil accumulation, if originally present, to survive undispersed. Small structures can nowhere provide room for major reservoirs, nor could such accumulations ever have occurred in the vast majority of sedimentary areas without the aid of the original but rarely coinciding necessary elements. The occurrence of petroleum has, indeed, a close relation to the thickness and extent of marine sediments, to the relative positions of ancient shore-lines, to suitable rock movements subsequent to the oil formation, and to physical and biological factors not yet fully understood.

It must follow from this that petroleum deposits, at best, would later be found on a major scale only in rare places, in trifling quantities at more, and at most not at all. Nor could there be question, unless by some unimaginable coincidence, that the latter-day political units could enjoy equal advantages, nor that oil occurrence could bear any relation to normal human needs or to agreeable surface surroundings. On the other hand, no Middle Eastern territory today existing could ever have been pronounced as entirely hopeless of possessing oil, since none is without some, and few without considerable, sedimentary areas.

Nor could the quality of the discoverable oil be foreseen. Crude petroleum, being always a mixture of many different gaseous, liquid, and solid hydrocarbon compounds, closely related but chemically and physically distinct, is never identical in any two locations; the proportions in which the various hydrocarbon series are represented, and the different—heavier or lighter, simpler or more complex—molecules of each series which are present, and the admixture of greater or lesser quantities of impurities in the oil, make some crude oils lighter, more fluid, and purer than others through a wide range of differences, of which those of specific gravity and sulphur content are the most practically important. They bear relation, no doubt, to varieties of original source material and to many vicissitudes suffered by the oil between its formation and the present age; but meanwhile the quality of oil which may be discovered in any one structure or region is as unforeseeable as its quantity.

## II. MIDDLE EAST OIL

The land units, with which this work will primarily concern itself, are the political units of the present-day Middle East. We proceed, therefore, to survey broadly (and indeed with the crudest over-simplification) the geological content of each territory, far as are the geographical, and still farther the geological, boundaries from coinciding with the political.

Turkey is a country in which a 'Median Mass', with areas of fairly deep sediment and capricious internal folding-lines, separates two arms of the great Alpine folding-system, one in the north fringing the Black Sea, and one, the Taurus, along the south. These ranges continue in the east to form the Elburz Mountains and the Zagros. South of the Taurus lies an area of sedimentation, a legacy of the sea-bottom of the Tethys; and farther east extends, within Turkey, the northern sector of the great Persian Gulf sedimentary area. Here on general grounds, given suitable conditions of deposition and preservation, important oil deposits could be expected, and folding or faulting might well have produced reservoir-structures.

Cyprus owes its final form to the same southern lines of Alpine folding, in which it forms a visible link; and close under Troodos lies a small Tethys-derived sedimentary area continuous, in olden days, with that of southern Turkey, north Syria, and 'Iraq. Syria itself, except for the southern sector of its coastal strip, belongs essentially to the same northern region of the Gulf sedimentary basin. It has continuity both in its sedimentary history and in some, at least, of its anticlinal folding; but with the Arabian Shield less deeply covered here by sediments, and with many signs of vulcanicity and faulting, only a part of the territory could be of oil-prospecting interest. Towards the south the further thinning of deposits renders the territory unattractive; but the rest of the area could never be dismissed as unworthy of exploration. Jordan has the character of southern Syria, but the north-east of the country is fairly sedimented and could be considered as forming part of the western 'Iraq geological province. The south must be without prospects, and the west—the Jordan Valley, Dead Sea, and Wadi 'Araba depression—belongs rather to the quite different system of the Lebanon, north-eastern Egypt, and Israel.

This Levantine area, aligned along the Mediterranean coast, owes its character not to the Taurus–Zagros folding and its effects on the Gulf geosyncline, but rather to the Tertiary phases of an ancient system of faulting, the result of opposing pressures in the

African-Arabian block itself: faulting which resulted in the sinking into deep depression of the Red Sea, the Gulfs of Suez and 'Aqaba, and the Dead Sea: the uplifting of the hills of Judea and of Jordan; and the continuance northward, to western Syria and Lebanon, of the same north–south trend in mountain-building which was the alternative result of similar pressure from east and west. The Lebanon and western Syria carry ancient as well as Tertiary deposits, not necessarily incapable of oil production; but the area is basically broken rather than folded, and surviving structures capable of containing oil are small.

In north-eastern Egypt the same deep fault or rift movement has broken the ancient continuity of Africa with Syria and Arabia, has in different periods of the Tertiary era thrown down the depressions of Suez and 'Aqaba, has sunk the Red Sea between parallel lines of mountains, and has tilted platforms of basic igneous side by side with sediments of various ages, so that the whole forms a complicated system of rigid and plastic rocks which was destined to prove baffling to the oil-prospector. The absence of deep and continuous sediments must in any case limit the oil possibilities of the country.

The main body of the Arabian peninsula consists essentially of a quadrilateral land-mass, elevated in the west and descending towards the Gulf geosyncline in the east. The territories of the three states which today form south-western, southern, and south-eastern Arabia—Yemen, the Aden Protectorate, and Oman—all represent a fringe of the continent, deeply sedimented by the transgression of the sea over it, all slope inwards towards the heart of Arabia, and all terminate southwards in a faulting system related to the depression which forms the Gulf of Aden. Thus Yemen and the Aden Protectorate are today uplifted areas where heavy (and not impossibly oil-bearing) sediments, with a base of granite rock in the Yemen and the complication of widespread vulcanicity, stand on the southern rim of the Shield. The coastal uplands of the Hadhramaut continue into Dhofar, the outlying province of Oman; and eastward therefrom they give place to the southern continuation of the vast sand-covered Ruba'al-Khali, before the high Oman mountains are reached. The Sultanate of Oman is dominated by a high and mainly north-west–south-east mountain ridge which, first uplifted in remoter ages, represents since the Tertiary mountain-building the southernmost branch of the Persian (Zagros) folding.[1] South and west of its mountains Oman contains broad and gently folded sedimentary areas where oil might well have accumulated.

Sa'udi Arabia includes, besides the central and western crystalline Shield, a narrow line of sediment on the Red Sea coast, washed throughout the ages from the plateau and volcanic mountains of western Arabia. It includes also the northern extension of the Shield itself, extending into Jordan and 'Iraq: and, more significantly, it covers the wide area of deep sediments which forms the western flank of the Gulf sedimentary basin. These sediments of the Tethys sea extend southward into the Ruba'al-Khali, and eastward disappear beneath the Gulf waters. The whole forms an area of the highest promise for petroleum wealth. The same is true, for the same reasons, of the lesser states of the southern Gulf coast between the northern tip of the Oman mountains and the base of the Qatar peninsula. The latter with its broad shallow arch: the visible anticline of Bahrain island: the sand-buried flatness of the Kuwait principality: all these belong to the same western area of the great geosyncline and emerged into modern times as a region of probable oil-storage.

The kingdom of 'Iraq includes a part of the mid-Zagros ranges, a submontane area in which the deep deposits south-west of these are gently folded, and a broad region farther west, astride both the great rivers. In the last of these regions the continued depth of the sedimentary rocks and their regular anticlinal folding extends to the north Syrian border and across it, but in the south and south-west prepares, with thinner sediments and less folding, to meet the north-eastern rim of the Arabian Shield. Persia contains more diverse geological elements. Its south-western foothill zone, where lie the oilfields, is more complicated than north-eastern 'Iraq, thanks to the broken and twisted later formations that overlie the great Tertiary anticlines and thanks also to the pressures of ancient salt-plugs. East of the main Zagros ranges the resistant 'Median Mass' of Persia is diversified by folding of its own, and a series of small basins contain possibly oil-bearing sediments. Northern Persia, where a main range of the Alpine–Himalayan system has given its modern shape to an area repeatedly crushed and uplifted in earlier ages, belongs essentially to the Russian zone and has

[1] Others dissociate the Oman mountains from the Zagros system and treat them as a purely Arabian phenomenon.

little relation to the 'Iraqi–Persian conditions of the Zagros foot-hills.

### III. SURFACE SIGNS AND EARLIEST USES

During all human history, and for millennia before, there have been in western Asia clear surface indications of the presence of petroleum. In places an oil-permeated rock-stratum outcrops on a hillside, elsewhere deposits of bitumen cover the ground, else-where gas or liquid oil seeps upwards through a crack or a weaken-ing in the cover-rock of a buried reservoir. Thus in Egypt the seepages at Jabal Zait earned that ridge its Roman name of Mons Petroleus, and other traces had long been noticed on the same coast, in the Sinai Peninsula, and in some of the Red Sea islands, notably the Farsan group. Oil-shales were known in the hinter-land of Aden. In the Persian Gulf signs of oil or bitumen marked the crest of the ridge on Bahrain Island and were visible in the desert near Kuwait. 'Iraq contained the great bitumen deposits at Hit and elsewhere on the Euphrates, the lighted gas escape—the 'burning fiery furnace'—near the future Kirkuk, traces of oil in the Upper Tigris, and abundant seepages at Qaiyara, Kirkuk, Tuz Khormatu, and in the Mandali district. In Persia traces of oil or bitumen were found in the north-west near Qasr-i-Shirin and conspicuously in ancient Edom. The Dead Sea was known for its indications of petroleum, and these were repeated in the villages of the Lebanese and 'Alawite tribesmen. Deposits of natural asphalt were found near Lattakiya. In Turkey shows of hydrocarbon substances occur on the Bosphorus, inland from the Black Sea coast, in the neighbourhood of Alexandretta, Antalya, Van, Diyarbakr, Siirt, and Jazira ibn-'Umar, and elsewhere in widely scattered localities. The connexion between such long-familiar surface appearances of oil and the presence of com-mercially valuable deposits is, in fact, uncertain and often mislead-ing; to primitive man, certainly, the conception of an oil-pool on the now familiar scale did not or could not exist; its use by human beings was inconceivable; and the trifling surface deposits were accepted as no more than minor mysteries of nature.

Even so, they were utilized. Bitumen was employed by all generations of men in Egypt, 'Iraq, and Persia as mortar or floor-ing-material by the builder, as domestic water-channel lining by the plumber, as caulking material by the shipbuilder. It helped in the construction of flood-dykes, was a resource for the potter, and was useful to the jeweller, toolmaker, and other craftsmen; it provided flares for lighting and a substitute for wood as fuel. In ancient religion the inflammable seepage-gases of Susiana or Khuzistan played a part, and their sites were marked by temples of the fire-venerating faithful. In war, arrows tipped with lighted petroleum showed the way to the 'Greek fire' of the Middle Ages; and in early modern times, or perhaps much earlier, men devised simple processes of distilling which gave, with abundant smoke and spluttering a serviceable kerosene for their lamps. Crude oil was prized in every land for its medicinal properties for man and beast.

The petroleum for this and every purpose was gained easily from the many seepages in use, sometimes by collection or skimming, potful by potful, from a surface trickle of the dark fluid. Rough galleries were made to improve access and shallow holes were dug by hand. Bitumen collected from the ground was taken on donkey or camel-back to a place of melting. Seepages on private land belonged to the landowner or, if on the royal estates, could be leased for an annual payment or bestowed outright by royal patent.

## IV. BIRTH OF THE INDUSTRY

Successor to these ancient ways, the modern petroleum industry was called into existence in the nineteenth century by both the domestic and industrial needs of fast-increasing populations. Until then animal and vegetable fats and oils had served all purposes, but they proved inadequate for the needs of growing industries and a public which demanded more and better illumination; and, from the mid-century, they were supplemented and finally replaced by mineral-oil distillation, by the first successful mechanical drilling for 'rock-oil' (in 1859), and by the rapid growth of the industry in its modern forms: production, tank-wagon and pipeline transportation, refining, and distribution.

By 1900 the oil industry in America, organized and yearly expanding, had produced fortunes and failures, had established a primacy in the petroleum trade which was long to endure, and was exporting products to the rest of the world. In Europe the new technique of drilling was applied in one country after another, wherever surface indications of petroleum could raise hopes. Production by this means was achieved in Russia from 1873 onwards and in Galicia and in Rumania from 1898. Refining and distributing activities were in the hands of scores of new or newly-specialized companies. In the United Kingdom, as elsewhere, the handling and marketing of imported petroleum products became in themselves an important trade; and the increasing interest of experts and financiers was aroused, year by year, in the oil possibilities of remoter territories.

Farther east the oil industry of Burma, which with hand-dug wells had already existed for a century, increased after 1890 with the modernization of its methods. The resources of the Netherlands East Indies also began to be seriously exploited by a Royal Dutch Company,[1] founded in the same decade. The family trading business of Samuel Brothers, London merchants, came, at the same period, to include first the distribution of petroleum products, then the acquisition of oil-bearing territory, and finally in 1892 the building of their first oil-tanker. Ten years of keen competition between the Royal Dutch and the Samuels, who founded the Shell Transport and Trading Company in 1897, ended in 1902 with the merging of their transport and marketing activities in the joint Asiatic Petroleum Company.

### V. MIDDLE EAST OIL IN THE NINETEENTH CENTURY

In the Middle East, where the nineteenth century could show no such record of petroleum development, the need for oil products—that is, for lamp oil—was increasingly felt with the rising living standards of the upper class. At the same time developments in the outside world, industrial as well as political, became better known with increasing contact and communications. But the countries themselves were little explored, repellent by their conditions and remoteness, and unattractive as a field for major foreign investment.

The Ottoman Empire continued throughout the century to keep its dead or dying hold not only on Anatolia but also on the Arab vilayets of Aleppo, Damascus, and Beirut,[2] which covered the modern states of Syria, Lebanon, Israel, and Jordan: on those of Mosul, Baghdad, and Basra, which covered the modern state of

---

[1] Its head was J. B. August Kessler, until his death in 1900; he was then succeeded by a young assistant, H. W. A. Deterding, the future giant of the Shell Group.

[2] And the two 'independent' sanjaqs of Dair al-Zor and Jerusalem.

'Iraq: and, with various degrees of intermittent feebleness, on the Hijaz, on the Yemen, and, after 1871, on al-Hasa and Qatar in the Persian Gulf. Its weak, capricious, and corrupt government was unsuited in every way to the initiation of major industrial enterprises; the mining law was ill-drafted and largely inapplicable, its execution uncertain: security was lacking outside the towns, antiforeign feeling was common, the courts venal, and the desire for progress still vague and inoperative.

It was not, in these conditions, surprising that in the Turkish Empire no petroleum enterprise existed, save humble and primitive local activity in the seepage-villages of Anatolia or 'Iraq, and some shallow wells or galleries at the Marmora shale-deposits and in a seepage area of Alexandretta district. Even so, the possibility of greater things was not excluded. Reports of oil occurrences, notably those in the Baghdad and Mosul vilayets, were studied in Istanbul; an able British-educated Armenian, Calouste Serkis Gulbenkian, son of a wealthy merchant, was notable among those who interested themselves in such possibilities. In the early eighteen-nineties he had submitted a report on Turkish oil properties to the Ministry of Mines. The Sultan himself took action in two directions. He decreed the transfer of the petroleum revenues from the Treasury to his own Privy Purse by firmans of 1890 and 1899; and through the Crown-lands (Saniya) Administration he secured for himself a number of the known oil-bearing lands. Moreover, on the grant of the first concession given to the German-owned Ottoman Railway Company of Anatolia, in 1888, a vizirial letter promised the Deutsche Bank (then and thereafter the effective controller of German enterprise in Turkey) a priority of rights in mining development, including petroleum. Applications from other foreigners and from resident Greeks and Armenians were made in the same period for development rights in one part or another of the Empire. German influence in Istanbul was constantly on the increase and redoubled after the Kaiser's visit in 1898; their companies and banks were certain to prove intolerant of rivals in their chosen sphere; but Englishmen or Dutchmen, in contact with Royal Dutch interests, or those of Samuel Brothers, did not fail to keep their companies aware of current affairs in Turkey, while Gulbenkian watched every tendency and did business with both British and Russian interests.

The greatest possibilities for Ottoman oil seemed to good

observers to lie in the Arab vilayets of Mosul and Baghdad. A mission of German experts had visited the territory in 1871 and had reported in glowing terms. The Wali, Midhat Pasha, had himself taken steps to develop the Mandali seepages and had built a short-lived refinery at Ba'quba. After the acquisition by the Privy Purse of the seepage lands of Tuz and Qaiyara in the eighteen-nineties, a French expert was brought to the latter. Efforts were made to increase the yield there by deeper diggings, while the treacly, viscous oil which was daily collected was distilled there and at Tuz on primitive lines, as also at Baba Gurgur near Kirkuk, where the seepages were owned under ancient firman by the local Naftchi family. The bitumen of Hit continued with little change to support an industry already 5,000 years old. These and the lesser petroleum occurrences of northern 'Iraq began to be noticed by foreigners in increasingly modern terms and were correlated to the regional geology by such European observers as M. de Morgan in 1892, A. F. Stahl in 1893, Colonel S. R. Maunsell in 1897, and Baron von Oppenheim in 1899.

In Arabia no move was made in these years towards oil inquiry or research. Persia offered a scarcely more attractive field, it seemed, for the investment of foreign capital; security was at a low and justice at the lowest level, commercial morality at the best uncertain, the administration capricious, venal, and incalculable. Nevertheless, even before 1900 there had been movements towards oil development, which the existence of known seepages seemed to render not impossible. The production of petroleum throughout the Persian Empire was included among the rights bestowed light-heartedly by the Shah in 1872 on Baron Julius de Reuter, a naturalized British subject, in a grandiose concession, which covered the construction of railways, a banking and customs monopoly, and the development of all minerals; but the concession, in every way absurd and frowned upon by the British Government, was soon afterwards cancelled—with confiscation of the caution-money deposited by the concessionaire.

The next stage was in 1884, when the firm of Hotz and Co. of Bushire were permitted to drill for oil, with the crude appliances of the time, near the seepages at Daliki in the Fars province. Their efforts failed. Five years later de Reuter, undaunted, obtained a second concession. It granted him a sixty-year privilege of conducting a note-issuing bank and the exclusive right of exploiting minerals, including oil. The Persian Government was to receive 16 per cent. of the net profits of whatever enterprises he should undertake. This concession led to the foundation of the Imperial Bank of Persia (which, with a change of name, continued to operate in Persia until its voluntary withdrawal in 1952) and of a Persian Bank Mining Rights Corporation. The latter drilled two wells at Daliki and another on Qishm Island, but without success. In 1899 the Government pronounced the Corporation's rights invalid. Production from the seepages at Shushtar, Daliki, Qasr-i-Shirin, and elsewhere continued on primitive lines.

In populous and relatively sophisticated Egypt, the period following 1882 was one of rehabilitation after half a century of gross misrule. Security was good, the penetration of Western ideas proceeded fast, foreign rights were protected, and industry in limited, semi-modern forms was not unfamiliar. It was in Egypt that, if Middle Eastern oil existed, its development seemed the most probable and the existence of surface traces was well known. In 1869 the holder of a sulphur concession, bestowed six years earlier by the Khedive, discovered the presence of oil at Gemsa (Jamsa), some miles south of Jabal Zait, at the mouth of the Gulf of Suez. The law provided for the exploitation of oil, as of any mineral resource, by licence and lease from the Government; and attempts were made accordingly during the next fifteen years to assess, by deeper hand-dug wells and galleries, the potentialities of the Gemsa and Jabal Zait section of the coast. In 1885 the Minister of Works superseded these efforts by inviting the services of a Belgian scientist to inspect the site. Favourably impressed, the expert arranged for the import of modern European equipment and Russian, American, and Rumanian 'borers'. Five wells of some hundreds of feet in depth were drilled at Gemsa, but no oil-flow was encountered; another unsuccessful well was drilled at Jabal Zait. The scale of the Egyptian Government's activity in the area was considerable; during the later eighteen-eighties a large settlement of workers, a light railway, a workshop, and wells up to 700 feet deep testified to their efforts and expenses. The failure of all these labours, however, did not destroy the continued interest of Egyptians and of foreigners in the possibilities of Egyptian oil. Small syndicates for prospecting in this or that area of the coast of Suez or Sinai continued to be formed; among these, that of Sir E. Palmer, a former Financial Adviser, worked at Gemsa for a year before abandoning hope.

## CHAPTER II

# BEFORE THE FIRST WORLD WAR

## I. THE NEW CENTURY

DURING the early years of the twentieth century the world oil industry was called upon greatly to expand its production, refining capacity, and organization. Production, which barely exceeded 4 million t/y in 1880 and 20 million in 1900, had in 1915 reached 59 million, of which a mere half million came from the Middle East. The use of oil fuel for steamers spread widely in merchant navies and by 1914 had become dominant in fighting fleets. The use of mineral oil for illumination purposes was general, save in the most backward countries, and had proceeded far in the field of lubrication. The use of bitumen as a road surface was widespread. More important than all these, the development of the internal-combustion engine changed the whole balance of the industry. The role of petroleum in peace-time, foreshadowed already, was fully established during these years: its part in war was soon to be not less evident.

During the period 1900–14 oil was for the first time exploited on a commercial scale in Mexico, Peru, Egypt, Persia, and Borneo, and further developed in the countries already producing—North America, Russia, Rumania, Poland, Burma, and the Dutch East Indies. No commercial oil had by 1914 been discovered in Venezuela, Sarawak, Arabia, 'Iraq, Colombia, or Ecuador, and little in Canada, Trinidad, or the Argentine.

In oilfield practice, some but not much of the earlier haphazard wastefulness was being corrected. Rotary drilling gained ground rapidly after 1912, offering greater depths and less deviation. Steel replaced wooden derricks. Pipelines were in general use. Refineries were moving, by new designs and procedures, towards greater efficiency. Geological information grew from all quarters, though its application to oil-finding was, as yet, imperfectly understood; geophysical methods of oil-structure discovery were under study from 1912 onwards.

New major oil companies came into flourishing existence year by year. In Europe and Asia the understanding between the Shell and Royal Dutch Companies was completed by the formation, in

1907, of joint integrated companies on a basis of three-fifths Dutch and two-fifths British ownership. These were the Anglo-Saxon Petroleum Company and the Bataafsche Petroleum Maatschappij with headquarters respectively in London and the Hague; the Royal Dutch and the Shell Transport and Trading remained as holding companies, and the combined group survived a period of intensive rivalry with Standard Oil. Though oil production in Europe was still important only in Russia, Rumania, and Poland, the business of refining, shipping, distributing, and marketing grew rapidly in these years.

## II. PERSIA AND THE A.P.O.C.

The interesting seepages of western Persia had attracted the notice in the eighteen-nineties of more observers than Hotz and the Banking Corporation (pp. 14–15). The French archæologist de Morgan had published in 1892 an account of Persian oil prospects; and this, with other technical notices, came to the attention of an Englishman, William Knox D'Arcy, who had made a fortune in Australian gold-mining. He formed in 1900 a small group—his own assistant, A. L. Marriot, a French ex-diplomat, and a Persian-Armenian high official—and set them to work in Teheran to obtain an oil concession. Some Russian opposition to D'Arcy's negotiators was reported and the Persians proved capable bargainers; but on 28 May 1901 a concession, regarded by all as highly speculative, was granted to D'Arcy by the Shah. Thus was permitted to work for Persia an enterprise from which that country was, for half a century, to derive enormous direct and indirect benefits.

The concession to find, exploit, and export petroleum was granted for sixty years, to end on 28 May 1961. It covered the whole of Persia except (thanks to Russian influence) the five northern provinces; it conferred the exclusive right to build pipelines to the south coast; and it granted comprehensive customs and taxation exemption. The concessionaire was bound to form within two years a company or companies to carry out the concession, and on the establishment of the first of these was to pay to the Persian Government £20,000 in cash and a further £20,000 in paid-up shares. A royalty equivalent to 16 per cent. of the annual net profits was due to the Persian Treasury.

Even before signature D'Arcy had sent a geologist to Persia and wild mountainous areas in the south-west and west of the country were inspected. In the summer of 1901 drillers, mainly Polish, were engaged. Drilling equipment was bought and, with infinite difficulty, conveyed to the first drilling site; this was the seepage area of Chiah Surkh, near Qasr-i-Shirin, a locality then on the Persian side of the Perso-'Iraq frontier. With the drilling gear went all technical and domestic supplies for the pioneer party forcing their way via Basra and Baghdad through barrages of obstruction. Security was poor on both sides of the frontier, rifle-shooting near the camp was habitual, stoppages of work were frequent, the blackmailing demands of local chiefs and landlords incessant; but drilling began under the tough and devoted G. B. Reynolds. The First Exploitation Company was registered in 1903, in compliance with the prescribed two-year period.

Operations in the summer of 1903 produced a slight show of hydrocarbon gas at 1,665 feet, followed by a trickle of oil. In June 1904 the second well, at a similar depth, gave a flow of oil, but a first output of 180 b/d fell rapidly to 25. Output of this order, so far from the seaboard, could not lead to 'commercial production'; and it was decided to try an alternative area, far to the south in the province of Khuzistan (or 'Arabistan), to which the approach was through Muhammara at the Karun mouth. The site selected was at Mamatain, near Ram Hormuz. Here the lack of all passable tracks, the vagaries and thieving of the tribesmen, the local deficiency of supplies, the demands of the powerful Bakhtiari Khans, who dominated the countryside, repeated the troubles of Chiah Surkh. In spite of all, late in 1906 a first well was begun and Reynolds was optimistic. Funds in London for the continuance of the work, after unsuccessful approaches to British and French financiers, were found (not without Admiralty assistance) by enlisting the help of the Burmah Oil Company and Sir John Cargill. The latter in May 1905 formed the Concessions Syndicate Limited with D'Arcy as a director to take over the assets of First Exploitation and to provide money for continuing operations. These funds were almost exhausted by the summer of 1907; and the two wells at Mamatain, having reached 2,170 and 1,940 feet, proved unproductive.

The rig was next moved, for a last attempt, to Masjid-i-Sulai-man, the site of an ancient fire-temple, where in January 1908 a first well was spudded in, and a second in March. Traces of gas were observed in mid-May and in the early morning of 26 May a strong flow of oil started from a depth of 1,180 feet. This moment, seven years after the signing of the concession, with the resources of the Syndicate exhausted and with orders to discontinue drilling already drafted or (as some say) dispatched, was in fact the triumphant turning-point of the whole enterprise and one of the most significant events of all Persian history. Ten days later oil and gas were reached in No. 2 well at 1,010 feet and work could proceed with full confidence.

The oil at Masjid-i-Sulaiman comes from a limestone reservoir-rock of lower Miocene to Oligocene age, 1,000 feet in thickness and folded in a spacious, but simple, anticline. The oil is of gravity 38 degrees A.P.I. The limestone, known as the Asmari from its surface outcrop in the imposing mountain of that name, is overlain by an anhydrite salt and shale series known as the Lower Fars, which is folded and contorted in a manner well calculated to conceal the anticline below. The surrounding terrain was in 1908 (and is today) a broken and uncultivable waste, in a climate of extreme severity, and totally devoid of all resources: a setting less favourable for modern industry could not well be imagined.

The discovery at Masjid-i-Sulaiman solved the immediate financial difficulties of D'Arcy and the Syndicate, and led directly to the formation in April 1909 of the Anglo-Persian Oil Company with an initial capital of £2 million. Lord Strathcona, then aged 89, became its first Chairman, with D'Arcy as a director until his death in 1917; Charles Greenway became Managing Director. Managing Agents, Lloyd Scott & Company—later Strick Scott—were appointed in 1909 to co-ordinate work from a headquarters at Muhammara, where J. B. Lloyd, C. A. Walpole, and T. L. Jacks were the pioneers of the organization; the first and third of these became, later, directors of the Anglo-Persian.

Developments in Persia from the spring of 1908 to the outbreak of the World War in 1914 proceeded at a pace which represented the maximum then practicable. Further drilling confirmed the existence of a great oilfield; many wells, to a total of some thirty by 1914, were deliberately stopped short of the pay-rock with the intention of later deepening. The first beginnings of permanent housing, amenities, and a settled social life were made at the oilfield; dry stream beds were made passable, a water-supply

C

provided, gathering lines and tankage erected, workshops and stores organized, a club and hospital appeared. As the first essential towards the export of oil, a pipeline to the sea across the high intervening ridges and the flat plain of Khuzistan was planned late in 1908. Its construction was started by a Glasgow contractor in 1909 and completed in June 1911 after victory over the many difficulties of unloading, river and animal transport, transhipping at the Karun rapids, and maintaining and teaching a totally un-accustomed labour force amid fierce heat, discomfort, and illness. The line, of 6- and 8-inch diameter, was designed to carry 400,000 tons of oil a year. Its construction and that of its pump stations and tankage at Tembi, Mulla Sani', Kut 'Abdullah, and Dorquain, owed much to the efforts of Charles Ritchie (who died in Basra in 1913) and J. A. Jameson, who was to give forty years of service to the Company and end as a director. The telegraph line which accompanied the pipeline was completed by 1911.

On the coast, the agreement made in July 1909 by Dr. Young—combined Medical and Political Officer—with the Shaikh of Muhammara provided the Company with an area of one square mile for the intended refinery on Abadan Island, an uninhabited mud-flat half-way between Basra and the sea. The refinery, whose construction occupied the Company's efforts from 1910 to 1913, was first designed for a capacity of 120,000 tons a year; but this plan was enlarged even before its completion. The course of erection was hindered by delays in shipping from Great Britain, by the need to recruit Indian and European as well as Persian staff, by an outbreak of cholera, by the necessity to provide or improvise scores or hundreds of items of equipment or material from local or 'Iraqi sources, and by unforeseen modifications in the design of the plant. Its completion, in consequence, lagged behind that of the pipeline; but a first distillation unit was tested in August 1912, and later in that year enough throughput was secured to begin to supply the Persian and 'Iraqi markets and to enable the dispatch of the first shiploads from the wharves. In 1913 the whole refinery was working, not without interruptions, and extensions were in immediate prospect. Persia had thus joined the ranks of the world's oil-producing countries, with an output of 43,000 tons in 1912, 80,000 in 1913, and 273,000 in 1914.

The interest of the British Government in the enterprise, in an age when navies were fast changing to liquid fuel, had been shown already by its word in season to the Burmah Oil Company in 1905; and in 1912 a Royal Commission pursued impatient investigations with the Anglo-Persian as to the supply of fuel to the Admiralty. Winston Churchill, First Lord of the Admiralty, emphasized in the House of Commons the necessity of reliable oil supplies, and late in that year a Commission which included John Cadman, a Birmingham professor, visited the Persian fields. Its fully reassuring report led to the recommendation that the Anglo-Persian should then and thereafter be financially supported by the Government. Additional shares in the Company were to be issued, the Treasury was to acquire 51 per cent., and two Government directors were to be appointed, with a right of veto to be exercised solely on matters of the highest policy. The Act of Parliament giving effect to these arrangements received the Royal Assent six days before the outbreak of war in August 1914. The investment, in spite of much contemporary criticism, was, in fact, destined to be an immensely profitable placing of public funds. A fuel-supply contract was concluded in May 1914.

In the next stage of the Company's operations, its field activities were to be pressed forward; tests outside the proved area were to be made—at Naftak nearby, at White Oil Springs, and near Ahwaz; the pipeline was to be trebled in capacity by a new 10–12-inch line, and the refinery increased by new distillation units. The Company's field at Chiah Surkh was thought likely, if it proved to be productive, to be of value should the projected Baghdad–Teheran railway be constructed.

Relations between the Company and the central Government were cordial and correct. The political struggles of Teheran were happily remote from the Company's works, and the central Government authorities showed little or no interest in the enterprise which they had authorized. After the revolution, the Shah's writ still ran but feebly in Khuzistan, and the local rulers—the Shaikh of Muhammara and the Bakhtiari Khans—who retained all their power, were the authorities with whom perforce the Company was most in contact. The subjects of these potentates formed the bulk of the scanty and shifting pastoral and agricultural population, who were of all men the least likely, it appeared, to settle to industrial tasks. It was possible, nevertheless, to arrange with the Khans, for cash, for the preservation of fair local security.

Unskilled labour was easily collected, though many workers departed seasonally back to their tribal tents. Others quickly acquired skill in the simpler tasks, and were joined by Persian artisans from elsewhere and by strangers from 'Iraq and India. The Company from the first adopted standards of pay and treatment for its workers which were far in advance of anything seen hitherto in that or any neighbouring country, and daily contact with reasonable and humane employers, fair and punctual payment of wages, an excellent medical service, and the opportunity to acquire higher skill and higher positions offered a new and hopeful element in the life of the Bakhtiari hills and the shores of the Shatt al-'Arab.

Lord Strathcona died early in 1914, and was succeeded as Chairman by Sir Charles Greenway. The formation in June 1914 of the D'Arcy Exploration Company as a wholly-owned A.P.O.C. subsidiary was intended to concentrate prospecting activities. Ten months later the British Tanker Company was registered. Meanwhile, the financial arrangements agreed with H.M. Government were carried out, leaving the latter as effective majority shareholder, and the Burmah Oil Company as the largest single other participant.

### III. EGYPT

The Egyptian oil industry, in a natural setting more desolate even than that of Persia, came into existence in the early years of the century, after the attempt by foreign, mainly British, enterprise and by the Egyptian Government to find oil had continued fitfully since the eighteen-eighties. The Cairo Syndicate obtained in 1904 two forty-five-year leases, one for land near Kenna on the Nile and one in the Sinai Peninsula; drilling was carried out in the latter, for which a Sinai Petroleum Syndicate was formed. From the enterprises of other small but hopeful companies no field work resulted; some lacked finance, some had no object but to sell the rights they had acquired. The plans of the Helouan Petroleum Company came to nothing effective, and the same was true of Egyptian Ventures Limited, of the Bedouin Syndicate Limited, and of the Western Sinai Petroleum Prospecting Syndicate.

Meanwhile, the Egyptian Petroleum Company, registered in December 1905, passed its licence for part of the Gemsa tract in 1907 to the Egyptian Oil Trust Limited. The Trust proceeded to drill; and two years later, early in 1909, it found the long-elusive

Gemsa oil in quantities then reckoned considerable. The oil, with a gravity of 39 degrees A.P.I., was found in Miocene sandstone at a depth of 1,290 feet and its presence was confirmed by another well in October. The Trust's area of fifty square miles was taken over in 1910 by Red Sea Oilfields Limited and the well, drilled forthwith by the new owners, continued their predecessors' success; no. 4 produced oil which reached the surface unpumped and no. 6, with a depth of 746 feet, was reported as a gusher.

The Shell group had long watched Egyptian developments with interest and now thought the moment opportune to intervene. Anglo-Egyptian Oilfields Limited, a Shell creation, was registered in July 1911. It acquired the properties and rights of Red Sea Oilfields Limited, of the Egyptian Oil Trust, and of the African Prospecting Syndicate, a connected body. These properties included the Gemsa discovery. In the new Company, whose capital was in 1912 increased to £1 million, 'A' shares were taken by the Anglo-Saxon Petroleum Company (p. 17), and 'B' shares by the vendor companies. In 1913 a block of 100,000 'C' shares was issued free to the Egyptian Government, carrying (with certain restrictions) a 10 per cent. equity in the Company. Management was placed in the hands of the Anglo-Saxon, and so remained for the next forty years. The royalty conditions under the 1912 lease included payment of 2½ piastres (about 6d.) per 100 gallons of crude oil won.

The properties at Jabal Zait acquired from African Prospecting were abandoned not long afterwards as valueless, after four dry wells had been drilled. Gemsa field, however, was put into immediate production and with the help of numerous shallow wells its output was increased from 2,793 tons in 1911 to 27,960 and 12,620 tons in the following two years. The necessary field installations—workshops, tankage, stores, a jetty, dwellings, a hospital —were erected, and all efforts were made to locate other oil-pockets which might probably exist. Shipments of crude were made in a small tank-steamer to tankage erected at the Company's depot at Suez. The construction of a small refinery at the latter place was soon completed and its output taken by the closely related Asiatic Petroleum Company. Surplus refining capacity was used profitably for the treatment of crude oil brought by sea from other countries.

Conditions at the oilfields were from the first severe but not intolerable. Labour was obtained from Kenna on the Nile and worked with fair contentment in a world wholly remote from the rest of the public. European staff, in this sandy and gravelly wilderness far from all humanity save a few nomadic tribesmen, settled down to live in normal, if isolated, cantonment conditions. Water and stores of every description were brought by sea from Suez. Exploring and surveying expeditions working inland used camel transport, with carrier pigeons as their means of telegraphy.

The next stage was the discovery in 1913 of another and more considerable oilfield at Hurghada,[1] some thirty miles to the south —an event which, no doubt, saved the Anglo-Egyptian enterprise from more or less imminent abandonment. Production was here obtained from two horizons in the Miocene series and one, more important, in the Cretaceous at depths from 1,600 to 2,000 feet. To this field Anglo-Egyptian moved its local headquarters in 1915, and it became its main and, latterly, its only supplier for twenty-five years. The leases covering Hurghada, granted between 1914 and 1923, provided for royalty payments similar to those at Gemsa.

The Hurghada oil was of sluggish viscosity, with a gravity of some 22 degrees A.P.I., a high sulphur content, and a heavy admixture of water; but in quantity, at least, it offered more than the already falling Gemsa supplies. The drilling of further wells was pressed on with; storage-tanks, a jetty and industrial buildings were erected. Every effort was made to explore the Hurghada field, which in 1914 produced four-fifths of a total Egyptian production barely exceeding 100,000 tons; but the enterprise continued at this stage to show a financial loss, which must have proved fatal to less resolute proprietors.

Other companies had been less successful. The Eastern Petroleum Company had been formed to acquire three concessions on the Gulf of Suez from the Gemsa Syndicate, two of which covered areas on the mainland, and one of which islands in the Red Sea. These properties were later transferred to the Suez Oil Company, a concern closely connected with the Eastern Company, with which it amalgamated in 1916. The Eastern–Suez group drilled wells at Jubal Island and Ranim Island, without success, and through a subsidiary, Gemsa Oil Reefs, carried out prospecting in Sinai. The outbreak of war in August 1914 stopped, for five years, these and all similar activities.

---

[1] The correct place-name is Ghardaqa.

### IV. THE TURKISH EMPIRE AND ARABIA

If, in spite of clear surface indications of their presence, the development of oil resources in the Ottoman Empire in this period was little attempted, the reason lay partly in the chronic maladministration of the Turkish provinces and the suspicious attitude of Turkish officialdom, and partly in the rivalries of would-be concessionaires, whose contending claims helped to postpone governmental decision. In fact, no enterprise in Turkey led to oil production in these years, nor, in spite of brief visits to 'Iraq by European geologists in 1905 and 1910 on behalf of the Government, was any serious or persistent research carried out. The Mining Law of 1886, amended in 1901, was in 1906 replaced by a new and relatively modernized code; and leases or licences under this were obtained in various areas by Ottoman subjects, usually with the intention of re-sale to credulous foreigners.

The Standard Oil Company of New York (since 1911 an independent fragment of the now dismembered Standard Oil) accepted such licences for lands in northern Anatolia and in Palestine. To the former area the Company dispatched geologists in 1914, but was forced by the war to withdraw them. In Palestine the decision was reached to drill near Kurnub, south of Beersheba. A road and buildings were constructed, lorries imported, and drilling equipment was ordered from America; but this, when war broke out, was unloaded at Alexandria, and the enterprise was abandoned for five years.

A Syria Exploration Company, registered in London in 1912, held licences in Syria and conducted some shallow drilling there; its intention was to interest larger concerns and sell its rights to these while retaining an interest. Jaffa Oilfields, an offshoot of Eastern Petroleum (p. 24), took up a lease of seven plots west of the Dead Sea. The Consolidated Oilfields of Syria, registered in 1913, was short-lived and failed to develop the bituminous property which it was founded to exploit. Leases for the seepages in Van vilayet were granted by the Turkish Government, but failed to interest foreign capital and lapsed. A British Ottoman Oil Syndicate acquired, or hoped for, rights in the Boyabat seepage area; but no more resulted from its efforts than from those of Anglo-Ottoman Oilfields Limited, which had been registered two years earlier to acquire unspecified rights, nor from those of the

Bagdad–Bassrah Concession Limited, registered with similar objectives. Of all these enterprises and of others now forgotten, the history was one of optimistic foreigners with or without capital, of hopeful and hungry local intermediaries, suspicious but venal Turkish officials, intrigue in high places, valueless maps and doubtfully valid documents, and a complete ignorance of geology and of the elements of petroleum development. No oil of commercial importance was produced, none located.

The island of Cyprus was in part explored for oil by a Cyprus Oil Trust which, registered in 1910, began to carry out some operations of research.

Of serious development in Arabia there could be little likelihood. Only in connexion with the west coast of the peninsula, where the Turkish overlordship clashed with the actuality of Arab rule, was some interest shown among the syndicates and licence brokers of Istanbul. At Salif, in the 'Asir province, the salt deposits attracted the interest of Europeans, and middlemen were ready with offers of licences for the northern Hijaz; the Turkish Petroleum Company itself (p. 30) had hopes in 1913 of a concession for this region or for the whole Hijaz, though the lack of security was recognized. Such a concession would replace or incorporate rights already granted (it was claimed) by Turkish ministers which had been acquired by Shell and which, under the agreement that bound it as a Turkish Petroleum shareholder, offered them to the latter Company in 1914. Negotiations for ratification were in hand when war broke out, and the validity of the rights remained dubious. A concession obtained by the Eastern Petroleum Company (p. 24) from the Turks, covering the Farsan archipelago, was transferred in 1912 to a company formed to develop it, the Farsan Islands Oil Company, and a geologist was sent to examine the islands.

In the Persian Gulf the threat of the Baghdad Railway, with all it could involve in disturbance of Great Britain's position on those coasts, caused the Government of India to arrange with the ruling shaikhs that development of their oil, should it exist, was to be entrusted to subjects of no Power other than Great Britain. Such an undertaking was given in October 1913 by the Shaikh of Kuwait, whom the Turks claimed as a subject while admitting his *de facto* independence and his British alliance; and in May 1914, in similar terms, by the ruler of Bahrain. The agreements current between the British Government and the shaikhs of the Trucial Coast stipulated that these also should enter into no relations with other Powers. A similar provision appeared in the agreement between Great Britain and the Sultan of Oman, who could count on British support as long as he parted with no portion of his kingdom to strangers and conformed in his foreign relations with British policy. In Qatar Turkish troops remained until late in 1914; but, although the agreement with Britain, which the Shaikh had accepted in earlier days on lines similar to those of the Trucial shaikhs, had been allowed to lapse when the Turks occupied the peninsula in 1872, the shaikhdom equally formed part of the region in which Great Britain claimed a special position. The al-Hasa province of Arabia was in 1913 occupied by 'Abdul 'Aziz ibn Sa'ud, ruler of Najd since 1901, and the Turks were expelled. No undertaking with specific reference to oil was asked by His Majesty's Government from the Sa'udi ruler; but in the treaty which he concluded with the British in 1915—a treaty superseded and replaced long before oil was discovered in Arabia—he agreed in general terms to grant concessions to foreign subjects only with British concurrence.

### V. TURKISH PETROLEUM COMPANY

The interest of the period from 1900 to 1914 in the territories west of Persia lies less in field operations than in the course of competitive claims and negotiations, on high levels, at the Turkish capital. The Ottoman Railway Company of Anatolia, which was controlled by the Deutsche Bank, retained in 1900 its claim to priority as a grantee of oil rights on the strength of the promises made to it in 1888; and to this was added, after signature of the Baghdad Railway Convention of March 1903, definite, though not exclusive rights, over a 20-kilometre strip on each side of the railway lines which the Company was now to construct through Anatolia to the head of the Persian Gulf. The Sultan by a new decree in December 1903 confirmed that of April 1890 as to his personal ownership of oil properties; and in July 1904 a specific option was granted by the Ministry of the Privy Purse to the Anatolian Railway (which transferred it to the Deutsche Bank) for one year's exploration for oil in the Baghdad and Mosul vilayets; if oil were found, a forty-year concession would be granted by Royal Decree, with division of the profits between concessionaire and Privy Purse in proportions to be decided later. An imposing exploration and geological party visited 'Iraq and compiled a report in favourable terms: but for whatever reason—probably lacks of funds—the option was not exercised. The Ministry declared it thereafter non-effective; the Germans demanded £20,000 for exploration expenses, which was refused, and maintained their claim to the option. It was with difficulty renewed annually until 1907, in which year its lapse was officially pronounced. This, however, was never accepted by the Company.

But the Germans were not alone in their interest in Turkish oil. The increasingly close relations of Shell and Royal Dutch, which led to the coalescence of the two groups in 1907, and the interest of both in discovering new oil-sources, placed at least one rival candidate in the field—the Istanbul office of Samuel Brothers and visiting representatives of Shell's London headquarters. Another applicant for Ottoman oil had already appeared; D'Arcy, after obtaining his Persian Concession in 1901, sent his representative, Marriot, to Istanbul with instructions to obtain an oil agreement for the Baghdad and Mosul vilayets. After spending eighteen months and some thousands of pounds in vain, Marriot was replaced in 1903 by H. E. Nichols.[1] The latter within a few months, and not without cost, claimed to have obtained a letter from Government conveying the promise of a concession in favour of his Ottoman Petroleum Syndicate, formed for the purpose. But normal Turkish procrastination and the force of German opposition prevented fulfilment of the promise. and the German option still, as they claimed, held the field. Yet another candidate was Rear-Admiral Colby Chester, who, sponsored by the New York Chamber of Commerce and aided by favourable contacts in Turkey made during service there ten years earlier, returned to Istanbul in January 1908 and was offered, in terms convincing to this too credulous negotiator, a variety of concessions for works, railways, harbours, minerals, and oil development in all parts of Turkey.

The military coup d'état and revolution of July 1908 and the reintroduction, after thirty years of suspension, of the Turkish Constitution involved the abandonment, or at least postponement, of all the negotiators' hopes and the re-submission of all offers. The oil properties of the Empire were re-transferred to the

[1] Later Managing Director of the Turkish Petroleum Company and a Director of Anglo-Persian.

Ministry of Finance by decree of September 1908, by which they ceased to belong to the Sultan or his Privy Purse; and this was confirmed in May 1909 by a further decree of the incoming Sultan, who succeeded 'Abdul Hamid on his deposition in April.

During the uneasy period between the first and second coups d'état—July 1908 to March 1909—no progress in concessionairing was possible; but after the latter date the pressure and tempo increased. Chester again urged his claims, and a concession granting him oil, mineral, and railway rights on an imposing scale was drafted in the Ministry of Public Works in 1909 and was ready for presentation to Parliament on behalf of his Ottoman–American Development Company in 1911. Other United States interests were represented by Dr. Bruce Glasgow, who spoke for the J. G. White Corporation and asked for rights similar to those of the Admiral. Nichols, who had come so near to success before, was active again in pressing the claims of the D'Arcy group, which was merged in 1909 in the newly-formed Anglo-Persian Oil Company. The Shell group, through Samuel Brothers, resumed their candidature, of which Nichols in 1910 became aware for the first time; and, associated with Shell, Gulbenkian remained keenly on the watch. The Anatolian Railway continued to claim its option for northern 'Iraq and to be refused by the Turkish Government.

A result of the success of the Young Turks, who professed liberal principles and now dominated the State, was a brief period of popularity for Great Britain—hailed as the liberal Power *par excellence*—and a corresponding brief eclipse of the all-influential Germans, whom the deposed tyrant had favoured. It led to the formation in 1910, by initiative of the British Government, and with British capital, of a National Bank of Turkey with Sir H. Babington-Smith (a British civil servant) as Chairman and Lord Revelstoke, Hugo Baring, Sir E. Cassell, and C. S. Gulbenkian as directors. The efforts of the last-named were now devoted to persuading the Bank to interest itself in Turkish oil development, and to reconciling British and German interests in that field, so that the threatened deadlock could be circumvented. Before the end of 1910 contact had been established and a measure of agreement reached, between the National Bank and the Deutsche Bank. It took visible form in the first days of 1911 by the registration in London of African and Eastern Concessions Limited, a company intended for oil operation throughout the Ottoman Empire. Babington-Smith became its Chairman. The Deutsche Bank, in return for its valueless options and outdated priorities, was given 20,000 shares free, the National Bank took and paid for 28,000, Gulbenkian retained 12,000 for himself and passed 20,000, in accordance with his prior agreement with Deterding, to the Royal Dutch Shell group. The capital was £80,000.

The entry of Shell into this organization and its association with British banking on the one hand and with German interests on the other represented the result of long efforts by Gulbenkian to produce this juxtaposition. He himself could pass his shares to others if the obligations became too onerous; and the National Bank had no intention of remaining other than as a spectator in the oil business. The Company's first directors were Deterding and Frederick Lane for Shell (more properly, Anglo-Saxon), Dr. Kliemke for the Deutsche Bank, Baring, F. E. Whittall, and Babington-Smith for the National Bank, and Gulbenkian for himself. The name of African and Eastern was changed to that of Turkish Petroleum Company in 1912. The Company proceeded to apply for a number of local licences and concessions in various parts of Turkey, and revealed in the process the lack of real cordiality between the Shell and German elements: but the major objective must be a comprehensive concession for the favoured vilayets of Mosul and Baghdad. Meanwhile the T.P.C. share-holders addressed the Company in agreed terms, to the effect that they would not interest themselves in the production of oil in the Turkish Empire in Europe or Asia otherwise than in association with their T.P.C. colleagues: the first occurrence of the self-denying rule to be consecrated sixteen years later as the Red Line Agreement.

Admiral Chester ceased after 1911, to his indignation, to be a serious candidate. The Turkish Parliament in 1910 and 1911 would have nothing to do with his draft concessions, in spite of some United States diplomatic intervention on his behalf. He lacked financial support and his claims clashed too obviously with those of the Baghdad Railway and other European interests. The Anglo-Persian, on the other hand, was formidable by reason of its conspicuous success in Persia, where it came in 1913 for the second time within an ace of success, which seemed to be prevented only by German intervention. The Company, whose reappearance in the field alarmed the T.P.C. constituents, was known to enjoy the favour of the British Government; and in 1913 both the National Bank and Gulbenkian received summonses from the Foreign Office that their shares should be made available for re-allotment. The intrusion of Anglo-Persian was, in fact, unwelcome to Deterding, though not unacceptable to the Germans as providing a broader basis for Anglo-German co-operation.

It was, indeed, by now in the clear interests of both Great Britain and Germany and of Turkey itself that the rival claims of the Anglo-German T.P.C. and the all-British A.P.O.C. should be so reconciled as to make practical progress feasible. Such reconciliation, which inter-Company conversations had failed to achieve, was effected finally at a high Government level. A Foreign Office meeting in March 1914 produced an agreement satisfactory to most (though resented by Gulbenkian as slighting his claims and position) and bearing the signatures of the companies and governments involved. The Anglo-Persian would cease to act independently and would take half the share-capital (now to be raised to £160,000) in the Turkish Petroleum Company, leaving the Deutsche Bank and Anglo-Saxon £40,000 each. The shareholding of the National Bank was to disappear and a 5 per cent. interest for Gulbenkian was to be provided in equal parts from the shares of Anglo-Persian and Anglo-Saxon. All shareholders reaffirmed the pledge not to interest themselves in oil development in the Turkish Empire otherwise than in association with the T.P.C.

The British and German Ambassadors could now confidently approach the Grand Vizier for the grant of an equitable concession, capable at long last of securing practical development of Turkish oil; the opportunity was indeed the more suitable as many Anglo-Turkish and Turco-German questions were simultaneously under discussion in government circles. Outstanding Anglo-German issues were settled by the never-ratified Grey–Lichnowsky Agreement of 15 January 1914; and a *démarche* of the two ambassadors in Istanbul was met by a letter of the Grand Vizier, Sa'id Halim Pasha, dated 28 June 1914 and addressed to them both. It stated that the Ministry of Finance agreed to lease the petroleum deposits 'discovered or to be discovered' in the vilayets of Baghdad and Mosul to the Turkish Petroleum Company and reserved to itself the right to decide later both its own share of the proceeds and the general terms of the concession. The

Company was to indemnify any third party's interest in the petroleum deposits concerned.

This letter, less authoritative than a legally sanctioned concession, was yet a formal and solemn promise given by the highest of all Turkish authorities and one whose fulfilment was, no doubt, prevented only by the outbreak of war five weeks afterwards. Ten years later it was to form the basis of the Turkish Petroleum Company's approach to the Government of 'Iraq, as the successor state in the two vilayets.

Meanwhile the Company sought to elucidate whatever problems of compensation to third parties it would be asked to face, and to move towards the drafting of a concession. But time was denied; little progress was made, the European War broke out on 4 August and Turkey and Great Britain were at war from 5 November 1915 for the next five years. It was ordained that neither Germans nor Turks were, after all, to have any part in the development of 'Iraqi oil.

## CHAPTER III

# THE FIRST WORLD WAR
# AND AFTER

## I. THE WAR YEARS

THE transformation of the Middle East into a theatre of war created during the five years from 1914 to 1919—and in 'Iraq and Turkey for longer—conditions of unsafety, disturbance, and preoccupation wholly inimical to industrial development. Persia was the scene of provocative German intrigue, of tribal uprising, of military invasion, and of almost total governmental impotence, and the years from 1919 to 1924 continued to witness gross maladministration and social confusion. Egypt was a major war base, its economy and manpower wholly devoted for five years to war purposes, and thereafter to political struggle not unaccompanied by violence. Every Middle Eastern sea during the war years was unsafe, convoys were decimated, and supplies interrupted. The Levant territories were afflicted by famine and harsh political suppression, followed by invasion and the clash of arms; and the post-war settlement of this region into four Mandated Territories was not quickly or easily accomplished. 'Iraq was the scene of a major campaign lasting from 1914 to the Armistice, which was followed eighteen months later by the outbreak of disorder over much of the territory; in the three years, however, which followed the establishment of an 'Iraq Government in October 1920, great progress was made towards a more permanent and encouraging régime. Turkey itself, with its every effort and resource strained for the prosecution of multi-frontal war, could give no thought to its mineral resources; and the Armistice of November 1918 was to be followed in this distracted but still vigorous country by a national uprising, a victory over invaders, and a total change of government and régime. In Arabia the possibility of oil exploitation was unanimously ignored during these years, when European enterprise and capital had far different preoccupations.

The part played by petroleum in the prosecution of the war was admitted at the time by every government and public, and was nowhere more apparent than in the Middle East. In civilian life the industry was placed in the conspicuous situation which it has held, increasingly, ever since, not least through the greatly accelerated development of motor transport and aviation and of the use of fuel oil in industry and at sea.

Three other effects of the war, or movements which coincided with it, were of profound significance. The first was the establishment of a British oil industry on a scale with which even the vast industry in America must seriously reckon. The second was the keen awareness of European Powers, notably France, of their need to secure oil supplies of their own, while the United States, alarmed at the foretold exhaustion of their own resources, determined not to be left behind with diminishing reserves and an increasing offtake. Finally, the new political structure in the Middle East, the Mandate system and the great increase of Western acquaintance with this region seemed to offer a new and yet unexplored oil world to the enterprise of the West.

## II. THE WAR IN PERSIA

By the autumn of 1914 the Anglo-Persian was producing and exporting petroleum products from Abadan at a rate of 25,000 tons a month, and formed an imperial and military asset of serious importance. If, therefore, the landing of British forces on the Shatt al-'Arab in November 1914 was the first move of an expedition whose object was primarily the defence of British political interests in the Persian Gulf, its second but no less real purpose was the defence of the Persian oil supplies. It was, indeed, evident that this supply would be an immediate Turkish objective, as was soon clear from their early requisition of the Company's oil stocks in Basra and Baghdad and their support of both Turkish and German agents penetrating into Khuzistan on trouble-creating missions. Nor were these unsuccessful; British control of Basra and Qurna was easily secured, but it could not prevent tribesmen from obeying the emissaries of the Turks and cutting the main oil pipeline between Fields and Ahwaz early in February 1915. The Bakhtiari and Shaikh Khaz'al himself remained steadfastly loyal to their undertakings, but the advance of a Turkish force, unhindered by the Persian Government, created a situation upon whose redressment must depend the continuation of all operations; and this required the dispatch of a British force to Ahwaz, the energetic rounding up of enemy agents, and finally the dispatch of greater forces which conducted successful operations of some weeks' duration. Thereafter the Company's area was not again disturbed, and the throughput of the pipeline was resumed in the summer of 1915, after some three months' interruption. British troops remained at Ahwaz throughout the war.

In other respects the operations of Anglo-Persian, encouraged as they were by the paramount contribution they could make to the British forces, were hampered by many wartime embarrassments. British staff were eager to serve in the armed forces elsewhere; communications were slow, tankers diverted or sunk by enemy action; supplies and skilled personnel were for five years difficult or impossible to obtain; military requisitions (including that of the Company's Karun barge fleet) were inconvenient or disastrous. Nevertheless, a great and systematic enlargement of the Company's operations took place between 1915 and 1919. Drilling was continued in Maidan-i-Naftun (still so called), while exploration for other fields went on. Improvements and extensions were made in the engineering, industrial, and administrative arrangements throughout Fields; road and bridge building began seriously in 1918; the use of mechanical transport grew rapidly and reduced the time required for the journey from Abadan to Fields from five days to eight hours. Increased use was made of electric power throughout Fields. The pipeline capacity to Abadan was more than doubled and by the end of the war stood at 3 million t/y. At Abadan refinery the construction of new units kept pace with pipeline increases, as these came progressively into operation; its capacity, 120,000 tons a year in 1913, was in 1918 over a million. Connected installations and services of all kinds expanded correspondingly, including extended wharves and jetties.

Production from the Persian fields grew from 273,000 tons in 1914 to comparable figures of 376,000, 449,000, 644,000, and 897,000 tons in the four succeeding years, to 1,106,000 in 1919, and to 1,385,000 in 1920. The staff and labour force of Persians (the vast majority), Indians, and British increased with the scale of work. Export from Abadan was carried increasingly in the fleet of the British Tanker Company (p. 22). As early as 1919, it is interesting to notice, spokesmen of the Company prophetically indicated the desirability, sooner or later, of a pipeline across Arabia to the Mediterranean. The British Government's investment in Anglo-Persian already declared itself as highly profitable, and seemed to be unaccompanied by the drawbacks prophesied by its critics; the profits of the concern, realized by its ever-increasing operations of refining, distribution, and sales outside Persia, rose annually after 1915.

To Persia, and more immediately to the public of Khuzistan, the Company's activity brought an infusion of wealth and an example of progress without parallel in the country's history; nor was this accompanied, as far as appeared, by any threat to local interests, governmental or private. To the wages paid, the stores and services purchased, and the contracts allotted among the public were to be added the more diffused benefits of higher local purchasing power, the opportunity to acquire higher skill, the example and attraction of the higher living standards and social services offered by the Company. The royalties and share-interest paid to the Persian Treasury up to April 1919 amounted to £1,325,000 and for the year 1919–20 were £470,000: a major contribution to the scanty Persian revenues of that period.

### III. PERSIA AFTER THE WAR

The end of the war in November 1918 permitted the Anglo-Persian not only to finish works in hand but also to inaugurate a period of ambitious development. Local conditions were un-affected by the miseries of the distant capital, and the tragic disorders of 'Iraq in 1920 had no echo in Khuzistan. Much was done to improve conditions of work for the local labour force, which exceeded 20,000 in 1922; a strike at Abadan in 1922 affected not Persian but imported Indian workers, some 3,000 strong, and was settled firmly by their repatriation. More attention could now be paid to the training of Persian workers; a beginning was made with instruction in many forms, and efforts were made, in spite of governmental apathy, to secure the establishment of technical colleges at Isfahan and elsewhere; the benefit to Persia and to the Company of the widest use of skilled Persians in its works was obvious. In the Company's administration, of which the highest authority in Persia was the head of the Strick Scott Managing Agency at Muhammara, the tendency from 1918 onwards was for the originally separate commands—fields at Masjid-i-Sulaiman, pipeline at Ahwaz, refinery at Abadan, geological at Muhammara—to coalesce; the conclusion of this process was the appointment in 1924 of J. A. Jameson as General Manager (Technical), with authority over all technical branches and operations. The General-Managership of Strick Scott, which became that of Anglo-Persian when in 1924 the contract for the Managing Agency was not renewed, was held from 1913 until 1920 by C. A. Walpole, with T. L. Jacks 'acting' at intervals. In May 1921 it devolved jointly upon the latter and Sir Arnold Wilson, who had been Vice-Consul at Muhammara from 1907 till 1913 and afterwards Acting Civil Commissioner at Baghdad. The transfer of Wilson to London in 1924, as General Manager of the D'Arcy Exploration Company, left the management in Persia in the combined hands of Jacks and Jameson.

The steady exploration and drilling at Maidan-i-Naftun continued, with the improvement and stabilization of all services and amenities. Drilling tests were carried out on promising structures in other parts of the concession area: at Qishm Island, at Deh Luran on the 'Iraq border, and elsewhere in the vast and desolate countryside; but success was for ten years denied to all these effort and production remained concentrated at the original location. It amounted to 1·1 million tons in 1919 and to 1·38, 1·74, and 2·32 millions respectively in 1920, 1921, and 1922.

Pipeline development continued, with the construction of a 12-inch line in 1921-2 and improvements, both mechanical and domestic, at pumping-stations. At Abadan refinery the works projected during the war were completed, though not without delays due to uncontrollable reasons. By 1922 refinery throughput capacity approached 3 million t/y.

The Company's increased profits permitted the payment of substantial annual sums in royalty and as dividends to the Persian Treasury; they amounted to £585,000 for the year 1920-1, and to £593,000 a year later. In these circumstances, a lively interest on the part of the Persian Government might have been expected, but in fact little was shown; almost no Persian in high places acquainted himself with the realities of the industry, and the policy of Government varied from mere uncritical acceptance to irritating pinpricks. Specific differences between it and the Company became explicit after the war. The interruption in 1915 of public security, which under the 1901 Concession the Persian Government was bound to maintain, led to the first of these. The Company claimed £500,000 for its loss sustained through the disorders of February to May 1915. The Government, disclaiming all responsibility, advanced counter-claims for damage done by Turkish troops in Persia: for a share of profits from the operations of the First Exploitation Company (which sold its oil at cost price to the Anglo-Persian) and from those of the British Tanker Company: and on various other accounts. Conversations in Teheran and London failed to resolve these questions, and in mid-1920 the Financial Adviser to the Persian Government, S. Armitage-Smith, was instructed by his ministers to negotiate a settlement. The resulting arrangement, concluded on 22 December 1920, dealt successfully with the question of compensation, settled the procedure for calculating future royalty payments, prescribed a lump-sum payment of £1 million by the Company in respect of all outstanding claims, and provided for the scrutiny of the Company's royalty calculations by chartered accountants in London to be named by the Persian Government. Unclouded relations between Company and Government were then resumed, amid general expressions of cordiality. But acceptance of the £1 million and, subsequently, of royalties calculated on the agreed basis did not prevent the Teheran authorities eight years later from alleging that the Armitage-Smith Agreement was and had always been invalid.

Another source of disagreement was of a different nature. The long-standing interest of Russia in northern Persia had become more explicit since the entry of Russian troops into the Caspian provinces during the war. It was marked in 1916 by the grant by the Persian ministers, without parliamentary ratification, of an oil concession covering the five provinces to a Georgian, A. M. Khostharia. He formed the Russo-Persian Naphtha Company, engaged geologists, and chartered a steamer; but the Russian Revolution halted his efforts, and the Persian Government showed early signs of repudiating the grant. Khostharia, thereupon, sold his rights to the Anglo-Persian, which, with a strange optimism, was willing to pay him £100,000, followed later by a greater sum; and North Persian Oils Limited was registered in May 1920, with a capital of £3 million and a board of Anglo-Persian directors, to operate the concession. The views of Bolshevik Russia on this development could not be doubtful; and the Perso-Russian Treaty of 26 February 1921, whereby Russia renounced all claims to economic privileges in Persia, was treated by them and by the Persian Government as ending all claims by Khostharia or his assignees. The protests of the Anglo-Persian were unavailing; no weight was given to their argument that Khostharia was not Russian but Georgian; and their last hope vanished when the Persians turned instead to an American company, the Standard Oil (New Jersey), and agreed in principle to grant it a concession. This action elicited indignant protests from both Russia and the Anglo-Persian; and to soften the blow and strengthen its position Standard Oil offered, without Persian authority, a half-share to the British company. The transaction was, however, rejected by the Persians, who, during the first weeks of 1922, persisted in refusing to countenance any British participation; and in June the Persian ministers offered a concession, for fifty years, to any all-American company which would conform to its stipulations. The share of the Government was to be 50 per cent. of all profits. Proposals were received from New Jersey and from the Sinclair Consolidated; but both offers were rejected in Teheran, where new terms were evolved and this time provisionally accepted by Sinclair. The abortive New Jersey concession was waved aside, and the way lay open for a concession for north Persia to the Sinclair group in return for an immediate loan of £10 million. A fifty-year Agreement, covering the northern provinces, was in fact signed in December 1923; but the project was doomed, after all, to frustration. The coincidence of the 'Teapot Dome' scandals, the suspicion of a private arrangement between Sinclair and New Jersey, and the loss of Sinclair's former acceptability to Russia, all combined with Persian suspicion and apathy to pass the year 1924 without progress, and in 1925 Sinclair withdrew.

### IV. EGYPT, 1914–23

The oil industry in Egypt was, in 1914, still tentative and unprosperous. The country's oil-producing capacity, as so far discovered, was small. The industry, from the outbreak of war, was faced by war-time difficulties of man-power and supply, in addition to world-wide shortages of materials and transport delays. But, within these enforced limits, it solved its problems with tenacity and well earned the thanks which the Egyptian Government later expressed. Even so, it had barely begun by 1919 to show a meagre profit.

Gemsa during these years produced a mere tenth part of the Egyptian output; the bulk was supplied by Hurghada, where

Anglo-Egyptian's operations were now concentrated; but even here output was sustained only by the drilling of many wells, often of meagre and disappointing output. The realized production of crude for the years 1914–19 amounted to no more than 103,000, 34,000, 55,000, 135,000, 272,000 and 232,000 tons. The quality of the oil and the high water admixture in it, which constantly increased, led in 1917 to the erection of a dehydration plant at Hurghada for its treatment before dispatch to Suez. In all operations, the difficulty of obtaining supplies was serious; many supply ships were sunk by the enemy. Nevertheless, the Hurghada field stabilized into a settled and not uncomfortable community; amenities increased, motor vehicles appeared, relations with the British military authorities and the Government of Egypt were excellent. Secure employment was found for an Egyptian labour force of 1,200 men. The Suez refinery was kept supplied in part by shipments of Hurghada crude and in part by the imported crude of other companies.

The first years after the war found the industry still hopeful of the better times which fresh sources of oil, if discovered, could bring; but this was not for long years to be achieved, and meanwhile the best use was made of existing resources. Production from 1920 to 1924 inclusive amounted to 156,000, 181,000, 169,000, 150,000 and 160,000 tons; and the improvement of installations and amenities continued with the easier availability of supplies and staff after 1919.

The new code of licensing and leasing procedure issued by the Government in 1921 encouraged in some measure the exploration of new areas, though to little avail; the only success was the discovery in 1921, by operations of the Egyptian Government itself, of a field at abu Durba on the west coast of Sinai. The field, of small output and low-quality oil, was in 1923 handed for exploitation, under a thirty-year lease, to a local company, the Egyptian Oil Syndicate. After producing a total of some 5,000 tons of crude from three producing wells (out of fifteen drilled) it appeared incapable of further commercial production and was, for the time, abandoned.

Another State enterprise was the erection at Suez in 1922 of a small refinery, which was intended to supply the needs of government departments by processing the royalty oil received in kind from Anglo-Egyptian. This self-contained refinery, at which two

Europeans and 300 Egyptians were employed, achieved an output of some 100 tons a day, including road asphalt.

Exploration for other oil-sources in Egypt by syndicates and companies formed for this purpose was resumed from 1919 onwards, after a four-year interruption. A 'Q.S.P. Syndicate' obtained Government licences and passed them to the British Burmah Petroleum Company, to be later acquired by the British Sinai Petroleum Company. The last-named of these carried out test drilling, but its operations were abandoned as unsuccessful in 1923. Egyptian Central Oilfields Limited held licences over two islands off the Egyptian coast and drilled on these, only to abandon hope five years later. The Suez Oil Company (p. 24) lasted till 1928, but was unrewarded to the last. The Anglo-Persian itself took licences for considerable areas of Sinai, drilled a well, and for a time was hopeful of an oil strike: but it was not to be. The Eastern Petroleum and Finance Company, registered in June 1921, was responsible for the drilling of two wells on the Sinai coast; both were dry. The prospects of Affiliated Oilfields, which through a subsidiary drilled at Tawila Island, appeared bright in 1928, but like the rest were to be disappointed. Oilfields of Egypt Limited acquired licences from the African Prospecting Syndicate for areas on the coast—Ras Bahar and Ras Dhib—and for the two islands of North and South Gaisum; serious drilling was carried out and three holes were taken to a depth of nearly 3,000 feet: but no favourable signs resulted, and the operation was abandoned. Nor were these the only enterprises in which foreign initiative and capital sought, with monotonous lack of recompense, to find oil in Egypt.

### V. LEVANT, TURKEY, ARABIA, AND 'IRAQ, 1914–23

During this period of political reorientation, in which these territories began a new existence as national states, the preoccupations of the time permitted little serious progress towards oil research or development. Most of the syndicates formed before the autumn of 1914 disappeared from view; and while the future of the territories (including that of their oil content) was a preoccupation of European statesmanship, local initiative had little to show. In southern Syria occasional drilling was carried out by German personnel of the Turkish Army; in Turkey some tunnelling at seepages was contrived by Russian invading troops in 1915;

but elsewhere the war period showed no activity in the production of petroleum.

But the years following witnessed a revival. The rights obtained before the war by Sulaiman Bey Nasif and the Syria Exploration Company (p. 25) in Transjordan and on the Dead Sea had already interested the D'Arcy Exploration Company (p. 22); the latter secured options and, under the Turkish Petroleum rules, offered them to its fellow shareholders. But the T.P.C.'s position was not yet effectively that of an operating company, and the licences were allowed to lapse after a visit had been paid to Palestine in 1922 by Anglo-Persian geologists on behalf of T.P.C. A 'concession' granted in 1920 by seven optimistic shaikhs of Transjordan on behalf of a self-styled National Government of Moab, shortly before the establishment of the Amirate there, was not taken seriously by the British Government. The concession was passed, nevertheless, by its proprietor to the Shell Group, who correctly offered it to the T.P.C.; but the Moab Government ceased to exist—if it had ever existed—and no more was heard of the concession. The licences which Standard Oil of New York had obtained before the war for the Kurnub area in southern Palestine were claimed as still valid after 1918, and a representative of the Company stayed for two years in Palestine; but he withdrew frustrated in 1921. The Middle East Development Company, resistered in London in 1919 as an Anglo-French enterprise to develop petroleum in Syria and Arabia, included the interests of Lord Inchcape; no field work, however, resulted from its efforts. A small London syndicate formed in 1920, the Eastern and General, was unnoticed at the time, but was destined later to play its part in great events.

In Turkey, for six years following the Armistice, the swift changes and uncertainties of the times and the antiquated mining law still in force precluded serious enterprise. At the first sight of a European or American geologist (such as the representative of the Omnium Company of Paris who toured Turkey in 1921-2) forgotten 'rights' were unearthed by local optimists and ancient permits deciphered; some of these—at Kighi, at Van, at Erzerum, and elsewhere—were offered to the Turkish Petroleum Company, but none was followed up. It was not easy to take seriously the efforts of Fuad Pasha to make attractive his 'exclusive rights' to the Van area, nor those of the Royal Family of Egypt to most of the rest of Turkey; nor did the Société Turque de Produits Pétrolifères, a Turkish and Belgian–French concern, achieve serious results. An enterprise planned in London by a group including Lord Cowdray, to obtain concessions in Turkey, came to nothing; nor was there the stuff of reality in the whispered promises of 'concessions' with which Turkish statesmen sought to gain interest at Lausanne.

In 'Iraq the seepages of Kirkuk and Tuz continued to be used as ever during the war. Those of Qaiyara were developed on a more ambitious scale by the Germans, who carried out shallow drilling, built galleries, removed 'refined products' by tank-lorry—and were heard even to speak of a pipeline to the Mediterranean! They were scarcely less interested in the Zakho seepages, where drilling and tunnelling were also carried out. The military use of the locally-distilled products of Qaiyara and Tuz was continued after the British occupation, and visits to 'Iraq were paid during and after the war by geologists whose employers were not unmindful of Turkish Petroleum's vizirial promise of 1914.

More significant for immediate results was the enterprise in 'Iraq of the Anglo-Persian, whose 1901 Concession in Persia covered also the Transferred Territories in 'Iraq, since these, with a total area of some 700 square miles, had been 'transferred' from Persia to Turkey by decision of the International Frontier Commission of 1913–14.[1] An experimental well in a smallish anticline astride the frontier, at Naftkhana, was 'spudded in' in 1919 and, after considerable delays, subsequent drilling struck a substantial oil-show in 1923—the first glimpse of potential 'commercial production' in 'Iraq. The Naftkhana field, whose trans-frontier portion in Persia is Naft-i-Shah, was later revealed as consisting of a closed limestone structure some 8 miles long by $1\frac{1}{2}$ wide; the reservoir-rock, 250 feet thick and its crest lying some 2,200 feet below the surface, is locally known as the 'Kalhur limestone' and forms a nearly symmetrical dome overlaid by unconformable later deposits. The development of this oilfield, both in 'Iraq and Persia, belongs to later pages.

The Turkish Petroleum Company could not but find its position full of delicacy after the war. The German shareholding had in

[1] Turkey had undertaken to treat any territory that she might gain as a result of the Commission as being covered by the A.P.O.C. Concession; the 'transfer' was, therefore, one of lands whose oil-rights were already engaged.

1915 been handed by the British Government to the Custodian of Enemy Property. The apprehension of the British shareholders in 1916 that the assignment of Mosul to the French sphere, under the Sykes–Picot Agreement, would be damaging to them had been met by a letter from the French Ambassador in London declaring that British oil rights in Mosul area would be unaffected. During the later years of the war the French Government (not without suggestions from Gulbenkian, then resident in Paris) hoped for transfer of the German share in the T.P.C. to a body representing French industry; and, after an exchange of letters in this sense took place between Lord Long and Henri Berenger, agreement was reached between M. Clemenceau and Mr. Lloyd George in December 1918 that the Mosul region should, after all, form part of British-controlled 'Iraq. This position became explicit when the decision was reached by the Principal Allied Powers that Great Britain should be awarded a Mandate for that territory.

The interests of both nations led them during 1919, accordingly, to put into final form the plan whereby France should succeed to the German T.P.C. shareholding, while itself in turn facilitating the passage of 'Mosul oil' (if any) across Syria to the Mediterranean. The Long–Berenger Agreement was developed on these lines and was ratified on 24 April 1920 in the form of the San Remo Oil Agreement,[1] which left Anglo-Saxon with 22½ per cent. of T.P.C. shares, Anglo-Persian with 47½, the French with 25, and Gulbenkian with 5.

The transfer of German shares to the French had been conditional in the mind of Deterding upon the formation of a French shareholding company in which Shell interests would predominate.

---

[1] The Agreement provided that the British Government should grant to the French Government or its nominees, at current market rates, 25 per cent. of the net output of crude oil which H.M.G. might acquire from the Mesopotamian oilfields, in the event of these being developed by government action; or in the event of this being done by a company the British Government should place at the disposal of the French a 25 per cent. share of such company. The company was to be under permanent British control, and, should subscriptions from the public be invited, native interests should be allowed to participate up to 20 per cent.; the French were to contribute up to 10 per cent. of such native participation. The British Government was to support arrangements by which the French might procure from Anglo-Persian supplies of oil, which might be piped from Persia to the Mediterranean through French Mandated Territory. In that event, the French agreed to the construction of two separate pipelines and railways from Mesopotamia or Persia through the French sphere to a port or ports on the eastern Mediterranean.

For this purpose a Société Française pour l'Exploitation du Pétrole was formed between Shell interests in France and the Union Parisienne; but with a change of government this Company was set aside and another formed in 1923 to be representative of purely French interests. This Company, the Compagnie Française des Pétroles, whose principal initial duty was to hold the Turkish Petroleum shares, was organized by M. Ernest Mercier and assumed its final form in 1931; from which date onwards the French Government held 35 per cent. of the shares but, by a special arrangement, 40 per cent. of the voting power.

Interest in Mesopotamian affairs had meanwhile been stirred in another quarter, that of the United States. The Open-Door policy in dependent territories, normally favoured there, was now specifically reinforced by fears of the exhaustion of oil supplies in North America itself; and the phrase, which stood for the equality of all comers in Mandated territories, appealed equally to the United States Government and to major American oil companies, which had previously adventured little in the eastern hemisphere. Standard Oil (New Jersey) proposed in 1919 to send geologists to 'Iraq, but was discouraged by its Government; it was joined in 1921 in a similar application by other companies,[1] with equal lack of success. Meanwhile a correspondence on Open-Door lines took place between the State Department and the Foreign Office, opened by a vigorous, but to some extent misinformed, letter by Ambassador Davis in May 1920. Lord Curzon replied that the American share of world oil was so predominant, and America's own exclusiveness in the past so marked that the United States could well acquiesce in British companies benefiting from the Turkish promise of 1914 which they held and which it was improper to ignore; in any case, the resources of 'Iraq would belong not to Britain but to the future state to be founded there. Subsequent letters between Bainbridge Colby and Lord Curzon prolonged the correspondence into 1921, but failed to render it conclusive.

It was, nevertheless, apparent on both sides of the Atlantic that some form of admission of American interests into Mesopotamian

[1] The Texas Company, Mexican Petroleum Company, Gulf Corporation, Atlantic Refining Company, Sinclair Consolidated Oil Corporation, and Standard Oil of New York. These, like New Jersey itself, had responded to an invitation by Herbert Hoover to interest themselves in overseas oil sources.

oil was desirable and must be arranged. The attitude of the T.P.C. shareholders to this was generally unfavourable, though Gulbenkian supported it and the major constituents were prepared to yield to governmental pressure. The question was discussed by Sir John Cadman during a visit to the United States in 1921, and in 1922 further conversations felt their way towards American entry on a basis which should conform to the Open-Door principle. Provisional agreement on behalf of the American companies was reached in 1922 and provided for American interest to the extent of one quarter, more or less, of the Company's share capital. The Company itself was to take leases for a limited number of plots in 'Iraq, to allow other areas to be taken freely by others, to confine itself strictly to functions of production and refining, and not to compete for any leases in 'Iraq outside its own plots. In further talks in 1923 it was agreed that the American shareholding should come wholly or substantially from the Anglo-Persian block of $47\frac{1}{2}$ per cent., the latter to be compensated by an overriding royalty, ultimately fixed at 10 per cent., on all oil produced by Turkish Petroleum. The incorporation of these conditions (other than the last mentioned) in the ultimate T.P.C. Concession of March 1925 and the effective entry of American oil companies as shareholders belong to later pages (p. 67). Agreement was, at the stage now reached, still imperfect, the American interest unofficial and provisional, and the dismay of Gulbenkian at the proposed lines of agreement (which restricted the area wherein he occupied a favourable position) still unappeased.

During and even after the earlier phases of this Anglo-American rapprochement there were disturbing influences at work. Admiral Chester, whose draft concession before the war had brought his Ottoman-American Development Company no valid rights, renewed his applications to the Turkish authorities after 1918. He was *persona grata* in Turkish governing circles, and received at least some measure, it was said, of American support; and the Grand National Assembly, at loggerheads with the British Government over treaty-making, was glad in April 1923 to ratify the 'Chester Concession' in terms which bestowed on him the mineral rights over a twenty-four-mile strip athwart the railway which Ottoman-American was to build into the heart of northern 'Iraq. But it was not to be; the Lausanne Treaty was signed in July 1923 and Turkey was in no position to make grants in the Mosul province. Ottoman-American, for its part, failed to carry out the first of its stipulated obligations; its 'concession' lapsed, and threats of legal action by the Admiral against the T.P.C. gradually died into silence.

By the end of 1923, with a king on the throne of Baghdad and a treaty signed between His Majesty's Government and the 'Iraq Kingdom, the first stages could be taken towards the long-delayed development of 'Mosul Oil'.

## CHAPTER IV

# OIL UNDER RIZA SHAH

## I. BETWEEN THE WARS

MIDDLE Eastern oil production, still humble in 1920 and barely exceeding 1 per cent. of world output, increased tenfold in the following two decades to a rate of some 15 million t/y, or 5·5 per cent. of the world's production: a rate of progress unsensational if judged by achievements since 1945, but accompanied by the highly fruitful discovery of oilfields in Arabia and 'Iraq, which later years were to see brought into production. Even by 1939, however, the future importance of Middle Eastern oil was still largely unrealized.

The region as one of oil production had great advantages. The administrations, officials, and social services of the States were improving from the nineteen-twenties onwards: modern communications were coming into use: security, though imperfect, was far superior to that of an earlier generation. The local governments were, in general, eager to see their resources exploited, to the profit of their treasuries: and great foreign companies, financially and technically competent, and capable also of an enlightened attitude to a task of trusteeship, were willing to undertake such development in the well-judged belief that world demand for oil would continue regularly to increase,[1] and to call for ever wider sources of supply. By far the greatest of the advantages of Middle Eastern oilfields was partly already manifest in Persia, partly awaited further demonstration in Arabia and 'Iraq: the extraordinary size of its oil-bearing structures, the vast scale of the reservoirs, and the productivity of single wells compared with the fields of North America or the Caribbean.[2] At the same time, the ownership of oil by the State and the elimination of vexatious competitive operation made possible 'unit development' of discovered struc-

---

[1] World oil-production was 70,000 tons in 1860, 4 million in 1880, 20 million in 1900, 59 million in 1915, 94 million in 1920, 148 million in 1925, 278 million in 1939.

[2] In 1947, for example, Persia was producing, from a few dozen wells, at the rate of 280,000 tons per year per well, and the average for the whole Middle East was 180,000 per year per well. The comparable figure for the United States, with its half-a-million wells, was 610 tons and for the Caribbean area 7,850 tons.

tures on the economic, balanced, and scientific lines best able to conserve the national wealth and to offer cheap and efficient production.

The period was one of great technical advance. In the search for oil structures, the geologist was better equipped, better instructed, more specialized than ever before; the geophysicist used with increasing mastery his gravity-meter, magnetometer, and seismic methods to discover the density and stratification of rocks deeply buried from view. Drilling itself, in which the rotary method usually though not universally displaced cable-tool equipment, was perfected in every part of its machinery and processes, and could attain greater depth, reliable well-head control, and almost complete straightness of the drilled hole. Oilfield science and the lore of reservoirs—the province of the Petroleum Engineer—advanced year by year. The installations of gas-separation and stabilization were improved; techniques were developed for re-injecting both unwanted products and pressure-creating gases into the structure, for recovering gasoline from 'wet' gas, for utilizing gas for industrial purposes, for dehydrating emulsified oil, and for sulphur recovery. Life in oilfields was transformed by the provision of abundant electric power, good water supplies, ranges of domestic as well as industrial buildings, modern amenities, full social services, and a wealth of transport and communication facilities. Every detail of pipelines, pumping installations, and tank-farms advanced in scale and efficiency. Refining, based on previous years of research, attained its modern forms and yielded products far ahead, in their diversity and quality, of those of the early days of the industry.

But, with all these natural and man-made advantages, the industry in the Middle East faced also its particular obstacles. If severe climates, roadless terrain, waterless sites, resourceless countrysides, and untrained labour forces could be supported or corrected (and indeed were not unusual features of oil country), the distance of the Middle Eastern fields from main centres of consumption was (and is) an adverse factor of serious weight. A distance of 6,500 miles to Great Britain from the head of the Persian Gulf, with Canal dues to be paid, gave Middle Eastern oil a passage to Europe 2,000 miles longer than from the Gulf of Mexico; and the shorter—but still 3,300-mile—journey from the eastern Mediterranean could be achieved only by the installation of highly expensive and vulnerable pipelines across the desert. This placed Persian, 'Iraqi, or Arabian oil at a clear disadvantage against American in the greatest of eastern-hemisphere markets.

The problems thus posed were economic or technical; others, of a political type, would prove less tractable, and these, still absent in the less evolved Arabian territories, appeared in Persia and the Fertile Crescent in the nineteen-twenties and nineteen-thirties to an extent which was already disquieting; they were to develop more fully after 1945. The underlying cause of the deep social and political unrest of the Middle East, which at the mid-century was all too obvious and seemed likely to persist, was connected with the painful and relatively sudden reorientation of these countries from the position of socially backward, industrially non-existent, politically fettered territories into independent States subject to all the strains and demands of the divided, competitive, and exacting twentieth-century world, and with the heightened self-consciousness of late arrivals ill-equipped in unfamiliar surroundings. Although in the Arab countries in the early nineteen-twenties a degree of European tutelage, by Mandate or treaty, partly restrained the cruder manifestations of local patriotism, it was inevitable that the emotional, unstable elements in the Middle Eastern character should prove difficult in dealings with the sober businessmen of the West, even when the charm, responsiveness, and humour of the best Arab and Persian society were well in evidence; and in their politics—which to a Middle Eastern évolué cover the industrial sphere as they cover the whole of corporate life—the appeal to national or nationalist emotion was certain to be used habitually to excite an inflammable and unreflecting public. The benefits brought by a great foreign enterprise to the Treasury, the nation, and its own workers would be appreciated only by a small proportion of the public; and, even so, material benefits can never on any level compete with emotional appeals in the Middle East, where efficiency is not especially valued and the 'greatest happiness of the greatest number' is not always the prime objective of politicians.

The nationalism to which local publicists appeal contained (and contains) a specifically anti-foreign element in its emotional content: a phenomenon capable, indeed, of analysis and explanation, but not the less embarrassing to the resident foreigner. Its appeal was the normal stock-in-trade of every politician, and was used at times on frankly competitive lines—the more anti-foreign, the greater the patriot! It was fed by a very human resentment at the mere presence in their midst of well-organized, well-established, rich, and thriving foreign enterprises, with wealth and standards too obviously in advance of anything indigenous: a resentment made up of *amour propre*, jealousy, and personal or corporate frustration. These feelings, given all the historical and psychological elements in the Middle East from 1920 onwards, were likely to prevail in all but comparatively rare political circles, and bound gravely to embarrass the companies, whose own merits or achievements were powerless to check them.

Meanwhile, there could be little doubt about the method or agency to be adopted for Middle Eastern development. The countries concerned were, save for limited areas, scantily populated. They contained wide areas of steppe country, barren hill tracts, and total desert. They were generally remote not only from the major markets, but also from main lines and means of communication. Resources were slight, skilled labour was rare, large-scale industry unknown. Their economies were in general primitive, concentrations of private wealth few (save in Egypt), poverty almost universal. In view of the minimum requirements of oil development in Middle East conditions, it was apparent that local private enterprise could not imaginably be adequate to the task; and local Governments (save in Turkey) did not as such enter the field on any considerable scale.

If the use of foreign capital be accepted, for lack of alternative, as a necessary evil, it could, except in rare cases, scarcely operate otherwise than through the grant by state authorities of 'blanket concessions' to such foreign companies as applied with suitable offers. This method was, in fact, widely adopted; and to it, as later pages will show, almost the whole of Middle Eastern oil development was in fact due. The grants thus made by sovereign states to British, American, Anglo-American, or international groups between 1924 and 1939, and covering for fifty-year or longer terms the whole or a great part of a country, carried conditions which were in every case the subject of long discussion and hard bargaining before the concession was bestowed; nor will it be found that these terms as agreed were in general over-indulgent in view of the risks taken and the tasks faced by the companies, nor that undue influences or pressures were brought to bear in

obtaining them. The subsequent attitudes and achievements of
the concession-holding companies will sufficiently appear in later
pages.

## II. THE NINETEEN-TWENTIES IN PERSIA

In Persia the period of great expansion in the oil industry which
followed the first war, continued for ten years unchecked: or
indeed for twenty, with the 1929–31 period of depression and the
concession troubles of 1932–3 as a partial mid-way halt. And while
the Anglo-Persian outside Persia built up its world-wide organization, upon which its prosperity wholly depended, it was served
within Persia by an increasingly evolved, loyal, and adequate
organization.

T. L. Jacks was appointed Resident Director of the Company,
with headquarters at Teheran, in 1926, and so remained till 1934.
At Abadan, J. A. Jameson held the General Managership until
1927, when he left Persia for a directorship of the Company in
London. He was succeeded for ten years by E. H. O. Elkington,
and the latter in 1937 by J. M. Pattinson. The General Fields
Managers of the period were J. Wright 1924–6, M. C. Seamark
1927–30, C. R. Clark 1931–7, and H. W. Lane 1937–45. In
London, Sir John Cadman who had joined the Company's board
in 1921, became Chairman in 1927; Sir Charles Greenway, raised
to the peerage, was appointed President of the Company.

The oilfield of Maidan-i-Naftun, renamed Masjid-i-Sulaiman
in 1926, was already in full production as this period opens; but
important additions were still to be made to its installations,
technical equipment, facilities, and amenities. Its electric supply
was secured by a new power-station at Tembi, its stores and workshops were developed, and a large range of industrial and domestic
building completed. The hospital was enlarged; branch dispensaries were opened. A Company-built bazaar and shops
erected by controlled private enterprise appeared. Roads feeding
the area and within it were improved and bridges constructed. A
light railway from Dar-i-Khazina to Fields was opened in 1924,
the Karun barge fleet multiplied. Air services began to run, landing grounds were levelled, and the variety and number of road
vehicles increased. The water-supply from Godar Landar on the
Karun was doubled by new pipelines, plant was erected for the
recovery of gasoline from natural gas, and the 'dry' gas was

utilized for all industrial and domestic purposes of heating, lighting, and fuel throughout Fields. The possibility of re-injecting gas into the structure, as a means of re-pressuring, was kept under consideration but not adopted.

The 're-cycling' of liquid hydrocarbons, however, became a characteristic practice in Persia and, like the 'unit development' of structures and multi-stage gas separation, was a major technical contribution of Anglo-Persian. The practice began in 1929 with the re-transfer, by pipeline from Abadan to Fields, of products for which, at the moment, there was no export demand. These, with the object of conserving them for later extraction, were re-injected into the structure through wells drilled into the highest or gas-cap portion and were thus re-absorbed into the pores and fissures of the limestone. The practice once established, economy demanded that the unwanted products should be separated at Fields; this was done by the erection there of a topping-plant of capacity of 1 million t/y, enabling the wanted products to be despatched to Abadan and the unwanted to be re-cycled.

Production from the Masjid-i-Sulaiman field amounted in 1923 to 2·9 million t/y and in the six years following to 3·7, 4·3, 4·5, 4·8, 5·3, and 5·4 million, after which in 1930, and thereafter, the Haft Kel Field joined it in production (p. 54).

The exploration which led to the last-mentioned development was no new activity. On the eve of the first war test drilling was in progress at various points in the concession area, and it was resumed in 1922. Further trials at Qishm Island were, with disappointment, abandoned after three costly years, and equal failure resulted at more than a dozen other sites in southern and western Persia.[1] The search was recommenced in 1926 by the work of a number of geological and geophysical field parties, upon the basis of whose reports drilling locations were selected or the areas dismissed. These inquiries resulted in a great majority of disappointments, and emphasized once more both the exceptional difficulty of locating oilfields, when the reservoir structures were covered by unconformable and misleading deposits above them, and the falsity of the hopes which could at times be raised by surface seepages. The record was one of failure at nearly all the locations

[1] During the whole period 1914–36 unsuccessful wells were drilled by the Company at Shahabad, Dalpari, Deh Luran, Zeloi, Pirgah, Gach Khalaj, Sar-i-Naftak, Yamaha, Kundak, Ahwaz, Mamatain, Chillingar, Sulabadar, Kuh-i-Mund, and Qishm.

examined; but the exceptions were such as to justify the whole of, and much more than, the great cost and effort involved. Even at locations later to be famous as centres of production the initial discoveries in the period 1926–30 were inconclusive. At Zeloi, in an area close to the later Lali field, early results were disappointing. White Oil Springs (later known as Naft Safid), in spite of its gas seepage and the light-coloured condensate found on the surface, was slow to reveal its buried stores; and at the remoter site of Gach Qaraghuli (later Gach Saran) the wells drilled in 1929, before the great depression halted operations in every area, revealed oil but left it incompletely proved for six more years. At Agha Jari, similarly, the proving of the field by further drilling was postponed till better times. At the small field of Naft-i-Shah, forming half of 'Iraq's Naftkhana field, a first well was drilled in 1927 and a second in 1928, but no production followed until six years later.

At Haft Kel, on the contrary, a field of the greatest, indeed almost unprecedented, richness was discovered in 1928. Marked by extensive seepages, it lies thirty-five miles south-south-east of Masjid-i-Sulaiman. The limestone reservoir, which forms an elongated dome, is overlaid with the usual uncomformable beds of the Middle and Lower Fars system and by a cap-rock of anhydrite. The productive Asmari limestone is 900 feet thick, the reservoir some seventeen miles long by three wide, and the oil of gravity 37 degrees A.P.I. Further wells were drilled from 1929 onwards, six producers being completed by 1930. Pipelines in that year were completed from Haft Kel to join the Masjid-i-Sulaiman–Abadan lines at Kut 'Abdullah. The field, 140 miles from Abadan, produced a million tons of oil in 1930 and greater quantities in each succeeding year. Thus augmented, the total production for Persia reached 5·9 million tons in 1930, fell to 5·7 in the slump year of 1931, and recovered to 6·4 million in 1932.

The throughput capacity of the main pipelines reached 17,000 tons a day, or over 6 million t/y, by 1930. The use of the Mulla Sani' pumping-station was discontinued, the installations at the others (Tembi, Kut 'Abdullah, Dorquain) were improved. Ahwaz, which was Pipeline Headquarters before 1930, was at this period a main station for stores, workshops, river, and road transport, with a Company's hospital and large European community; but from the depression of 1930 onwards it was greatly reduced in scale.

At Abadan the record was consistently one of growing expansion realized and of difficulties overcome: an increasing community to be housed, fed, and cared for with services and amenities of every kind: vaster tank-farms for crude oil and products: the installation of new plant and equipment on lines indicated by the increasing scale of throughput and by the improved processes which technological advance made possible and which the markets demanded. By 1930 refining capacity reached 13,000 tons a day, or nearly 5 million t/y. New crude-distillation units erected in 1929–30 were followed by thermal cracking plant, whose products could meet the demand for a greater proportion of gasoline, and this of higher octane-rating.

Development of Abadan as a port kept pace with increased tanker liftings, and loading facilities improved and multiplied. In 1925 agreement was reached with the Port of Basra for the dredging of the Fao Bar, which restricted the entry of shipping into the Shatt al-'Arab, and a loan of £500,000 made by the Company to the port enabled the latter to begin operations with dredgers on the selected Rooka Channel. A year later the proportion of lightering at the bar could be reduced, and in 1928 was brought down to a negligible figure. The loan was repaid; and the dredged channel became a permanent boon to the traffic of Basra, Abadan, and Muhammara.

The policy of the Company towards its workers increasingly declared itself in these years as one of 'model employment' with the maximum of Persianization of its staff. Since of formal organization or unionization of labour there was at this period neither possibility nor demand, the attitude to the workers was of necessity paternalistic; the Company offered spontaneously such conditions as seemed to it suitable and generous. These were beyond question far superior to those offered by any Persian employer, and went far beyond any legal or contractual obligation; but the fact that they were bestowed by a foreign management, in which as yet no Persian played a responsible part, detracted from the value given them by their recipients. Nevertheless, alien as the Company must remain, the pride of Persian workers in its service was apparent, their skill developed and was used, promotion to higher positions grew commoner, and the annual wastage due to workers' seasonal reversion to their own homes and herds became a less constant feature.

The administration of the Company's labour force, which by

1931 exceeded 20,000 Persians, was carried out with close regard to careful recruiting, high physical standards, regular pay and holidays, and a code of detailed regulation both humane and reasonable. Employment officers became expert in handling grievances and promoting welfare; all were Persian-speaking. Many hundreds of houses were built for Persian workers, model bazaars were erected, shops were built or licensed, and in times of scarcity essential food supplies were offered at favourable prices. Medical services were comprehensive and included an all-embracing sanitary and preventive system such as Persia had never known. Dispensaries were ubiquitous, central hospitals with British doctors and nurses were established at Masjid-i-Sulaiman, Ahwaz, and Abadan, with specialist services available. Electric light and power were provided everywhere, fresh-water supplies were assured from rivers by pipeline and pump, bathing facilities were made available. The orderly layout of all premises and settlements, with their broad, well-kept roads, their gardens, clubs, and playing-fields, gave a healthy setting to the lives of workers. Generous help was given to Persian municipalities, at Abadan itself and at Ahwaz. At the former a populous city arose beside the Company's refinery areas, and its Persian authorities received the comprehensive support due to a township which the Company's enterprise alone had brought into existence.

The training of Persians for higher posts in the Company was encouraged equally by common sense, by economy, and by policy. From 1923 onwards increasing care was given to the education and training of workers and potential workers, in workshops and manual training centres and in a training school under European teachers. Schools for the workers' children were built and staffed, and help was given to government schools. All teaching was free, an English educationalist was brought to Persia to co-ordinate and advise, and plans were made to send Persians to the United Kingdom for higher studies. Every effort of policy, expenditure, and goodwill was forthcoming from the Company before 1932 towards improving the capacity of Persian staff and workers, with no limit to the level which lay open to them in the Company's system.

The impact of its operations on the public of Khuzistan was strong and favourable. It was the source of wealth and vitality, offered secure employment in good conditions, and afforded direct benefits in its medical services, communications, and schools, with others less direct in the stabilization of society, the increased circulation of wealth, and the force of example. Relations with the neighbouring shaikhs or khans, herdsmen and villagers were generally friendly, and the Company stood wholly aloof from local politics, even when these removed from the scene its veteran friend Shaikh Khaz'al of Muhammara. To the public of Teheran the Company was little known; to the politicians and intelligentsia it represented primarily an issue which, since it concerned foreigners, could be made political; but the magnitude of the enterprise in Khuzistan, its mastered difficulties, its enormous financial investment, its expanding and beneficial social influence, its vast technical and industrial feats accomplished, these were almost wholly unrealized. Few indeed were the critics in Teheran who, to see for themselves, made the journey to Abadan or to Fields.

The relations of Riza Shah himself (crowned as such in 1925) with the Company were correct and outwardly cordial; he had by 1932 twice visited the Company's operations, with great expressed satisfaction.

Some signs of interest were shown in Persian oil during the middle and later nineteen-twenties, by others than the Anglo-Persian. A firman granted fifty years earlier to a Persian notable was reaffirmed in 1924 in favour of a surviving kinsman and his friends, who formed the Kavir-i-Khurian Company for the exploitation of oil in the Semnan district; and a controlling interest in this enterprise was acquired soon afterwards by none other than Khostharia (p. 38), who in turn sold a majority shareholding to the Soviet Government and smaller blocks of shares to Persian and French investors. Some drilling was carried out, without favourable result. This work, however, and the interest of the French shareholders led in 1927 to the formation in Paris of a Franco-Belgian group, the Syndicat d'Etudes Franco-Persanes. This became a candidate for a larger north-Persian Concession; and in June 1930 a Société Franco-Persane de Recherches was formed, with the Syndicat as a participant in it. Geologists were sent to Persia for a beginning of exploration, but no active operations followed. The Company was renamed Franco-Iranienne in 1935.

### III. 1933: A NEW DEAL

Persian statesmen had convinced themselves by the later nineteen-twenties that the 1901 Concession, even as interpreted by the

Armitage–Smith Agreement of 1920, was no longer adequate to the present scale of the Company's operations, nor to the change of times. Hostile critics of the Company did not hesitate to allege that the original concession was invalid, that Persian rights were ignored, that their receipts were unjustly diminished by devices of accountancy (by the exclusion, for instance, of subsidiary companies, and by the sale of oil to the British Fleet at less than commercial rates), that the process of Persianization was too slow and the concession itself too extensive. The Company on its side felt the need of more explicit provisions, a longer concessionary period to justify the immense financial investment existing and contemplated, and a more definite guarantee of undisturbed possession.

Initial discussions through 1929 to 1931 led to no result; Persian demands appeared to the Company excessive and unreasonable. Conversations, however, limited to the calculation of profits, were begun late in 1931, and in February 1932 the Council of Ministers agreed to a draft embodying new principles. This, as initialed by plenipotentiaries, was sent to Teheran in May 1932 for ratification. But at this point appeared a further factor disturbing to the Government: the Company's accounts for 1931–2 showed substantially diminished profits, a natural consequence of the severe world-wide depression; and the Government, which had received £1,436,000 for 1929 and £1,288,000 for 1930, was to receive only £307,000 for 1931. Confronted with this, it resentfully declined to ratify the draft agreement, requested (in vain) that a mission from the Company should visit Teheran, stated that its own counter-proposals were en route—and on 27 November 1932 suddenly announced its outright cancellation of the concession, while simultaneously expressing its willingness to negotiate another. The Majlis on 1 December confirmed the decision, which was conveyed to the Company and elicited its strongest protests.

These were followed next day by a letter from the British to the Persian Government declaring the cancellation to be inadmissible and reserving the right to 'take all the legitimate measures' to protect British interests; and a few days later it was stated that unless the Persian letter of cancellation was withdrawn within a week, the matter would be referred to the Permanent Court of International Justice. The Persians refused to admit the competence of this Court; whereupon the Foreign Office referred the dispute, as one of urgency, to the Council of the League of Nations, under Article 15 of the League Covenant.

While the Company's operations in Persia were allowed to proceed without interruption, the reference to the League was followed by the tendering by both Governments of the full statements of their case to the Council. Mr. Beneš of Czechoslovakia was on 24 January 1933 appointed as rapporteur; two days later both Governments, through Sir John Simon and M. Davar respectively, stated their positions orally to the Council; and, after a week of negotiations by the rapporteur with both, he announced that each had agreed to a temporary withdrawal of the case from the Council's consideration, in hopes of reaching direct agreement. The Council concurred. During February direct negotiations continued in Geneva and Paris; in April, still with the close cognizance of the rapporteur, they were transferred to Teheran whither Directors of the Company and, finally, the Chairman proceeded. After hard bargaining by the Shah and his ministers—grotesquely misrepresented in later years as dictation by the Company to a powerless Government—a new Convention was signed on 29 April, was ratified by the Majlis and the Shah a month later, and was announced by M. Beneš to the League Council as an effective disposal of the dispute. Both Governments expressed their satisfaction at the amicable settlement, which contained in its Articles 21 and 26 a specific guarantee by Government against premature determination; [1] both thanked the League Council and its rapporteur for their good offices, and both addressed the Registrar of the Permanent Court with the request that the Court should accept in certain cases, should these arise, the duty of appointing an umpire to assist in arbitration.

The new Agreement extended the Company's rights for a further thirty-two years—to the end of 1993—but limited them to a defined area (one-quarter of the original D'Arcy grant) in south-west Persia: an area which was by 1938 to be further restricted to one of 100,000 square miles. A new basis for the assessment of royalties was provided. These would be calculated at 4s. sterling per ton, with allowance made for increase in this rate in the event of a depreciation of sterling in terms of gold, and with a guaranteed

---

[1] It was in return for these explicit guarantees of security of tenure, and the extension of the period, that the Company agreed to the reduction of area.

minimum of £750,000 in any year; and to this was to be added, first, 9*d.* per ton as commuted taxation (to give a minimum total sum of £225,000 a year) and, secondly, a sum equal to 20 per cent. of any distribution made to the Company's ordinary stockholders in excess of £670,000 in any year and, upon expiry of the concession, a sum equal to 20 per cent. also of the difference between the Company's General Reserve on that date and that on 31 December 1932. The royalties for 1931 and 1932 were to be recalculated on the new basis; they amounted to £1,339,000 and £1,525,000 respectively. A payment of £1 million was made additionally in settlement of all or any outstanding claims. The Company bound itself to produce, refine, and sell oil through a separate Company in the province of Kirmanshah, where the Naft-i-Shah field had been left undeveloped. An expedited process of Persianization of employees was envisaged, with an annual grant for the professional education of Persian students in Great Britain. Arbitration procedure was laid down, to deal with any later dispute that might arise.

By the new settlement thus freely negotiated and ratified by the Persian Government and endowed with all the sanctity of an agreement blessed by the League of Nations, whose good offices had secured it, it seemed that the further operations of the Company in Persia, whatever risks or adverse fortunes they might encounter, must at least be beyond the reach of political criticism or disturbance.

### IV. FIELDS AND ABADAN, 1933–9

Relations between the Persian (Iranian) Government and the Anglo-Persian Oil Company—renamed Anglo-Iranian in 1935, to conform with Riza Shah's changed name for his country—remained generally satisfactory throughout the last third of the period between the wars: even inveterate critics of the 'Foreign Company' had for a time little to say, though the essential uneasiness of the situation—that of a highly prospering foreign enterprise confronting a suspicious and emotional Persian nationalism—still tacitly obtained. The terms of the new concession, favourable as they were to the nation and questioned by no single voice as to their validity and authority, were punctiliously observed—or rather, as was habitual, far surpassed—in the services rendered by the Company. The decision in the one controversial issue which

arose was conceded as an act of grace by the Company: that
the calculation of royalties be allowed on a basis of metric tons of
2,014 lb., instead of long tons of 2,240 lb. The increased royalties
were paid and accepted without incident or question; only at the
end of this period, in 1938 and 1939, was some Persian dismay
expressed at their failure to increase. These contributions to the
Persian Treasury [1] had long since become necessary to the
stability and almost to the existence of the state, and represented
a main part of Persian receipts from all sources.

The duty imposed by the 1933 Agreement to limit and define
the concessionary area was duly carried out and notified to Government in 1938. The finally selected 100,000-square-mile area was
bounded on the north by an irregular line running parallel to the
main trend of the Zagros ranges, from its north-eastern point on
the 'Iraq frontier to its south-western end on the Straits of
Hormuz.

Another direct consequence of the new Agreement was the
development of the Naft-i-Shah field. The Kirmanshah Oil
Company, an *ad hoc* subsidiary, was registered in London in
June 1934. Drilling recommenced on the small but productive
structure—or half-structure—which was soon equipped with
necessary installations and buildings in readiness for production.
A small topping-plant was erected, enabling products not wanted
at the refinery to be 're-cycled'. A 3-inch pipeline was constructed
to Kirmanshah, 158 miles distant across mountainous country
rising in places to 5,000 feet; with four pumping stations, it conveyed Naft-i-Shah crude for treatment at a small refinery erected
three miles from the city. This was soon brought into operation
with an output of some 100,000 t/y, and took its place in the
northern area of the Company's internal supply and distribution
system.

The scene of another development of the period was the wide
region of Persia which had now been excluded from the Anglo-
Iranian's area. Of Khostharia, North Persian Oils, and the Sinclair group no more was to be heard; but in 1937 the grant of a
concession for fifty years was made to the Amiranian Oil Company,

---

[1] For the years 1933–7 inclusive they amounted to £1,812,000, £2,189,000,
£2,220,000, £2,580,000 and £5,545,000; in 1938 the payment fell to £3,307,000
and for 1939, not surprisingly, to £2,770,000, thus producing a situation which
special steps were taken to meet when it arose (p. 124).

an enterprise registered in Delaware, U.S.A., and controlled by the Seaboard Oil Company of that State. The Agreement covered a wide area of northern and eastern Persia, which was to be reduced within fifteen years to one of 100,000 square miles. The royalty payable was 4s. a ton, with security against currency fluctuations and with the addition of 20 per cent. of profits. The Amiranian Company proceeded to two years of extensive geological survey; but although attractive structures were not lacking, no such prospects were discovered as to compensate for the unfavourable inland situation of the concession, and it was abandoned in 1939. In May of that year an exploration licence was granted to a Dutch mining company, the Algemeene Exploratie Maatschappij, covering the five northern provinces. If oil were found, the licence would be superseded by a sixty-year concession; the Persian public were to be allowed to subscribe up to 40 per cent., in the event of public subscription being invited; no shareholding other than Dutch or Persian was admissible, and the latter Government was to receive 50 per cent. of profits realized. The outbreak of war, however, prevented the undertaking of field operations, and the licence was abandoned in 1944.

The Anglo-Iranian was more fortunate. The period from 1933 to 1939 was fruitful in its confirmation of the new sources of supply, which had been located before 1930, and in fresh discoveries. These were achieved by strenuous exploration and test-drilling, which were restarted with all the encouragement of the new concession as the period of depression came to an end. These operations were both costly and arduous in their necessary provision of roads, transport, water and fuel supplies, drilling and technical equipment, and shelter, maintenance, and domestic necessities for staff and workers, Persian and British, in locations often the most remote and inaccessible. A number of seemingly hopeful sites had, as a result of this campaign, to be reluctantly dismissed; but thanks to persistence and the advance both of regional knowledge and of structure-finding technique—since all geophysical methods had by now come into use—good prospects were revealed both in new areas and in some which had been formerly abandoned, and early in 1934 arrangements were made for test-drilling at a number of chosen locations.

At Zeloi, where the probability of a buried anticline similar to that of Masjid-i-Sulaiman had led to the drilling of three wells in

1927 and 1928, a fourth well was begun in 1936 and carried to 11,190 feet (one of the world's deepest at that time), but found no oil. A move was then made northward to Lali, immediately adjacent. Here a well sited by geophysical means and drilled in 1938 entered gas-bearing limestone at a depth of less than 4,000 feet. Later exploration confirmed the presence of oil in a spacious anticline in which the limestone reservoir-rock was 1,200 feet thick. Production, however, was not to be realized for ten more years.

Simultaneously with the work at Zeloi, a well was drilled ten miles north-west of Haft Kel at Naft Safid, where earlier attempts to find oil had failed. Those now made, from 1934 to 1937, were successful: a limestone structure of the usual type, fifteen miles long by two broad, was found to contain oil and gas.

Sixty miles south-south-east of Haft Kel, at Agha Jari, where an oilfield had been discovered before the depression stopped work, drilling was resumed in 1935 and soon confirmed the existence of oil deposits of great magnitude stored in the usual type of domed limestone anticline overlaid, with the usual disharmony, by some 4,500 feet of Upper and Lower Fars. Progress, however, towards production, which would call for major Fields' installations, buildings, and a hundred-mile pipeline, was not far advanced by the outbreak of war. At Pazanun, some fifteen miles south-east of Agha Jari, drilling at the same period revealed an extensive gasfield, but no oil: this was left, for the time, unused.

The Gach Saran structure, located before 1930, still awaited proof and development. A well drilled in 1935, and others thereafter, satisfied the Company that in spite of the higher gravity of the oil (32 degrees A.P.I.), this field was the first candidate for development among the newer discoveries. The oil-bearing limestone, itself 1,500 feet thick, lay at a depth of 3,000 feet and formed a dome some twenty miles long and nearly five wide. By 1936 a development scheme was drawn up for progressive fulfilment; further wells were drilled, the necessary gathering lines, multi-stage gas separators, and tankage were assembled and erected, pipe was ordered for the necessary 160 miles of line to Abadan, and the construction of domestic and industrial buildings made progress. A project was formed, but not immediately realized, for constructing a sea outlet, and possibly a refinery, for this oil nearer to its source, perhaps in the neighbourhood of Bandar Shapur on the Khor Musa inlet, the terminal of the trans-Persian railway.

Thus the short period from 1934 to 1939, in which the confidence inspired by the new Agreement was shown by the vast expenditure incurred, brought into being no fewer than four major oilfields and one gas-field, additional to the three already under exploitation. Meanwhile, production in these years was limited to Masjid-i-Sulaiman and Haft Kel fields, with a yearly greater proportion being contributed by the latter. Completely equipped between 1933 and 1936, it was already by 1934 giving 2 million t/y, and over 6 million by 1939. Its oil was carried to Abadan by further pipelines constructed between 1933 and 1938. The total of Persian production amounted to 7·08 million tons in 1933, from 1934 to 1938 reached 7·53, 7·48, 8·19, 10·16, and 10·19 million, and in 1939, thanks to the market disturbances and sea dangers resulting from the war, fell to 9·58 million. These figures, except the last, indicate a gradual rise in production; but they do not fully reveal the progress, consolidation, and improvement achieved in all the varied and increasingly complex installations necessary for the development of oilfields to the highest economic and technical standards, the many ancillary and supporting operations of land and air transport and communications, the scrupulous maintenance of vehicles and machinery, the erection, upkeep, and equipment of buildings, the background of scientific research, the services and amenities provided for staff and workers and their families.

The great Abadan refinery increased during the same half-dozen years in scale and flexibility and in the quality of its products. The crude oil reaching Abadan by the pipeline system was there subjected to processes of distillation, of cracking (for which a capacity of 100,000 b/d was available by 1938), and of acid treatment, on lines suited to each of various products and processes; and then, in many cases, of re-distillation. Secondary products prepared at Abadan were 'white spirit', vaporizing oils, a small quantity of aviation spirit, and, in 1938, road asphalt and the barrel-factory for which this called. A chemical manufacturing plant provided, from the solid sulphur recovered in Fields, all the sulphuric acid used in the refinery.

The storage capacity at Abadan amounted in 1938 to some 6 million barrels, mostly in the form of 70,000-barrel tanks. It was situated in two great tank farms, one between the refinery and the Bahmashir River and the other at Bawarda on the Shatt al-

'Arab three miles below Abadan. Ten loading jetties had been built along the Abadan–Bawarda foreshore and arrangements were made for a further loading-area at Khosrawabad, seventeen miles downstream. Marine equipment included a workshop and floating dock. A powerful water pumping station had been erected. Steam for use throughout the refinery was provided centrally as well as by individual batteries of boilers. Electric power was supplied from a powerful modern power-station which provided not only for Abadan refinery and town, but also for the city of Khoramshahr (formerly Muhammara), eight miles away.

During the decade preceding the Second World War the small quantities of crude exported from Persia went to the United Kingdom and Australia for the Company's own refineries and to Egypt for that of Anglo-Egyptian. Refined products from Abadan supplied Persia itself and southern 'Iraq, India through the Burmah-Shell organization, the Middle East and East Africa through Consolidated Petroleum Limited, and the Far East, Africa, and Europe through the Company's own marketing subsidiaries. The Company's tankers provided at this period from 75 to more than 90 per cent. of the south-to-north tanker traffic through the Suez Canal.

The conclusion of the 1933 Agreement was followed by the development of the Company's services in favour of its Persian workers on lines already well established. Such were its health and medical services, its housing estates and town-planning, its water and sewage systems, its active assistance to the municipalities of Abadan and Ahwaz. A 'General Plan' was agreed in 1936 with the Government for the substitution of foreign by Persian staff as rapidly and as completely as could be found practicable. It was hoped to reduce non-Persian employees from a proportion of 17½ per cent. of the skilled grades in 1936 to 13½ per cent. by 1943; unskilled workers were, of course, already exclusively Persian. The Company with this policy (which was its own) and apart from its educational benefactions in Khuzistan and Teheran, completed in 1939 its admirably equipped Technical Institute at Abadan and carried out the training of young Persians by a carefully graded service of vocational training courses. This programme, agreed in detail with the Persian authorities, was the object of meticulous care as well as ungrudged expense on the part of the Company and represented a great and continuing effort, for which it was given too little credit.

## CHAPTER V

# HOPE AND FULFILMENT IN 'IRAQ

## I. NAFTKHANA

WHILE diplomacy, both governmental and industrial, was still busy with the greater problems of 'Iraqi oil disposal, it was at Naftkhana in the Transferred Territory that the first 'Iraqi oil in 'commercial quantities' was discovered. After the success of the well drilled here by the Anglo-Persian in 1923, the High Commissioner, Sir Percy Cox, suggested to the Government that the moment was opportune to make explicit the rights due to this Company under the Perso-Turkish Agreement of 1913. He received the reply that that Agreement was unratified, but that the 'Iraq Government was not unwilling to accede to it and to grant reasonable terms; among these would be a royalty of 20 per cent. of profits (as compared with the 16 per cent. provided in the Persian concession) and the right to participate in the price-fixing of such products as were marketed in 'Iraq. These conditions were debated for many months; and on 30 August 1925 a concession was granted to Anglo-Persian on terms closely similar to those of the Persian Concession of 1901. The obligation was added to build a refinery near Khanaqin for the supply of 'Iraq's own needs, with the privilege of bringing Persian oil into 'Iraq for this purpose if necessary. A year later, however, the evident difficulty of calculating 'profits', and the recent precedent of the Turkish Petroleum Company's concession (p. 69) led to revision and a new Agreement, which, instead of a share of profits, prescribed a royalty of 4s. (gold) per ton. The Khanaqin Oil Company had meanwhile been registered in London as an Anglo-Persian subsidiary and took over from its parent all the responsibilities, operations, and assets of the latter in 'Iraq.

Drilling on the Naftkhana structure began again late in 1925 for the development of the field, which lay twenty-five miles from Khanaqin and railhead. Few wells, however, were needed, and it was possible to discontinue drilling in 1928-30. The field was equipped with normal production installations, a water supply was assured, a power-plant provided, domestic and industrial buildings

erected. The construction of a 4-inch pipeline to a site on the
Alwand River outside Khanaqin was begun in January 1926 and
completed by April of the following year. A 1-inch water-line
took water to Naftkhana from Alwand. The refinery, which was
opened in state by King Faisal in February 1927, was a simple
topping-plant with a throughout capacity of some 150,000 t/y.
It was destined to supply northern and central 'Iraq with products,
while southern areas continued to draw from Abadan. Pipelines
led from Alwand to Khanaqin railway station five miles distant,
where a tin factory came into operation and the loading of cased
or bulk products was carried out. The distribution and marketing
organization of Anglo-Persian in 'Iraq was progressively improved; prices charged for locally-manufactured products were
lower than those of equivalent imports, though Government did
not cease to ask for further reductions. Practical help was given
repeatedly by the Company to oil-using irrigation-pump owners,
whom bad times compelled to live on credit. In March 1932 a
separate marketing company, the Rafidain Oil Company, was
formed by Anglo-Persian to take over all activities of the K.O.C.,
other than those of production and refining.

'Iraq thus became, early in its modern development, fortunately
self-sufficient, or nearly so, in oil products. The quantities of
these issued from Alwand averaged less than 100,000 t/y in the
period from 1927 to 1934, but by 1938-9 had risen to almost
150,000. Nearly 1,000 'Iraqis were maintained in regular employment by the Company. The royalties paid to Government—its
first taste of such revenues—amounted in 1927 to Rs. 105,000
(£7,800) and grew to annual sums ranging between £20,000 and
£30,000.

Drilling at Chiah Surkh, in spite of previous failure, was
resumed in 1924 and again in 1929, but difficulties were once
more encountered and no commercial production was forthcoming.

## II. THE RED LINE

Even with important questions to be settled between the constituent groups, and with the French shareholders and Gulbenkian
still uneasy at American intrusion, the situation within the Turkish
Petroleum Company was thought, nevertheless, sufficiently stable
by the end of 1923 to permit the taking of steps towards validation

of its rights in 'Iraq. The Americans, six [1] of whose companies were still interested, were content to postpone their purchase of shares until they could obtain more satisfaction regarding the conditions of participation and until the value of the enterprise should further declare itself. The position in 'Iraq, however, with an 'Iraq Government established and an Anglo-'Iraq Treaty signed, seemed sufficiently assured—even though the expected League of Nations Frontier Commission, which was to recommend a settlement of the long-debated 'Mosul question', had still to appear.

While the Qaiyara seepages were still worked on a humble scale by the British Military authorities, and those of Kirkuk and Tuz Khormatu by the Naftchi family and the Government respectively, and while the spokesmen of the heirs [2] of Sultan Abdul Hamid were stating their claims to inherit the fabulous riches of the Privy Purse, including all 'Iraqi oil resources, Turkish Petroleum's negotiator, E. H. Keeling, reached Baghdad late in

---

[1] These were Standard Oil (New Jersey), Standard Oil of New York, Gulf Corporation, Atlantic Refining Company, Mexican Petroleum Company and Sinclair Consolidated Oil Corporation. The Texas Company dropped out in 1923, and Pan American Petroleum and Transport Company replaced Mexican in 1927, when the Sinclair Corporation gave up its participation. Six companies, therefore, were left to form Near East Development Corporation (p. 69) in 1928.

[2] The claims of these, an ever-growing body of Turkish princes and princesses, had little effect on the development of Middle Eastern oil. With many bitter factions amongst themselves, they stood together in their assertion that all the oil rights transferred by Abdul Hamid to his Privy Purse were their rightful property. They claimed that the decree of 1908, re-transferring the properties to the State, had not been ratified by Parliament: that of 1909 had been neither ratified nor officially published, and both were extorted under duress. The successor Sultan had in January 1920 issued a decree, re-transferring all to the Privy Purse, and in 1922 the Court of Qasamat had recognized the heirs' claims. The latter added that the Turkish Republic had no power or right to assign these properties, as it had done by Article 60 of the Treaty of Lausanne, to the successor states.

Their lawyers were active at Lausanne in 1923 and subsequently at Geneva. In 1926 began the formation of companies to acquire and seek to validate these claims—the Anglo-Hellenic Finance Corporation, the Valideh Trust Limited and the Aegean Trust Limited. Many applications were made to the 'Iraq Government, which ignored them, and to the Turkish Petroleum Company. In 1930 both the Anglo-Turkish Mixed Arbitral Tribunal and the Italo-Turkish Mixed Arbitral Tribunal declared the claim to be beyond their competence. Four other companies were subsequently registered in Canada to deal with the claims, and American lawyers found a fluctuating but agreeable income from the diminishing purses of the princes and princesses. That any one of the successor states should at any time concede any part of these claims, remained inconceivable.

1923. He was to find his task of gaining a 'blanket' concession for 'Iraq, in fulfilment of the 1914 promise, complicated not only by the general preoccupation in Baghdad with politics, but also by the efforts of competitors. One of these represented the Phoenix Oil and Transport Company, another, fresh from successes in Arabia, was the Eastern and General Syndicate, another a group supported by Lord Inverforth, while in 1924, another, from the Pearson (Lord Cowdray) interests, visited Baghdad or whispered in London in the hope of swaying the 'Iraq or British Governments away from Turkish Petroleum claims and favour. Keeling continued his negotiations, with interruptions, until March 1925; and on the 14th of that month a Convention was signed with the appropriate Minister and ratified by the Council of Ministers—in the absence, as yet, of a Parliament.

The Turkish Petroleum Concession of 1925, covering for seventy-five years the whole of 'Iraq except the Transferred Territories and the Basra vilayet, provided for a royalty of 4s. (gold) per ton of crude oil: for the supply by the Company of 'Iraq's requirements in refined products: and for an obligation to begin drilling within three years with five drilling rigs working simultaneously, and thereafter to maintain a drilling footage of at least 12,000 feet a year. The concession allowed for the selection by the Company, within thirty-two months, of twenty-four 8-squaremile plots for its own exploitation, while, acting as agent for the Government, it was to offer by auction at least twenty-four others to all comers: a provision intended to meet, by an arrangement which could scarcely have been workable, American insistence on the Open Door.

While active operations began and proceeded in 'Iraq, the longdrawn attempt at reconciliation of conflicting interests among the groups filled, behind the scenes, the years from 1925 to 1928; and the compromise finally agreed permitted no independent acquisition of rights by T.P.C. constituents except in the twenty-four (or more) plots not chosen by the T.P.C. itself, and, even then, such acquisition was allowable only to the Americans. On this basis, and greatly helped by the sensational oil-strike at Kirkuk in October 1927, a working agreement could at last be reached between all the groups; and the Americans, formed *ad hoc* into the Near East Development Corporation, accepted transfer of half the Anglo-Persian shareholding, the latter company in return being compensated by an overriding royalty of 10 per cent. on all T.P.C. oil. The final shareholding in the Company was thus adjusted to its long-familiar form of 23·75 per cent. for each 'major group', and with 5 per cent. for Gulbenkian, and a definitive Group Agreement—the well-known Red Line Agreement—embodying these arrangements was signed on 31 July 1928. The T.P.C., limited strictly to functions of production and transport, was to act henceforward in the capacity of non-profit-making supplier of cheap crude oil to its constituents, one of whom would buy the Gulbenkian share at a just valuation.

The Red Line Agreement, variously assessed as a sad case of wrongful cartelization [1] or as an enlightened example of inter-national co-operation and fair sharing, was to hold the field for twenty years and in large measure determined the pattern and tempo of oil development over a great part of the Middle East.

### III. BABA GURGUR

Meanwhile much had happened in 'Iraq. The Mosul province had been finally awarded to that kingdom by the League of Nations in December 1925, and, under a treaty between 'Iraq and Turkey, the latter was for twenty-five years, to receive 10 per cent. of 'Iraq's oil revenues derived from the T.P.C. Concession. The general attitude of both Government and public, though not of all politicians, was friendly to the Turkish Petroleum Company, and its field work could begin in good conditions. A first geological mission headed by Professor H. de Bockh, toured 'Iraq in 1926, and on its evidence drilling sites were selected and a programme for ten wells was established for 1927–8. H. C. H. Bull proceeded to 'Iraq as General Manager and H. A. Hammick as Fields Manager: in London Sir Adam Ritchie, as General Manager until 1929, succeeded H. E. Nichols, who had been Managing Director since 1921.[2] Twelve modern rotary or combination drilling-rigs were dispatched to 'Iraq with staff, equipment, and supplies of every kind; a Fields' headquarters was established near Tuz Khormatu; and an organization for drilling and for all connected services was brought into rapid existence. Some 2,500 'Iraqi workers and fifty

---

[1] For instance, in the report of the Federal Trade Commission (1952).

[2] Sir John Cadman became Chairman of T.P.C. in the same year, 1926, suc-ceeding Nichols who acted as such in 1924–6. From 1919 to 1924 the Chairman had been C. H. Smith and from 1912 to 1919, Sir H. Babington-Smith.

British engineers and technicians were mobilized, and the provision of water-lines, domestic and office buildings, workshops,
store sheds, garages, vehicles, and much more could proceed.

Drilling began on 5 April 1927 at Palkhana, six miles south of
Tuz, with a ceremonial spudding in in the presence of King
Faisal. It was followed by a second well three weeks later; but
the drilling of these wells had to be suspended owing to mechanical
difficulties at depths of 2,200 and 1,900 feet, without reaching the
'main limestone'. Immediately after these a well was begun at
Tarjil, southward from Kirkuk, but penetrated only the edge water
of the Kirkuk structure. In May a beginning was made in the
Jabal Hamrin, where a well at Khashm al-Ahmar was abandoned
after encountering high-pressure gas and heaving shales, and
another at Injana was for similar reasons not taken below 3,500
feet. A well at Jambur, south of Kirkuk, met with minor shows
of oil and gas. Results at Qaiyara, west of the Tigris, were more
significant: on 13 October oil in seemingly important quantities,
but highly viscous and sulphurous, was struck in limestone at a
depth of some 800 feet.

The well spudded in at Baba Gurgur, immediately north of
Kirkuk, on 27 June 1927, was in contrast to all these disappointments destined profoundly to alter both the economic fortunes of
'Iraq and the oil-history of the world. The strike at Baba no. 1 on
15 October, when the oil by the violence of its force broke all
control, flowed 'wild' for a week, and cost the lives of two drillers,
indicated an oilfield so important as to lead the Turkish Petroleum
Company, a few months later, to abandon for some years all
operations in other areas. It concentrated thereafter on the Kirkuk
structure, where from six to nine drilling rigs were continuously
active for the next four years, and two or three thereafter.

A second well at Qaiyara early in 1928 repeated, with copious
but viscous oil, the experience of the first. Two more wells were
drilled at Palkhana in 1928 and 1929, only to meet with high-
pressure water and gas. Three more were drilled without success
on the Injana structure. At Khormor, forty miles south-east of
Kirkuk, a well was taken to 6,500 feet in January 1931, but then
abandoned after insignificant shows of oil. West of the Tigris two
wells were drilled on the Khanuqa anticline, south of Qaiyara, but
found gas without oil. Preparations for drilling were made at
Najma, north-west of Qaiyara. In January 1929 a well at Quwair,

on the Greater Zab, penetrated 1,000 feet of the main limestone, but was perforce abandoned as a 'dry hole'. Finally, the anticlinal structure at Chamchamal, half-way between Kirkuk and Sulaimaniya, was drilled early in 1930, but yielded no more than a show of gas. A high-pressure gas-field was located in the Bai Hasan anticline, between Kirkuk and the Lesser Zab.

The first few wells on the Kirkuk structure, and the completion of tests, revealed it as a field of immense capacity. It is a simple and relatively narrow anticline, productive throughout a length of sixty miles from a porous and fissured limestone reservoir-rock of Miocene to Middle Eocene age, unusually permeable. The main limestone, corresponding to the Asmari in Persia, is covered by a Lower Fars series of anhydrite, silty marls, and thin limestones and, above these, the Upper Fars group of sandstones and silt-stones. Separated by low saddles, there are three domes of decreasing amplitude in the structure, those of Baba Gurgur, Avana, and Khurmala. The exploratory drilling carried out between 1927 and 1934, before the extraction of oil began, determined with much accuracy the great commercial possibilities of the field, its extent, pressures, and reservoir peculiarities. This, with the comparative simplicity of technical operation and the high ability of those in technical control, made the Kirkuk structure a model of economical and efficient oil production. By the end of 1930 twenty producing wells had been completed on the structure, with others for oil–water and gas–oil level observation. One season's work in 1928–9 was carried out, at a number of locations, by a team of geophysicists using the seismic method.

Simultaneously with drilling, costly and laborious ancillary works proceeded: road-making, a water supply, piped from the Lesser Zab, store-sheds and their multifarious contents, garages and workshops, offices and laboratories, dwellings, canteens, and a hospital. The Fields' topping-plant was in operation by 1929. The Fields' Headquarters of the Company moved from Tuz to Kirkuk in 1930. J. C. Templeton succeeded Hammick as Fields Manager in 1929 and was himself replaced by G. W. Dunkley in 1930 and by W. E. D. Cole in 1931. The labour force mounted in scale, with an average of some 2,000 'Iraqis, 125 Europeans, and 30 Americans in this early period. The conditions of work were stabilized and improved and employment with the Company attracted workers not only from Kirkuk and its Turkoman and

Kurdish villages, but also from Mosul, Baghdad, and elsewhere. Security was good, relations with the Government and the public were satisfactory. Medical services of high quality were already in existence within the organization, and the training of 'Iraqi workers for higher technical and clerical functions could begin.

J. Skliros succeeded Sir Adam Ritchie as General Manager in London in January 1930 and held the position of Managing Director from 1934 to 1949. G. W. Dunkley became first Agent, then General Manager in the Middle East, resident at Haifa from 1931 to 1939.

### IV. REVISED CONCESSION AND B.O.D.

The 'plot system' incorporated in the Turkish Petroleum Concession of 1925 was popular with nobody. The 'Iraq Government feared embarrassing rivalries between foreigners; the Company disliked the restriction to an area perhaps insufficient to cover the whole of revealed structures and the liability to competitive drilling —and, no less, the prospect that other rich structures, yet to be located, might fall into others' hands. When early in 1927 the Company requested extension of the period provided for its choice of plots, on the ground that a part of the concessional area on the Turkish frontier had been inaccessible to exploration, a year's prolongation was granted; a second request in 1928 was similarly granted and had the same effect of postponing the date by which the Government must make its own selection of the plots to be offered for competitive bidding. In 1929, however, application for yet another deferment was refused; the Government was becoming impatient, and the Permanent Mandates Commission at Geneva were under pressure to intervene and prevent further delays in plot-selection. The T.P.C. in November of that year notified its selection; it had, however, by this time become probable that no such plot-system would, after all, be applied. The Company confessedly desired a radically revised Agreement, and the Government, though unwilling for political reasons to propose this to Parliament, was prepared nevertheless, on terms, to favour the suggestion. The technical and economic reasons which made a 'blanket' concession preferable to a régime of competitive plot-holding were in fact powerful, if 'Iraq was to enjoy the long-term benefits of 'unit development' by a fully reliable operator.

A new factor in the case had rather helped than hindered this trend of policy. Even before 1925, another body founded in 1924 by a small English group which included Lord Inverforth, F. W. Ricketts, and Sir E. Manville, and which later was to become the B.O.D. Company,[1] had made contact with the 'Iraq Government. In 1928 an approach by its Chairman, Admiral Lord Wester-Wemyss, to the Chairman of the T.P.C. failed to indicate a way by which B.O.D. could, by agreement, be gratified in its desire to enter the field of 'Iraqi oil; and a brief flirtation with a company representing the Sultan's heirs (p. 68) availed it no better. The Government rejected the offer of a 12½ per cent. shareholding in B.O.D., but was interested in their suggestion to build a Tigris–Mediterranean railway; and meanwhile the Company, inadequately financed for major operations, made overtures to Italian industrialists for support.

Negotiations between Turkish Petroleum and the Government, with the B.O.D. as an embarrassing third party at the door, continued from mid-1928 to the late winter of 1930–1: a leisurely tempo explained by the over-supply of oil in world markets which had now supervened, by the economic crisis which had already spread from America to Europe. and, to some extent, by differences of viewpoint between the Company's constituent groups. The Company agreed, at the Government's suggestion, to consider a Mediterranean railway project, to proceed with early construction of a Kirkuk–Mediterranean pipeline, and to make substantial interim annual payments to the 'Iraq Treasury, on condition of receiving a concession, even for a reduced area, in which the whole included acreage should be its own. A revised Convention on these lines was, after protracted bargaining, agreed and signed on 24 March 1931, and thereafter ratified by Parliament.

With the royalty rate of 4s. (gold) unaltered, the new Agreement provided for the abandonment of the plot system and for the restriction of the Company to an area of 32,000 square miles in the Mosul and Baghdad vilayets, east of Tigris. The Company was obliged to build a pipeline to the Mediterranean, with a capacity of not less than 3 million tons a year,[2] to complete it before the end of

---

[1] The initials signify British Oil Development, but B.O.D. Limited was the registered name.

[2] At least 50 per cent. of this capacity was to be taken to the Bay of Acre until the pipeline should attain a capacity of at least 4 million tons; this stipulation was, however, removed by an Agreement of 25 May 1939.

1935, and to pay forthwith £400,000 (gold) a year, of which half would be recoverable from future royalties. No railway-construction duty was assumed and no drilling obligations were specified. The supply of refined products to 'Iraq was to be 'secured' by the Company—a task in fact transferred, with government consent, to the Khanaqin and later to the Rafidain Oil Company.

A consequence of the revision of the 1925 Concession was an alteration in the rate of Anglo-Persian royalty (p. 70) from the territory covered; instead of 10 per cent. of the oil obtained from the intended twenty-four plots, the T.P.C. groups agreed that a royalty of 7½ per cent. should be payable to their colleague in respect of oil won under the 1931 Concession.

While the Iraq Petroleum Company, so called since 1929, now saw its way clear to full exploitation of its oilfield, the Government of 'Iraq had at its disposal further areas to allot. It received for a time no offers for its southern province; but for the north-western area now released by I.P.C. there was a ready candidate, the B.O.D. Company. This group, which during 1930-2 was constrained to accept a majority of foreign shareholding,[1] applied to the Government in the latter year for rights over the ex-T.P.C. area west of Tigris, and negotiations proceeded. A concession covering all 'Iraq, west of the Tigris and north of the 33-degree line (some 46,000 square miles), was granted on 25 May 1932 and later ratified by Parliament. It prescribed a 4s. (gold) per ton royalty, with a minimum of £200,000 (gold) per year. Dead-rent payments, pending production, were to begin at £100,000 a year and to rise to £200,000; the Government was to be entitled to 20 per cent. of all oil produced—a remarkable addition to the I.P.C. terms; the Company was to drill with three rigs within eighteen months and to increase these to nine within a year of striking oil.[2] A pipeline to the Mediterranean, with a capacity of at least 1 million t/y, was to be built, provided always that the oil be of marketable quality, within seven and a half years—a period extended, in the event, for a further seven.

[1] Shareholding in 1931 was 46 per cent. British, 30 per cent. Italian through the parastatal A.G.I.P., 12 per cent. French-Swiss, 12 per cent. German and Dutch (through Ferrostall, Dutch associate of Krupps, and Deutsche Fruehand, a banking and industrial combine).

[2] The drilling obligation was altered in May 1939 to one of 12,000 feet a year.

### V. MEDITERRANEAN PIPELINE

A pipeline to convey 'Iraqi oil to the Mediterranean was, from the first, understood by all to be a necessary means of commercial development. Specified in the San Remo Agreement, it was prominent from then onwards in all calculations affecting the ultimate form of the 'Iraqi oil industry, and its construction became a definite obligation under the revised I.P.C. Convention of March 1931.

The planning of this line or lines involved not merely determination of the route to be followed but also the selection of terminal points on the coast. This problem gave rise to prolonged intergroup discussions, in which the degree of protection (if any) from weather offered by various ports, the mileage from Kirkuk to each of these, the degree of security prevailing in the various tribal areas, and the relative advantages of transit across, and terminals in, French or British mandated territory were all considered. The choice of ports limited itself to Haifa and Tripoli; and, since British and 'Iraqi feeling favoured a southern route through Palestine, while the French preferred a northern to the Lebanon, the compromise decision was reached for a double line of wishbone pattern. Two lines, each of 2 million t/y capacity, were to run parallel from Kirkuk across the Tigris to the Euphrates, and to cross the latter near Haditha, 148 miles from Kirkuk; they were there to bifurcate, the one running across Transjordan and Palestine to Haifa, the other by way of Syria and the Lebanon to Tripoli. The length of the southern line would be 620, the northern 532 miles.

Early in 1931 Skliros visited the capitals of the four transit-States and obtained from each, in almost identical terms, agreements for the passage of the pipelines and erection of the necessary works. During the summer detailed demarcation of the routes was carried out. The selection of terminal locations began and sites were decided for the main-line pumping-stations, of which the design called for twelve. Land acquisition was undertaken, mid-desert water supplies organized by search and well-drilling, and the building of railhead depots at Baiji on the Tigris, at Homs in Syria, and at Mafraq in Transjordan was begun.

The construction of this, the first of the great Middle-Eastern pipelines, called for the solution of many problems posed by the vast and inhospitable territory, the lack of water, shelter and supplies, the rough desert tracks and river barriers. Simultaneous tasks were the organization of a numerous and varied staff and labour supply (with its limiting condition of recruitment only of nationals of the country concerned), the supply of these with every necessity of life in scattered mid-desert camps, the maintenance of vehicles and installations, the establishment of telegraphic and wireless communications. The main lines themselves, of 12-inch and locally of 10-inch diameter, were strung, welded, wrapped, and buried by four main-line construction gangs. Of the main stations, seven (including three double stations) lay in 'Iraq, three in Syria, and two in Transjordan. At each not only large-scale pumping plant [1] and connected installations, but also tankage,[2] power, light and water, stores, repair shops and telecommunications, with housing accommodation for all types of staff and labour, were provided. Telegraph lines ran parallel to the oil line throughout its length and wireless telegraphy was provided at all stations and terminals. Every station had its landing-ground and each its vehicles. Two hundred thousand tons of materials were brought from overseas, 37 million ton-miles were carried by the railways of the countries concerned, 23 million ton-miles were run by the Company's main transport fleet. The twelve main pumping stations were each a veritable township in itself, lying on the fringes of inhabited country or deep in the desert.

The work was carried out with no serious delay or dislocation between 1932 and 1934. The line came into use late in the latter year and was officially declared open by King Ghazi of 'Iraq at a ceremony at Kirkuk in January 1935; whereafter the record of the years 1934–40 was one of steady pipeline operation,[3] with such improvements and additions as experience indicated. The greatest welded pipeline then existing had been constructed and 'Iraq could take, in a day, a high place among oil-producing countries. Since, however, the productive capacity of its field vastly exceeded the

---

[1] Each double station (K1, K2, and K3) had six and each other station three sets of pumps and engines, each set being designed to handle 1 million t/y.

[2] K1 station was provided with six 97,000 barrel tanks, each of the other stations with one of 30,000 barrels.

[3] Production from Kirkuk structure from 1934 to 1939 inclusive was (in million tons), 0·96, 3·58, 3·91, 4·14, 4·16, 3·81. Pre-pipeline production, from 1927 to 1933, had been (in thousands of tons), 81, 39, 32, 41, 32, 16, 43.

limits imposed by two 12-inch pipelines, the study of market possibilities and further outlets for 'Iraqi oil engaged all the attention of the I.P.C. directors. The decision to double, or more than double, the pipeline was reached in principle in 1938; it approached, in 1939, a stage near to practical execution, of which the intervention of the war led to so grievous a postponement.

Meanwhile, the development of the Kirkuk field had proceeded far. Production wells on the Baba Gurgur section, suitably grouped, supplied the three de-gassing stations of Shurau, Baba, and Hanjira. Other wells for later production and for structure-observation were drilled both on the Baba dome and on that of Avana, north of the Zab. Drilling on other locations was discontinued and rigs working at Kirkuk were reduced to three and later to two. The slow processes of land acquisition took their course. The 'Iraqi workers were treated on lines far in advance of current 'Iraqi levels in remuneration, security, and provision for welfare. Local purchase and the use of 'Iraqi contractors spread more widely the direct benefits of the industry. Increased help was given to the Kirkuk township and to technical institutions in Baghdad. Communications and services in Fields were improved: the power-house was extended, a new topping-plant finished, more industrial buildings erected, roads improved, new offices completed, the hospital at K1 station enlarged, a compact housing estate laid out for the foreign staff, personal transport organized for local workers. To remove the objection raised in some quarters against the delivery at seaboard of 'sour' crude, the erection of a stabilization plant in Fields was undertaken in 1936 for the removal of obnoxious elements from the oil before pumping it to the sea. This plant, which involved modification in the design of the de-gassing stations, came into operation in 1937.

The devaluation of sterling in 1931 led to a controversy between Government and Company as to the effect of this on the dead-rent and future royalty payments which the concession expressed in '£ (gold)'. The Company's decision to pay in sterling at the Bank of England's gold-sterling conversion rate, though accepted by Government only provisionally and with reservation of its rights, increased materially its sterling receipts. Apart from the continuing payments by the B.O.D. and the Basrah Companies, (p. 82) which by 1939 were together contributing £400,000 (gold) or about £665,000 sterling annually, those of the I.P.C.

itself amounted to nearly £1½ million a year in the period 1934–7 and substantially exceeded that sum in each of the years 1938–9. Recovery of half the dead-rents paid in 1931–4 was completed in 1937. This 'oil revenue' of over £2 million per year [1] exceeded any other single source of 'Iraqi revenue at this period, except their Customs receipts, and formed more than a quarter of the total revenues of the State.

## VI. WEST OF TIGRIS

The grant of the B.O.D. Concession in May 1932 was followed in that Company by an immediate reorganization and the collection of new capital. Mosul Oilfields Limited, with British, Italian, German, Dutch, French-Swiss, and 'Iraqi shareholding, was registered in December 1932 for the purpose of acquiring the share capital of B.O.D., while leaving the latter to operate in the field; Lord Goschen became Chairman of both Companies and Lord Glenconner, Managing Director. A technical committee was set up in London. Drilling equipment was ordered from Germany, representing the German share of capital contribution. Geologists and production experts visited the territory on behalf of the incoming Company. After an intensive period of preparation and organizing and the opening of a headquarters at Mosul drilling could begin where that of the I.P.C. had left off, and with the advantage of the latter's recorded experience. British drillers were engaged for the work, using cable-tool equipment until the arrival of heavy German rotary equipment in 1934.

The first well drilled by the new Company was completed, without success, at Mishraq, half-way between Qaiyara and Mosul, and another at Qaiyara itself. In 1934 further exploration was carried out with rotary equipment at Qaiyara; wells, which revealed only low-quality oil, were completed on the adjoining Najma, Jawan, and Qasab anticlines and others were drilled with no greater success at Sadid and Hibbara and, far to the north, at 'Ain Zala. In 1935, while drilling with nine rigs continued and orders were placed for more German equipment, the earlier B.O.D. project of a Qaiyara–Mediterranean railway was again considered

---

[1] Sums paid by I.P.C. to the Government in 1934–40, were (in thousands sterling), £1,294, 753, 763, 913, 1,563, 1,514, and 984. (The payments for 1935–7 were decreased by recoveries of half dead-rents for the period 1931–4). These were exclusive of B.O.D. and B.P.C. payments.

and directors visited 'Iraq and Syria to assess its possibilities. The plan was in general terms approved by the 'Iraq Government, who visualized the creation of a Government refinery at Qaiyara; it was equally welcome to the railway concessionaire companies in Syria, as seeming to offer the possibility of good oil and general traffic. The cost of the railway, which would be built by an affiliated Mosul Railway Company, would be recoverable by the B.O.D. from oil royalties payable to the 'Iraq Government.

But, future railways apart, the highly expensive organization necessary to conduct current B.O.D. operations was, meanwhile, taxing its resources to the limit, and beyond it. Further British capital could not, on suitable terms, be attracted; the Italians had by 1935 become majority shareholders, with a 52 per cent. holding; the German proportion was less but considerable. The directors were five Italian, one British and the Chairman, one French and two German. But the financial strain grew ever greater and with it the difficulty of paying the 'Iraq Government its dues, which had now increased to a rate of £200,000 (gold) a year. Egyptian participation appeared at one moment to be probable, but did not materialize; 'Iraqi shareholding was insignificant. The solution, if any, must come from another source.

Early in 1936 conversations began between the Italian element in Mosul Oilfields and the Managing Director of I.P.C., which Company was on various grounds not averse from regaining the lost areas west of Tigris. By March 1936 an advance of cash had been made to M.O.F. through an American intermediary; by August, I.P.C. directors were in session with those of M.O.F., and a new concern, Mosul Holdings Limited, was registered in October 1936 to acquire the shares of Mosul Oilfields. This it proceeded rapidly but discreetly to do. Those held by the Italians and Germans were bought, and their representatives retired from the scene. By the beginning of 1937 the I.P.C. interests were in effective charge and in 1941 Mosul Holdings, renamed the Mosul Petroleum Company, received the assignment from B.O.D. of its 1932 Concession. Both B.O.D. itself and M.O.F. were liquidated and disappeared in the same year.

In acquiring the B.O.D. Concessions and interests, the I.P.C. groups added to their territory, though upon terms markedly less advantageous, an extensive tract with numerous well-marked structures already proved to contain oil. It remained to be seen whether, as a result of further operations, which were bound to be expensive, a grade of oil would be discovered superior to that of Qaiyara and the adjacent structures, whose problems of viscosity and impurity were still all unsolved.

The operations west of Tigris, under I.P.C. management from the spring of 1937 onwards, were now redirected and reanimated. George Heseldin, from the I.P.C., became Fields Manager. A building programme was carried out at Qaiyara, with the erection of residences, an enlarged hospital, a club, cinema, swimming-pool, and many industrial buildings. Some 1,500 'Iraqis were in employment; foreigners—British, German, Italian, French, American, Polish, Rumanian, Swiss, and White Russian—varied in numbers between sixty and seventy. The protection of the Company's camps and communications continued to be ensured by contract with the Chief of the Shammar tribe.

Deep test wells were drilled on the Addaya and Jabal Makhul structures, and on those of Butma and 'Alan, north of Mosul. Other wells were drilled on those of Zambar and Qusair, west of Mosul towards Sinjar, others again on structures already tested, including that of 'Ain Zala. A location at Sinjar was sited though never drilled. At Qalian, where a depth of over 9,000 feet was reached, light oil was found, but in small quantities; elsewhere, to the disappointment of all hopes, no commercial possibilities were revealed. In the Euphrates area wells were drilled at Awasil and abu Jir near Ramadi, at Hit and at 'Ain al-Naft, and at 'Ana and al-Qa'im, while a geophysical party sought new structures in that region. Nearly twenty locations in all were tested and a total of 150,000 feet had been drilled by the middle of 1938. The maintenance of drilling camps at these distant locations, involving the erection of many temporary buildings, heavy transport of men and materials, and often the provision of water-lines from the rivers, was a formidable task.

From October 1938, the time of Munich, German and Italian staff began to leave 'Iraq, the German drillers being replaced by American. In July 1939 the drilling programme was reduced to one of four operating rigs; but one of these at long last succeeded, a few days before the outbreak of war, in locating deposits of light oil, at a depth of 5,000–6,000 feet, in the limestone of the anticlinal structure at 'Ain Zala; and it could be hoped that some reward for twelve years of costly and disappointing efforts west of the Tigris was at last to be gained.

## VII. THE BASRA PROVINCE

The efforts of the 'Iraq Government, after its grant of the 1925, 1931, and 1932 Concessions, to find suitable concessionaires for the exploitation of its oil—if any—in southern 'Iraq, met with little response; and this in spite of recurrent rumours and the visits to Basra, incognito or otherwise, of various oil company representatives. But the proving of important fields in Bahrain and al-Hasa from 1932 onwards led the I.P.C. groups by 1937 to consider seriously the acquisition of a Basra concession. Since none of the I.P.C. constituents could apply independently, that Company itself must undertake the task. An Agreement for seventy-five years, covering all 'Iraq not already allotted,[1] was concluded accordingly between the I.P.C. and the Government on 29 July 1938, upon terms closely similar to those of the B.O.D. Concession. A Basrah Petroleum Company, similar in constitution to the I.P.C. and to Mosul Holdings, was formed. The terms included a royalty of 4s. (gold) with a minimum of £200,000 (gold) a year;[2] provision for royalty revision after twenty years: payments for commuted taxation: a dead-rent of £200,000 (gold) a year pending export of oil: the duty of delivering to the Government, at well-head, 20 per cent. of oil produced: a drilling obligation of 12,000 or, after striking oil, 20,000 feet a year: and an obligation to commence within seven and a half years the transport to seaboard, at least, of 1 million tons of oil a year, or 2 million tons if oil resources within the concession proved comparable to those of Kirkuk.

Expectation of the presence of oil in the Basra area was high, both on regional grounds and by reason of the discovery in 1938 of the great Burgan structure in Kuwait territory. The new Company lost no time in organizing a base and supply depot at Makina, outside Basra city, and dispatching its geological parties to examine the territory. A geophysical survey was carried out between March 1939 and May 1940.

[1] That is, all Iraq south of the southern boundary of the B.O.D. and I.P.C. Concessions, including the 'Iraqi interest in the 'Iraq–Sa'udi Neutral Zone; some 93,000 square miles.

[2] This sum was to be doubled in the event of the discovery of oil comparable with that of Kirkuk.

A supplementary Agreement between the Government and all three companies of the I.P.C. group in 'Iraq was concluded in May 1939. Under its terms an interest-free loan equivalent to £3 million sterling was to be made by the Companies, payable in six half-yearly instalments and later recoverable out of royalties. In return, the Government consented to certain modifications of the existing Agreements, notably an alteration of the B.O.D. drilling obligation (p. 75), and a seven-year extension of the period within which that Company must produce oil on a commercial scale.

## CHAPTER VI

# THE LEVANT BETWEEN THE WARS

## I. TURKEY

To the rulers of Kemalist Turkey, once firmly established, no means of development of their country's resources appeared practicable save those of *Etatism*, the domination of industry by the State. Oil, more particularly, was present in the minds of the planners of Ankara after their experiences at Lausanne, their claims to Mosul and its alleged oilfields, and the importunities of Admiral Chester; and American experts on behalf of the Government toured the Mardin area, some coastal regions, and the Anatolian plateau in 1925. Their report was guarded and on balance unfavourable; but it was far from denying the possibility of oil deposits.

Legislation in the same year provided that grantees of mineral rights must be of Turkish nationality, or Turkish-controlled companies; and early in 1926 the existing regulations, which governed mining, were replaced by a law so conceived as to render almost impossible the attraction of foreign capital to the task of Turkish oil development. The latter became, instead, a specifically governmental undertaking capable of delegation to private enterprise only with niggardly reluctance. Plots for allotment to members of the public for exploration were rigidly limited in size and shape and carried inordinate drilling obligations; and the area ultimately grantable to a concessionaire under a thirty-year mining lease could not exceed thirty-five hectares per producing well. Royalty was fixed at 20 per cent. of production, payable in cash or kind.

The publication of this law, nevertheless, did not immediately suspend the traffic in concessions and licences held or claimed by oil-minded Turks and resident Europeans. In 1927 the Turkish Petroleum Company was thus offered 'exclusive rights' in Erzerum district; in 1928 a Turkish syndicate sought to dispose of a bundle of ancient *permis de recherches* to French interests. Meanwhile the T.P.C. itself made what movements it could towards persuading the Turkish Government to modify, in its own interest, the present discouraging regulations; but it could make no progress. In 1933 the British Government was informed, and informed the I.P.C. (as the Company had now become), that the old licences of Fuad Pasha for the Van area were reputed to be still valid; the Company, however, showed no interest. Even so, the advice given to it by many 'old hands'—to keep out of a field where foreigners were unwelcome and where ultimate profits were clearly destined only for the Turkish State—was not yet wholeheartedly accepted; the Company still hankered for the chance, at least, to study Turkish potentialities. Foreign interest could, however, scarcely survive the further stages of *Etatism* reached in 1933–4, when, under the Five Year Plan, the Eti Bank was founded to finance the work of the Mining Research Institute—the M.T.A.[1]—and the latter thereafter assumed complete charge of all oil-finding activity. The visits of 'Iraq Petroleum geologists to the Boyabat and other seepages in 1934 revealed an atmosphere of increasing restriction; the relations between the Company and certain Turkish publicists and parliamentarians in 1934 and 1935 could lead to no more than unrealized aspirations to modify the law or to secure consent from the Grand National Assembly to a 'blanket concession' for some promising area. Little more, in fact, was heard of private enterprise in Turkish oil development for the next eighteen years.

The M.T.A., meanwhile, aided from time to time by American experts and drilling-contractors, settled down to a campaign of energetic search, and between 1934 and 1940 drilled a score or more of wells on various structures, usually in the vicinity of seepages. Initial hopes were highest in the neighbourhood of Murefté on the Bosphoros, where eight wells were drilled: those of Van and of Sinop in the east and north-east: detached locations in central Turkey: the plain of Adana: the Alexandretta (Iskenderun) area: and the district athwart the Upper Tigris from Mardin to Siirt. At all these one or more wells were drilled, American equipment being used and a number of Texan and Canadian drillers employed. Among efforts which raised the highest hopes were those in 1935 at Basbirin, where a depth of 4,500 feet was reached, but only salt water discovered: and at Hermis and Kerbent, at both of which, at depths of 3,000–3,500 feet, insignificant traces of oil were encountered. These wells were all abandoned and nowhere else was any deposit approaching 'commercial

[1] Maden Tetkik ve Arama Enstitusu.

quantities' located. Simultaneously, geophysical parties covered wide areas; and with the increase of geological data and after many local disappointments, the search appeared by 1937 to be narrowing to the Adana plain and to that part of the great Persian Gulf geosyncline which covers the provinces of Diyarbakr, Mardin, and Siirt. In 1939 hopes were concentrated on the Raman Dagh anticline near Diyarbakr and drilling there was put in hand.

Up to 1935 the bulk of Turkish imports of petroleum products were of Russian or Rumanian origin. Thereafter, arrivals from Rumania diminished and Russia was decreasingly willing to spare her petroleum for export. The market was by 1939 predominantly in the hands of the Shell Company and of Socony-Vacuum, and the supplies were mainly American in origin. At this time, however, in spite of efforts at industrialization, Turkish needs barely reached 200,000 t/y of products.

## II. THE LEVANT STATES: PIPELINES AND TERMINALS

Syria and the Lebanon, Palestine and Transjordan passed during these years, 1923–39, through closely similar experiences in their relationship with the oil industry. All four acquired importance as territories across which oil passed in transit from 'Iraq to the sea; two of them, Palestine and Lebanon, were furnished also with important terminal and oil-loading installations; and in them all a serious search for native oil supplies was set in motion for the first time with modern methods and upon an important scale.

The decision by the Iraq Petroleum Company in 1931 to construct a pipeline from the Kirkuk oilfield to the Mediterranean involved the laying of trunk lines through 267 miles of Syrian territory, 17 of Lebanese, 205 of Transjordanian, and 40 of Palestinian. In Syria three main pumping-stations were to be erected (T2, T3, and T4), in Transjordan two (H4 and H5); the terminal installations at Haifa and Tripoli were to be on an imposing scale.

Agreements with the High Commissioner of Palestine, the Amir of Transjordan, and the ministers and Presidents of the Lebanese and Syrian Republics were obtained for the Company in January and March 1931 by its negotiator, J. Skliros: agreements which, differing essentially as they did from concessions for oil exploitation, were closely similar to each other. While favourable to the

Company, the terms which they embodied were in no way un-favourable to the States. The agreements were for seventy years. They gave almost complete customs and taxation exemption and permitted the Company to use, on payment, all local services and resources, to construct all necessary works, and to use all public communications. The Government was to assist the Company in obtaining the necessary lands and wayleaves. No charge was made for the right of transit as such, partly in deference to the inter-national Convention to that effect [1] and partly in anticipation of general benefits to the transit countries' economy.

The headquarters of the enterprise was established at Haifa in the summer of 1931. Offices were opened in Beirut, Tripoli, Homs, and 'Amman and the detailed survey was completed by the autumn. Steps were taken in each country towards land acquisi-tion, contact and co-operation with all local authorities, the use of railways, and the recruitment of staff and labour in a wide range of categories. With the first arrival of materials from Europe and the United States to Haifa, Beirut, and Tripoli early in 1932, the physical work of construction began in the spring of that year. The course of the line and its construction through Syria and Transjordan had all the features already described as encountered in 'Iraq (p. 77), and others were involved in the lines' transit across intricate cultivated lands in Syria, Lebanon, and Palestine, the forbidding lava-country of Transjordan, where a formidable feat of road construction was necessary, and the deep Jordan Valley depression, where a relief station was constructed. The five main-line stations were duly established, equipped, and per-fected; the railhead depots of Homs and Mafraq were, and re-mained, scenes of ceaseless activity as bases and forwarding stations. The passage of the line through Lebanon and Palestine raised more complicated questions of land acquisition, which were successfully resolved.

Oil was pumped into terminal tankage at Tripoli from T4 station, a distance of 111 miles, and to that of Haifa from H5 station 138 miles away. At Haifa the tank-farm of ten 93,000-barrel tanks was situated on sand-dunes on the Bay of Acre, with five more tanks (added later) close to Haifa Harbour and its oil dock. At Tripoli fifteen 93,000-barrel tanks were erected four

[1] Barcelona Transit Convention, 1921.

miles north of the town on the lower slopes of the hills overlooking orange-gardens and the sea. At both the necessary industrial buildings, offices, stores, communication centres, and repair shops were installed, fire-fighting arrangements organized, marine signal stations erected, and submarine lines laid on the sea-bed to loading berths a mile or more from shore. Both terminals were served by railway sidings, both could draw their electric power, at least in part, from public supplies. At the Tripoli loading berths little protection from the weather, except from the west, was available; at Haifa some protection was given to the sea-berths by the Carmel promontory and the port of Haifa was improved in other respects by the construction by the Palestine Government between 1930 and 1933 of a modern harbour, to which an oil dock for the Company's use was added later and came into use in 1935.

The landing arrangements, by sea-line at Tripoli but by both sea-line and oil dock at Haifa, were the subject of agreements made in 1934 with the Lebanese and Palestine Governments. These provided for the detailed procedure of loading, the relation of the Company's needs and installations to those of the State and public, and the consolidated payment (2d. per ton for sea-line and 5d. for oil dock loading) to be made for services provided. At each terminal the Company acquired not only the lands immediately required but further and considerable adjacent areas for possible future refineries.

The work of construction called in each State for the rapid organization of a staff and recruitment of workers drawn from the nationals of the country, with a minimum of British, French, or American supervision. All efforts were made to use the skill of local doctors, engineers, technicians, and artisans to the greatest possible extent; semi-skilled and unskilled labour was, as a matter of course, found locally. In the peak period of construction the numbers employed were, by any previous standards in these territories, formidable; in the summer of 1933, 1,400 Palestinians, 4,250 Transjordanians, 2,600 Lebanese and Syrians were in employment. Though by the end of 1932, and thereafter, these numbers were substantially reduced, yet the direct contribution made to local society by such employment and by the scale of the purchases made and contracts given in each country was both economically and educationally considerable. The end of the construction period itself was no clearcut line; further work, the erection of additional buildings and tankage, was in constant progress between 1935 and 1939 and provided further economic benefit to the workers and the public. Relations of the Company with its employees and with local authorities were almost uniformly excellent. In Palestine the necessary but uneasy balance was held between Arab and Jewish claims to employment and a similar balance was maintained in every territory between the Muslim majority and the Christian minorities. Every care was taken to provide working conditions well in advance of prevailing local usage, medical and commissariat services were fully developed, living quarters built where necessary, facilities for sport and social life provided.

The pipeline came into use in the later weeks of 1934, in advance of the formal opening ceremonies in each country. Its operation was uninterrupted and efficient. The throughput, shared equally between the northern and southern lines, approached 4 million tons in 1935 and slightly exceeded that figure annually thereafter.

The crude oil [1] delivered at seaboard became, once loaded, the property of the constituent groups. The share of the Socony and the New Jersey Companies went to their respective refineries in France and England: that of the Compagnie Française to France: of Anglo-Iranian to its refineries in Great Britain and France: of Shell to its refineries in France and Belgium.

The outbreak of war, which frustrated the Company's intention, formed in 1938–9, to increase the pipeline system, came, fortunately, too late to stop another major development of the industry in Palestine, the construction of a refinery. Already in 1933 the Anglo-Iranian had obtained transit rights across Transjordan and Palestine: and agreements reached in 1938 between that Company and the I.P.C., and between both and the High Commissioner for Palestine, permitted Anglo-Iranian to enjoy the facilities and privileges of the I.P.C. for handling and loading products. To carry out the refinery project, which fell within the Consolidated area (p. 65), Consolidated Refineries Limited had been registered as early as 1935, with equal Shell and Anglo-Iranian participation. It proceeded in 1938 to construction on a site adjoining the Kishon River in the Bay of Acre. Work had proceeded so far by September 1939 that the first distillation unit could be completed in December

---

[1] 'Sour' crude until completion of the stabilization plant at Kirkuk in 1937, and thereafter 'stabilized'.

by the Company's own staff, after the departure of the American contractors in December; it was brought into operation in that month with an initial capacity of 1 million t/y—an immense war asset as the event proved. The original design, which included two 300,000-gallon reforming units, could not for the time being be carried out. Even so, the establishment on this coast of a modern refinery marked a significant step in the development of the oil industry in the Middle East; and the strategic, no less than the financial importance of the new oil route across the desert, was obvious. A new weapon, moreover, for bargaining or a new hostage had been given to whatever political forces in the transit States might care, some day, to use it.

Meanwhile, the requirements of the Levant countries in oil products in these years were humble enough. The demand in Palestine, which in 1928 was less than 50,000 tons of all products combined, did not reach 200,000 tons in 1938 and was still less in each of the other three territories. These needs were met by the established distributing companies: Consolidated Petroleum (in the guise of the Shell companies of Syria and of Palestine), Socony-Vacuum, and a half-dozen minor local distributors with or without affiliations with American, Rumanian, or French parent-companies. The products themselves came from Rumania, Persia, the Netherlands East Indies, and Egypt.

### III. THE LEVANT STATES: THE SEARCH FOR OIL

In the Levant States, throughout the nineteen-twenties, small progress was made in the search for oil otherwise than by the accumulation of geological information in government files, until this situation of comparative neglect was changed by three succeeding events. The first of these was the influx of oil-minded Europeans and Americans into the Levant countries in connexion with the 'Iraq–Mediterranean pipelines. The second was the discovery of oil in rock of Cretaceous age at Bahrain Island: an event which both enlarged the geologically hopeful field of search and warned the pioneer companies of the Middle East that newcomers were in the field. Thirdly, and partly under pressures resulting from these influences, the local governments proceeded to the preparation of modern oil codes.

As a first step, an Iraq Petroleum Company geological office was opened in Jerusalem in 1932; and thereafter expert examination of areas in Palestine led the Company to apply for and obtain licences for the exploration of considerable areas of the centre and north of the country. A geophysical party worked for a season in 1934 in the Gaza district. By the time the Mandatory Government brought its new mining law and rules into force in 1938, a substantial body of geological studies had been carried out in areas for which the Company's licences remained valid. Others were held by the veteran prospector D. A. Sutherland, covering blocks on the shores of the Dead Sea, where the seepages had been long recognized. The I.P.C. extended its researches and its candidature for licences into neighbouring Transjordan.

On the issue of the new law, the Company, in the guise of Petroleum Development (Palestine) Limited, obtained licences under it for an area of some 5,000 square miles; and it faced thereby the immediate obligations of these, which included drilling within stated periods on each of the two groups of permits. A second geophysical party was brought to Palestine in 1939 and worked for some months towards the definite establishment of drilling locations, where work was intended to begin forthwith. The Sutherland permit areas, abandoned by their holder, were allotted to the Palestine Mining Syndicate, the parent of the Palestine Potash enterprise. The mining law provided for the grant to successful licence-holders of a thirty-year mining lease for half of the licensed area, with the obligation to pay an annual dead-rent and, in addition, a royalty varying between 2s. 6d. and 6s. per ton of oil.

In Transjordan less progress could be made. The Amir's Government was slow to produce a modern mining law; and in spite of survey work sufficient for the selection of licence areas and the Company's application for these, none was in fact obtained. The I.P.C. group formed Petroleum Development (Transjordan) Limited in February 1938 for future operations in that territory.

In Syria French governmental geologists were active from the early nineteen-twenties in exploring the territory and in September 1933 obtained the enactment of a mining code with specific provision for liquid hydrocarbons. In spite of serious defects in this law and of the inadequacy of the information then at its disposal, the I.P.C. showed eagerness to take part in exploration. Early in 1934, it obtained permits valid for a four-year exploration period, and carrying obligations of mapping, geological report, and test drilling. They included areas believed adequate to cover the observed structures at Jibissa,[1] Jabal Bishri, and Chamba, all in the Shamiya desert, and the long-known Changan structure in the province of Alexandretta. Other permits were applied for between 1934 and 1937 for areas in the districts of Dair al-Zor and Rakka, at Darro, Tuwal 'Abba, Sabkha, 'Azaman, Shaikh Mansur, Qubaiba, Sirrin, and Baidha. A further licence in Alexandretta, that of Husainiya, was applied for and another covering a structure in Qarachauq Dagh, in the extreme north-east of Syria—the 'Bec de Canard'—was acquired from its owners.[2]

The I.P.C., which formed Petroleum Concessions (Syria and Lebanon) Limited in July 1936, busied itself from 1934 to 1938 with the statutory mapping, delimitation, and detailed reports on the licence areas which it successively obtained or applied for under the revised regulations which in 1936 superseded those of 1933. These operations were carried out by mobile parties, with lorry-borne camps based on a headquarters established at Dair al-Zor. The drilling prescribed under the licences was carried out with cable-tool equipment and was completed at Jabal Bishri, Jibissa, Chamba, Darro, Changan, and Qarachauq.

But increased investigation during the years following 1934 revealed so many possible oil-containing structures that a régime of isolated licences and leases could not appear the best adapted for Syrian oil development; and the first half of 1937 was spent in Damascus by a negotiator on behalf of P.C. (S. & L.)—the present writer—in attempting to arrange a 'blanket concession' for the territory. The preoccupations of the Syrian Government with political matters, and notably with Turkish claims to Alexandretta, precluded agreement at the time; but in February 1938 an agreed concession was signed by the responsible ministers for later ratification (p. 140), covering for seventy-five years all Syrian territory (except the Alexandretta district) north of the latitude of

---

[1] French spelling of these names is Djebissa, Djebel Bichri, Tchembé, Tchenguene, Derro, Toual Abba, Gbeibé, Sirrine, Beida, Husseinie, Karatchok.

[2] This licence obtained by the Karatchok Syndicate had been registered in the name of the Société Industrielle des Asphaltes de Lattaquie, which controlled the Syndicate and was itself controlled by the Union des Mines. The Société now sold to Petroleum Concessions (Syria and Lebanon) Limited its holdings in the Syndicate, and P.C. (S. & L.) thereafter obtained control of the Union des Mines majority shareholding in the Société. The latter Company continued thereafter to be controlled by the I.P.C. group.

Damascus. The Agreement prescribed an immediate payment of £50,000, a dead-rent rising from £15,000 in ten years to £80,000 a year, and a sum of £100,000 to be paid on commencement of the export of oil—or double that sum if the oil were of lighter gravity than 20 degrees A.P.I. The rate of royalty was fixed initially at 4s. (gold) per ton or less if the oil were of low quality. A refinery was to be built to supply Syrian needs after the export of oil had begun. If no oil had been discovered within ten years, or no commercial export had begun within fifteen, the concession would become null and void. The monetary unit, in which all sums were to be payable under it, was described as 'English gold pounds'.

Opposition parties in Syrian politics were, on general grounds, loud in outcry against an 'unjust' concession, while the Company for its part continued with vigour its exploratory work in satisfaction of the obligations prescribed and treated as in force. At Dubaiyat, forty-five miles north of Palmyra, at Sharifa,[1] forty miles west of Palmyra, and at Darro, twenty miles north of Dair al-Zor, drilling camps were set up, equipment and materials moved to the sites, labour housed and fed, and wells drilled with rotary equipment into and through sedimentary beds of various ages from Miocene to Devonian. These expensive and initially hopeful operations, conducted in 1939 and 1940, met unfortunately with no success greater than a whiff of gas in the Jibissa well; and thus largely discredited such hopes as had been placed on the Palmyra, Bishri, and Jabal Sinjar areas.

The detachment of the Alexandretta–Antioch province from Syria, to become the Hatay province of Turkey, was completed in 1938–9, and the Company's licences in that area were thereby lost beyond hope of recovery. In Syria herself, a single competitor for exploration rights had appeared, representing the Nobel group; but the licence for which he applied seemed to overlap an area already granted to P.C. (S. & L.) and was never allotted. His claim, however, persisted and, after the failure of his efforts to sell his rights to the I.P.C., a British geologist was temporarily installed in the licence area. No sign of Syrian enterprise appeared.

In the Lebanon, where the same mining code was in force, a licence was taken by the I.P.C. in March 1938 to cover the area

[1] French spelling, Cherrifé.

of Jabal Terbol, lying immediately behind the Company's terminal at Tripoli. The outbreak of war prevented the commencement of drilling.

The island of Cyprus was visited by a geologist of the I.P.C. late in 1936. A reconnaissance was carried out, and in April 1938 a two-year exploration permit, covering 2,000 square miles, was issued to a Company registered for the purpose, Petroleum Development (Cyprus) Limited. The Company proceeded to further studies towards the discovery of structures capable of containing oil deposits.

## IV. EGYPT: RENEWAL OF HOPE

In Egypt the period between the wars was one of constant and reasonably rewarded effort to keep the oil industry in existence and to expand it. The country retained its place as a minor oil-producing territory, and was thus more fortunate than any other in Africa or the Levant. Its native supply of crude, with a refining industry slightly exceeding this in scale, was a considerable though not a dominant national asset, whose expansion through a new discovery might be reasonably hoped for at any time.

The scale of operation was, in fact, small during most of this period; but 1937 and the two succeeding years witnessed an infusion of new life into both production and exploration and seemed to open new prospects for the industry in Egypt. With Gemsa now exhausted—it was abandoned, provisionally, in 1929—and abu Durba never important, Hurghada remained for twenty years the only producing centre in the country until, immediately before the Second War (exactly as Hurghada itself before the First), a new and greater oilfield was discovered.

The problems of Hurghada, meanwhile, were handled as best might be. All efforts were made to increase output by the drilling of some half-dozen wells a year, with cable-tool equipment: wells usually of meagre or precarious productiveness and a world removed from the standards of the Middle Eastern oilfields elsewhere. The exploration of adjacent and remoter areas continued, but none was found to be oil producing. Drilling at Ras Gharib, among other sites, was undertaken in 1921 and 1923 but abandoned, as without hope, after two years, and test wells elsewhere were no more successful. Drilling on Ashrafi Island, some forty miles south of Ras Gharib, was begun in 1925 but abandoned two

years later. At Hurghada itself the installation of electric dehydration plant in 1926 was designed to pass the crude oil to the refinery in a less corrosive form; but it could not augment the still
disappointing crude output which, from 1924 to 1927 by a serious
decline from the wartime figures, never exceeded 180,000 t/y. In
1928 a northern extension of the field was located, whose development lifted production to more than 260,000 t/y for the next five
years, after which it again declined.[1] The problem of locating
major reservoirs, in the complicated and fragmented geological
formations of Egypt, remained unsolved. Hurghada was visited
by the King of Egypt in 1926.

Refining operations at Suez were extended in two ways. The
Anglo-Egyptian plant, which continued until 1939 to use its surplus capacity for the treatment of imported crude, was both enlarged and improved. Alterations were made in the distillation
units in 1927 and the erection of a thermal cracking plant was
completed in 1929. A gasoline recovery plant was installed and a
plant and drum-factory for the production and packing of asphalt
emulsion, for application cold on road surfaces, was erected in
1929. Loading facilities were improved by construction of a new
petroleum basin, opened by the King in 1929. The usual range of
tankage, railway siding, stores, workshops, laboratories, transport,
and living quarters for staff were provided, and working conditions
maintained which were markedly superior to those prevalent elsewhere in Egyptian industry.

The use of geophysical methods for locating sub-surface structures led, late in 1937, to the selection of a drilling site close to a
location previously tested but abandoned, that of Ras Gharib; and
here at last, using rotary equipment, the Anglo-Egyptian drillers
struck oil in the first weeks of 1938. Five wells were rapidly completed, the relatively important value of the structure was established, and 75,000 tons of oil produced from it in 1938. Good
progress was made in the provision of housing, shops, services, and
amenities, and the erection of tankage, pumps, and a loading jetty.
Total Egyptian production rose in 1938 to 225,000 tons and next
year almost to 600,000 tons. The oil at Ras Gharib, with a gravity
of 25–26 degrees A.P.I., was obtained at depths from 1,500 to

---

[1] The figures from 1924 to 1927 inclusive (in thousands of t/y) were 160, 175,
169, and 180; from 1928 to 1937 they were 264, 267, 277, 280, 260, 228, 211, 173,
174 and 168.

1,750 feet, mainly from a series of sands of Carboniferous age lying below Miocene beds. This structure, a faulted monocline of pre-Miocene age, was to become the mainstay of Egyptian production for the next ten years. The lease granted for it to Anglo-Egyptian in 1938, for thirty years with a permitted extension of fifteen more, provided for a royalty of 14 per cent., payable in kind or cash at the Government's discretion; the dead-rent, of L.E.2½ per hectare, was to be deducted from the royalty payable. The Government retained a limited right to buy oil, additional to royalty-oil, on favourable terms from the Company. Labour employed must be 90 per cent., and staff 50 per cent., Egyptian.

The marketing of Anglo-Egyptian products was carried out by the Shell Company of Egypt. This Company, founded in 1911 as the Asiatic Petroleum Company (Egypt) and renamed in 1927, was itself controlled after 1928 by Consolidated Petroleum Limited; the latter was formed in that year to acquire all Shell and Anglo-Persian installations and marketing interests in the Levant, Egypt and the Sudan, Aden, and much of East and South Africa. The Anglo-Persian at the same time acquired a share in Anglo-Egyptian, of which the Shell group continued to provide the management.

After a long inactive period [1] a great impetus to exploration was given by the publication in 1937 of revised Governmental regulations on the subject, in supersession of the highly restrictive code in force. An exploration permit covering 100 square kilometres for three years, or by renewal for four, could now be followed by a prospecting licence for four kilometres for one year, renewable to two. Work must be energetic and continuous, with a maximum employment of Egyptians. The striking of oil could be followed by the bestowal of exclusive rights under a mining lease, upon the terms already mentioned as governing Ras Gharib. The new conditions at once attracted eager permit seekers. These included, notably, Shell, Anglo-Iranian, Socony-Vacuum, Standard of California, Standard of New Jersey, and the Texas Company, and also, in order to increase the possible holdings of each (otherwise restricted to one hundred licences per applicant), a large number of their subsidiaries. Shell and Anglo-Iranian applied jointly for permits in the names of seven companies, Socony-Vacuum in

---

[1] Between 1910 and 1930 fifty exploration wells were drilled in Egypt, all dry save two; between 1930 and 1935, none.

those of five, California-Texas in those of seven, New Jersey in those of six. In all 846 licences had been applied for by the end of 1938, covering an area of 84,600 square kilometres. Geological and geophysical parties, assisted at times by air survey, hastened to their chosen areas, which included the Western Desert as well as the Red Sea coast and hinterland and the Sinai Peninsula. An aggregate of some millions of pounds sterling was spent, including large local disbursements for labour, supplies, and services. The outbreak of war found the main surviving operators—Shell, Caltex, New Jersey, Socony-Vacuum—embarked on serious programmes of drilling, for whose success the discovery at Ras Gharib was encouraging: Anglo-Egyptian were drilling in an area west of Gharib and at al-Diba, Socony-Vacuum at Wadi Dara, Giftun Saghir, and abu Sha'ar, New Jersey were about to drill at Ras Bakr, north of Ras Gharib.

Meanwhile the country's own needs in petroleum products, some 750,000 t/y with another million for bunkering, were by far the largest of any Middle Eastern country and could be met only in part from its own supplies. Additional crude for refining at Suez was brought from Persia, and refined products were imported from Rumania, Persia, the Netherlands East Indies, Russia, and the Netherlands West Indies. Lubricants, produced neither in Egypt nor elsewhere in the Middle East, came from the United States, Great Britain, Rumania, and Belgium. Marketing throughout the country was in the hands of the local Shell Company, Socony-Vacuum, and minor importers. Shipments of oil through the Suez Canal, from south to north, had grown by 1939 to some 4 million tons a year. A proposal to construct a pipeline for refined products from Suez to Cairo was under formulation shortly before the war.

## CHAPTER VII

# THE BEGINNING IN ARABIA

## I. FIRST STEPS

NOTHING came, as we have seen, of attempts to secure oil rights in Arabia in the years between 1918 and 1922; political stability there was not yet established,[1] little inducement to persuade the great oil companies to seek entry was yet apparent, the level of security was low. But, as the middle nineteen-twenties approached, more signs of a practical interest appeared. Two American geologists, on behalf of Standard Franco-Americaine, were allowed in the first days of 1923 briefly to visit the Yemen. The rights obtained for the Farsan Islands, years ago, were again on the market in London in 1920 and were offered to any taker. More significant was the interest of the tough and patient New Zealander, Major Frank Holmes, of the Eastern and General Syndicate (p. 42). His first chosen field of operation was eastern and north-eastern Arabia, containing as it did a number of separate political units.

The first of these was the small principality of Kuwait, with its single seaport, its arid waste of hinterland, and its sparse nomadic population; its ruler was the sagacious Shaikh Ahmad ibn Subah, who, loyal to his British protectors, had preserved the independence of his House. Next southward came the al-Hasa district of the dominions of 'Abdul 'Aziz ibn Sa'ud, a province which contained, besides its forbidding deserts and shallow seas, a number of well-watered oases and coastal villages. Poor and simple in its economy of pastoral life, garden cultivation, and cottage industries, and quite unpenetrated by Western influence, it was governed for ibn Sa'ud by a loyal and stalwart kinsman. The Bahrain group of islands, lying some twenty miles off the coast of al-Hasa, consisted of one larger and some smaller islands and, with its capital at the considerable town of Manama, formed an independent but British-protected principality. Its aged ruler, Shaikh Hamad al-Khalifa, had some familiarity with

---

[1] 'Abdul 'Aziz ibn Sa'ud, Sultan of Najd, which included the al-Hasa province on the Persian Gulf, conquered and annexed Jabal Shammar from the dynasty of ibn Rashid in 1921, and the Hijaz from its Sharifian ruler, King Husain, in 1925.

Western ways and those of India and 'Iraq, thanks to regular steamship services and international telegraphs.

East and south-east of Bahrain, across shallow seas, lay the flat and arid peninsula of Qatar with scarcely more permanent settlements than its village capital, Doha, no cultivation, and almost no vegetation, no water drinkable by Europeans, and a population of a few thousand starveling tribesmen and fisherfolk. These lived under the rule of the veteran Shaikh 'Abdullah al Jasim al Thani, who had assumed his government in 1906. To the south-east of Qatar, and stretching eastward and north-eastward to the Straits of Hormuz, lay the Trucial Coast, a wilderness of dune and salt marsh with the scantiest of inhabitants. It included the seaside villages of abu Dhabi, Dibai, Sharja, 'Ajman, Umm al-Qaiwain, and Ras al-Khaima, each the domain of a separate and independent shaikh who acknowledged no overlord but was bound by treaty with the Government of India. Eastward again, and forming the south-eastern corner of Arabia, lay the Sultanate of Oman, with its narrow date-planted coastal strip on the Gulf of Oman, its arid south coast on the Arabian Sea, and its great range of mountains between the Batina coast and the Empty Quarter of Arabia. The young Sultan of Oman, Sayid Sa'id ibn Taimur [1] was far, however, from enjoying undisputed authority; not only were the outlying nomadic tribes almost wholly independent of his rule, but the heart of the territory, the folk of the valleys and villages in the main mountain massif, obeyed a rival potentate, the Imam of Oman, whose little-visited territory was ruled by a primitive theocracy.

Throughout eastern and south-eastern Arabia the British position, as overlord and protector, was more than a century old. Through a Political Resident, stationed at Bushire on the Persian side, and Political Agents at Kuwait, Bahrain, and Muscat, the Government of India had for many years striven to suppress piracy, the slave-trade and the arms-traffic, had regulated the succession in the various states, and had kept the peace. The British position, one of well-earned primacy but equally of thankless effort and expense, was unique and valued, and invasion by outside Powers or interests into so backward and sensitive a world was not likely to be welcomed.

After a sojourn in Bahrain, to which he was attracted by known

---

[1] He succeeded his father, Sayid Taimur, who abdicated in 1928.

oil seepages, Holmes formed the ambition of entering the main-land of Arabia as oil concessionaire. In the winter of 1922 he followed the negotiations between Sir Percy Cox and the Sultan of Najd regarding the Kuwait–Hasa frontier, which at the Con-ference of 'Ujair ('Uqair) in December 1922 solved the problem by the formation of a Neutral Zone in which the two rulers would have equal and undivided rights; and Holmes on this occasion presented to ibn Sa'ud his suggestions for an oil exploration licence to cover the al-Hasa province. The Sultan, advised by Cox, was wisely cautious; nevertheless, a permit in the desired sense was issued to Holmes in May 1923, involving the carrying out of exploration and the payment of a small annual sum and including an option valid, for two years, for a subsequent concession. A Swiss geologist was sent to the area by Eastern and General late in 1923 and test-drilling was contemplated; but in the event, since the Syndicate could not itself face the costs of development and failed to interest any acceptable major company, the licence and option were destined, after two renewals, to lapse in 1927.

Meanwhile, Holmes's next move was to Kuwait, where he hoped to acquire rights both over that State and, in so far as Shaikh Ahmad al-Subah could grant them, over the Neutral Zone. In the former he was unsuccessful; the rival interest of Anglo-Persian, the cautious counsels of the Political Agent, and the natural suspicion of Shaikh Ahmad forced Holmes after some weeks of conversa-tions to postpone his hopes. For the Neutral Zone he obtained exploration rights in May 1924 and an option from both rulers for a future concession. Returning next to Bahrain, he undertook for Shaikh Hamad a programme of water well drilling; then left the island, visited Aden and the Red Sea, and began inquiries for a concession for the Farsan Islands. Back at Bahrain late in 1925 he received from the Shaikh an exclusive exploration permit and option for the whole island principality: a permit which would, under the Shaikh's undertaking of May 1914, be transferable to others only with British concurrence.

While the Eastern and General Syndicate faced the task of dis-posing profitably of their rights thus acquired, the first serious drilling in Arabia was starting elsewhere; the Shell group had accepted the transfer to themselves of exploration rights recently obtained for the Farsan group from the Idrisi ruler of 'Asir. The Red Line Agreement was not yet signed, the allegiance of this Red

Sea archipelago was anyhow doubtful; and Shell, feeling justified in retaining its rights, registered in January 1927 the Red Sea Petroleum Company, as a subsidiary of Anglo-Egyptian Oilfields. Their geologists were favourably impressed; an expedition was dispatched and drilling started in the same year; but some months' work and a test well at Zifuf, which penetrated great depths of salt, were enough to disappoint immediate hopes. The party withdrew and the enterprise was abandoned in 1929.

The Shell group also, represented at Aden by their agent, the justly famous Anton Besse, was from 1925 onwards a candidate for the rights over the Sultanate of Shihr in the Eastern Aden Protectorate. Drafts and counter-drafts of a concession were exchanged for three years, and the proposed rights, in the form finally established, were offered in 1928 by Shell to the Turkish Petroleum Company; but the geologist of the latter saw little interest in the territory and rejected the proposal.

In 1924–5 geological exploration—the first since the days of Pilgrim, twenty years earlier—was carried out in the Oman Sultanate by geologists of the Anglo-Persian. Restricted by lack of security and the presence of a rival potentate in the hinterland, they inspected the coast lands of the Batina, part of the central Jabal Akhdhar massif, and something of the remote Dhofar province. Valuable information was gathered on Arabian tectonics, but no immediate oil prospects were revealed.

## II. BAPCO

The efforts of the Eastern and General to 'place' their licences and options were long unsuccessful. Offered to both Shell and Anglo-Persian, they were declined; the Tertiary reservoir-rocks, so rich in south-western Persia, were in Bahrain exposed on the surface, nor was there, as yet, in the region any evidence which suggested the existence of pre-Tertiary oil. In America some interest was shown; the prospect was studied by the Standard of New Jersey; but the territory was remote, the risk considerable, the geology of doubtful promise, and British exclusiveness was feared; and it was not until a week before the date when the Bahrain rights must lapse—7 December 1927—that the Gulf Oil Corporation accepted an option on the Holmes rights, and concluded separate agreements with his Syndicate for Bahrain and for the mainland.

Geologists of the Gulf Corporation were sent to the island before the end of 1927. After a strenuous season, their report was favourable; but their own prospects were blighted, thus early, by factors from another quarter. The Corporation was still a member of the American group to whom Turkish Petroleum shares were to be allotted; and the conclusion of the Red Line Agreement in the summer of 1928 involved the obligation on Gulf to offer its Arabian rights to T.P.C., or the necessity to be authorized by its colleagues to retain them in isolation. The answer to both was negative; the T.P.C. would neither accept the Bahrain option for itself, nor allow Gulf to retain it.

Thanks to timely encounters at a Chicago meeting late in 1928 and the willingness of the Standard of California to try its fortunes in the East and the attractiveness of the Gulf geologists' report on Bahrain, the Holmes rights were safely passed, by purchase, to the California Company in December of the same year. The British authorities had, indeed, already hinted that the Shaikh of Bahrain would be advised to permit transfer or to extend the licence period only in favour of a British company: no surprising provision, in view of the hitherto exclusive British connexion with Bahrain, which owed its independent existence to British protection. The question of nationality was after all, however, met amicably after a short Anglo-American diplomatic correspondence by the formation early in 1930 of a Canadian company, the Bahrein Petroleum Company ('Bapco') as a subsidiary of the Standard of California.

Even before the registration of Bapco its first representatives had reached the island, and the erection of a camp and provision of a road, transport, equipment, and materials were put in hand forthwith in the favourable conditions which the island afforded. Drilling on the central portion of a large and simple anticline, the 'Awali structure, was begun in October 1931; and oil in considerable quantities of 33–35 degrees A.P.I. gravity was struck on 31 May 1932, its reservoir in porous limestone of Cretaceous age at a depth of 2,000–2,500 feet. The event was of high significance for the whole of Arabia, whose oil prospects were thenceforth to be reconsidered with a new interest by companies encouraged (or perturbed) by the Bahrain discovery.

The two years following were occupied by Bapco in the drilling of further wells for production and observation and the prepara-

tion of the field for production by the construction of gas separation and storage installations, a pipeline to the east coast of Sitra
Island, and the extension therefrom of submarine lines to tanker
berths. The Bapco foreign community,[1] British and American
with a few Indian and non-Bahraini Arab and Persian artisans and
clerks, settled down at their new-built oil town of 'Awali. By 1938
it contained its hospital, school, commissary, club, swimming-pool,
cinema, sports ground, and living quarters for some 110 married
and 200 unmarried foreign staff. Most of the non-European personnel and nearly all the Bahraini labour-force lived in Manama
town, using Company transport for their daily journey. The
export of crude oil began in 1934 with 40,000 tons in that year.
This figure rose to 170,000 and 620,000 tons in 1935 and 1936
respectively, after which production was for many years to approximate to, or slightly exceed, 1 million tons a year.[2]

The social effect of the well-provided employment offered to the
Bahrainis, the increase of spending power among the public, and
the direct benefit to the Shaikh's Treasury were all the more notable
since the pearl trade, traditionally the island's chief occupation and
asset, had some years before entered a period of severe depression.
No community or government, indeed, has been more suddenly
and timely rescued from economic disaster than those of Bahrain
in 1932.

The difficulty of finding markets [3] for the crude oil of Bapco led
early to the decision to erect a refinery on the island. The first installation, designed for some 10,000 b/d, was completed in 1937
at a site intermediate between the 'Awali field and the coast
opposite Sitra. A second crude still, with cracking, reforming,
and treating plant, and all necessary supplementary facilities to
increase capacity to 25,000 b/d were added during 1937. The
capacity of the crude stills was in 1938 further increased to
30,000 barrels, a polymerization plant added, and subsequent
alterations to the crude units permitted distilling capacity to reach
33,000 b/d before the outbreak of war.

The rights obtained by Holmes in 1925 were replaced in 1934

---

[1] The numbers concerned were, in 1938: 250 British, 100 American, 450
Indians and 550 'Iraqis, etc., and, not living at 'Awali, over 2,000 Bahrainis.
[2] Figures for 1937–40 were (in thousands of tons) 1,055, 1,110, 1,015, 943.
[3] Shipments of crude in the early years were to Japan, southern Europe, and
rarely America.

by a mining lease. This limited the area to 100,000 acres on Bahrain Island, and thereby excluded a part of the main island as well as the smaller islands and reefs. The lease gave comprehensive customs and taxation exemption, and established the royalty at Rs. 3 as. 8 per ton with a minimum annual payment of Rs. 75,000 (later Rs. 150,000). The 'Bahrain unallotted area', being the difference between the 100,000 acres and the whole extent of the Shaikh's dominions, was from 1934 to 1940 the subject of lengthy negotiations between the Shaikh, Bapco, and another candidate, the Iraq Petroleum Company.

Meanwhile an assured market was needed for the Bahrain products, and successful efforts were made to provide it. The California Company had no eastern marketing organization, the powerful Texas Company possessed one but lacked a convenient source of products wherewith to supply it; and an arrangement agreeable to both was made in July 1935. It provided for a 50 per cent. participation by Texas in the Bapco enterprise, in exchange for 50 per cent. of their eastern [1] marketing facilities. The marketing of Bahrain products was thereafter arranged by the California-Texas Oil Company, or 'Caltex', refined products being shipped from Sitra to existing and expanding Caltex markets in the Middle East, Far East, and India.

One further consequence of the Bahrain development and of the concession acquired soon afterwards on the Arabian mainland (p. 107) remains to be recorded. The Companies—Anglo-Persian, Shell, and Near East Development—already operating in the Middle East and possessed of European or Far Eastern markets, could not be indifferent to a new and major source of petroleum products so situated; and they were occupied,[2] 1932–9, in discussions among themselves, and abortively with Caltex, as to the possibility of acquiring all or part of the California Concessions or a voice in the disposal of the oil produced. The difficulty encountered was that of the Red Line, and, arising from it, the uneasy task of persuading the French group and Gulbenkian that their rights under the 1928 Agreement would not be diminished by the desired partial waiving thereof. No conclusion could be

---

[1] A half-share of the Texas Company's *European* marketing organization was acquired by Standard of California in January 1947.
[2] The authority for this paragraph is pp. 72–82 of the Federal Trade Commission's report, 1952, on the (alleged) International Oil Cartel.

reached and meanwhile the refinery at Bahrain was built and the California-Texas arrangement consummated. Other inter-group possibilities were discussed, only to be rejected in 1938–9; and a reconciliation of the producing and marketing interests of the I.P.C. groups, or some of them, with those of Caltex was, after all, to await the years after the second war, and even then to be steered on no easy course.

### III. QATAR

Holmes had been from the first not alone in his interest in the Arabian territories. Anglo-Persian had in 1924 sent its geologists to Oman, had wished to explore al-Hasa, and had prejudiced Holmes' prospects at Kuwait: and in June 1930 its representative, acting on behalf of the I.P.C. with full Red Line propriety, visited the Qatar capital of Doha and obtained from the aged Shaikh 'Abdullah permission for two years' exploration of this most desolate of territories. The initial survey and map were finished early in 1933.

In the meanwhile the discovery well at Bahrain had been completed; and the groups which composed the Iraq Petroleum Company could not be indifferent to the possibility, already in part the certainty, of the flooding of markets from such new sources of supply. Of the decision to compete for the al-Hasa province of Sa'udi Arabia more will be said later (p. 107): meanwhile the Qatar prospect could not but be followed up, and a negotiator was sent to Doha, to act nominally on behalf of Anglo-Persian so as to avoid confusing the old ruler with apparent rivalries, but in fact to acquire rights for the I.P.C. The Political Resident at Bushire felt it well to advise the Shaikh to make the award to a British company and discouraged accordingly a tentative Californian démarche; he was aware also that Holmes and his Syndicate, who appeared with offers for the Qatar Concession, were middlemen scarcely to be preferred to a fully competent operating company. The prospects for the Anglo-Persian negotiator were, therefore, favourable; but the course of the conversations was slow, the Shaikh senile and suspicious, and agreement was reached, after a change of negotiators, only in May 1935.

The Qatar Concession, duly assigned soon afterwards by Anglo-Persian to the Iraq Petroleum Company, gave for seventy-five years exclusive rights over the territory of Qatar, consisting of

4,000 square miles bounded on the south by an arbitrary line. Provision was made for customs and taxation exemption, for full freedom of construction and operation, and for payment of a royalty of Rs. 3 per ton. A payment of Rs. 400,000 was to be made on signature, and annual sums of Rs. 150,000 (after five years, Rs. 300,000) were due in addition to royalty.

Signature was followed by the considerable period necessary for further and detailed examination of the peninsula. Before drilling could begin all physical preparations for the work must be completed and all stores and necessaries imported, since the territory was totally devoid of resources. The drilling of water wells was put in hand, though with little success; communication was established with Bahrain, where an office and depot were opened; camps were formed on Qatar territory, an unloading point was organized, a jetty built at Zakrit, and materials assembled for every purpose. Qatari labour, wholly unskilled and weak through malnutrition, improved progressively with good food and treatment; it was supplemented by imported Arab and Indian artisans and soon represented a large part of the whole manpower of the shaikhdom. Security was imperfect, pilfering incessant.

The first well was spudded in during October 1938 on the Dukhan structure, an anticline marked by a line of low hills in the south-west corner of the concession area. Conditions were arduous and exceptional drilling difficulties encountered; but in the last weeks of 1939 penetration into a limestone formation of middle Jurassic age, at a depth of 5,500 feet, revealed the presence of oil. The capacity of the first well was assessed at some 5,000 b/d; the oil was of 36 degrees A.P.I. gravity. Subsequent drilling was to confirm the important potentiality of the Dukhan field, which added another to Arabia's roll of oil-producing territories, and fully assured thenceforward the economic future of Shaikh 'Abdullah's principality.

### IV. CASOC

Since the life of Holmes's permit and option for the al-Hasa province of ibn Sa'ud had become extinct by 1928, negotiation, by whatsoever party, for rights in the territory must be recommenced. Entry therein, to the extent of free exploration, was sought in 1930 by the Standard of California, but refused: the discovery well at Bahrain in 1932, however, added to the general tendencies of the time, made it certain that the adjacent mainland would soon be in demand.

The Hijaz, meanwhile, had been visited in 1931 by an American mining engineer, Karl Twitchell, on behalf of the millionaire philanthropist and arabophile, C. R. Crane. Although his quest for artesian water was unsuccessful, he aroused the interest of ibn Sa'ud in mineral possibilities and was allowed to cross Arabia in search of indications of petroleum; and at the moment when the Bahrain well revealed itself as a producer, Twitchell was back in America with the King's instructions to find a suitable company to explore his country's oil resources.

Political conditions in Sa'udi Arabia were by this period reasonably stable, the King's authority unquestioned. But the territory was economically at the lowest ebb. Never self-supporting in food, without minerals or industry or any other resources, the Arabian population had long lived at the barest level of subsistence; the great Mecca pilgrimage itself, sole support of the Treasury was in 1930 greatly reduced in scale, and the King was in desperate straits to maintain a court and government in existence.

Twitchell was unsuccessful in his first contacts. The Texas Company rejected his suggestion; the Gulf Corporation was by now bound by Red Line obligations; the American shareholders of the I.P.C. did no more than pass his offers to that Company in London. But the Standard of California, encouraged by events at Bahrain, were willing to take further risks and determined to ask for a comprehensive concession for the mainland territory. Their negotiator, Lloyd Hamilton, accompanied by Twitchell, reached Jidda for this purpose in March 1933.

The Iraq Petroleum Company had this time decided to contest the issue. Their representative (the present writer) arrived at Jidda to find negotiations in progress between Hamilton and the Sa'udi ministers and was invited to make his own offers. Both negotiators interviewed the King, both advanced their proposals, each was assured that his Company and nationality would, all things being equal, be the more acceptable to the Sa'udi King. But the I.P.C. directors were slow and cautious in their offers and would speak only of rupees when gold was demanded. Their negotiator, so handicapped, could do little; and agreement was reached without difficulty between Hamilton and Shaikh 'Abdullah

Sulaiman on 29 May 1933 for a sixty-year concession for the al-Hasa province.

The territory covered was the whole of 'eastern Sa'udi Arabia' as far west as the Dahana, with assurance of future preferential treatment over wide further areas which included the Sa'ud's half-rights in the Kuwait Neutral Zone. An initial payment of 30,000 gold sovereigns was counted out at Jidda a few weeks later; an annual minimum payment of 5,000 sovereigns, two loans of 50,000 sovereigns each when commercial oil should be discovered, and a royalty of 4s. (gold) per ton, were the other financial considerations. Exemption was granted from taxation and customs duties. Unwanted lands were to be progressively released. Refinery obligations were limited to the erection of a small plant, after the discovery of commercial oil. The concession was assigned by Standard of California to an affiliate created for the purpose, the California Arabian Standard Oil Company, or C.A.S.O.C., in November 1933. Three years later the basis of C.A.S.O.C. itself was broadened by the admission of the Texas Company to a half-share, as in Bapco.

Geologists of the California Company landed on the al-Hasa coast late in September 1933, lodged with their Sa'udi agents, hired camels, and soon located their first promising structure at Jabal Dhahran, five miles inland from the coastal village of Dammam. Moving to the oasis of Hofuf, and joined by other geologists and motor transport, the parties ranged the barren wastes for long distances under Sa'udi escort. In the spring of 1934 they acquired an aircraft and discovered an apparent folding at Qatif, another far to the north at abu Hadriya, and in 1935 exposures of Eocene rocks at Abqaiq (Buqaiq), al-'Alat, and elsewhere: but the cover of sand and recent sediments prevented, almost everywhere, all reliable knowledge of the substructure until other means for discovery of underlying formations had been brought to bear.

The intention to drill the Dhahran structure led, late in 1934, to the establishment of a permanent camp, the import of equipment, materials and necessaries for every industrial and domestic purpose, and, in due course, the arrival of drillers. Fresh water was obtained from a spring under the sea; a road was built between Dhahran camp and the coast; and in April 1935 the first Dhahran well was spudded in.

Success came slowly. In a location of high promise, successive wells revealed only minor shows of heavy oil and gas in the zone which was productive at Bahrain. Efforts, however, did not slacken, buildings at Dhahran multiplied, and in the early weeks of 1938 well no. 7, deepened to 4,550 feet, revealed oil in important quantities in the porous Upper Jurassic limestone, 300–400 feet thick, of a broad gently domed structure, four miles long and three wide.

The discovery well, completed in March, was a foretaste of the immensely productive series drilled in one oilfield after another in the vast spaces of Sa'udi Arabia, with the direct and early consequence of a total transformation of Sa'udi economics. The months following the discovery were full of varied activity. A building scheme was undertaken and its execution was to extend far into war years. All modern amenities, family and bachelor dwellings, sleeping and living quarters for Sa'udis, clubs and a hospital, bath-houses and a swimming-pool, store-sheds and all their contents, garages, workshops, a power plant, a water system, and the installation of air-conditioning units: all these were completed. Telegraph communication was established between all points and wireless contact made possible with parties operating far inland and with the Company's office at Jidda, which was maintained for liaison with the King and his ministers. The drilling of further wells proceeded, those already drilled were deepened. Oilfield installations, gathering lines, gas-separators and tankage were constructed. A 6-inch pipeline was laid to the coast at al-Khobar, from which barge loads of oil could be sent to Bahrain. For shipping greater consignments by deeper-draft vessels it was necessary to find and improve whatever suitable channel might exist; the choice fell on Ras Tanura, a low-jutting spit to the north of Dammam, and a forty-three-mile 10-inch pipeline to this point was completed by the spring of 1939. The channel leading inshore to Ras Tanura was marked, tankage was erected, a loading jetty and submarine lines were constructed, and all was in readiness to receive tankers for the export of oil by May 1939. The sailing of the first cargo on 1 May was the occasion of a visit in great state of King 'Abdul 'Aziz ibn Sa'ud. The export of oil from Sa'udi Arabia amounted in that year to 525,000 tons; this was dispatched overseas, partly in crude form to Caltex-owned refineries and partly as refined products, after passing through Bahrain, to their markets in the East.

Test drilling was undertaken during this period at abu Hadriya, 'wild-cat' wells were drilled at Ma'qala and al-'Alat (but later abandoned), and seven rotary drilling rigs in all kept working in the concession area. The close of the year 1939 found five producing wells completed on the Dhahran structure and four more under drilling. Three storage tanks, sea lines, and a loading terminal had been completed at Ras Tanura.

The extent of the concession area itself was widely increased by a Supplementary Agreement between Casoc and the Government, concluded on 21 July 1939; it bestowed, for sixty years, not less than 85,000 square miles of additional area, of which one block [1] lay in the far south-west of the country, another in the extreme north, abutting on 'Iraq and Transjordan. The King's half-rights over both the Neutral Zones were included and a west-central tract remained subject to Casoc's 'right of preference'. The size of the exclusive area was by this Agreement increased to some 440,000 square miles. A sum of £140,000 (gold) was paid by the Company on signature and the minimum dead-rent raised from £5,000 to £25,000 (gold) a year.

### V. KUWAIT

The success of Holmes in 1923 in obtaining rights for the Kuwait–Sa'udi Neutral Zone, but not for Kuwait itself, has been mentioned (p. 100). Though his Neutral Zone permit was for a time kept valid by renewals, the parties to the Agreement of November 1927, whereby Eastern and General's mainland, as well as island, rights were assigned to the Gulf Corporation, were faced—as at Bahrain—by the Red Line restrictions on Gulf as an I.P.C. constituent and by the obstacle (easily surmountable, as Bahrain had proved) of its non-British nationality. In any case, the Neutral Zone permit lapsed at last, while rights over Kuwait, which had been specifically excluded from the Red Line and for which Gulf were therefore eligible, remained ungranted.

But if Gulf's interest in this stayed alive and was shown by the presence of Holmes at Kuwait as their representative, the pressure of their Anglo-Persian rivals had not diminished. The latter was permitted to view the territory and even to drill two shallow boreholes; and, though these tests were inconclusive, the Bahrain dis-

---

[1] Part of this block was surrendered in 1940.

covery could not fail to redouble interest in the region and the stage was set for direct competition between the two groups. Gulf, it seemed, could succeed only by bluntly outbidding its rival and by overcoming, as best it could, the obstacle of nationality: and on the latter point the State Department took on its behalf the same steps as it had taken in respect of Bahrain, representing to the British the evils of national exclusiveness and closed doors. The two candidates were of equal industrial standing and of equal ability to develop whatever oil might prove to exist; neither the Shaikh nor the British Government was willing to reject either applicant, nor would either retire. A compromise was indicated; and, after two years of dragging negotiations, the two Companies decided to apply jointly for the concession. An agreement between them on 14 December 1933 provided for combined use of the Eastern and General's facilities or priorities, for joint acquisition of these by a cash payment to the Syndicate, and for the formation of a Kuwait Oil Company to be financed and administered equally [1] by the two groups. Neither party was to dispose of its interest therein except with the consent of the other, and each would abstain from action damaging to the other's marketing position. Oil would be produced to an extent demanded by either, Anglo-Persian being allowed, if it wished, to substitute Persian for Kuwaiti oil in fulfilment of all requirements. The Kuwait Oil Company was formed, on the lines proposed, in February 1934. Concession negotiations with the Shaikh were continued by joint negotiators and concluded on 23 December of that year, twelve months after the inter-company agreement had been reached.

The terms of the concession were favourable. The area was of 6,000 square miles, the period seventy-five years, the initial payment Rs. 470,000, the annual dead-rent Rs. 95,000, and the royalty Rs. 3 per ton with an annual minimum of Rs. 250,000. All taxation was commuted for a payment of As. 4 per ton. These payments, trivial by comparison with those current in 'Iraq, were in 1934 of rare value to the ruler and public of Kuwait and would be much increased by the money spent locally and the employment given in the course of the Company's operations. The country, with its sand-strewn, desolate surface, absence of water, and low

[1] The Anglo-Persian half-shareholding was later transferred by it to the D'Arcy Exploration Company, that of Gulf to a Gulf Exploration Company registered in March 1937.

rainfall, lacked all agricultural possibilities. Its trade of pearl-fishing was gravely depressed, its industry of boat building un-prosperous; its value as a transit centre for inner Arabia was limited, and the long-established traffic of smuggling into 'Iraq could bring profit to no more than a few pockets. The petroleum industry, if fortune favoured, would bring salvation to Kuwait as it had already brought it to Bahrain.

The settlement of concessionary rights in the Neutral Zone did not keep pace with that of Kuwait. It lay within the Red Line; it depended upon two rulers instead of one; Holmes's rights had long lapsed and the Sa'udi half-rights, or a preferential claim to them, had been granted in 1933 to Standard of California. With I.P.C. shareholders individually excluded, that Company as such could be a candidate for the Kuwait half-rights, and its representative visited Kuwait in 1935 to negotiate in that sense. But the Shaikh was hesitant and the Political Agent advised inaction until the position was clarified on the Sa'udi side, where an Arabian Mining Syndicate, led by a Syrian creditor of ibn Sa'ud, was hopeful of supplanting Casoc as grantee of the King's rights. A joint I.P.C.-California company appeared as the probable solution; but, in fact, no step in that direction was taken and the zone remained unallotted.

Operations in Kuwait showed no such delays. Eighteen months from the date of the concession sufficed for the preparation of all staff, labour, equipment, vehicles, and services adequate for the commencement of drilling; and on 31 May 1936, a day of violent sandstorm, the first well was spudded in at Bahra in the presence of Shaikh Ahmad and a large concourse. This well, taken to a depth of almost 8,000 feet, encountered no horizon capable of com-mercial production and was abandoned. The next stage was to cover nearly the whole territory, during the winter of 1936-7, with a campaign of geophysical search by magnetometer, gravi-meter, and seismograph. It led to the selection of the second drilling location near the bitumen seepage in the Burgan area, twenty-eight miles south of Kuwait town and fourteen inland from the coast. Drilling here began on 16 October 1937. Oil shows were encountered below 3,400 feet of depth; and in April 1938, at 3,675 feet, the drill entered a high-pressure oil and gas sand, and the pressure was with difficulty controlled. A second and further wells were immediately put in hand, the completion of which was to confirm the presence of an oilfield of the very greatest magnitude.

The productive area of the Burgan field was proved, in due course, to be pear-shaped, narrowing to the north. It covers some thirty square miles in a broad anticlinal structure with its major axis north–south and a length of twelve to fifteen miles. The productive formations are of Middle or Lower Cretaceous sandstone, capped with impermeable shale; the oil-bearing horizon, 3,500–4,500 feet below the surface, is some 1,000 feet in thickness. The structure has been claimed as the petroleum engineer's ideal, with only slight faulting and the ability to produce at high rates without 'making sand'; pressures are moderate and the sand is of high porosity. The gravity of the oil, which contains some 2 per cent. of sulphur, varies according to depth from 36 to 30 degrees A.P.I. gravity.

Between the discovery well and the outbreak of war much progress was made towards the equipment and preparation of the field with a view to the production and export of oil. An intensive search was made for drinking water and preparations for another exploratory well at Madaniyat, between Burgan and Kuwait, were put in hand.

### VI. WEST, SOUTH, AND SOUTH-EAST

The unsuccessful effort of the Iraq Petroleum group in 1933 to obtain the al-Hasa Concession has been mentioned (p. 107) and their interest, equally unrealized, in the Neutral Zone (p. 112). These steps represented early moves of the Company towards embarking on enterprises outside their first area in northern 'Iraq, enterprises to which the spacious areas still unexplored within the Red Line (and the interest of others in them) might well dispose them. Though the companies of the group differed in their commitments and their marketing interests, and were not always unanimous in their eagerness for further production from this or that Middle Eastern territory (which could adversely affect the acceptability of production elsewhere), yet all must dislike the prospect of uncontrolled operation by outsiders. It was, therefore, rather in prudent self-defence than in a spirit of self-aggrandizement that the I.P.C. looked abroad in 1933 and thereafter.

A significant move in this direction was the formation in October 1935 of Petroleum Concessions Limited, with ownership and shareholding identical to those of the I.P.C. It was intended that this Company should create an affiliate in each country for the development of concessions obtained, on lines which, as they occurred in the Levant, have already been recorded (p. 91).

In pursuance of this policy, it was decided early in 1936 to apply for rights in the Hijaz province, with 'Asir, on the east coast of the Red Sea: a region which, though largely volcanic, was known to be bordered seawards by a thin strip of sedimentary rocks. The resulting concession, duly negotiated and signed (by the present writer) at Taif on 1 July, was to cover for sixty years a strip 100 kilometres in depth, stretching from the Transjordan boundary to the Yemen, but excluding a central area around the Holy City of Mecca. Two-thirds of the concession was to be surrendered within three years of the commencement of drilling and half of the rest five years later; and the concession would be null and void if no commercial oil had been discovered within ten further years. The Company, which proceeded to form Petroleum Development (Western Arabia) Limited, was exempt from all taxation; exploration and drilling obligations were moderate. An initial payment of 35,000 gold sovereigns, or their sterling equivalent, was to be made and annual dead-rent payments were to rise, until oil should be discovered, by stages from 7,500 to 10,000 sovereigns. Small quantities of refined products and 1 per cent. of crude oil produced were to be handed annually to the Government.

Early steps were taken for the carrying out of the concession. An office was opened at Jidda and two geological parties were sent to operate, one in each of the two coastal blocks, in the winter of 1936–7. The researches of neither, unfortunately, could reveal any hopeful prospects; and the same verdict was given by a geological survey party, for whom, early in 1937, permission was obtained from the Imam of the Yemen rapidly to explore a restricted coastal strip of his kingdom, from Hudaida northward. The known seepage, however, on the Farsan Islands (where Shell had drilled ten years earlier) suggested the desirability of further research in that archipelago, which the present Hijaz Concession included. Two seasons' work by a geological party of Petroleum Development (Western Arabia) was carried out in 1937–8 and 1938–9. With the help of the Aden and the Kamaran Island authorities a suitable mobile and amphibian organization was created and good use was made of the resources, manpower, and transport (by dhow and launch, camel, and handcart) of these primitive and little-visited communities. Core drilling to depths from 450 to 1,600 feet was carried out in seventeen wells spread over eight of the islands. Geophysical methods were adopted at the same time on the adjacent mainland near Jisan (Gisan) to assess the underlying structure, but with discouraging results; no hopeful formation was located below the deep overlying salt. The failure to find prospects of interest, either on the islands or on the mainland, seemed, in the end, to condemn the Western Arabia Concession as of little value.

The Aden Protectorate, from which came persistent rumours of oil shales and seepages, might offer more encouragement and had not been examined by geologists since Little's visit in 1920. An exploration licence for the whole territory was granted by the Governor of Aden to Petroleum Concessions in January 1938 and in anticipation of its issue a party of geologists visited the Hadhramaut in the winter season of 1937–8. They were able to add a limited range of aerial survey and photography to their travel by animal and mechanical transport, and covered much of the coast, the high hinterland, and the great Wadi itself. In spite, however, of the abundance of sediments, no structure worthy of the drill was located in the regions visited; and insecurity in the no-man's-land between the Protectorate and the Sa'udi and Yemen frontiers prevented exploration of some areas from which surface indications were reported.

Petroleum Concessions was active also in south-eastern Arabia, on the Trucial Coast, and in the Sultanate of Oman. The half-dozen ruling Shaikhs of the coast were visited in 1936 by a Company's representative based on Bahrain and were offered agreements, similar to those current at Bahrain and Kuwait, for the exploration and development of their oil resources, should these exist. The rulers, living in abject poverty and governing by the simplest form of patriarchal absolutism, knew nothing of boundary lines across their sand-covered wastes and could guarantee little security; but by patient negotiation and the slow victory over suspicion and avarice, it was possible in 1937 to reach agreement for modest immediate payments and annual dead-rents in return for concessions over the lands of Dibai and Sharja. Agreement proved easier at Muscat, where the Sultan was visited at the same period; he was glad to relieve his financial straits by granting concessions or options for concessions for the main block of Oman (of which he effectively controlled less than a third) and, separately, for the detached southern province of Dhofar. Late in 1938 a permit was obtained for the shaikhdom of Ras al-Khaima and another for the village-state of Kalba; and early in 1939 the Shaikh of abu Dhabi, whose almost uninhabited country comprises three-quarters of the whole Trucial Coast and an unknown area of hinterland, awarded a concession for its oil resources. In all these agreements the royalty was fixed at Rs. 3 a ton; and the area covered was in each case defined as including the 'territorial waters and islands' belonging to the ruler. A five-year exploration licence for 'Ajman was granted in March 1939.

The Shaikhs of the coast, upon whom no agreement was forced against their will, and some of whom preferred a short-term permit to a long-term concession—while one refused to grant either—found themselves prosperous to an extent without precedent as they collected their annual rentals, paid some of their debts, rode in their new cars, and filled their hospitable coffee-pots; but their people could at this stage benefit little or nothing from the exchange of documents between their ruler and the Company, until field-work should begin. A geological party spent the winter of 1938-9 on the coast of Oman, on part of its mountain-mass and western foothills, and along the Trucial Coast and nearer hinterland. Since the western slopes of the Oman mountains, and doubtless also the sand-covered flatness beyond, contained well-folded sedimentary rock masses and lay on the fringes of the great geosyncline, the area could not but be of interest; but it was insecure, allegiance to the Sultan slight or withheld, inter-tribal anarchy prevalent, law non-existent, the terrain difficult; and the war broke out before exploration could be further pursued. A brief visit was paid to Dhofar.

## CHAPTER VIII

# SECOND WORLD WAR:
## 'IRAQ AND PERSIA

### I. 'IRAQ CATASTROPHE

THE outbreak of war in September 1939 had in 'Iraq, as elsewhere, immediate effects on the oil industry, in spite of efforts to maintain it at the full or increased production for which war necessities would certainly call. The project to double the 'Iraq–Mediterranean pipeline was postponed: a decision wholly unavoidable but one which, restricting 'Iraqi production to some 4 million t/y for a further ten years, has been deplored by the publicists of that nation, as well as by the Company itself. Exploration work in the Basrah Company's area was continued on a reduced scale; but the geophysical survey, begun early in 1939, was brought to an end in May 1940. Some American staff left 'Iraq for their own country on the outbreak of war and a number of the British were allowed to join the fighting services.

The interruption of supplies and communications was an immediate and serious handicap to all operations. The insecurity of the Mediterranean interfered with, and indeed temporarily suspended, shipments of oil from Haifa and Tripoli, and, thereby, diminished pumping from K1 station. The effect on exported tonnage and on the Government's receipts was perceptible but not serious, since after three weeks normal export could recommence; 'Iraqi exported production, 4·16 million tons in 1938, in 1939 was 3·81; nor was production affected by the Franco-British prohibition of the export of 'Iraq oil to any but French or British assignees, since these could gladly absorb all that was available. In June 1940, however, the entry of Italy into the war produced such shipping conditions in the Mediterranean as to preclude any production by the I.P.C. in excess of what could be processed at the Haifa refinery or at the new Tripoli 'raffinerie de poche'. The consequent fall in production was now more marked, and the stoppage of all pumping on the northern line to Tripoli, consequent on the fall of France and transformation of Syria–Lebanon into enemy-dominated countries, was to last for many months.

'Iraqi production for export fell in 1940 to 2·5 million tons, and in 1941 to 1·4 million.

The German overwhelming of France had the further result that the latter, under its subservient Vichy Government, became, for the British, enemy territory; the shares of the Compagnie Française in the I.P.C. were passed to the Custodian of Enemy Property and its tankers could till 1945 lift no quota of 'Iraq oil. Gulbenkian, resident in France, was similarly classified as an enemy alien in spite of his diplomatic status as Iranian Commercial Attaché, but was reinstated in his rights as a British national in 1943, when he moved to Lisbon. The effect on its structure of these temporary withdrawals from the I.P.C. comity will be mentioned later (p. 174): meanwhile oil after August 1940 was sold to such groups as could receive it, at a price fixed by an expert American oil-broker invoked for the purpose; and protests from the legal representatives of both Gulbenkian and C.F.P. were unheeded. Oil at this period was taken, in the form of refined products from the Haifa refinery, by Anglo-Iranian, Shell, and Socony-Vacuum, none by New Jersey, the French, or Gulbenkian.

In 'Iraq it was possible amid increasing difficulties to maintain drilling in the 'Ain Zala field, where by the spring of 1941 five wells had been completed to depths ranging from 5,100 to 6,000 feet, and simultaneously to continue the search for others by geophysical work. The completion of the Mosul–Baghdad railway in July 1940 was helpful to the Company. At Kirkuk drilling with two strings continued until May 1940, with production assured from some fourteen producing wells in the same 9-mile section of the structure. The internal needs of 'Iraq continued to be met by the products of the Alwand refinery and, in the south, by import from Abadan. A system of rationing for petroleum products was introduced by Government soon after the outbreak of war; it was especially stringent for lubricants, which neither Alwand nor Abadan produced.

The effect of the events of May 1941—the usurpation of power by the Prime Minister, Rashid 'Ali al-Gailani and his Golden Square of 'Iraqi Generals in anticipation of German help and British discomfiture—were immediate and unfortunate, but short lived. A state of war was produced overnight by the surrounding of the British garrison at Habbaniya by the 'Iraq army; and the considerable British colonies at 'Ain Zala, Qaiyara, Kirkuk, the pipeline stations, Khanaqin, and Naftkhana were bidden first to send their families to safety and then themselves to concentrate. Of the women and children, part were dispatched by way of Haditha to Palestine, part by air to Basra. Of the men, a few from Alwand were detained by 'Iraqi police at Ba'quba, others shared the month-long captivity of almost the whole community of their fellow countrymen in the British and American Embassies in Baghdad. Most of the I.P.C. foreign personnel were detained for the same period under close house-arrest at Kirkuk—in Fields headquarters or a local school or their own homes—while the staff of B.O.D., European and American, were brought from 'Ain Zala and Qaiyara to Mosul for incarceration in the British Consulate. Treatment of captives at all locations varied from the courteous to the truculent.

During this month of May when 'Iraq civil or military authorities replaced the Company's executives in directing all oil installations and supplies, in the expectation of handing these shortly to German technicians, all production was brought to a standstill. The attitude of the Company's 'Iraqi staff and labour varied between steadfast loyalty and frank adhesion to the momentarily winning side. At Alwand, where interruption was brief and never complete, maintenance was well secured, little property misused, and all records preserved. At Kirkuk little deliberate sabotage occurred, though some dwelling-houses and Company's stores were looted. There, as elsewhere, almost all transport vehicles were seized and only a part recovered subsequently in more or less usable condition. At K3 plant and machinery were badly damaged and stores stolen. At H2 the sabotage and looting were at their worst, at other stations the losses and damage were less serious. At Qaiyara camp looting and destruction cost the Company most of its stores and furniture; at 'Ain Zala it was less but considerable. The field camps of the Basrah Company's geophysical parties were looted.

## II. RECOVERY IN 'IRAQ

The rehabilitation of damage at Kirkuk and restoration of Fields to operation could proceed during June 1941 and thereafter, in a restored atmosphere of confidence. Nevertheless the progressive loss of irreplaceable staff and the impossibility of obtaining regular supplies were but a part of the factors which prevented full recovery or expansion. No further work, except for some continuing geological reconnaissance, was attempted throughout the war in the Basra area nor in that of the B.O.D.[1] At Qaiyara, occupied by British troops, a footing was retained by the Mosul Company on a basis of care and maintenance, and quantities of road-bitumen were supplied to government and the British forces. 'Ain Zala, which also quartered a military force, was not reoccupied by Company personnel. Security arrangements with the shaikhs of the Shammar continued in force.

Elsewhere, the country from the summer of 1941 onwards was filled with British and British-Indian troops, and the supply of these became a principal consideration for the Companies. The army's many and varied vehicles, their movable and fixed installations, and their reserve stocks at strategic points called for quantities of refined products which, added to normal civilian needs, needed extraordinary steps to make available. The refinery at Alwand was increased in capacity by improvisation and 'revamping' during and after 1942 and crude was supplied to it not only from Naftkhana but from Naft-i-Shah across the frontier by a new 'flexibility' linking of the two fields. Kerosene also was piped from Naft-i-Shah (by the old one-inch Naftkhana–Alwand water-line). To the 4-inch crude line from Naftkhana was added a new six-inch line. The Alwand output was doubled from 1939 to 1945—from 150,000 to 300,000 t/y—and distribution arrangements were correspondingly augmented. A black-oil pipeline was laid between Abadan and the Royal Air Force cantonment (now a vast military base) at Shaiba, additional networks of pipelines were installed in the Basra port area and in connexion with the Rafidain Company's depots at Baghdad. At Kirkuk units of the stabilization plant were used for the production of gasoline capable, with treatment, of supplying military vehicles and the topping-plant worked to capacity. Fuel oil for the fleet was 'slugged' down the pipeline to Tripoli. Tin factories were erected at both Kirkuk and Mosul and were worked until the threat of invasion by German troops from the north had disappeared and military forces could be reduced. A 4-inch pipeline 110 miles in length was built from Kirkuk to Mosul. Help to the Forces in miscellaneous supplies, in

---

[1] Henceforward to be known as the Mosul Petroleum Company; the B.O.D. Concession was assigned to it in 1941 and B.O.D. and Mosul Oilfields ceased to exist in 1943.

the provision of quarters, in telecommunications, in workshop facilities, and in the loan of specialist staff was given abundantly by all the Companies at all levels.

Such services, which were, indeed, a matter of course as contributing to the British war effort, could not save the I.P.C. from a heavy militarily-inflicted blow. In 1942, in face of a not impossible southward advance of enemy forces, the Military Command decided that precautionary measures must include the destruction of nearly all of the producing wells in the Kirkuk fields. All except six were 'plugged' by Royal Engineers so effectively as to preclude all hope of reopening and thousands of tons of stores and equipment were moved to Basra. It was fortunate that these works of 'denial' stopped when they did; a closer enemy threat, or a more impetuous local commander, might well have placed Kirkuk beyond the power to produce oil for years to come. In the event, the six producing wells that were spared—and the close knowledge of the field which fifteen years of study had made possible—sufficed to maintain full production to the limits with which the western terminals of the pipeline could deal. Similar 'denial' measures cost the Company all its wells at 'Ain Zala and all but one at Qaiyara.

Production in 'Iraq of all companies amounted to some 3·25 million tons in 1942, 3·78 in 1943, 4·25 in 1944, and 4·62 million in 1945, by which year full I.P.C. output had been regained and the Government's receipts fron its oil royalties, dead-rents, and commuted taxation amounted again to over £2 million a year. But the impossibility in these war conditions of fulfilling all the obligations of the three major concessions—those of 1931, 1932, and 1938—led the I.P.C. and the Mosul and Basrah Companies in 1943 to ask the Government for a moratorium in respect of these; and an agreement made between the Government and the Companies in March of that year provided for a 'period of suspension' for the drilling, production, and export obligations of the Mosul and Basrah Companies. The period was to terminate and all the prescribed duties were to be resumed two years after the Armistice with Germany or Japan, whichever should be the later. The Company in return made an immediate interest-free loan of £500,000, with another £1 million to follow at the Armistice. These were repayable on terms similar to those of the loan given in 1939.

As the war drew to a close both the Companies and the Government were maturing plans for the future. The latter, with motives mainly political but in part financial, held to its intention to build a refinery of its own for which cheap supplies of crude would be assured; the former were reviewing their plans of 1938–9 to duplicate its Mediterranean pipeline and thus provide greater outlets for 'Iraq's waiting resources.

The maintenance of the 'Iraqi labour force in Fields and at pipeline stations during the war presented unusual difficulties. The numbers involved, indeed, increased little until late in the war; but the cost of living doubled and redoubled in the later war years, thanks to the country's restricted supplies of food and commodities, the profuse military expenditure, and the steeply rising world prices. The real value of pre-war wages and salaries was thereby halved and halved again. A system of living-allowances was evolved by the Company to obviate hardship and maintain its workers' standard of living and further assistance was given in the form of supplies of grain and other foodstuffs and clothing, which were made available to workers at prices far below those of the bazaars.

### III. RECESSION IN PERSIA

If in 'Iraq the oil history of the war was one of limitation and disturbance followed by full operation and valuable work for the war effort, in Persia it was one of painful restriction for nearly two years and then, after one critical month, a call to wider expansion than ever and fruitful work alike for the Allied cause, the Persian public, and the industry itself. In this opportunity, thanks to the more varied scope of its industry and to its direct sea-outlet, Persia was more fortunate than 'Iraq; it could not merely maintain but could increase and diversify its output. In both countries the wartime background of the industry was one of relative isolation, of irregular sea communication, a resented censorship, inadequate supplies, difficulty or crisis in the local economy, and the depletion of experienced staff. In both every care was taken that the petroleum needs of the local public should take a high priority— far higher, indeed, than any civilian public in Europe. In neither was any advantage taken of the abnormal conditions by the responsible companies, *vis-à-vis* Government or consumer or

labour force, nor any attempt made, otherwise than by free agreement, to escape from obligations.

The outbreak of war enabled the Germans in Persia, swollen in
numbers and long prepared for the event, to redouble their efforts
to lower Persian morale, foment anti-British feeling, and preach
the certainty of Hitler's success. Nor did the Shah's strict neu-
trality preclude the display of evident favour by his officials to the
German cause and agents, until the events of midsummer 1941
produced a clearly necessary reorientation of the Persian attitude.

Meanwhile the state of war announced in September 1939 halted
the extensive and costly schemes for development in fields and
refinery, which had been conceived a year earlier, were already in
hand, and were planned to reach fruition in 1943. The project of
expansion had envisaged the use of three drilling rigs at each of
Lali, Naft Safid, and Gach Saran and four at Agha Jari, with full
production installations at all the new fields; fresh tests were
planned in other areas, including Ahwaz, and extensive housing
projects were in hand for the older fields and Abadan. Instead of
pursuing these the Company was forced to suspend almost all
new work and to undertake, instead, security measures against
German-inspired sabotage. Such were the barbed-wiring of pump-
stations, the expanded-metal fences around wells, additional
patrolling, and the 'mudding off' of wells not in use; and, at
Abadan, a system of personal passes, the building of fire walls
round tanks, the digging of shelters, and, after the bombing of
Bahrain in October 1940, the imposition of a blackout and the
extinction of gas-flares.

With all this, however, an important step forward was taken
by the completion of a 12-inch pipeline to bring crude 165
miles from Gach Saran to Abadan, and of a stabilization plant of
perfected type at the new field and other Fields' installations.
Gach Saran, the remotest of Anglo-Iranian fields, took its place
thenceforward as a supplier of some 1·5–2 million tons a year.

The pause in intended development elsewhere was not necessitated only by the sudden interruption of transport, supplies, and
foreign recruitment; it was indicated, no less, by the diminished
demand for products, since Anglo-Iranian markets in much of
Europe were lost in a day. Production, over 10 million tons in
1938, fell in 1939 to 9·5 million. In 1940, when the Mediterranean was unsafe and Europe overrun by German armies, demand

slackened still further to some 8·6 million tons and, in 1941, with the adoption of the 'short haul' system to economize tankers (which in effect suspended shipments to Great Britain) to 6·6 million, the lowest figure for ten years.

Correct as were the relations between the Persian Government and the Company since 1933, the fall in production and consequent decrease in royalties could not but dismay the Government—in effect, the Shah; the payment in respect of 1938 had been £3,300,000, for 1939 it was £2,770,000. In August 1940 on representations by the Persian Government, the company agreed to pay immediately an additional £1½ million in respect of 1939 and thenceforward to secure by similar payments that the Government revenue should not fall below £4 million in any year up to that of the Armistice. Payments so made were accepted by the Government in each of the years 1940–3; thereafter the normal provisions of the 1933 Concession secured, thanks to increased tonnages, an oil revenue for the Government exceeding £4 million. The arrangement involved the Company, in effect, in a free gift of some £5½ million to assist the Persian Government in its difficulties, and this at a time of great commercial uncertainty.

The first phase of the war ended, for Fields and Abadan, with an event which Hitler's invasion of Russia in June 1941, and the needs of the Russian forces made inevitable for Allied strategy. It consisted in securing, by British and Russian forces, a position in Persia which could control and fortify that country. The dominating position of pro-Germans in the Court and Ministries of Teheran and the potential 'fifth column', which might at any time threaten oil production or block the Shatt al-'Arab, were additional reasons for the adoption of this step by the British War Cabinet. There was, indeed, little Persian reaction in favour of Rashid 'Ali's attempt at usurpation in 'Iraq, though leading figures in that abortive movement found easy sanctuary in Teheran; but the presence of British troops in 'Iraq thereafter and their organization there of bases and communications made access to Persia the easier.

The Shah, who refused to believe in the danger of a 'fifth column', gave inadequate replies to British and Russian requests for the expulsion of most of the Germans from the country. It became necessary, therefore, to take other steps. Operations of invasion started with the sinking of a Persian sloop by H.M.S. *Shoreham* in the Shatt al-'Arab, followed by that of another by

H.M.S. *Yarra*. The invasion of Abadan by land forces, which was to be carried out simultaneously, was dislocated by a first transport grounding on a mudbank; and Indian troops, landing at Abadan from a second, were opposed by Persian troops and suffered some casualties, but obtained possession of the water‧front. Persian resistance continued for some hours outside the refinery fencing and in overcoming it Indian troops, in the misunderstanding of a confused and unexpected engagement, shot three and wounded a very few more of the Company's staff. A morning of sporadic but dangerous firing ended with the cessation of Persian resistance by noon; neither the Persian police nor the main body of their troops had taken part. The Company's staff at all levels showed coolness, and men on shift worked without interruption.

Contact was established between the force which now occupied Abadan and that which, crossing the river at Tanuma, had occupied Khoramshahr after a brief but spirited resistance and advanced up the Karun on Ahwaz. Another force landed at Bandar Shapur, the terminus of the Persian railway.

Europeans at Kut 'Abdullah pump station were arrested, taken to Burujird, and there released. At Masjid-i-Sulaiman some days of keen tension passed, with British staff concentrated as a precaution in two central buildings; but work was not interrupted. On 25 August, the day after the Abadan landing, Persian troops arrived, occupied key positions, stopped work and collected Company transport; and, after two days of not ill-humoured captivity, the staff was driven off in buses by way of Shustar to Andimeshk. They returned, however, in good order to Fields on the 29th to find nothing disturbed. At Haft Kel troop-carrying aircraft landed Indian troops in the early morning of 25 August. These disarmed the Persian garrison and secured the oilfield. The European and Indian staff at Agha Jari and Gach Saran were arrested and taken to Behbehan for a two-day internment. These releases, after the briefest of campaigns and captivities, followed the signing of a cease-fire with the central Persian authorities on 29 August.

The operations of the 8th Indian Division in Khuzistan were synchronized with those of the 10th Division in the north. It entered Persia at Naft-i-Shah, Tang Ab, and Qasr-i-Shirin and seemed likely to meet more resistance than in the south; considerable forces had already been concentrated at the Paytak Pass, at the Kirmanshah refinery and at pumping stations on the line from Naft-i-Shah. But no fighting occurred and no damage was sustained; the working of Naft-i-Shah and of the refinery were uninterrupted and British forces entered Kirmanshah on 30 August.

The occupation of Persia by British and, in the north, by Russian troops was followed two weeks later by the abdication of the Shah, by the conclusion of an Anglo-Russo-Persian Treaty, which ranged the country on the side of the Allies, and by the restoration of conditions in which industrial activities could pursue their work in confidence.

This turning point in Persian history had been preceded by one month by the death of Lord Cadman in July 1941. He was succeeded as Chairman of the Company by Sir William Fraser.

### IV. PERSIA: THE WAR ACHIEVEMENT

The first consequence of the establishment of new conditions in Persia and higher morale and security at Fields and Abadan was not, unfortunately, an immediate increase in output. Fewer tons of oil were produced and processed and fewer tankers called at Abadan than for a dozen years past; the prospects of better progress seemed dubious; the added bustle of traffic in Khuzistan, the visible road improvements, indicated military activity but not oil shipments. Meanwhile, the defensive precautions at Abadan were considerably increased; they became for the first time a direct military responsibility, and one judged to be serious. A balloon barrage was established, the fire service increased, shelters were improved, and the routines of civilian passive defence adopted on the British model. A dummy refinery was constructed of gas flares, lights, and other decoying devices and a smokescreen prepared with hundreds of smoke-generators. Anti-aircraft batteries were brought into position, the Shatt was watched for the dropping of mines, camouflage was attempted, and fighter aircraft were provided on the landing grounds. Relations between the Company and the Military Command were admirable. The former's British staff,[1] eager in most cases to serve in the forces, were with difficulty

---

[1] These numbered nearly 1,700 in September 1939 and 950 two years later.

restrained; and the instruction published by Order in Council in December 1941, to the effect that the Company was an 'essential undertaking', brought them but partial consolation.

It is, indeed, not possible easily to distinguish between the strictly industrial operations of the Company from 1941 to 1945 and those designed to help the complex and massive operations of the Military Command, of which the maintenance of troops in forward areas and the convoying of supplies to Russia were the chief. Continuous and varied help was given to the operations of unloading and transporting by the Company's Karun barges or otherwise, railway engines, tanks, and vehicles of all kinds for the Russians, and in the supply of vast quantities of liquid fuel. The capacity of the Abadan tin factory was doubled between 1941 and 1944, from 600,000 tins to more than a million. Bulk depots for fuel were established all over Persia. Pipelines for products connected Abadan and the railway at Andimeshk. Additional staging posts and filling stations were erected in all parts. Asphalt in large quantities was supplied for military roads and depots, the production at Abadan rising from 85,000 tons in 1941 to 225,000 tons three years later.

Nor were British forces alone in calling for co-operation. Parties from the Russian Army visited Abadan to draw stores and vehicles; the United Kingdom Commercial Corporation depended for all fuel and for many services on the Company; the public and Government of Persia were entitled to, and received, a very high priority for their supplies: and the American forces, which appeared in June 1942, called for, as well as contributed, constant and multifarious services. These were the more difficult to render and the more necessary, since the interruption of the Company's own normal supplies; and the impossibility of obtaining from harassed Europe the needed equipment and materials compelled a high measure of self-sufficiency. Stores accumulated in 1939 for the development programme were used and re-used, adapted and re-adapted during the next five years, with rigid avoidance of waste and great ingenuity in improvisation.

The entry of Japan into the war in December 1941 and the loss of Allied oil resources in the Far East and Burma led to further calls on Abadan. Demands increased again with the preparation of the Allied offensive in North Africa in 1942. The era of diminished demand was at an end, new prospects opened, and these were to grow yet wider when the Mediterranean was reopened to shipping by the Allied landing in Sicily in July 1942. The reply was a production of nearly 9·5 million tons in 1942 (little less than in 1939), 9·75 in 1943, 13·25 in 1944, and nearly 17 million in 1945.

To achieve this output it was necessary to return urgently to the 1938–9 programme, formidable as were the supply difficulties to be surmounted. The Agha Jari field was the first to be brought into production, a result achieved in 1944 by obtaining an allotment of 50,000 tons of steel, finding somehow all other needed materials, and completing a 12-inch pipeline to Abadan; twelve wells had been drilled and the field supplied with water, power, stores, and workshops, and a stabilization unit of some 2 million ton capacity constructed of such materials as could be mustered. Work was begun at Naft Safid, and the necessary 10–12-inch pipeline to Wais on the Fields pipeline system was finished in 1945. At Pazanun special plant was installed in 1943 for utilizing the valuable distillate, into which a part of the gas can be made to condense, and which forms a valuable constituent of aviation spirit.

It was in large measure to meet the insistent demand for the latter that the expansion of producing power was put in hand; and the exigencies of the time demanded for it the utmost speed and effort. To procure further equipment capable of the highly specialized tasks required, J. A. Jameson visited America, ordered and collected all that could be found, and arranged for shipping. The precious cargo was sunk in the Atlantic, and twice more equipment re-ordered was sunk; but in April 1942 a beginning was made in the erection of the plant in a Special Products Area at Abadan. The design of this plant and of the connected processes was the most advanced of that time for the production of the special constituents of high-octane sulphur-free aviation fuel, for the blending of these, and for the production of the finished article in great quantity. The first of the production units was in operation by August 1943, the second five months later, a third sixteen months after that, just as the war in Europe was ending. By that time the output of aviation spirit exceeded a million tons a year: a truly remarkable achievement which made a priceless contribution to victory. The 100-octane spirit produced met a large proportion of the requirements of the British and American Air

Forces and provided great quantities also for the Russians. Simultaneously, important additions were made to the other refining installations at Abadan, whose combined capacity rose in 1939–45 from 10 to nearly 17 million t/y. The war-time demand for unlimited aviation spirit and other military needs involved the production of large quantities of unwanted products, to dispose of which recourse was had to a temporary extension of 're-cycling' into structures both at Masjid-i-Sulaiman and, for a time, at Haft Kel.

If the task of recruiting trained staff in Persia for the urgent expansion was one of formidable difficulty and involved the importation of citizens of many nations—Czechs, Danes, Greeks, Palestinians, and Swiss, as well as British—the care of the Persian labour force had, in all the circumstances of the war period, scarcely soluble problems of its own. The housing schemes, initiated in 1939 but interrupted until 1942, could thereafter proceed but haltingly; the result was a shortage of accommodation, which the Company, with full knowledge, was physically unable to avoid. It led inevitably to overcrowding, to low living standards in Abadan township, and to some discontent. In spite, moreover, of the admirable training, medical, safety, and amenity services provided by the Company, which retained all their high quality, the abrupt rise in living costs after 1941 compelled the adoption of special measures to safeguard workers' living standards. Local market-gardening and dairy-farming were undertaken by the Company, which also imported the grain required for the whole oil area, mainly by tankers returning from Australia. In 1943 a rationing system was drawn up to feed over 100,000 persons daily, of whom half were Company employees. Company shops were opened, where foodstuffs and clothing were available at subsidized prices. The ration of flour, tea, and sugar was free and additional to wages; it was replaced by a cash allowance at the Government's request in 1946.

### V. RUSSIAN CONCESSION

The Anglo-Russian occupation of Persia in 1941–5 appeared to the Russians to offer them advantages of a particular order. In the south no incorrectness of behaviour, no departure from concession terms could, unless with sheer falsity, be alleged; in the north the position lent itself well to the acquisition of Soviet rights in Persia which the previous twenty years had failed to extract.

Late in 1943 representatives of the Shell Group arrived in Persia to negotiate for an area in east Persia left unbestowed since the Anglo-Iranian delimitation in 1938. Conditions for negotiation were adverse, progress slow, the Persians reluctant: and in 1944 two more competitors for the same or neighbouring areas appeared, of whom one represented Sinclair interests, the other those of the Standard Vacuum, a joint subsidiary of Socony-Vacuum and New Jersey. The Persian Government, not unwilling to bargain, invoked independent American consultants to advise it and these stayed for some months in Teheran while conversations dragged on.

In September 1944, eleven days after a Cabinet decision to grant no concessions to anybody during the war, the situation was transformed by the sudden appearance at Teheran of a Soviet Vice-Commissar for Foreign Affairs, Sergei Kavtaradze,[1] with a large staff. Receptions were offered, audience with the young Shah obtained, and all publicity invited. The possibility that Russian ambitions might be limited to a greater exploitation of their rights, current or previous, in the Kavir-i-Khurian Company (where some shallow drilling had taken place since 1942) were the pretext for the visit: but the Commissar's demand was in effect for full freedom to explore most of north Persia for five years, with the assurance of a concession thereafter. Against any such proposition (contrary in any case to the recent Cabinet decision) all Persian suspicions revolted; it was, they felt, to admit Russian power into the heart of their country, with troops in the foreground, bases at Azerbaijan, and a mere façade of industrial functions. The proposals were discouraged, and the British and American negotiators were informed at the same time that no proposals would at present be entertained. Accepting the position, they left Persia.

The Persian refusal, conveyed to Kavtaradze in mid-October, was followed by a storm of protest by the Russophile press of Teheran. The advantage of a Russian-operated concession was emphasized, and the dangerous unfriendliness implicit in a refusal. Demonstrations were organized by the Communist-sponsored Tudeh Party [2] and Russian troops paraded in the towns.

---

[1] The name was improved by Persian wits to Kaftarzadeh, 'hyena's son'.

[2] Founded, not without liberal elements, in 1942 it fell rapidly under Communist domination and became a Russian instrument.

The Prime Minister resigned; but his successor could adopt no different attitude. Representations made by the British and American Ambassadors at Moscow endeavoured to relieve the pressure. Early in December a politician of hotly nationalist views and strangely wayward eccentricity, Dr. Muhammad Musaddiq, secured from the Majlis the adoption of a law designed to prevent, under heavy personal penalties, all further oil negotiation, unless by specific consent of the Majlis. At the same time Persian promises or half-promises, that in due time a Persian Company with Russian technicians might be formed for north Persian development, were offered to the Soviet Embassy; but their reception was uncertain and no action followed. Kavtaradze left Teheran: but north Persia was still Russian-dominated, and all Russian objectives remained.

## CHAPTER IX

# SECOND WORLD WAR: ARABIA AND THE LEVANT

## I. THE FORTUNATE: SA'UDI ARABIA

IN September 1939 the Dhahran field of the California-Arabian (Casoc) Company in al-Hasa was already in production, on a small scale, from eight completed wells. Since all essential field installations had been or were being erected and a sea outlet provided, it was foreseeable that production would rapidly increase. Meanwhile a test well was being drilled at abu Hadriya, 100 miles to the north-west.

The war had immediate effects; communication with America became difficult, the seas insecure, markets disturbed and partly inaccessible. The numbers of American staff were reduced from the spring of 1940 onwards; 150 out of 370 had gone home by the end of the year and another 100 by mid-1942. Nevertheless, progress was for a time continuous; the Dhahran stabilization plant was completed, with a capacity of 45,000 b/d and a small topping-plant of 3,000 b/d capacity was completed at Ras Tanura late in 1940. Export of crude from al Khobar and Ras Tanura amounted to 510,000 tons in 1939 and in the four succeeding years to 665,000, 565,000, 590,000, and 640,000 the bulk of which was destined for the Bahrain refinery.

The abu Hadriya well was completed as a good producer at a depth of over 10,100 feet in porous Jurassic limestone; a second well was left uncompleted. 'Wild-cat' wells were drilled at Ma'qala and al-'Alat, but were suspended and later abandoned. At Abqaiq (Buqaiq), in sand-dune country forty miles south-west of Dhahran, drilling began at a location revealed by structure-drilling and oil was found at a depth of 5,700 feet in November 1940. A second well was spudded in but suspended. Later development, as will be seen, was to prove the Abqaiq field one of the greatest in the world. In February 1943 a 'wild-cat' well was started at al-Jauf but later abandoned as a dry hole.

The interruption of transport and supplies rendered all operations in this period especially difficult; but it was possible to offer help to the Sa'udi Government by the drilling of many water wells, by loans of vehicles for movement of food, and by skilled maintenance of government transport. The Company's social and educational work on behalf of its workers continued; schools were started at Dhahran, al-Khobar, and Ras Tanura, and vocational training was increased. Wireless and telegraphic facilities were installed between Jidda and Riyadh. An agricultural project at al Kharj, fifty miles from Riyadh, was undertaken at the Government's request in 1941, and full administration of it from 1943; pumping plant was installed, wells developed, canals dug, and some 2,000 acres of land levelled and brought under cultivation.

The geological exploration of the vast Casoc Concession area, including wide districts of the Ruba' al-Khali, proceeded during 1940–2 by rapid reconnaissance, detailed mapping, and, for smaller areas, geophysical survey and structure-drilling.

All these activities, whether of exploring, drilling, or field engineering, were, nevertheless, running by the middle of 1943 at a decreasing tempo and one after another had been curtailed. From that period onwards a great change came over the Sa'udi scene, thanks to the decision of the United States Government that rapid wartime development in Arabia should be undertaken: a decision caused in part by the urgent wartime need for petroleum products and uneasiness at the heavy drawings on American oil, and in part also from certain Arabian anxieties felt in Washington. It was uneasy at the dominating position of Great Britain in that area of Asia, partly shared Casoc fears that England would gain ground in Sa'udi favour, was dubious of the future of the country if King 'Abdul 'Aziz should die, and remembered the British Government's position as majority shareholder in Anglo-Iranian. At midsummer 1943 the project of a direct United States Government shareholding in Casoc was proposed by H. L. Ickes and approved by the President. The plan, however, was rejected by Casoc's parent companies, dismayed at the new status offered them, and it came to nothing; and they declined equally to accept the Government as a minority shareholder. But early in 1944, while the DeGolyer Mission of American geologists was still touring the Middle East, it was announced that the California and Texas Companies had agreed with the Petroleum Reserves Corporation for the construction by the Government of a Sa'udi–Mediterranean pipeline (at a then anticipated cost of $130 to

$160 million) for which Casoc would provide the oil, repay the cost within twenty-five years, and maintain large reserves of oil at the Government's disposal.

This plan, though it provided a market for Sa'udi oil, displeased strong elements in American industry and in the Senate, as being a dangerous incursion by the Government into private enterprise; and the President agreed not to approve it unless suitably amended. The scheme was dead by April 1944; the Mediterranean pipeline was, after all, to be built by private enterprise five years later. But the considerations which had prompted the proposal, and the necessities of the war in the Far East, were still insistent. They gained for Casoc—now renamed the Arabian-American Oil Company, or Aramco—authority immediately to construct a major refinery at Ras Tanura, at its own expense. This project, for which the supply of steel, materials, and transport was given a high military priority, involved not merely the erection of the refinery but also that of a construction camp on the Tanura peninsula, new storage tanks, loading lines, services, and a pier and wharf with full marine installations. The year 1944, therefore, in contrast to 1940-3, was one of strenuous activity. Difficulties of every sort which confronted the Company and its contractors— those of materials, transport, staff, housing, storage—were all sur- mounted, and the refinery, with an initial capacity of 50,000 b/d, came into partial operation in September 1945 and to full working in December. It contained plant for atmospheric and vacuum distillation, for thermal reforming, and for chemical treatments, but not for cracking. The Tanura topping-plant ceased to operate in 1945.

A 12-inch partially submarine pipeline, thirty-four miles in length, from Dhahran to Bahrain was completed in April 1945, as part of the same expansion programme. That of a thirty-nine- mile 12-inch line from Abqaiq to Dhahran was begun in the same year. Drilling in the former field was re-started and five wells were completed; at Dhahran twenty-three were in production. Sa'udi output, which came entirely from this latter source, amounted in 1944 to more than 1 million tons and in 1945 to more than 2½ million. A field at Qatif, near the coast, was discovered in 1945 at a depth of 7,000 feet, and upwards, and steps were taken to prepare it for production.

The series of annual increases in Sa'udi production had now well begun, though the astonishing upward sweep of the next few years was still unpredictable. Aramco ended the war in a position, which its last eighteen months of intensive development had rendered highly advantageous, thanks to its part in the war and to the vast resources of American industry; it could supply anything in any quantities—provided only that markets became available.

## II. THE FORTUNATE: BAHRAIN

If Aramco and Anglo-Iranian passed through a two-year period of restriction before rising to their full war-time prowess, Bapco was more fortunate. Bahrain already possessed its refinery, capable of processing some 35,000 b/d, and assured markets; the routine of barge traffic from the mainland had been established in 1939; the installations, residencies, and amenities of Bapco's oil town of 'Awali were all in being. It followed that all the processes of production, refining, and export were little disturbed by the outbreak of war; only a measure of interruption of supplies and markets need be feared.

In fact, although drilling ceased late in 1940 for six years and although the fear of enemy attack—Bahrain was bombed by the Italians in October 1940—was not remote, full operation continued throughout the war; native production of crude ranged from just below to just above 1 million t/y, and the refinery, helped by Sa'udi crude, maintained a steady throughput from 1939 to 1943 of between 1·4 million and 1·5 million t/y.

The long-awaited ruling of the British Government on the sovereignty of islands and shoals on the fringes of the Bahrain archipelago had been issued in 1939, in terms favourable to the Shaikh. This result was embodied in July 1940 in a Supplementary Agreement between Bapco and Shaikh Hamad, who was succeeded by his son in 1942. The fifty-five-year period, for which it provided was further extended by the grant in December 1942 of a moratorium affecting most of the Company's obligations. It bestowed exclusive rights over the entire present or future dominions of the Shaikh, including all islands, shoals, and sea-bed within a defined area. Rs. 400,000 (£30,000) was paid on signature; the minimum annual royalty was raised to the equivalent of £95,000 for the first fifteen years, or to £127,500 if oil be discovered in the additional territory; but these minima were to be reduced after fifteen years to £11,250 and £22,500 respectively. The tonnage royalty remained at Rs. 3 as. 8. The Company undertook to drill, within the additional area, on any suitable structure. Nothing was payable in respect of oil imported from Sa'udi Arabia for refining, but a minimum proportion of the total oil refined must be Bahraini.

The decisions made in Washington in 1943, as dictated by the course of the war, have been mentioned (p. 133) as affecting war-time Sa'udi Arabia. The results there had their close parallel in Bahrain. Dominating the years 1944–5, this great and sudden increase in the scale of work at Bahrain covered all operations except drilling. The pipeline from Dhahran made possible the supply of more than double the previous quantities of crude to the refinery, which in turn received substantial increases in its size and scope; these, begun late in 1943, included a third crude distillation unit, a catalytic cracking unit to produce high-octane spirit, a gas recovery and a stabilizer unit, and others for the manufacture of special products. In 1944 a drum manufacturing and filling plant was added, for the packing of aviation and motor spirit; large additions were made to tankage (at the refinery and at Sitra), pipelines, services, amenities, and housing. The throughput of the refinery was raised from 35,000 b/d in 1943 to 37,500 in 1944 and to 65,000 in 1945. The aviation spirit plant was, as such, shut down in October 1945.

New work was undertaken simultaneously at the Sitra loading terminal; a new T-shaped wharf, affording space for four tankers, was sited at the end of a three-mile causeway. Begun in 1944, it was finished two years later. A dozen pipelines of various dimensions connected the shipping tank-farm and the wharf.

### III. THE UNFORTUNATE: QATAR AND KUWAIT

While Sa'udi Arabia and Bahrain were destined to end the Second War as oil territories in full career, neighbouring States were less favoured, thanks to their failure, in spite of abundant oil already revealed in 1939, to reach the stage of export by the first year of the war: to their lack, that is, of production equipment and marine loading facilities. Moreover the war-time requirement was for refined products, not for crude; and in the circumstances of the war refinery materials could be furnished by the United States alone, and that country was unlikely to afford them as readily to British or half-British companies as to all-American.

The condemnation of the oil development of Qatar and Kuwait to years of inaction, if easily explained and perhaps inevitable, had unfortunate results. It gave throughout the Middle East an impression (still noticeable ten years later) that the tempo of American development far exceeded the British; it delayed the achievement of British sources of supply alternative to Abadan ; and it deferred the benefits which it was hoped to confer on the peoples and rulers of those States.

On the Qatar peninsula the oil strike on the Dukhan structure in December 1939 has been already mentioned (p. 106). The first well was completed in January 1940. A second producing well was drilled in the same year, some ten miles south of no. 1. A third, three miles eastward, proved to be 'off structure'. Thereafter all operations were, under official instructions, suspended for the whole duration of the war. The wells were plugged as a 'denial' measure against enemy—presumably Japanese—invaders: strangest of contrasts to the prospering current operations at Dhahran and 'Awali! The field equipment was removed to Basra and Bombay.

At Kuwait the record from 1942 to 1945 seemed to be similar, though both the oilfield and the scale of current development were greater. After the Burgan discovery well, others were drilled on that structure between 1939 and 1942; the completion of these fully confirmed early anticipation of the great importance of the field, whose reserves the DeGolyer Mission estimated at 7,000 million barrels. A further well was drilled, but abandoned, at Madaniyat, fifteen miles north of Burgan. Early in 1942, however, all operations ceased, wells were plugged with cement, and most of the materials and equipment were removed from the country.

But the Kuwait operations were half-American in ownership and had reached a stage in advance of those of Qatar. Their reinstatement, therefore, had a decisive priority: and it was ordered early in 1945 as part of the Allied programme of increasing available supplies both for the Japanese war, should this be prolonged, and for the oil-thirsty early years of peace. The immediate target was a production of crude at the rate of 30,000 b/d or 1·5 million t/y. Work in the Kuwait principality was restarted in October 1945, staff and materials reassembled, and buildings reconditioned. It proved possible to clean out all the existing wells (except the discovery well itself) to gun-perforate them and to prepare them for production, with all necessary field installations, by the early summer of 1946. The provision of gathering-lines, gas-separators, storage tanks, and pipelines to the marine loading terminal improvised at Fahahil, was actively in hand as 1945 closed. The Kuwait enterprise had been resuscitated in time to take a high place as an immediate post-war oil supplier.

No steps were taken throughout the war towards allotting rights over the Kuwait–Sa'udi Neutral Zone; the other Neutral Zone, of Sa'udi–'Iraqi joint interest, was by now fully allotted (to Casoc in 1939 and the Basrah Company in 1938 respectively) in undivided half-shares, but no arrangement for joint working had been suggested.

To the Trucial Coast and the Oman Sultanate the advent of the World War could bring nothing but postponement of all further exploration by the concession-holding companies. The expeditions planned for the winter of 1939–40 did not take place, and no field work was possible throughout the war. The rulers were notified that they must show patience; all stipulated annual payments continued to be made and the Company's staff remained in friendly personal touch. The option to convert exploration rights into a concession over the Oman Sultanate was exercised in 1942. The permit for Ras al-Khaima was converted into a Concession in 1945 and another was signed in the same year for the Shaikhdom of Umm al-Qaiwain. The drilling obligation at Sharja was postponed in consideration of an immediate payment.

In the Aden Protectorate the exploration licence of Petroleum Concessions Limited was renewed bi-annually throughout the war, the impracticability of field work being recognized. In western Sa'udi Arabia nothing in 1939–41 occurred to enhance the apparent low value of the concession, nor was further field work contemplated; Petroleum Development (Western Arabia) closed its office in Jidda in 1941 and the concession was formally abandoned.

### IV. TURKEY AND THE LEVANT

The course of the war, in which Turkey was never a belligerent, was bound by its many preoccupations to restrict, though it did not halt, oil search in which M.T.A. (p. 85) had been ceaselessly engaged since 1934. Further efforts were made to find commercial oil at the site of the well-known Kurzot seepages, at the

north-eastern extremity of Lake Van, and a party sent by the
M.T.A. renewed operations there in 1938, 1943, and 1945, but
without encouraging results. A more hopeful issue seemed to
await the drilling at Raman Dagh on an anticline some sixty miles
east of Diyarbakr. Work started there with cable-tool equipment
in the last weeks of peace and continued through the winter of
1939–40. On 20 April 1940 the first discovery of oil (other than
seepage-oil) in Turkey was made; Raman Dagh well no. 1, at
3,450 feet, produced oil which rose by natural pressure nearly to
the surface. The news spread throughout Turkey and the world,
the Prime Minister and high dignitaries rushed to the spot, and the
discovery was for some weeks the greatest news in Turkey. But
disillusion was to follow; the oil, originally some 75 b/d, rapidly
diminished in quantity and the quality was low, with a gravity of
20 degrees A.P.I. and a high sulphur content. The site was, however, well worth further effort. Six more wells were drilled between 1940 and 1944 on the same structure. Five were failures,
one gave a small output of oil at 3,050 feet; but, although this
yield was slightly increased by acidizing, it fell again almost to
nothing and the well was abandoned in 1944.

Though there was still belief in the possibilities of Raman Dagh
and drilling was continuous, the end of the war found Turkish
hopes again dissipated among other areas. These included Polatli
and Bolu on the Black Sea coast, the shale deposits of Ismir, and
the plain of Adana.

In Cyprus, Petroleum Development (Cyprus) Limited could
carry out no work during the war. In the four Levant States the
record was that inevitably imposed by the strains and restrictions
of the time. The search for native oil sources ceased in Palestine
early in 1940, with the withdrawal of the geophysical party and the
grant by the Government of a moratorium suspending the licence
obligations. In Transjordan nothing was attempted. In the
Lebanon a moratorium was announced by the Government in
1942, whereunder the duties involved under exploration licences
were postponed until after the Armistice. In Syria the drilling
already described (p. 92) was, perforce, discontinued in 1940
when, after the fall of France, the position in Syria became constitutionally dubious and practically insecure. A 'period of suspension' from drilling and production obligations was granted by
the Syrian Government. In the meanwhile the 1938 Concession

had at last been ratified by the Council of Directors, the authoritative body for the purpose since the Syrian Constitution had been suspended in 1939. The payments due on signature were made in Syrian currency converted from 'English gold pounds' at the current Bank of England rate; the Syrian Government accepted the payments, thus calculated, under protest and reserved its rights to the 'gold pounds' which it demanded.

To the position of these States as transit or terminal countries, the war gave additional importance. Every effort was made at the Kirkuk end of the pipeline to maintain full throughput, with success except for the two-month interruption in the spring of 1941 and the longer break in the operation of the northern line from mid-1940 till mid-1942, due to the political vicissitudes in Syria–Lebanon and the closing of the Mediterranean. Pumping installations on the pipeline were maintained, not without difficulty, in full efficiency. The trunk lines were watched constantly for erosion and leakage: and the stations themselves, oases of industry, supply, and communication in the desert, played a valuable part in the operations of war, not least during the mission of troops from Palestine to 'Iraq and the invasion of Syria by Allied forces, both in 1941. The land-line and wireless facilities of the pipeline were widely used by military Signals, and the landing grounds at stations and the depots at Mafraq and at Homs were habituated to military traffic.

At the Tripoli Terminal, from which crude oil was ferried by sea to Haifa for refining from 1943 onwards, part of the tankage was made available to the naval or military authorities. All installations were maintained, defence was provided by fire walls and otherwise against air attack, and crude passed to the rapidly improvised 'pocket refinery' which was erected in the early months of the war by the technical services of the High Commissioner. By a simple topping process and some chemical treatment, usable gasoline, kerosene, and fuel oil were obtained with a total throughput of 200,000 t/y. The plant was operated by French engineers and artisans and Lebanese labour. The cost of construction was gradually reimbursed to the High Commission by the supply of free crude oil by the I.P.C., who were to acquire the plant after the war. It performed a valuable war-time service for the civil public, for whom the problem of obtaining hydrocarbon products must otherwise have been scarcely soluble. The refinery output, apart from supplies to the Allied forces, was divided between existing local marketers—Shell, Socony-Vacuum, and four Lebanese distributors, all grouped for the purpose into a 'consortium'.

At the Haifa Terminal cordial, if intricate, relations were maintained with British military and naval authorities. The export of crude ceased ; that of refined products, mainly for the Allied forces in the Middle East, took its place. All crude received by the pipeline from 'Iraq was diverted to the Consolidated refinery and, as the northern line came back into partial and then full operation, was supplemented by cargoes from Tripoli. The refinery, which first came on stream in December 1939 with an intake of some 20,000 b/d, was enlarged by a second distillation unit early in 1941, and later in the year, after the stoppage of May–June, could double its original throughput. Bitumen manufacture for road and airport construction was undertaken from 1941 onwards, and a drum plant, created out of materials improvised from all quarters, was erected. The output of gasoline, kerosene, gas oil, and fuel oil was raised to a rate of 3·5 million t/y by the completion of a third distillation unit and, by the middle of 1944, to 4 million by the adaptation of other equipment for the processing of additional crude.

The Haifa refinery took its place by 1944 as the largest single industrial asset in Palestine. Its value during the war years—and that of the I.P.C. crude which supplied it—was immense, not only to the civil population but also to the Navy and land forces. To the latter in Egypt and North Africa, from 1941 onwards, tankers carried the supplies without which they could not have waged war ; the bunkering at Haifa was a great convenience to His Majesty's ships ; and the supply of fuel in Palestine and Transjordan made possible the maintenance of forces in those countries. These considerations explain the repeated enemy air attacks, during some twenty-seven of which one hundred bombs of big or small dimensions fell inside the refinery area and three times that number outside it. An assault by Italian bombers in September 1940 caused considerable damage. During an attack made in the spring of 1941 by German aircraft, based on Aleppo (then Vichy-controlled), 600 tons of sulphur was ignited and damage to refining plant led to reduced production for some weeks. The measures taken to minimize risks and damage—cement pipe-protection, shelters, tank-walls, blackout, and smoke screen—were, with the dispersed lay-out of the refinery itself, responsible for restricting the harm done. The demolition of walls and restoration of normal conditions at both the terminal and refinery were welcome features of the later months of 1945. Others were the resumption by the I.P.C. of its own facilities for telecommunications, reoccupation of many of its own premises, rearrangement of its tanks and lines at Haifa in anticipation of peace-time working, rehabilitation everywhere of store sheds, workshops, and garages, and the restoration of the Company's air traffic to its Haifa landing ground. Still more encouraging was the decision of the I.P.C. directors to proceed immediately with the construction of new pipelines from 'Iraq —a work regretfully deferred in 1939—and the beginning of work to this end at Haifa even before the Armistice.

## V. EGYPT IN THE WAR

The presence in Egypt throughout the war of an Allied military base of high importance gave to the country's oil industry a significance out of proportion to its scale. Helped by the Ras Gharib discovery in 1938 and the rapid steps taken to profit from it, Anglo-Egyptian Oilfields was able to give valuable help to the war effort, while not ceasing to serve Egypt itself.

Egyptian crude production, which reached 650,000 tons in 1939 —more than double the output of any previous year—passed 900,000 in 1940 and thereafter attained a figure close to, or in 1944 and 1945 exceeding, 1·25 million tons. Hurghada contributed a fifth of this in 1939, a tenth in 1940, but later a proportion decreasing to one-twentieth in 1945; the field was, in fact, approaching exhaustion. The output from Ras Gharib was maintained, not easily, by intensive drilling; ninety-eight wells were completed there from 1939 to 1944. Drilling continued with cable-tool equipment at Hurghada, and another attempt was made. without appreciable success, at Gemsa.

At the Suez refinery the established practice of using surplus capacity for other companies' oil was abandoned from 1938 onwards; indeed, only by vigorous adaptation and addition, within the limits of current supply possibilities, was the refinery able to deal with native crude supplies. A second cracking unit had come into service in 1938 and all steps for 're-vamping' and improvement, by every means, were taken to double the throughput. This was effectively achieved, though construction materials were three

times sunk at sea en route for Suez. Products were divided between the civilian consumers of Egypt and the Allied forces. To
the former went, through existing Shell Company distribution,
about half the gasoline, most of the kerosene, and a quantity of
fuel oil. Egyptian State Railways, largely adapted for liquid fuel,
drew their supplies from Suez. The British and Egyptian armies
and navies were provided with almost all their gasoline requirements, with asphalt, with bottled gas, and with fuel oil.

The war service of the industry in Egypt did not end here. It
was able to provide technical and administrative assistance to the
Allied forces, to help in distribution of their requirements, and to
operate military supply depots such as those at Nafisha on the
Canal (connected by pipeline with Port Said) and at Agrad,
between Suez and Cairo. A 6-inch white-products pipeline was
built by Shell between the latter two cities for the army, to facilitate supply to the capital. Elsewhere the services of the industry
were used for the construction of asphalted roads and landing
grounds.

Damage by enemy action was appreciable but, with the vulnerable targets offered, might well have been far worse. In spite of
anti-aircraft protection at Suez, the refinery was attacked from the
air in August and September 1941 with some loss of stocks and
tankage, and buildings were damaged in July 1942. Later in that
year a tanker at Ras Gharib was hit and sunk, with loss of life.

The revival in exploratory drilling which marked the years 1938–
9 did not cease during the war, except between 1941 and 1943;
despite highly unfavourable conditions, the incentives were very
powerful. Anglo-Egyptian Oilfields itself drilled seven exploration wells in 1939–40, all of which proved dry; five were in the
areas immediately north and west of Ras Gharib, one at al-Daba,
and one at Shagar. The Company in 1944 still held 240 exploration licences, for some of the obligations of which the Government
granted a moratorium; and, taking steps during 1944–5 to restart
its suspended drilling activity, it rehabilitated its field-base at Ras
Matarma on the west coast of Sinai, drilled yet another exploration
well north of Ras Gharib, mobilized three drilling rigs and crews,
and agreed with Socony-Vacuum on a programme of drilling on
joint account in licensed areas in Sinai. Socony completed nine
exploration wells during the first two years of the war, at Ras
Shukhair, Dasht al-Diba, Wadi Dara, abu Sha'ar, and Wadi

Maraikha; all were dry. New Jersey, through its affiliate the Standard of Egypt, drilled six wells in 1940–1 and 1944 in the Ras Bakr area north of Ras Gharib and one at Ras Ruahmi; and turned, as the war ended, to new locations in Sinai and near the Pyramids. Caltex, through its subsidiary South Mediterranean Oilfields, drilled in these years, with equal lack of success, at Khatatba, near Cairo; and, as the war ended, decided on a complete withdrawal of its exploration activities from Egypt. In all, twenty-five wells were drilled in 'wild-cat' areas of Egypt between 1939 and 1944.

Guy Charvet, after a long tenure of office, handed over the General Managership of Anglo-Egyptian Oilfields and of the local Shell Company to D. R. Mackintosh in 1943.

## CHAPTER X

# THE TRAGEDY OF PERSIA

## I. RUSSIAN CONCESSION

THE presence of Russian troops and the revealed Soviet determination thereby to acquire the concession of the Caspian provinces made it unlikely that the departure of Kavtaradze to Moscow in December 1944 was their last move. The population of Azerbaijan is mainly non-Persian—Turki or Kurdish—and these differences had already been exploited by the Russians; and this process continued throughout 1945, with local autonomists gradually reducing the authority of Teheran to nothing. The last date for the evacuation of foreign troops from Persia had been agreed as 2 March 1946. The Americans anticipated this date, the British conformed to it, but the Russians, in spite of Persian appeals to the United Nations, declined to evacuate until 'the situation was clarified'. Meanwhile, a Russo-Azerbaijani coup d'état in December 1945 had swamped the province with Communists, deposed the Persian Governor, and proclaimed a Republic.

In the absence of effective support by the United Nations, the Persian Premier in February 1946 entered into negotiations with Russia. Agreement was reached and announced on 4 April: the Persian complaint to United Nations would be withdrawn and a Soviet-Iranian Oil Company would be formed forthwith for the exploitation of north Persian oil. During the fifty-year life of the Agreement (which required ratification by the Majlis) the Russians would hold 51 per cent. of the Company's shares for the first twenty-five years and thereafter 49 per cent., and would provide all the necessary capital, equipment, and higher staff. The area concerned lay north of a line running from Mount Ararat southward by Lake Urmiya to Miyanduab, then east to the Perso-Russo-Afghan frontier point of junction, with a southward salient to include the Semnan area.

Russian troops, after some weeks of uncertainty, evacuated Azerbaijan by June 1946, leaving a body of civilian-clad agents to assist the Azerbaijan Republic. The province was gradually re-absorbed into Persia. The Russian-sponsored Tudeh party remained aggressively active.

Elsewhere, the indignation among the tribal and settled public in south Persia, traditionally suspicious of Teheran governments, led them to demand a rupture of relations with Russia, the dismissal of Communist ministers, and the rejection of the Agreement. These moves, combined with a popular movement of almost separatist type in the south, were met by the Tudeh Party with fanciful accusations of British intrigue and with further and successful efforts to disrupt the Anglo-Iranian's organization, first by mass demonstrations and mob oratory, then by intimidation, and finally by the creation of a general strike at Abadan in July 1946. Some industrial unrest had, indeed, been visible there for some time, due to the reactions of normal post-war psychology and to high living costs; but the workers' grievances were at the time under sympathetic treatment in joint consultative bodies, and the violence which followed the declaration of the strike in mid-July was both politically inspired and the product of long preparation. The danger to British lives and property led to the dispatch of troops from India to Shaiba as a safeguard, but they were not invoked. The Prime Minister had proclaimed on 23 June that he would deal severely with the abuse of workers' organizations for political ends, and the Governor-General of Khuzistan intervened with disciplinary measures, when, on 14 July, rioting broke out accompanied by bloodshed. The situation was restored with the cessation of immediate political inspiration, and normal work at Abadan could be resumed.

Following the pacification of south Persia and the conclusion of long-delayed elections for a new Majlis—delayed while the Azerbaijan position was fully restored and local Communism brought under control—the oil agreement with Russia was submitted for parliamentary sanction in August 1947. Two months later it was rejected with unanimity (save for two Communist supporters), to the high indignation of the Soviet propaganda machine, which hailed the rejection as the work of 'Fascist Imperialists' and as presaging foreign attacks on the Soviet Union. The law of 22 October 1947, proclaiming the Agreement to be null and void, bade the Government study the oil wealth of the country, so that the Majlis could later prepare 'through enactment of the necessary laws' for its commercial exploitation; meanwhile, no concession and no share in a company would be granted to any foreigner whatsoever, and the ominous words were added: 'In all cases where the rights of the Iranian nation, in respect of the country's natural resources, whether underground or otherwise, have been impaired, particularly in regard to the southern oil, the Government is required to enter into such negotiations and take such measures as are necessary to regain the national rights, and inform the Majlis of the result.'

## II. DEVELOPMENT IN PERSIA: THE LAST PHASE

If, in a favourable post-war situation which promised still further Anglo-Iranian expansion—and yet greater benefits for Persia—fears could exist that either marketing limitations or new rivals in Arabia could restrict outlets for the Company's oil, these were largely removed by an arrangement formulated in 1947 between A.I.O.C., Standard of New Jersey, and Socony-Vacuum. The latter two companies needed assured supplies of crude for their existing or planned refineries, while Anglo-Iranian welcomed a reliable purchaser for crude which would be surplus to its own needs. The directors of New Jersey agreed accordingly in September 1947 to buy 106 million tons of Anglo-Iranian oil—to be obtained, at the seller's option, from Persia or from Kuwait—over a twenty-year period, at a price to be fixed on a 'cost-plus' basis. Socony-Vacuum agreed similarly to buy 27 million tons within the same period, an amount increased to 60 million under a second agreement in March 1948.

The execution of these arrangements was, initially, to depend on the conclusion of another joint enterprise, that of a large diameter pipeline from the Gulf head to the Mediterranean. In this project, for which Middle East Pipelines Limited was formed in December 1947, Anglo-Iranian took a 60·9, New Jersey a 24·7, and Socony-Vacuum a 14·4 per cent. interest. With pipe of 36- and 34-inch diameter, the line was to have a capacity of 535,000 b/d or 26 million t/y. The system, with 500 miles of its length in 'Iraq and 280 in Syria, would allow for seven pumping stations, five in 'Iraq and two in Syria, and would deal with oil both from Kuwait and from Abadan. The pipe was to be obtained in the United States immediately after the needs of Tapline (p. 206) had been satisfied, and it was hoped to see completion of the M.E.P.L. line by 1951. In the event, though wayleaves and terminal facilities were duly obtained in Syria, it proved impossible to arrange for transit through 'Iraq; that Government, convinced that additional Persian or Kuwait output would prejudice its own development, refused to facilitate that process, unless on prohibitive terms. The initial survey ended, negotiations languished, and by the end of 1949 the project, for which much preparatory work had been done and orders placed, appeared to be dying. The tripartite oil-purchase arrangement had, therefore, to be reviewed; this was done in August 1949 on the basis of sea instead of pipeline transport for the oil, and the arrangement came into effect on 1 January 1952.

The last five years of Anglo-Iranian operation in Persia were a period of remarkable accomplishment. Its oilfield and refinery expansion, planned in 1938 and partly accomplished in 1943–5, was still at the latter date partly outstanding and called for completion. It was clear, moreover, that, American purchases apart, both world economic needs and the Persian Government would call for yet greater development. Technical and engineering demands, those of housing and of the social services, and those of the establishment of industrial relations in modern forms, called at once for the Company's best efforts. Capital was spent on an unprecedented scale; production rose in Persia at a rate substantially more rapid than the average of other territories; the remarkable group of oilfields in the provinces of Khuzistan and Fars were brought into, or remained in, balanced and economic production; Abadan easily retained its place as the world's greatest refinery; and the direct and indirect benefits to the Company's workers and to the Persian State and public were increased on a corresponding, or a greater, scale.

In spite of the re-examination of former drilling sites and researches at new ones, no major discovery of fresh sources of supply was made during this period. Drilling and field development, on the other hand, did all that was required of them. Up to a dozen drilling rigs were constantly at work and annual footages of 50,000–100,000 feet were drilled. In the small Naft-i-Shah field, operated, perforce, in nationalistic isolation from its close neighbour in 'Iraq, a single well in production could give the required 125,000–150,000 t/y of crude, and feed the Kirmanshah refinery. In the main group of fields, Masjid-i-Sulaiman continued to contribute from thirty producing wells kept in operation at any one time or often from half that number; about 280 wells were drilled in all in that field between 1908 and 1951. Its contribution, ranging from 3–5 million t/y, diminished proportionately to the total of other and later-developed fields, as these increased their output.  It still contained Fields' administrative headquarters and, with its great workshops and stores, laboratories and research institutions, offices, clubs, hospital, and residential quarters, where a large part of its 6,000 employees were housed, was the most complete and mature of the Company's establishments outside Abadan.

Due north of Masjid-i-Sulaiman, at Lali, where oil had been located but not proved before and during the war, a successful well was drilled in 1946 and was followed by others.  After completion of a 10–12-inch pipeline to join the main system, Lali produced some 0·5 million t/y in each of 1948 and 1949 and 0·75 million in 1950.  By 1951 four wells were in production, and yielded crude of a distinctive sulphur-free—but rather heavier—type from a Cretaceous horizon, which a test well had penetrated.

Haft Kel was for some years the main producing area; its yield, from some twenty-five producing wells, was of not less than 10 million t/y during this period, when the field reached and, perhaps, passed its maximum economically exploitable capacity.  By its cumulative production of some 130 million tons (by 1951) it had already overtaken Masjid-i-Sulaiman and ranked justly among the world's largest single fields.  The adjacent field of Naft Safid, prepared for production during the war and joined to the main pipeline system in 1945, came into operation next year.  With its great gas dome but lesser oil capacity it maintained a contribution of approximately 1 million t/y thereafter.  The rarest of occurrences in Anglo-Iranian fields, a well-fire, took place here on a spectacular scale from a fierce ignited gas-blast at 'Rig 20' a few weeks before the cessation of the Company's operations in Persia; its extinction by Myron Kinley was an outstanding feat of skill and courage.

No production after the war took place at Pazanun, where the gas wells were plugged and the presence of liquid oil remained uncertain.  At the great field of Agha Jari was found, however, the true successor of Haft Kel as the main contributor to A.I.O.C. output for, in all probability, many years to come.  In 1951 it had a score of producing wells, had been provided with every refinement of Fields' equipment, contained its own hospital and its 'industrial area' with important stores, and workshops, and employed the largest concentration of labour—some 3,500—out-side Abadan and Masjid-i-Sulaiman. Production from this field rose from 4 million tons in 1946 to 15½ million in 1950. The original 12-inch pipeline to Abadan was tripled in succeeding years, and first a 12-inch and in 1948 a 22-inch line connected it to the loading port of Bandar Mashhur, forty miles distant. Gach Saran, with its longer pipeline and its heavier-gravity oil, received, after the war, only limited development. It had by 1950 three producing wells, smaller installations, a labour force, and a production barely reaching 2 million t/y; this could, if needed, have been at any time expanded, and already the 12-inch pipeline to Abadan had been looped for greater throughput.

The combined output of these fields, still rising rapidly year by year, amounted in 1945 to 16·8 million tons and from 1946 to 1950 to 19·20, 20·19, 24·87, 26·8, and 31·75 million tons respectively. General Fields Managers after H. W. Lane were H. S. Gibson in 1945–8 and P. T. Cox in 1948–51. The General Managership of the Company in Persia was held after Pattinson had left for London in 1945, by I. M. Jones, 1945–9, G. N. S. Gobey 1949–50, and A. E. C. Drake 1950.

The oil, produced from between seventy and ninety producing wells at any one time, was, after de-gassing, and in part after topping-plant treatment, transmitted by pipeline from field tankage to Abadan or Bandar Mashhur. From the former of these and from the loading berths at Khosrawabad, fifteen miles downstream, refined products and smaller quantities of crude were loaded; the latter was brought into existence as a loading station in 1946 and equipped with the necessary wharves, jetties, tankage, and accommodation. Crude oil from Agha Jari was exported from Bandar Mashhur in quantities of 2·5 million tons in 1949 and nearly 6 million in 1950; these would in future years have been greatly increased. Pipelines of the Company's main system, which included 1,990 miles of pipe, had a combined capacity of 650,000 b/d. In the 12-inch lines from Gach Saran and Agha Jari to Abadan and the 12- and 22-inch from the latter field to Bandar Mashhur, the descent of the oil to the terminals could, thanks to the elevation of the fields, be by gravity; elsewhere, pumping stations were required. The other four fields—Masjid-i-Sulaiman, Lali, Haft Kel, and Naft Safid—were connected to Abadan by six 12- or 10-inch lines. Topping units existed at Masjid-i-Sulaiman and small distillation plants at the other fields for local fuel needs.

Power-plants for the supply of electric power and light were maintained in all fields. Water was supplied from the nearest river or, at Gach Saran, from wells. All fields were connected by roads, which carried a heavy traffic; the main Abadan–Masjid-i-Sulaiman highway was re-made on all-weather lines in 1950, that from Abadan to Bandar Mashhur was still unfinished in 1951, and that between the latter and Agha Jari was superseded by a metre-gauge railway which connected the port to the oilfield: it was opened for traffic in 1948 and was linked with the Persian main line at Sar-i-Bundar. The old Dar-i-Khazina–Tembi light railway was dismantled in 1950. The bulk of materials for Fields (other than Agha Jari and Gach Saran) was landed at Bandar Shapur and conveyed by railway to Ahwaz. Karun river transport ceased in 1950 to be used above Ahwaz and below that point was used for limited purposes. For passenger traffic the air, since the early nineteen-thirties, had superseded both land and water transport. There were landing grounds at all fields and at Ahwaz and Bandar Mashhur.

Persian needs in refined products, amounting to about 1 million t/y in 1951, were met by supplies from Abadan and Kirmanshah and distributed throughout the country. Lubricants were imported annually from the Anglo-Iranian's refineries in Great Britain. The import of Russian products into north Persia was irregular and had diminished since 1939.

Apart from the Kirmanshah refinery, all refining was concentrated at Abadan, where output in 1946 was already 17 million t/y (double that of 1939) and rose to 23·25 million in 1949 and to more than 24 million in 1950. The output included the entire range of products from aviation spirit to bitumen, with the exception of lubricating oils, for the manufacture of which, for the needs of Persia and 'Iraq, a plant was on the verge of completion in the summer of 1951. The Abadan refinery, truly impressive for its scale and scope and its vast yet orderly design, covered 400 acres in addition to its tank-farms and housing estates. Installations for the production of electric power and steam, substantially increased between 1946 and 1951, were on the scale of a great city. Tankage for crude oil and its products was similarly enlarged. The many processes carried out in the refinery for the manufacture of a wide range of products cannot here be described; the difference from refining as practised in smaller plants or at earlier periods lay chiefly in the great gain in flexibility, the infinitely ingenious splitting and reforming of hydrocarbon constituents for special purposes, the avoidance of waste, and the high quality of the final products. These characteristics would have been further increased by the addition of the catalytic cracking plant which, begun in 1947, was brought into operation in the first weeks of 1951.

The navigation of the Shatt al-'Arab continued to be controlled by the Port of Basra, but the A.I.O.C. maintained also five dredgers to facilitate use of the jetties. The latter were between fifteen and twenty in number, with loading speeds up to 750 tons an hour for white oils and 1,250 for black; three were reserved for general cargo and for bitumen. A dozen sea-going tugs and two dozen barges for use on the Shatt and the Karun were constantly busy. Extensive facilities had been provided for marine repair work. The scale and equipment of Abadan placed it among the world's great seaports.

There is little to record on petroleum activity in these years outside the Anglo-Iranian concession area. The organization of an all-Persian Oil Company was reported in 1947 and its revision in 1948; to assist this the oil experts of Industrial Consultants Incorporated, advising on seven-year-plan matters, were available, and other American help and equipment were invoked. A party of Swiss geologists were engaged and in 1949-51 examined the more hopeful areas of central Persia; and out of eight zones defined by Professor Heim, the decision was reached to drill first in the Qum area of the Persian 'Median Mass', where work began early in 1951. The two first wells reached 6,730 and 2,130 feet, and in the summer of 1952 oil was declared to be proved, to the extent of 1,000 b/d, from a well 7,310 feet in depth; but the propaganda needs of the moment and the manner and suddenness of the announcement rendered the 'strike' suspicious, though not impossible. The transport problems from a Qum oilfield would, in any case, be formidable.

### III. THE ANGLO-IRANIAN AS EMPLOYER

If under Middle Eastern conditions the physical and social care of their employees, which elsewhere belong to the normal institutions of the country, devolved admittedly upon the oil companies, since large concentrations of workers were and are commonly maintained in remote areas: and if, at least theoretically, different companies could take different views of such responsibilities, from mere neglectful profit-making to a policy of model employment: what was the Anglo-Iranian record, with their 60,000 workers and five times that number of dependents, in the hungry and inhospitable area of their enormous enterprise?

It is certain that perfection was never reached. The climate and terrain in Fields and Abadan alike were unusually severe, the amenities, indeed the necessities, of normal life had all to be created from nothing. Between human types so far removed in psychological and social background as the Persian worker and the British executive, complete mutual comprehension was no matter of course; though workers were treated with genuine consideration, based on personal liking and human respect, and though the response of the majority was one of toleration or even loyalty, yet there was inevitably room for occasional misunderstanding in addition to the daily monotonies or disappointments common to industrial life; and the fact that the Persianization of the higher grades of the executive had inevitably still far to go could add a racial or nationalistic element to the frustrations of the impatient. And it was in the interest of some Persian political elements, especially since the strong Communist infiltration, to magnify all or any anti-foreign and anti-Company trends and to unite and exploit, against the Company as a convenient foreign scapegoat, a complex of bitter and violent political emotions originally quite unconnected with it. Moreover, the Company's task as provider could never be finished and was rarely foreseeable. A regular, even a rapid, growth of demands for housing, services, and welfare could be met; but a position of difficulty could not but be created, in and after 1945, by the simultaneous occurrence of acute shortages of supplies, materials, and staff with the sudden increase of the communities to be catered for. In 1940 18,000 were employed at Abadan, 7,800 in Fields; in 1945 the corresponding figures were 32,750 and 9,500; and in 1949 they were 38,000 and 17,000.

On the other hand, there was reason for reassurance in the enlightened attitude of the Company's management, its full awareness of modern procedures and spirit in industrial relations, its material ability to provide generously, and its realization that in its treatment of workers and of Persia its good name was at stake.

Workers' satisfaction with their conditions of work was usual, hostile criticism and discontent the exception. Wages and allowances, hours of work, paid holidays, the working environment, disciplinary provisions: all these compared more than favourably with those offered by any other employer in Persia.[1] A Trade Union organization among workers, which first appeared in 1945 and was legalized by the Labour Law of 1946, was largely vitiated by inherent weaknesses; its internal factions and hostilities precluded constructive, unified action, it concentrated its efforts less on principles than on individual cases, and its easy penetration by the Tudeh Party gave at times a strongly political and destructive colour to its activities. Well-rooted and well-organized Unions would have been of great benefit to both workers and the Company. Formal management–labour relations were maintained by the Company's institution in 1943 of joint Departmental Committees, which enabled representatives of both sides, at all locations, jointly to discuss questions of common interest; and by the Workers or Factory Councils, the Arbitration Boards, and Boards for the settlement of disputes, which were set up by the Labour Law of 1946. These bodies were representative of the Government, management, and workers and were compulsory, but their practical value was very limited.

That the Company's premises were everywhere, as far as topography and function allowed, orderly, convenient, and spacious, need hardly be said. Electric lighting, piped water, and an impeccable sanitary service were matters of course: and, at Abadan, clean streets, gardens, lawns, considerable institutional buildings, shops and restaurants and playing-fields. The Persian municipality, which had grown up beside the Company's housing estates, received continual and very substantial help from the latter in town cleaning and improvement, road-making, drainage, and the provision of light, water, and sewerage: functions which, in Fields, necessarily devolved everywhere on the Company itself. Much assistance was given to the municipalities of Ahwaz and Khoramshahr.

Housing for workers, for which the 1939 programme had been regrettably interrupted, was the object of great efforts from 1945

---

[1] The State Railways, employing some 15,000 men, ranked next after A.I.O.C. as large-scale employers; the other comparable concerns were the statal or private factories.

onwards; of the 21,000 houses built for its employees, 9,500 were erected by the Company between that year and 1951. These, whose completion unhappily still left thousands of workers ill-housed, were all to the design of architects satisfied only with the best of materials and conveniences—light, water, heating, sanitation—which were hitherto unknown in Persian dwellings. At Abadan four housing estates for Persian labour had been constructed; in Fields' areas about half the Company's workers were housed in Company-built accommodation. The housing effort,[1] which by 1951 was catching up with post-war deficiencies, was conceived, in fact, on an immense scale: apart from dwelling houses, provision was made for shops and stores, canteens and restaurants, cinemas, swimming-pools, social and athletic clubs and sports grounds; and this endeavour to offer workers at Abadan a healthy and varied life was reflected in similar efforts at every location. The Company's agricultural projects, elsewhere mentioned (p. 129), were continued or increased after the war and practical encouragement was given to local cultivators. Transport in the form of bus services was provided in all areas for workers and for school children, and hundreds of bicycles were sold to workers at low prices.

The Company's medical services were among the most appreciated of the visible benefits provided. They included not only hospitals and dispensaries but a complete Public Health and preventive service, dental treatment, schools' medical service, and a training scheme for nurses. The medical staff included 100 doctors (including ten specialists), seven dentists, and nearly 150 nurses. Hospital beds available in Company areas—Abadan, Masjid-i-Sulaiman, Agha Jari—numbered 850 in 1951. Thirty-five clinics and dispensaries were largely attended. The preventative services had had notable effect in diminishing malaria, eye disease, typhus, smallpox, and intestinal diseases; no epidemic of cholera or plague occurred after 1926. The cost to the Company of its medical services was £2 million in the year 1950.[2]

[1] A visiting Commission of the I.L.O. in 1950 recorded that 'The observer cannot fail to be impressed by the vast number of modern houses and amenities which the Company has been able to provide in a comparatively short time, in spite of exceptionally unfavourable circumstances.'

[2] A senior British Medical Association spokesman visiting Abadan in March 1951 recorded 'Abadan must be one of the best cared for industrial communities in the world.' The I.L.O. Commission in 1950 noted that the Company's medical facilities were used extensively by the workers' families and even by people who have no connexion with the Company.

The planning and provision of safety measures everywhere were the responsibility of a specialized department, with representatives at all important points. Every effort was made to produce 'safety consciousness' among workers by instructional classes, posters, the showing of films, by mechanical safeguards, and by a full range of equipment for personal protection.

The import and distribution of domestic supplies (p. 129) were continued after the war and helped materially to ensure to workers a reasonably-priced supply of necessities. Eight shops at Abadan and others in Fields were provided for wage-earners. The purchase of food and clothing, tobacco, cotton cloth, and other domestic needs was regulated by a system of ration cards.[1]

In its educational and training system the Company had three objectives: the first to provide or assist Government to provide an education for the children of workers—and often for the adult workers themselves: the second, to increase the supply of trained men: the third, the preparation of the ablest of these for increasingly responsible executive posts. Of this great and continuing effort, which cost the Company more than £2 million in 1950, only certain phases can here be mentioned. Active help was given to the Government in its campaign for adult education, by paying teachers and arranging for English teaching. Buildings for thirty-five primary and secondary schools were constructed by the Company and handed over to the State in Khuzistan and a contribution made in money equal to three-quarters of the cost of their maintenance. The Company completely equipped the laboratories and workshops of the faculties of Engineering and Science at Teheran University; paid the expenses of scores of Persians proceeding for higher or technical education in Great Britain; and had built and maintained, at its own expense, the Technical Institute in Abadan, an institution of imposing scale and of the highest standard, which, operated by the Company, was recognized by the State as part of the structure of Persian higher education. The Institute catered for the three departments of engineering, science, and commerce. Apart from this, the Company carried out

---

[1] The I.L.O. Mission pronounced this system a 'remarkable achievement': it 'resulted in the provision of vast quantities of commodities which would not otherwise have been available, has contributed towards holding down prices, of supporting the purchasing power of wages . . . the continuance of the scheme would seem to be an absolute necessity.'

vocational training courses in accordance with industrial needs and with the availability of young Persians adequately educated to benefit from them; these were all paid while under instruction, which was partly 'on the job', partly in apprentice training shops, and partly at the Technical Institute. There existed a five-year course for artisan apprentices, a four-year for commercial apprentices, a five-year in petroleum technology and engineering, and two-year courses in practical work for graduates of Teheran University or Technical College. Various courses were designed at all centres for young men of lower educational standard, with the aim of producing more and better artisans and skilled workmen.

The Persianization of higher and skilled categories, envisaged in the agreed Plan under the 1933 Concession, had continued progressively in spite of the war. Unskilled labour being already all-Persian, the proportion which it was desired to reduce was that of foreign staff to the total of staff and skilled employees; this proportion was 14·84 per cent. in 1936 and 10·45 per cent. in 1950. In this process of Persianization there was no conflict of aim or interest between the Company and the Government; but with impatience and a political viewpoint on one side and cautious regard to industrial practicability on the other, it resulted that Persian national pride, both at Abadan and Teheran, could be and was afflicted by the continuing spectacle of so much leadership and so many of the higher executive powers being exercised by foreigners.

Of all the Company's social services and benefits it is fair to summarize that, being habitual and widely scattered and in part unperceived, they were accepted by the Persian workers and public rather with nonchalance or criticism than with gratitude. They were a matter of course; they were given without effort or sacrifice by the foreigner out of his vast profits; they were not always what the Persians, if asked, would have chosen; and they could have been yet greater. This attitude, familiar in every country in similar circumstances, does not in truth diminish the magnitude of the Company's effort or its genuine benevolence in these provisions, which far exceeded any contractual or legal obligation. The whole of this effort, the whole of a half-century of generous and enlightened treatment of its own workers and the public was, in the final destiny of the Company in Persia, not only treated as of no account, but attacked in terms suggesting not mere neglect but the crudest exploitation. It had done nothing to appease the rancour of Persian politicians nor to rally even its own workers, apathetic and easily perverted, actively to its side: a lesson not to be ignored by the similarly situated oil companies in 'Iraq and Arabia.

The suggestion had sometimes been made that a company so placed should seek to play a still larger part in the country's economics and society, should undertake works of development outside its own sphere, and should thereby show its will to assist a more rapid general evolution and to encourage alternative sources of wealth. Such a policy can appear attractive; but the suspicions of local publicists, the jealousy of threatened vested interests, and the inevitable accusations of 'interference' would probably invalidate such a programme and perhaps, paradoxically, harm the company itself. This policy was, in any case, not adopted by Anglo-Iranian; its attitude was one of concentration on its own sphere of operations, with willingness to assist governmental or local authorities at their request in limited fields, while providing the funds to the central Treasury for use in any direction the Government might choose.

But the benefits of oil development to Persia did not stop at the pay rates of its workers (a small fraction, after all, of the Persian public) or the amenities and services which they enjoyed or the gains of a wider circle of Persian suppliers and contractors or the material enrichment of the country by the Company's capital expenditure. The royalty payments, a major part of Persia's total Treasury receipts—more than one-sixth in 1950—amounted in 1945 to £5·6 million and in the five years following to £7·1, £7·1, £9·1, £13·5, and £16 millions respectively; the last four of these payments would, under the 1949 Supplementary Agreement, have been increased by a total of £40 million. These sums, which were habitually advanced by the Company before due dates to ease the Government's successive financial crises, were essential to the maintenance of the Persian administration on any but the very lowest scale, and on them rested the sole hope of such development projects as the ambitious Seven-Year Plan, formulated in 1949 and elaborated by American consultants. Other payments were scarcely less important: by manipulation of the exchange rates between rials and sterling the Persian Treasury realized a profit, varying between £3 and £8 million a year, on the sums imported by the Company to meet its payments in Persia. Persian receipts

from Customs duties on non-exempted imports amounted to from
£1·5 to £2·5 million a year and the income tax on the salaries of
foreign staff to some £1 to £2 million. The heavy excise duty on
locally sold petroleum products (made possible by the lowness of the
Company's prices for these) brought £5 to £7 million in revenue.
These receipts, which in 1950 amounted to some £18 million
apart from £16 million of royalties, brought the total Anglo-
Iranian contribution to the Persian budget to an amount equivalent
to one-third of the total.

As regards the purposes on which these sums were spent by
the Persian Government, precision is difficult. Some effort was
normally made, on paper, to reserve them for capital works; but,
as the Government published no accounts, there is no evidence
and little probability that they were, in fact, so used; and instructed
observers believed that prior to 1949 not more than a very small
proportion had been used otherwise than for routine needs of the
State. Even with a separate development budget for the Seven-
Year Plan, very little of the oil revenues was effectively diverted to
it—and none, it appears, with productive results.

If not to development, at least to current needs in foreign exchange, the Company's contribution was of the first importance.
The requirements of Persia in this were for years obtainable
mainly through the Company's operations, which supplied some
60 or 65 per cent. of the total; and the foreign exchange needs of
the Seven-Year Plan would have been met in their entirety from
the same source.

### IV. AGREEMENT, DISAGREEMENT, AND NATIONALIZATION

It is time to pass from consideration of the Company's achievements in Persia to the record of those events which led in a few
months to the loss of its entire status, rights, and assets in the
territory.

No action, seemingly directed against the Company, was taken
by the Government as a consequence of its law of 22 October 1947
(p. 146), under which it was 'particularly in regard to the southern
oil . . . required to enter into such negotiations and take such
measures as are necessary to regain national rights.' The law did
not appear to the Company to be a threat. During 1947, however,
certain matters had been raised for discussion by the Government;

and the Company, aware that the current British policy of dividend limitation (to which the Company adhered) must affect Persia's immediate receipts—since 20 per cent. of such dividends, over a certain sum, was due to the Persian Treasury—itself proposed in 1948 to send representatives to Teheran to discuss this position, as one clearly prejudicial to Persia.  Discussions, which at no time even remotely suggested repudiation of the 1933 Concession, continued from September 1948 until August 1949.  They dealt with the further progressive Persianization of the Company's staff, and with an increased scale of payments to the Treasury.  A 'half-and-half' sharing of profits in place of the current 'tonnage royalty plus a sum equal to 20 per cent. of dividends', was proposed and discussed.  It failed of acceptance because the Persian negotiators wished it to be applicable to the Company's profits made from refining and marketing *throughout the world*, instead of to those due to operations within the country of origin.  Nevertheless, agreement on new formulas was reached on 17 July 1949 and a Supplemental Agreement was signed.  It provided that royalty should be raised from 4s. per ton to 6s.[1]: that sums equal to one-fifth of those placed to the Company's general reserve should thereafter be paid annually [2] to the Government, an immediate payment exceeding £5 million being made in respect of allotments to general reserve since 1947: that the Company's annual payment, covering Persia's share of divisible profits and allocations to reserve, should never fall below £4 million: that the tax commutation payment of 9d. per ton of oil exports should be raised to 1s.[1]: that prices charged to purchasers of oil products in Persia should be yet further reduced: and that the arrangements made in 1933 to allow for variations in the gold–sterling exchange rate should remain operative.

The financial terms of this Agreement were certainly the most favourable enjoyed at the time by any Middle Eastern country.  Its immediate effect on ratification would have been to offer Persia, as the difference between sums due under the 1933 and

---

[1] These amounts, with the allowance for gold-sterling fluctuation, represented 8s. and 12s. respectively, and the tax commutation represented 2s.; the Persian 'take' was, therefore, 14s. per ton *in a year of no profit*.

[2] Instead of, under the 1933 Agreement, being payable only at the end of the concession.  Moreover, payments in respect of amounts placed to reserve ('sums equal to 20 p.c. . . .') were to be calculated prior to the deduction of taxation on them and not on the net amounts actually so placed.

1949 Agreements, an additional £9½ million for 1948, £9½ million for 1949, and £16½ million for 1950. As compared with a formula of 'half the profits of operation within the country', such as was introduced during 1950–2 in neighbouring oil-producing countries, it offered revenues which, if inferior in a period of high profits, would be certainly superior in a less prosperous period; and these were offered 18 months before any profit-sharing offer had been made to any other government in the Middle East.

The Supplemental Agreement, requiring Parliamentary sanction, was passed immediately to the Majlis; but no adequate account of its provisions was ever given to the Deputies, nor was it ever analysed, scrutinized, or debated. Attacked by Opposition Deputies, led by Dr. Musaddiq and his National Front, for tactical political reasons almost completely unconnected with oil, the validating law was not passed by the end of the session, ten days later. Elections for a new Majlis took their protracted course and produced a new body of Deputies only in February 1950; and in June of that year the Supplemental Agreement was passed to an *ad hoc* Parliamentary Oil Committee of eighteen members, with Dr. Musaddiq as its Chairman. A new Prime Minister, General 'Ali Razmara, closely identified with the Army and with the Monarchy, replaced 'Ali Mansur at the same time; but, like his predecessor, he restrained the Company from giving, for the present, any publicity to the terms of the Agreement, which remained unknown to the public.

The Oil Committee reported to the Majlis on 12 December that the Supplemental Agreement was unacceptable, as not satisfactorily safeguarding Persian rights and interests: and on the 26th the validating Bill was withdrawn. In January 1951 Parliament, in plenary session, accepted the Committee's adverse verdict and charged it to formulate proposals on the matter within two months. Strongly under National Front influence, the Committee was less interested in the economic than the political aspect of the affair; and Razmara was unwilling to appear as the champion of agreement with the Company, or of authoritarian government. The Company's suggestion that the Agreement might, if desired, be reconsidered on the lines of the 'half-and-half' Agreement, recently announced as between the Sa'udi Arabian Government and Aramco (p. 210), or indeed on any other reasonable basis, was not followed up nor communicated to the public. This silence, pointedly unhelpful to the Company, strengthened the position of Dr. Musaddiq and the National Front as advocates of strong and immediate anti-Razmara and anti-Company measures, among which the nationalization of oil offered itself as a patriotic and appealing proposal. The Oil Committee, in reply to its direct question to the Prime Minister on 19 February, was told that, on the authority of the experts whom he had consulted, nationalization was impracticable. The experts' report in this sense was broadcast on the Teheran wireless; but the reply of the now inflamed adherents or allies of the nationalization party was prompt: the Prime Minister was murdered on the following day. Within twenty-four hours the Oil Committee adopted on 8 March a resolution requesting an extension of its life for a further two months in order to study the execution of the 'proposal to nationalize the oil industry throughout the country', which it had considered and accepted. A Bill granting this request and confirming the Committee's decision—at present one of principle only —was approved by the Majlis on 15 March and by the Senate five days later. Government stood thus committed, by its own law, to nationalize the industry, a step of which the implications had not been considered.

An initial protest, addressed to Teheran by the British Government, regretted that Persian opinion had never been properly informed of the 1949 Agreement or of later proposals and referred to the 'regularly negotiated Agreement valid till 1993', which was currently in force, an Agreement which specifically forbade unilateral abrogation and provided for the settlement of disputes by arbitration. These representations and those of the Company itself, and the general publicity which the latter had in recent months given to the subject, had no effect. The Oil Committee, working in great haste and unaided by anyone acquainted with the scale, conditions, or essential structure of the industry, proffered a law which in nine clauses provided for the precise manner of nationalization and referred to the Anglo-Iranian as 'the former Company'. The rising tide of enthusiasm swept from office the Prime Minister, Husain 'Ala, who had succeeded Razmara, and substituted the prime mover of the nationalist campaign, Dr. Musaddiq himself. The appointment was greeted with enthusiasm by mass Tudeh-organized demonstrations in Teheran, with parades of anti-Western and pro-Soviet placards. Interest-free advances by the Company to the Persian Treasury, against future royalties, had been made during 1950 and the first three months of 1951; these were now discontinued when pronounced by the Government to be 'partial payments against' its 'claims against the Company in respect of the past'.

Dr. Musaddiq secured forthwith the passage of the Nationalization Law, which was approved by Parliament on 30 April and signed by the Shah the next day. It set up immediately a mixed Board of Senators and Deputies to depose 'the former Company': to examine the latter's claims and Persian counter-claims for reference to the Majlis: to audit the Company's current accounts, since, as from 1 March, 'the entire revenue from oil and its production is indisputably due to the Persian nation': to 'closely supervise exploitation': to draw up a statute for the National Iranian Oil Company, with its executive and expert bodies: to replace foreign experts and send Persian students abroad: to allow 'all purchasers of products derived from the wells' to buy oil henceforth up to their normal past requirements: to send its recommendations to the Oil Committee of the Majlis: and to finish its work within three months.

The ratification of this naïve and totally inadequate law—henceforward to be the inviolable basis of all discussion and negotiation—was followed by an enthusiastic popular and political campaign of abuse and misrepresentation, directed against the Company. The latter's call for arbitration, as provided for in the 1933 Agreement, was ignored; and on 26 May the British Government instituted proceedings against the Persian Government before the International Court of Justice at the Hague on the grounds that a British national had been treated in a manner contrary to International Law.

The prospects of a settlement, such as to permit the industry to continue in operation, grew daily poorer; forces of dangerous, indeed of bloodthirsty, fanaticism were allied to and largely dictated the moves of the nationalizers, who became the prisoners of their own law and of their broadcast promises of wealth and happiness for all; and the contributions of certain American diplomats and consultants, who professed to see the situation as one of Anglo-Iranian 'colonization' or mere reaction or as a legacy of unspecified Anglo-Iranian misdoings in the past, encouraged even responsible Persians to expect American approval.

Nevertheless, the Persian Government on 30 May expressed a wish for the Company's help in completing its nationalization arrangements, and, in the hope of an opportunity for reasonable discussion, a delegation under the Deputy Chairman, B. R. Jackson, arrived in Teheran on 11 June. But the seeming hopefulness of this opportunity was an illusion; the Government spokesmen refused out of hand to consider the Company's suggestion for the setting up of a Company, with mixed Persian and British directors, to operate in Persia on behalf of the N.I.O.C., after the vesting in the latter of all Anglo-Iranian's local assets; the sole Persian demand was for the precise application of every word of the law of 1 May, whereby the Company would in effect be immediately deprived of everything it possessed in Persia, with no assurance, and indeed little prospect, of redressment or compensation, and none that the industry would be properly and reasonably conducted. The Jackson Mission returned to England.

Meanwhile the anti-Company campaign throughout Persia was intensified, with its spearhead at Abadan. There had already been in April persistent and evidently Communist-led strike movements at the refinery and in the oilfields, with mass demonstrations and violence that cost two British lives and made operation for a time impossible; the Government, unable as ever to control its supporters, imposed martial law in Khuzistan. During June representatives of the N.I.O.C. began to assume nominal (though actually ineffective) charge of operations at the refinery, confused or stultified the existing administration, and ordered tanker captains to sign receipts for their cargoes in a form which assumed Persian ownership of the oil. All refused, and export of oil ceased; tankers at Abadan and Bandar Mashhur sailed empty and no more arrived after 26 June. One oilfield after another ceased production and pumping stations on the main pipeline came to a standstill. Supplies of products no longer moved to 'Iraq. The General Manager at Abadan—A. E. C. Drake—unable to comply with Persian instructions and risking thereby accusation of 'sabotage', was ordered to proceed to Basra. The evacuation of British women and children from all locations in south Persia began. Engagements offered by the N.I.O.C. to British staff, as individuals, were refused: nothing appealed to them in the mixture of cajolery and threats with which they were treated. Conditions, as June ended, became daily more confused, Persian aggressiveness more marked, their perversion of the Company's Persian staff more blatant, the continuation of operation less probable. A British warship, H.M.S. *Mauritius*, anchored in the Shatt al-'Arab as a measure of precaution and the arrival of some British troops in 'Iraq was reported; but none of these, in the event, played any part.

At Teheran the Company's office, and later the private house of its chief representative there, N. R. Seddon, were raided, and hooligan activity against the Company was rather encouraged than suppressed. A suggestion from American sources to Dr. Musaddiq —which might with advantage have come earlier and more forcibly —did nothing to deflect him from his policy, from which indeed any retreat must now endanger his power and probably his life, nor his supporters from a campaign of insult and crude vilification. The arrival as adviser, at Persian request, of the Italian expert Count Caraffa, the generally moderating advice given by resident foreign diplomats, and a communication from Mr. Nehru in India were all without effect. The Prime Minister was barely persuaded to drop his Anti-Sabotage Bill, a measure designed to incriminate the British in case of any misadventure in future at Abadan.

The International Court, to which Great Britain had appealed, but to which Persia denied jurisdiction in a matter which she claimed to be strictly domestic, pronounced nevertheless on 5 July that, pending its fuller consideration of the case, neither side should do anything prejudicial to the interests of the other or likely to extend the dispute or stop industrial operations; the former management should remain in charge, supervised by a joint Board of Supervision, to be appointed by the Court. The Court's interim order was accepted by Great Britain, rejected *in toto* by Persia, and remained ineffective.

While conditions in Abadan quickly deteriorated, deliveries of crude from the fields ceased, and refining operations were one by one discontinued, an intervention by President Truman led to the arrival at Teheran on 15 July of Averell Harriman on a peacemaking mission. In spite of Communist-led rioting in Teheran against 'Imperialism', his discussions at the capital were thought by him to reveal some hope of compromise, based on British acceptance of the principle of nationalization (the law of 15 March) though not of its detailed procedure (law of 1 May). On this specific basis a British Cabinet Minister, Richard Stokes, was deputed to Teheran and arrived on 3 August. The practical proposals which he made after seeing all parties and visiting Abadan, included the vesting of all A.I.O.C. assets in the Persian Government, payment by the latter of assessed compensation, operation of the industry by an *ad hoc* agency on behalf of N.I.O.C., and the sale of oil on long-term contracts to a 'buying organization' outside Persia. These proposals were rejected; Persian insistence on the whole law of 1 May was reiterated. The field in which the Persian Government would accept negotiation grew ever narrower; it could henceforth, in the atmosphere of rabid anglophobia which had been created, include nothing which permitted visible British control of operations. Harriman and Stokes left Persia; and 'revised proposals' sent by Dr. Musaddiq to the former in New York in mid-September, with a time limit for acceptance, were such that he declined to forward them to the British Government.

The last phase of Anglo-Iranian's operations in Persia could not now be far distant. The certainty that the United States would withhold support from any direct British military intervention, such as a landing at Abadan, and the danger (which was and is variously assessed) that Russian forces would in that event invade north Persia [1] and install a puppet Communist government seemed to the British Government of the time to preclude such forcible action as would unquestionably have been taken in earlier years, and might possibly have been taken now by another British Government. In the event, speeches in the British Parliament, repeated *démarches* by the Ambassador at Teheran, the withdrawal by the British Treasury of the exceptional sterling-conversion privileges, which Persia as a source of valuable sterling oil had been allowed, encouraging messages to A.I.O.C. staff at Abadan from the British Prime Minister and Foreign Secretary—none of these could influence the landslide of events. All refining had ceased on 31 July in an Abadan now anarchic and paralysed. All foreign employees had been called in from Fields late in August. Kirmanshah and Naft-i-Shah had been handed over; four-fifths of the foreign staff at Abadan, as their duties came per-

---

[1] They were in that case likely to adduce the terms of the Russo-Persian treaty of 1921, though these (which allowed for Russian counter-intervention in the case of pro-Czarist forces operating from Persia) would have been in fact inapplicable.

force to an end, had been repatriated. The seizure of their offices, stores, vehicles, and dwelling-houses by Persian delegates of the N.I.O.C. or their friends, the demoralization or intimidation of the Persian staff and labour, the cessation of all operations without visible hope of restarting, made the end inevitable. Their residence permits cancelled and their occupation gone, the last party of British staff left Abadan for Basra or Great Britain on 3 October 1951. The Company's representative in Teheran left a month later.

### V. AFTERMATH, 1951-3

Events in the international field which followed the departure of the Anglo-Iranian from Persia contributed nothing to Middle Eastern oil development and wholly failed to rescue Persia from its plight or the Company from its losses. Nevertheless, they will be recounted here as indicating characteristic groupings of world opinion, the sad powerlessness of international bodies to correct even a flagrant wrong, and the resolution in self-destruction to which Persian political leaders could induce their public.

The reference by Great Britain of the dispute, as one in which Persia had flouted the ruling of the International Court, to the Security Council of the United Nations was made a few days before the Anglo-Iranian staff's departure from Abadan: a few weeks, therefore, before the change of Government in Great Britain from Labour to Conservative. The British demand for an order from the United Nations for obedience to the Hague ruling of 5 July 1951, resumption of negotiations, and avoidance of aggravating action, was opposed at Lake Success by Dr. Musaddiq in person. The decision of the Security Council was to await the Hague Court's ruling as to its own competence. The Persian case was supported by the U.S.S.R. and evoked the sympathy of the Arab States, whose anti-Western attitude enabled them to ignore both the practical and the ethical aspects. Opinion in the United States was, by majority, unfavourable on moral and self-interested grounds to the Persian tactics of contract-breaking and virtual confiscation of foreign assets, but remained resolutely opposed to the use of force, which was not indeed (it is believed) at any time seriously contemplated by the British Government.

Dr. Musaddiq returned to his country in December 1951, after a visit to Cairo marked by sympathetic demonstrations. In Teheran serious riots led to violence in suppression which, causing many deaths, created dismay and terror. The tone of the Premier's public utterances grew wilder: he found 'the British' in every street brawl and sought popularity by the expulsion of British and American journalists. Accusations of A.I.O.C. 'interference in Persian politics', bribery of officials, and 'use of unjust economic pressure', were effective with the Persian public: and the closing of British Consulates throughout Persia in January 1952 was a step gratifying to Persian feeling, in which the merits or demerits of the Oil Company were not, and indeed have never been, seriously considered in the emotional obsession of an anglophobia indispensable to Dr. Musaddiq's position.

An attempt by the International Bank, by missions to Teheran in December 1951 and February 1952, to produce a temporary *modus vivendi* seemed for a time promising, but was rejected by Persian insistence that the Agency, which the bank would create to operate the industry, should be responsible to them alone, should accept their control, and should discriminate against all British participation. None of this, nor the implied acceptance of nationalization, was consistent with the bank's position.

While a régime of demonstrations and sporadic violence continued in Teheran, another success was acclaimed on the withdrawal of the British Bank of Iran from Persia. Hearings of the case, which Great Britain had placed in March 1952 before the International Court, were attended in April by Dr. Musaddiq, whence he returned to Teheran to resign from the premiership. His replacement for four days, 17–21 July, by the veteran Quwwam al-Sultana, on lines that promised a more realistic attitude to oil and other affairs, was cut short by organized rioting, which decided the frightened Shah—who refused to allow use of the armed forces —to restore Dr. Musaddiq. The pronouncement of the International Court on 22 July 1952, that it had no jurisdiction [1] in

---

[1] Persia in 1932 accepted the compulsory jurisdiction of the Court on 'all disputes arising after ratification of the present declaration with regard to situations or facts relating directly or indirectly to the application of treaties accepted by Persia and *subsequent to the ratification of this declaration.*' The Court, contrary to the British claim, held that the last seven words quoted refer to *treaties*, not to *situations or facts*: in which case Persian acceptance would be only in respect of treaties accepted by Persia after September 1932; and the treaties which contain most-favoured-nation treatment for Great Britain, and upon which Britain, therefore, relied in the Anglo-Iranian case, were those of 1857 and 1903. The second British argument, that the 1933 Concession was in effect a Treaty, was not accepted by the Court.

the Anglo-Iranian case, was taken as strengthening the position of the Persian Government.

A fortnight later a new offer of negotiation with the Company was made by Dr. Musaddiq, but in terms which condemned it as unacceptable: the losses inflicted by Anglo-Iranian called for compensation, settlement must be in strict terms of the law of May 1951, disputes would be referable to the Persian Courts, and very large sums must be paid immediately to the Persian Treasury. These suggestions were not followed up: but late in August joint proposals from President Truman and Mr. Churchill were conveyed to Dr. Musaddiq. These proposals were for unconditional reference of the compensation issue to the International Court: for immediate negotiations between the two parties to arrange 'for the flow of oil from Persia to world markets': for a relaxation of the British ban on Persia's use of sterling: and for an immediate grant of funds to assist that Government. These proposals were immediately pronounced by the Persian Premier as 'quite unacceptable'; he proposed, instead, on 25 September that compensation should at most be limited to the Company's physical assets at Abadan, that the A.I.O.C. should make good all Persian losses since nationalization, that such provisions of the (rejected) 1949 Agreement as were favourable to Persia should be carried out with effect from 1947, and that £49 million,[1] partly convertible into dollars, should be 'advanced' to Persia. These suggestions, which indicated a ten-day time limit for acceptance, were unlikely to lead to a settlement: and the same was true of the half-mysterious visit of a prominent American oil executive to Persia in the same period.

A British–American reply to Dr. Musaddiq's 'offer' was sent early in October and endeavoured to correct his misunderstanding of the Truman–Churchill proposal and to refute his wilder charges. He replied on 9 October by an invitation to 'the former A.I.O.C.' to discuss in Teheran his proposals of 25 September, having first paid £20 million (all convertible into dollars) and accepted the liability later to pay £29 million more. This suggestion was rejected by Her Majesty's Government, as involving the payment of a 'fictitious debt of £49 million, in return for the Company abandoning its right to claim just compensation.' The Persian

---

[1] Claimed as 'due' under the 1949 Supplemental Agreement.

reply was to break off diplomatic relations with Great Britain, whose chargé d'affaires and staff left Persia.

The later weeks of 1952 brought no sign or hope of agreement. No helpful British step presented itself: no moderating or realistic influence in Teheran could hope to be felt: and in the United States nothing for the moment emerged from many exchanges of view between oil interests and the State Department. The latter announced, under 'independent' pressure, that the purchase of oil from Persia, though claimed as British property, would be a matter for private buyers' discretion—a decision highly acceptable to Persia.

On 9 January the court at Aden pronounced, after six months of proceedings, that the oil cargo of the *Rose Mary*, a small vessel chartered by an Italian firm which had loaded oil at Bandar Mashhur and called at Aden, was Anglo-Iranian property; a second Italian tanker, the *Miriella*, took a cargo from Abadan on 20 January and was, in due course, the subject of lawsuits brought by A.I.O.C. in Italy. Further sailings of tankers to Italy were reported, and cargoes bought—at the 50 per cent. discount advertised by the N.I.O.C.—by Japanese interests and conveyed to Japan (to the evident embarrassment of the Japanese Government) were immediately the subject of litigation there.

Further proposals by the American Ambassador at Teheran, early in 1953, reflected renewed consultations between London and Washington. They included the principle of sole Persian responsibility for its oil industry: extensive purchase of Persian oil by an international company: provision of immediate funds to the Persian Treasury: and arbitration, on the subject of compensation, according to one of two alternative procedures acceptable to A.I.O.C. These proposals, pronounced by the British Foreign Secretary to be 'reasonable and fair', were held by Dr. Musaddiq on 20 March to be a mere variation of former offers and unacceptable. His summary—a curious judgement on half a century of Anglo-Iranian's beneficent services to Persia—was, no doubt, wholly consonant with Persian political feeling: 'What the A.I.O.C. did formerly was sheer looting, not business.' Meanwhile a Persian Government Commission, investigating its own counter-claims against the 'former Company', had reported that these, under the 1933 Agreement, amounted already to £82 million.

The damage done to British and sterling area economy was in

fact severe,[1] since refined products from Persia had for a time to be replaced at great cost by others from dollar sources, and in some territories physical shortages, especially of aviation spirit, were felt for some months. But the elasticity of world supply, the increase in European refining capacity, the co-operation of the international companies, and the rapid re-deployment of tanker fleets (notably that of the British Tanker Company) succeeded to a remarkable extent in avoiding hardship and providing consumers with their supplies. The total Middle Eastern production, fortified by the extraordinary increases from Sa'udi Arabia, Kuwait, and 'Iraq, continued its upward course and, in terms of crude oil, easily made good the loss of the Persian output; already by 1952 there were those who saw more embarrassment than satisfaction in the reappearance of major Persian supplies on the market. Anglo-Iranian itself, strong in its worldwide organization, its grown and growing refineries outside Persia, and its crude supplies from Kuwait, 'Iraq, and Qatar, had suffered a heavy, but not fatal blow.

Oil activity in Persia after 3 October 1951 consisted of the prospecting and drilling in the Qum area, already recorded (p. 152), the working of the Naft-i-Shah field and Kirmanshah refinery plant, the distribution of existing stocks [2] of products throughout Persia, and the partial replacement of these by the operation, for a few days at intervals, of a distillation unit at Abadan. A limited production of crude—by the simple opening of a valve—continued from the main south Persian fields. Work was found for the idle and malcontent oil workers on roads and unfinished buildings; installations were carefully maintained, within the limits of Persian competence; and stories of achievement and progress were issued to the world. Squabbles among managers and directors, experts and politicians, marked the administration of the N.I.O.C. The Shah paid his first visit to Abadan, which Dr. Musaddiq had never seen.

---

[1] It was estimated in mid-1952 by the head of the Petroleum Division of M.S.A. that the dollar cost arising from the loss of Persian oil would amount to $215 million in 1952 and had been in 1951 at a rate of $40 million a month. It was foreseen that A.I.O.C. would cease to require non-sterling crude by the end of 1952, thanks to other supplies; the need for purchases of dollar refined products would be eliminated by early 1953.

The same authority assessed the replacement value of Abadan refinery at over £320 million, of which at least 15 per cent. would be dollar expenditure.

[2] A.I.O.C. left more than 13 million bbl. of products stored at Abadan; Persian consumption averaged 14,000–18,000 b/d.

No partial expedient and no propaganda could, however, diminish the weight of Persia's self-inflicted blow. Although nine-tenths of the population, accustomed to abject poverty and never visibly beneficiaries from the country's oil royalties, could be philosophical at this last achievement of their Government, yet all hopes of better times, of security and progress, of effective social services, must be dashed by this sudden immobilization of the country's greatest source of wealth, sole reliable contributor to its Treasury, sole pioneer in efficient industry, and almost sole provider of foreign exchange. Such loss was, indeed, no inevitable consequence of nationalization as such; a nationalized industry could, in Persia as elsewhere, give satisfactory results, but only if certain conditions existed. The non-existence of these, unrealized by the enthusiasts of Teheran, caused the fiasco so disastrous to Persia. If Persian executives were capable of performing many practical functions in the industry, they were patently incapable of the administration of the whole integrated enterprise, lacked all research and scientific facilities, had no contact with the international oil industry, and no knowledge (much less possession) of the worldwide transportation, distribution and sales network whereby virtually the whole of production in Persia had been placed on the world's markets; and these were neither susceptible of Persian nationalization nor likely to be placed at their disposal. It must, in these circumstances, be judged that the nationalization (in effect the confiscation) of the industry in the form adopted by Persia was not only repugnant to commercial and international morality but offered a sad record of practical ineptitude.

Though much of the action taken, or permitted to happen, in Persia was the result of excitement, naïve irresponsibility, and a 'political' atmosphere of violence, malice, and fear, yet it is reasonable to ask what were the more serious pretexts or reasons which must surely have existed for a course of action held with so much persistence? Differently assessed by different observers, they certainly included a childlike, but politically exploited, belief that if the industry became 'our own' all must be well: the feeling that it was unworthy of a great nation (or was even a derogation of sovereignty) that an important foreign corporation should work and prosper on such a scale in its midst: the suspicion that the Company must be 'interfering' in State affairs, corrupting politicians, and perverting loyalty: the allegation (which readers of these pages can judge) that the Company's workers were ill-treated and dissatisfied, the training of Persians neglected, their claims for promotion disallowed: the belief that 'other countries received more' for their foreign-developed oil: the vexed realization that the British Government received more from the Company than did Persia: the pretext that the 1933 Agreement was invalid: and the claim that nationalization, in some or any form, was, without more ado, the right of any sovereign government. Some of these pleas found a measure of support in the United States and some in limited British circles. It was in places believed or alleged that the Company's sympathy with Persian aspirations or sensibilities had indeed been imperfect: that it had driven too hard and too deliberate a bargain in 1933, or even in 1949; that it was caught unprepared in 1950 by an inadequate appreciation of Persian mental and political movements: that it had done too little to place its achievements before the Persian public and nothing to ensure that its royalties were spent for true Persian benefit. The present writer cannot find that more than a small fraction of this criticism is valid; nor does he venture to assess the suggestion that there was room for, and might have been safety in, an imaginative gesture by the Company immediately after the war, inviting more visible Persian partnership in the enterprise and simultaneously offering, with full publicity, greater immediate benefits.

The view of the Company, the British Government, and the great body of world opinion [1] remained that the Company's rights had been bestowed upon it with every legal and moral validity, blessed by the League of Nations, and accepted by Persia for eighteen years without question; that its operations had been conducted with entire correctness and notable benevolence, much to the benefit of Persia: that the unilateral cancellation of these rights (expressly forbidden in the 1933 Agreement) and the refusal of arbitration were improper and immoral: that nationalization in the form adopted was, in fact, confiscation: and that, meanwhile, the Company's assets in Persia remained its property.

[1] Outside the U.S.S.R. and its satellites, and the Arab world.

## CHAPTER XI

# MID-CENTURY IN 'IRAQ ·

## I. END OF THE RED LINE

IF the I.P.C. was both willing and able to press forward with development in 'Iraq as soon as war restrictions were removed, this did not imply that there were no traces of discord among its constituent groups. The circumstances which had deprived the Compagnie Française and Gulbenkian—and, for other reasons, New Jersey—of their quota of 'Iraq oil for a period beginning in 1940 have elsewhere been recorded (p. 118). The 'enemy alien' status of Gulbenkian was revoked in 1943, that of the C.F.P. in 1945, whereafter both (but not New Jersey) submitted claims to be compensated for their loss of oil allotment. That of Gulbenkian, advanced in 1943, was finally settled in May 1945, that of C.F.P. only in 1950.

The events of the war had, however, a deeper effect than this on I.P.C. group interrelations. The eagerness, but final failure, of the American groups in 1935–9 to secure relaxation of Red Line restrictions, so as to let them participate in Arabian development (p. 104), did not diminish; such restrictions as were implicit in the Red Line Agreement on the freedom of its signatories to enter whatever fields of development or trade they wished had always been disliked by the American groups. These proceeded late in 1946 to inform their I.P.C. associates that the Red Line should now be considered as no more, and followed this by the announcement of their own agreement to acquire considerable shares in Aramco. Protests came from the French and Gulbenkian but were unheeded, and their plea for equal admission to the Arabian field was refused. The suit brought by the Compagnie Française in February 1947 against N.E.D.C. and the other I.P.C. groups sought a declaration that the 1928 Agreement remained valid. The reply of N.E.D.C. was to file a statement of claim denying this.

The long preparation of this highly complicated case gave time for continuing efforts to settle it out of court. Nearly two years were spent in inter-group negotiations to regulate the position or establish a new one, and at the same time to determine the pace of future development in 'Iraq. The Americans desired to make good their entry into Aramco, the French needed more and more oil, Anglo-Iranian had to consider their greater commitments elsewhere, Shell stood for moderate development in 'Iraq. Agreement was reached at last between the four major groups in the summer of 1947, but was rejected by Gulbenkian: and a further eighteen months of negotiations between the lawyers of both hemispheres resulted, in November 1948, in a revised Group Agreement. Under its provisions Socony-Vacuum and New Jersey were free to enter the Aramco enterprise, a specific development programme for 'Iraq was laid down, and a general price formula and prices for inter-group sales were prescribed. Special provisions governed the Gulbenkian rights and the acquisition, or re-acquisition, of concessions.

The Heads of Agreement thus reached in 1948 remained to be drafted in full detail during succeeding years. The terms, which, nevertheless, were treated as already operative, contained nothing unfavourable to the development of the territories concerned.

On the death of Lord Cadman in 1941, the chairmanship of the Company was assumed by Sir Francis Humphrys and in 1949 by Admiral of the Fleet Sir John Cunningham. J. Skliros was succeeded, after twenty years as the executive head of affairs, by H. S. Gibson, of Anglo-Iranian, in January 1950. The Company's Board, with two directors from each major group and one from Participations and Investments, had been increased in 1934 by the appointment of a Managing Director, J. Skliros, and in 1951 by that of two executive directors, G. W. Dunkley and H. H. Wheatley. The place of the latter, who died by tragic coincidence two days before his appointment was to be confirmed, was taken by G. H. Herridge in 1953.

## II. KIRKUK AND THE I.P.C.

The fair possibilities of early expansion that opened before the I.P.C. in 1945 were not to be easily realized. The shortage of skilled workers was a limiting factor, foreign staffs were not re-assembled in a day, all equipment needed rehabilitation or replacement, foreign currency restrictions continued, and output of new equipment by British or other non-dollar factories was limited. Nevertheless, every commercial and political consideration called for expansion; and the 'period of suspension' arranged with the

'Iraq Government in 1943 was to end two years after August 1945.

The production of crude oil from the Kirkuk structure, which had fallen to 1·4 million tons in 1941 but rose again to 4·3 million in 1945, maintained this level in the two years following; it fell, for reasons which will appear later, to 3·1 million in 1948 and thereafter rose to 3·8 million in 1949, 6·1 in 1950, almost 8 in 1951 and 15·5 in 1952.[1] These latter increases reflected the additional pipeline capacity which progressively became available. The structure had by the end of 1952 given a total of 85 million tons and would exceed 100 million by September 1953.

Drilling on the Kirkuk structure was re-started with one string in 1943 and continued with two in 1944–5. Thereafter enough wells were completed on both the Baba Gurgur and the Avana domes—forty-four on the former and eighteen on the latter—by April 1953, to permit the assured supply of all quantities of oil which would be required and to allow fully for reservoir observation. At the end of 1952 some thirty-five wells were in production, not all simultaneously, with another twenty shut in or reserved for observation. At Avana two groups of five wells each had been prepared for early production; it was planned to obtain Kirkuk's full anticipated output of 22 million t/y in the proportion of three-fifths from Baba Gurgur and two-fifths from Avana.

A deep test-well was drilled in 1951 to a depth of 11,150 feet, and below the main limestone found a Cretaceous limestone of 'Ain Zala type. Tests to prove oil-bearing structures elsewhere were made at locations off the Kirkuk structure: at Bai Hasan in 1948 (where high-pressure gas was again encountered), at Quwair in 1950 for observation, at Chamchamal, where no oil was found, and at Khormor, where early in 1953 drilling was still in progress in the main limestone. Meanwhile the ability of Kirkuk to support alone the formidable future offtake for many years was not in doubt.

Production facilities kept pace with drilling and with pipeline increases. Two of the original three de-gassing stations were enlarged, another was completed at Qutan, and two more—Sarbashakh and Saralu—were erected north of the Zab; oil from the latter was pumped, on 17 March 1953 for the first time, by a 24-

---

[1] Output from the Kirkuk structure exceeded 7 million tons in the first four months of 1953.

inch pipeline, across a new Zab bridge built for the purpose, to the stabilization plant at Baba. A third de-gassing station at Avana was to be completed late in 1953. The stabilization plant, to which four new units were added in 1947–9 and another was under erection in 1953, continued to turn sour crude into sweet. The 'new industrial area', serving Fields and K1 station, was planned and constructed in 1948–51 and contained the topping and stabilization plants, laboratories, railway station, workshops, store sheds and yards, garages and power-house. At K1, with its 'service-unit', residential quarters, hangars, and main hospital, increased tankage was provided and the pumping installation vastly enlarged. A new and imposing power-house, completed in 1950, supplied all Company requirements and those of Kirkuk city, to which abundant power was supplied free of charge. Water from the Zab was doubled by new pumps and pipelines, from which again Kirkuk city was a chief beneficiary. The old topping-plant was superseded by a new two-unit distillation plant with capacity of 1,500 b/d. Further railway facilities were added, the Company's internal transport system was perfected, and the aviation service linked K1 daily with all parts of the Company's system.

If the Kirkuk oilfield, so favoured by nature, was thus in well-designed and well-provided production, appropriate efforts had been made for the welfare of workers. Trade Union organization, though permitted by 'Iraq law, was in practice discouraged by successive governments and its place at Kirkuk was in part taken by Joint Committees of workers and management, working in friendly consultation. Visible unrest among workers occurred only when political agitation from outside—as in the Communist-inspired strike [1] of 1946—was patently the cause. Pay-rates and allowances were in advance of those of other employers in 'Iraq and a long-matured system of recruiting and administration was based on justice and good sense, with treatment more favourable in all respects than that prescribed in the Labour Code. Paid holidays were the rule. Substantial benefits on retirement, in replacement of a previously existing contributory Provident Fund,

---

[1] An unfortunate episode, when a prohibited strikers' meeting in Kirkuk town (not on or near the Company's quarters) was broken up by the 'Iraqi Police, with loss of life, was maliciously attributed by Baghdad journalists to I.P.C. brutality.

awaited employees of all grades. A voluntary Savings Scheme encouraged private thrift among workers. The health of workers was safeguarded by a comprehensive system of preventive medicine, by healthy premises, pure water, and regular work under good conditions. The Company's hospitals and dispensaries reached the highest standard. Accidents were minimized by every known device and by continuous training. Canteens were provided throughout Fields; and, when supplies were scarce, 'commodity assistance' was given by the Company to ensure workers' needs at subsidized prices. Sports facilities and grounds were provided, clubs were opened for 'Iraqi and foreign staff, bus transport was furnished for workers where required, and thousands of bicycles were sold to them at low prices.

The proximity of Kirkuk, with its 85,000 inhabitants, failed to solve adequately the housing problem of the Company's workers, and the decision to create a housing estate was taken in 1947. The houses, of a high standard of construction and convenience, were in part occupied in 1949, in part were still under construction in 1952. All services were provided, rents moderate, and the well-being of the tenants assured. A similar but smaller estate was erected on the Lesser Zab. Other plans for assistance in improving workers' housing in Kirkuk by 'assisted purchase' and otherwise were, in 1952, passing into the stage of active realization.

The period saw great advances in the vocational training of 'Iraqi employees. Besides much and varied unofficial instruction by executives throughout the Company's system, the course at the Training School at Kirkuk, spent partly in class and partly in the technical departments, led to trade tests and promotion to higher places in the industry. To this was in process of being added, in 1952, an Apprenticeship Training Scheme, which would offer, at an admirable Technical Training Centre which was under erection, a four-year course to some sixty carefully recruited candidates a year. These, who were paid while learning, would supply in future most of the Company's needs in the engineering and commercial fields. The sending of artisans for practical training in the United Kingdom and that of pupils for university or higher courses in Europe continued on an increasing scale. The advantage to the Company of substituting properly qualified 'Iraqis for foreign employees, whenever and wherever possible, was evident; the present relative paucity of 'Iraqis in the higher levels of the Company's hierarchy was due solely to the actual lack of trained men willing to join the Company's service and to serve it in outstations; few were willing to leave Baghdad or Kirkuk, and many after completing their training sought employment elsewhere.

W. E. D. Cole, Fields Manager from 1931, was succeeded on his death in 1945 by M. S. Mainland; the latter, followed six years later in Fields by G. Hopkinson, became General Manager (I.P.C. Fields and Pipeline) in 'Iraq. In the same year, 1952, Sir Herbert Todd became the Company's Chief Representative in 'Iraq. The post of General Manager in the Middle East, with headquarters at Haifa and later at Tripoli, was handed by G. W. Dunkley to M. M. Stuckey in 1939; and the latter was succeeded, on his death in 1947, by G. H. Herridge. The post ceased to exist in 1952 when, under an amended organization, a General Manager and Chief Representative was appointed in each separate national territory.

### III. THE NEW PIPELINES

The 12-inch trans-desert lines, completed in 1934, were certain in the first years of peace to be the object of careful rehabilitation and even before the Armistice such work was in progress. Roads were improved, telegraphs overhauled, a renewed effort made to improve water-supplies for stations. The main line itself, now twelve years old, was in many places corroded, in spite of its 'dope' and wrapping, and the exhumation, repair, and re-burial of the pipe through its course was an important work of 1945–8. At the stations repair and replacement were comprehensive and, with this, urgent tasks were put in hand in connexion with the new lines whose construction had been decided.

The 12-inch line, hailed in the early nineteen-thirties as an outstanding engineering feat, was to seem, in the later nineteen-forties and thereafter, no more than a picturesque pioneering work; and the 16-inch lines built in 1945–9 were in their turn to be dwarfed by a later giant. Nevertheless, the 16-inch line, which cost £40 million and called for 180,000 tons of pipe, was a formidable task, and its ultimate failure to deliver its full throughput was due to world events against which no company (and no government) could prevail. The decision to build it with all speed was taken by the I.P.C. directors in 1944, the limitation of the diameter to 16-inch being enforced by the inability of sterling-area manufacturers to produce larger pipe and the equal impossibility of obtaining dollars. The plans made for its construction were on principles closely similar to those of the 12-inch line and it was to follow the same alignment; the completion of the work was designed to bring total capacity ex-Kirkuk to 270,000 b/d, or 13 million t/y, since each 16-inch line would equal approximately the throughput of the double 12-inch.

Work on the south line began late in 1946. The line, two-thirds rolled in British and one-third in French mills, was delivered progressively from 1946 to 1949. The work of providing and organizing the transport fleet, enlarging the railhead depots, and erecting construction camps was pressed on in advance of main-line construction. The latter involved, simultaneously, the erection of pumphouses and installation of batteries of pumps, the general expansion of station buildings and accommodation, the doubling or trebling of tankage at all points, and the stringing, welding, wrapping, and burying of the pipe itself. The labour force for these operations was recruited and administered, fed and sheltered, to a total number, at the peak of construction, of some 15,000 in the five countries.

Progress on the Haifa line during 1947 was so satisfactory that, with only the Palestine section to be completed, operation well in advance of anticipated dates could be expected. But the disorders in Palestine in 1948 and the stoppage, by 'Iraqi decision, of oil pumping to the State of Israel ended all hope of utilizing either the new or the old southern lines; they were condemned to lie idle and empty in the earth, the south-line stations to lose their usefulness for an indefinite period, and the Company and 'Iraq Government (and the western hemisphere) alike to lose the benefit of an oil export exceeding 6 million t/y. The pumping of oil to Haifa ceased on 17 April 1948. Suggestions to divert the line to an outlet on the Lebanese coast were considered, but not adopted.

Work on the northern line began only late in 1948; but accelerated effort succeeded in so far advancing both station and line construction that by the middle of 1949 sections of the line could be brought into use. The combined northern lines gave in 1949 a throughput nearly double that of the single 12-inch, and in 1950, with a delivery of more than 6 million tons, had trebled the former capacity. Construction work was progressively completed on machinery installation, tankage, and buildings; temporary arrangements were replaced by permanent, and the north-line project was effectively completed during 1951.

This achievement and the tragedy of the wasted southern line both yielded in interest to the new and greater project which reached the stage of detailed planning in 1949 and of execution from 1950 to 1952. This was the construction of a single 30–32-inch pipeline from Kirkuk to a Syrian terminal at Banias, fifty-five miles north of Tripoli. The designed capacity of the line, with four pumping stations, was 14 million t/y. It was to follow the existing alignment from K1 station to a point west of Homs and, thereafter, to bear north-westward to the sea. The pipe, apart from ninety miles of 26-inch for the most westerly section, was half 30- and half 32-inch, so designed to minimize shipping costs by nesting pipe within pipe. The pipe, of which the first consignment left Los Angeles in September 1950, was shipped simultaneously to Tripoli and Basra. It filled thirty-five shiploads. The length of the line was 555 miles, as against 532 from Kirkuk to Tripoli, the weight of pipe required was 165,000 tons,[1] and the cost slightly to exceed £40 million.

The Company on this occasion entrusted the task of main-line construction to a contractor—the American firm fresh from closely similar experience on the Trans-Arabian project (p. 206), with British and Lebanese firms in association. Labour employed by the Company and its contractors on the work amounted in 1951 to 7,000 'Iraqis and Syrians, 90 Americans, 300 British. Progress in the successive stages of main-line and station construction, machinery erection, and tankage was smooth and harmonious, and disturbed by little labour uneasiness, though on occasion by abnormally unfavourable weather; the construction of the entire work occupied no more than seventeen months, from November 1950 to April 1952.

The pipe from two ports of entry was carried, to a total of 800 trainloads, to Baiji and Homs, where living quarters (largely movable), mess halls, offices, stores, and repair shops were established. While construction of powerful new generators and pumping-plant at K1, K3, T2, and T4 proceeded, and the Employment, Commissariat, and Medical departments were extended to fulfil unprecedented requirements, the work of

---

[1] The pipe was wrapped in 40,000 miles of fibre-glass and coated with 21,000 tons of tar enamel.

receiving and stacking pipe in its 30-feet lengths proceeded at the depots. It was followed by the successive operations of ditch-making [1] by mechanical excavators and of stringing, aligning, and cleaning the pipe. This, already assembled in welded three-pipe lengths at the base depot, was brought to the line by specially designed pipe-carrying six-wheeled vehicles of 250 h.p., capable, with their 'dollys', of carrying 65-ton loads. The final tasks were those of welding the lengths together, testing welds by gamma-ray detectors, covering with tar, fibre glass, and asbestos wrapping, and finally lowering from the side-boom tractors which held the pipe in mid-air throughout these processes. Ten additional storage tanks, each of 24,000 tons capacity, were added to the pipeline stations. Communication between stations and the terminal were improved by the installation of automatic telephones and tele-printing. By comprehensive provision of the necessary generating plant, lines, rectifiers, and bed-plates 'cathodic protection' was afforded to the pipeline (and simultaneously to pre-existing pipe-lines) against the corrosion which burial in soil must ultimately cause.

The flow of oil, recorded on its course by delicate instruments, began, in advance of completion of the whole work, by the use of the idle 12- and 16-inch lines of the eastern section of the Haifa lines. By this means the 30-inch line achieved a throughput of more than 8 million tons in 1952 and the whole I.P.C. pipeline system [2] one of 15·5 million tons, a figure likely to be increased to 19 or 20 million in 1953. The new line was ceremonially opened by King Faisal II at Kirkuk and by the Head of the Syrian State at Banias in November 1952.

Everything feasible was done to render life at mid-desert pump stations agreeable for the workers, in spite of isolation, monotony, and the severity of the climate. The stations contained good (and constantly improved) residential accommodation, facilities for messing and shopping, clubs and reading-rooms, opportunities for sport, swimming pools and a cinema, medical and dental service, and adult evening classes. There was at each a Company-built school for workers' children of both sexes, with staff and supervision provided by the local Ministry of Education.

---

[1] Three million tons of earth were excavated to form the ditch.

[2] Excluding, therefore, 'Ain Zala–K2 (of the M.P.C.), and Zubair–Fao (B.P.C.).

## IV. 'AIN ZALA AND THE M.P.C.

The end of the war brought back for solution the problem of viscous oil and long disappointment west of the Tigris, where the B.O.D. had, since September 1941, become the Mosul Petroleum Company. The seven-year postponement of obligatory production, granted by the Government in 1939, had since then been further extended by the 'period of suspension' allowed under the 1943 Agreement; but the necessity to export major quantities of oil had but been re-dated and was now to fall due in March 1953; and no marketable oil, save a doubtful quantity in the Cretaceous limestone of the 'Ain Zala structure, had yet been located. A merging of the Mosul production and export obligation with those of Kirkuk was unacceptable to the 'Iraqi authorities, partly because the Mosul concession gave them greater advantages—a fifth of all oil produced, free of charge, in addition to royalty. The oil, therefore, must be found, production facilities must be created, and a pipeline built; and to these tasks the M.P.C. perforce addressed itself in the autumn of 1945.

Eighteen months were devoted to the rehabilitation of the Company's camps, buildings, power-station, airfields, communications, and equipment at Qaiyara and 'Ain Zala and the repair of military damage. 'Ain Zala camp, destined thereafter to be the Company's operating headquarters, was enlarged, a depot on the railway at Tel Hugna was established and the M.P.C. labour force rose by the middle of 1947 from a few dozen men to some 700. Drilling with old German equipment recommenced early in that year with the reopening of one of the 'junked' wells. Others were spudded in, modern rigs and equipment (obtained not without difficulty and delay) superseded the older materials, and the full drilling campaign gained impetus. Six wells, of average depth of 5,250–5,500 feet, were completed at 'Ain Zala in 1948, but gave results not more favourable than those of the first 'Ain Zala wells at the same location in 1939–40. A trial made twenty miles off at Mashura Dagh gave a dry hole at 7,600 feet. Stratigraphic and geophysical surveys were carried out in different parts of the M.P.C. area in 1948 and every year thereafter.

The experience of drilling in the two years following was similar and, on balance, disappointing; the productiveness of wells in the 'first pay' of the hard and erratically fissured limestone was improved by acidizing, but still seemed doubtfully adequate to support long-term production. A well at the former location of Qasab was drilled, without success. A further attempt was made in 1951–2 at Butma, a structure eight miles from 'Ain Zala, and a limited output of oil was found. At 'Ain Zala itself deeper tests revealed a not unpromising 'second pay' and this seemed likely to be the main supplier for M.P.C. export.

The provision of facilities for the latter process began seriously in 1951 with the commencement of work on a de-gassing station, the planning of flow lines, tankage, a pump station, and an electric generator. A 12-inch line from 'Ain Zala to K2 station, 135 miles distant, was designed, and work on this and on new offices and domestic buildings proceeded throughout 1952. In October oil flowed into the tanks, was pumped to K2, and thence by an unused 12-inch line to K3 station, where (being itself sulphur-free) it could be added to the Kirkuk stabilized crude and pass to waiting tankers at Tripoli. At 'Ain Zala drilling proceeded for further exploitation of the 'second pay' at some 5,500 feet of depth: the more necessary since early production from the 'first pay' caused an abrupt drop in pressure. By the end of 1952 production under the M.P.C. Concession had amounted to 270,000 tons.[1]

The changes made in the terms of this concession during 1951–2 will be mentioned on a later page (p. 191). Time would show what processes, if any, could best be adopted to render marketable the great stores of viscous oil known to underlie Qaiyara and its adjacent structures; and world demand would indicate how far the exploitation of this economically marginal production would be feasible. From 'Ain Zala and structures near it where lighter oil was available—but on a scale niggardly compared with Middle Eastern reservoirs elsewhere—the maintenance of production seemed probable, but would call for constant effort. If, or when, the great expenses incurred in the area since 1927 would be reimbursed, remained to be seen; that oil of one type or another was abundant and that every resource and technique would be available to develop it were, fortunately for 'Iraq, certain.

Meanwhile the community at 'Ain Zala—1,000 'Iraqis and fifty foreigners—was typical of modern oil-company organization in similar conditions. The 'Iraqi labour, drawn mostly from the

---

[1] 'Ain Zala production for the first four months of 1953 was 448,000 tons.

neighbouring villages, needed and received training in every form of skill. A number were Mosulawi and returned for each week-end in Company buses to their city homes. The disposition of industrial and domestic buildings and gardens was carefully planned, and an extensive building programme of enlarged and improved living quarters was in 1953 in course of fulfilment. Cheap and clean food was provided in a Company-built restaurant, a cinema was shared by all grades of personnel, a library of Arabic and English books catered for the literate and an 'Iraqi sports committee organized games. A hospital cared for the sick and other medical and sanitary services were comprehensive. Water was piped from the Tigris, six miles away. A commissariat shop was well stocked, Company plant provided ice and mineral water. A Welfare Committee met monthly for the free discussion of all questions of amenities, comfort, and well-being. Workers from 'Ain Zala were eligible candidates for the Training Centre at Kirkuk, and an unlimited career in the Company's service awaited the able. In general, the presence in this remote area of northern 'Iraq of an industrial centre from which radiated a diffused and prosperous activity and the example of higher living standards, with every prospect of 'Iraqi participation at higher and executive levels, could not be other than a valuable asset to the region.

### V. ZUBAIR AND THE B.P.C.

In the area of the Basrah Petroleum Company, not only had geological parties, interrupted and looted in the troubles of 1941, kept in being during the war and amassed information, but in the later war years the Company felt justified in ordering drilling equipment and arranging for early geophysical research. The latter activity was pressed strenuously during 1946–7 with a number of parties in the field, where the dead-flat silt or sand-covered terrain, concealing all its secrets from the eye, called in-sistently for the science of the geophysicist. By the end of 1947 great progress had been made in the extension and equipment of the Company's main depot at Makina, in the selection of drilling sites at Zubair (fifteen miles south-west of Basra), Nahr 'Umar (thirty miles up-river), and Ratawi (in open desert west of the Euphrates), in the building of workers' and staff dwellings and service installations at these sites, and in 'rigging up' preparatory to drilling.

In 1948, while prospecting continued elsewhere, drilling began at Zubair in February, at Nahr 'Umar in March, and at Ratawi in November. The Ratawi well was abandoned, as a dry hole, in 1949 at the great depth of 12,690 feet; but at Zubair and Nahr 'Umar the drill penetrated oil-bearing sand at depths of 10,250–11,000 feet and 8,000–8,500 feet respectively. The first tests at each proved oil to be present in important quantities, stored in flattish anticlinal structures of Cretaceous sandstone. That of Nahr 'Umar was of 43 degrees A.P.I. gravity, the lightest oil yet discovered in the Middle East; the Zubair oil was 35·5 degrees. In September 1948 Government was informed that oil in commercial quantities had been discovered.

The second well at Nahr 'Umar yielded, disappointingly, salt water and was 'plugged back' for use as an observation well; and the uncertain potentiality of this structure and its greater distance from a sea-outlet determined the Company to concentrate at Zubair, where, with four and later five rigs in operation, a series of wells was completed, so spaced as to explore the dimensions of the structure. At the same time preparations were pressed forward to equip the field for the earliest possible exploitation; and while at Makina the depot became a populous centre of many activities and services, the Zubair field—the deepest so far discovered of all Middle Eastern producing fields—evolved and stabilized into a carefully-designed and fully-equipped centre of production. A single five-stage de-gassing station of 70,000 b/d capacity was erected, to serve fifteen producing wells; and the oil, after moving from this to flow-tanks, was pumped to central storage before its despatch to Fao, at the mouth of the Shatt al-'Arab, seventy-four miles distant, by way of 12–10-inch pipeline. Finished and tested in 1950, the line (unlike those of northern 'Iraq) was laid above ground on concrete sleepers to avoid corrosion from the salty ground. At Fao eight storage tanks were erected, two loading jetties constructed, and facilities provided for loading at high speeds.

Oil flowed to field tankage early in October 1951 and the first loading at Fao took place on 21 December. An inaugural ceremony for the new field and pipeline was held on 10 January 1952, attended by the Prime Minister of 'Iraq and a large gathering of ministers, diplomats, the public, and the Company's directors and superior staff. Production by the end of 1951 had amounted to

121,000 tons of oil and in the year 1952 reached 2·24 million tons.[1]
L. Teyssot was Fields Manager, later General Manager, of the
B.P.C. from 1951.

The growing-pains of the oilfield, which employed some 2,000
'Iraqis and a handful of Europeans, included some phases of labour
unrest which culminated in a general strike in March 1951. This
was settled by changes of procedure in matters of transport and
allowances, and industrial relations were, thereafter, on the whole
excellent. Joint Welfare Committees were instituted, on the model
already successful at Kirkuk; good canteen accommodation at
Zubair and a club for 'Iraqi staff in the suburbs of Basra were
appreciated. A voluntary Savings Scheme was launched. Buses
conveyed workers daily between Zubair and Basra, a small proportion also being housed at the field. Workers and their sons were
sent to the Artisan Training Course at Kirkuk and others to the
newly instituted Apprentice Training Course. Students continued
to be sent from Basra to the United Kingdom for higher study.
Cordial relations were enjoyed with the local authorities of Basra
province and with the public, to whom the immediate economic
benefit of the Company's payrolls, purchases, and locally-given
contracts was evident.

In spite of the great depth of wells in the Zubair field and the
heavy handicap of long sea transport and Suez Canal fees, which
its output must face, neither the Government nor the Company
was likely long to rest content with a production merely satisfying
the concession obligations. The increase of output from the Basra
field became an item in the new Government–Company arrangements discussed during 1949–52. The result, agreed by the
Company even before the cessation of Persian supplies in 1951,
provided that Zubair production should, from the end of 1955, be
raised to a rate of 8 million t/y. The anticipation of this increase
led from 1950 onwards to continued drilling [2] and construction
activity in Zubair field, and to further prospecting elsewhere for
alternative sources. A second multi-stage de-gassing station was
to be completed by 1954 to serve a group of new wells, and a third
was planned; a limited programme of house building for 'Iraqi
staff and workers was begun, tankage at Fao was increased, a

---

[1] Zubair production for January–April 1953 was 962,000 tons.
[2] 91,000 feet were drilled in 1951, 109,000 in 1952, and a footage of 130,000
was expected in 1953.

second jetty completed, and the laying of a 24-inch pipeline [1] from Zubair to Fao, parallel to the first line, made rapid progress in 1952 and was ready for use by March 1953.

Whatever other fields southern 'Iraq might prove to contain—and their existence was scarcely doubtful—and whether or not Basra oil would have its part in some future trans-desert pipeline, the Zubair structure was likely to be in important production for many years as a major source, if all went well, of 'Iraqi prosperity. Meanwhile the decline in Basra Port revenues, due to the cessation of Abadan traffic, was in part compensated by that of the B.P.C.; Zubair crude was supplied to the Muftiya refinery, erected for the Government by the Khanaqin Oil Company in 1952; and the direct contribution of the B.P.C. enterprise to the economy and stability of southern 'Iraq was appreciable.

### VI. NAFTKHANA AND THE K.O.C.

The great, greater, and greatest fields of the I.P.C. group—'Ain Zala, Zubair, Kirkuk—did not exhaust the list of 'Iraqi producing areas. There remained the oldest and smallest—the half-structure of Naftkhana on the Persian frontier. From this, the Siamese twin of Naft-i-Shah but administered since the war again in complete separation from it for political reasons, more than 5 million tons of oil had been taken by the Khanaqin Oil Company by the end of 1952 and refined for consumption in 'Iraq. Such limited drilling as was necessary to ensure a balanced annual offtake up to 500,000 t/y was carried out, and by 1952 a score of wells had been completed into the productive Kalhur limestone, 3,000 feet below the surface, though no more than three, or sometimes one only, were in operation at one time. The attempt to find marketable oil at Chiah Surkh, scene of the Anglo-Persian's earliest efforts, was repeated in 1950-1 and the years following. The 'Iraqi workers at Naftkhana lived in Company-built quarters or in the neighbouring villages: clubs and canteens were provided, necessary domestic supplies ensured, medical services excellent. Labour was not organized in Unions, but procedures of joint consultation with the management ensured healthy and co-operative relations. Royalty payments to the 'Iraq Government from 1926 to the end of 1951

---

[1] This was the first occasion on which pipe of this diameter became available from British (or sterling) mills.

(when such payments ceased under the new form of agreement) amounted to £1,900,000.

As long as supplies of products from Abadan were available for southern 'Iraq, until the summer of 1951, crude production at Naftkhana and refining at Alwand (which celebrated its twenty-fifth anniversary in 1952) did not exceed 375,000 t/y: in 1951 the total reached 437,000 and in 1952 was 492,000 tons. Products from Alwand passed as ever through bulk storage at Khanaqin railway station, and in part through the tin-factory there, and were thereafter distributed throughout 'Iraq by the Rafidain Company. There was no export from 'Iraq. Neither aviation spirit nor lubricating oil was manufactured.

The important changes which affected the work and status of these companies as the result of an agreement with the 'Iraq Government signed on Christmas Day 1951 will be described on a later page (p. 193).

### VII. COMPANIES AND GOVERNMENT

As in field operations so in oil-diplomacy in 'Iraq, the war afforded a period of relative tranquillity; but the complaints and demands which 'Iraqi publicists and their Government had formulated before the war were certain to reappear in the earliest days of peace, with the return of normal political life.

The first of these issues concerned the receipts due to the Treasury from the four companies. Government had long requested clarification of the royalty-revision formulae provided in the concessions and was unlikely to await patiently the end of the twenty-year period for which a royalty of '4s. gold' per ton was prescribed. Nor had the 'gold question' itself ever been settled; and the sums at stake in the controversy were all the greater since the war-time price of gold in Middle Eastern bazaars had far exceeded—had doubled or trebled—the 'Bank of England price', upon which the Companies based their calculations: if gold were to mean the sterling equivalent of gold sovereigns, according to the Baghdad money-changers' tariff, then the Company's outstanding debt was formidable.[1] Next, the question of 'Iraqi shareholding had not been forgotten; the concessions provided that, in the event of a public issue of the Company's shares, 'Iraqis should

---

[1] The gold conversion rate was controversial for the I.P.C. Concession only; in the M.P.C. and B.P.C. Concessions it had been precisely defined.

be given the preferential opportunity to acquire 20 per cent. of such issue, and the Government demanded this measure of participation for itself or for its public, even though no public issue of shares had in fact ever occurred.

Further points raised by 'Iraqi Ministers were those of increasing the output of 'Iraq oil to a higher minimum rate and the more rapid substitution of 'Iraqis in the higher positions in the industry. Negotiations on these matters, which were pressed by 'Iraqis for both economic and political reasons, occupied much of the attention of both parties between 1947 and 1952, during which 'Iraqi Ministers and Company spokesmen exchanged visits repeatedly between Baghdad and London, while awaiting the outcome of the simultaneous and not dissimilar negotiations between the Persian Government and the Anglo-Iranian. The companies of the I.P.C. Group sought, but Government rejected, 'pooling' of the obligations of all three companies: and 'Iraqi negotiators had, as ever, the delicate task of reconciling, if they could, what was industrially reasonable with what was politically acceptable. Not until August 1950 was agreement reached on an increase of the basic royalty-rate from 4s. to 6s.: an evidently provisional solution which had touched neither the 'pooling' question nor that of the gold-rate. Payment at the new rate of royalty began as from 1 January 1950 in anticipation of parliamentary sanction, and was expected to yield a royalty income of nearly £6 million in 1950 and more than three times that sum on completion of the Banias pipeline.

The gold question, however, was one of too great a sensitivity in 'Iraqi politics for such solution, nor was this diminished by the second British devaluation of sterling in September 1949.[1] The natural recourse to the arbitration procedure indicated in the concession was unwelcome to the 'Iraqis, who requested the Company, instead, to let the case be tried in a British court. A remarkable assembly of leading counsel on both sides prepared in mid-1951 to dispute the case; but by the date of the first hearing Government–Company conversations on other and connected matters had proceeded so far that the case was at the last moment withdrawn for settlement out of court.

These conversations had been stimulated by a new element in the case; that of the announcement of the new Aramco-Sa'udi basis

[1] To a level of 248 shillings per fine ounce of gold, or 58 shillings per sovereign.

of payments (p. 210), which appeared to offer (at least in years of prosperity) both a more generous formula than anything yet proposed in 'Iraq and also one likely to be intelligible and, perhaps, acceptable in Baghdad. The Company, who would on this basis be at least free of future 'gold' complications, agreed at once to negotiation on the basis of one of many possible 'half-and-half' formulas; but, since the national fiscal systems of its different constituent groups were not identical, alternative means to attain a result acceptable to each group and to 'Iraq were various and intricate, and long negotiations between groups and their lawyers were required before agreement was so near as to justify withdrawal of the imminent gold case. It was reached, subject to detailed re-drafting and to parliamentary approval in Baghdad, on 13 August 1951, to be effective from 1 January of that year. Although rejected by a section of 'Iraqi politicians, partly through misunderstanding and partly by conviction, and largely or chiefly through political animosity against the Prime Minister and 'the foreigners', the Agreement was signed in its final form on 3 February 1952 and, in spite of an abortive 'general strike' called by Opposition politicians, was ratified by Parliament late in that month.

It covered many important issues, which had long been the subject of disagreement. The Government was now assured that the production of 'Iraqi oil would, subject to *force majeure*, be maintained at the high level already made possible by new pipeline construction and oilfield development; the M.P.C. and I.P.C. together were to produce 22 million t/y from 1954 onwards and the B.P.C. to raise its production from 2 million to 8 million t/y as from the end of 1955. The income of the State from its oil was, however low a level future profits might reach, never to be less than 25 per cent. of the seaboard value of oil exported by the I.P.C. and M.P.C. and 33 per cent. of that of B.P.C., with due regard to market price fluctuations. The equal division of operating profits, *before* deduction of foreign taxes, was accepted; and the Government was allowed to take in kind, as part of its total half-share, one-eighth of all the oil produced for export and either to re-sell this to the Company or to offer it on the open market. The difference between these receipts and the whole Government share would be provided by a varying level of income tax. The Treasury could, under this Agreement, look to receive not less

than £30 million in both 1953 and 1954 and not less than £50
million in 1955 and thereafter; in fact, greater sums than these
could be hoped for. In the event of such *force majeure* as would
preclude oil production, the Companies would pay a minimum
sum of £5 million annually for two years. Crude oil for the 'Iraq
Government refinery was to be supplied at Baiji at the nominal
price of 5s. per ton. 'Iraqi representation on the companies'
boards was to be increased by a second director. The existing
Company policy and efforts towards the replacement of foreign
employees in responsible posts by 'Iraqis were confirmed and
would be intensified; 150 'Iraqis would be maintained by the
Company while studying at universities in the United Kingdom,
and technical education at Kirkuk would be further developed.

Government–Company relations were, after the passage of this
agreement into law, duly regulated by it, the administrative and
educational arrangements carried out, the payments made. The
rate of the latter, whether considered as shillings per ton of oil or
as total sums payable per year, would, of course, thereafter depend
on the 'posted prices' for 'Iraqi crude at Banias, Tripoli, and Fao
—prices which neither the Company nor the Government could
control. The Treasury's receipts from the three Companies
amounted in 1951 to £15 million and for 1952 to £34 million. The
'Iraqi Minister of Economics in April 1952 advertised the sale
(preferably for hard currencies) of its 12½ per cent. share in kind of
the Company's 1953 production: this was announced as amounting
to 2,650,000 tons of Kirkuk oil, 162,500 of 'Ain Zala, and 350,000
of Zubair. The corresponding figures in his similar announcement in April 1953, referring to 1954 production, were 2,850,000,
162,500, and 400,000 tons.

The 'gold case', which it had been hoped—and as indeed it
was in July 1951 arranged—to solve as part of the main settlement,
was, in fact, settled instead as a separate issue in 1952.

But the Government of 'Iraq had still other cares than these. It
had to deal also with two matters close to the daily life of the nation:
first, the status of the twin Companies—Khanaqin and Rafidain—
producing, refining, and selling oil products in its own country:
and, secondly, its long-standing project of erecting and operating a
refinery of its own.

The latter had been designed before the war on the assumption
of location at Baiji, a capacity of 350,000 t/y, and a cost of £1½

million. Its realization, on a greater scale, after the war was delayed by the Government's grave financial shortages in the years 1945-9; but after an 'Iraqi expert had visited the United States in the latter year and consulted possible suppliers, the Minister of Economics was charged in 1951 with the carrying out of the enterprise at a cost now assessed at £4-£5 million, of which the National Bank of 'Iraq would lend half. An American firm was accepted as contractor for the erection of a plant of 24,000 b/d capacity, or 1,250,000 t/y, at a cost, inclusive of all pipelines and connected works, of £8 million. The refinery, ample in scale for 'Iraq's needs for some years to come, was to be situated, after all, not at Baiji but at Daura, a left-bank suburb downstream of Baghdad. A 135-mile 12-inch pipeline would bring crude from I.P.C. supplies at K2 station. Completion was expected in 1954-5.

But the expectation of this project did not satisfy immediate 'Iraqi aspirations, and there were few to whom a State enterprise, in place of a foreign company, as manufacturer and distributor at home of 'Iraqi oil products did not appeal. Simultaneously, therefore, with the I.P.C. negotiations, a new *modus vivendi* was being sought between the Government and the local Anglo-Iranian subsidiaries, the K.O.C. and R.O.C. It was reached in the Agreement of Christmas Day 1951. The Government was to buy the Alwand refinery from the Khanaqin Company at a valuation, retaining temporarily the Company's staff and organization as a government agency. Crude oil for the refinery would continue to be supplied by the K.O.C. from Naftkhana, where the Company's rights of production would remain valid. This crude production, when no longer needed for local refining—that is, after the opening of the Daura refinery in 1955—would be available for export, and the profits from such export would be divided on a basis similar to that applicable to the I.P.C.; if no export had occurred before 1959, the K.O.C. rights would lapse. The Daura refinery would be operated by the Khanaqin Oil Company for a fixed fee, pending availability of 'Iraqi personnel, for a period not to exceed ten years. The import of lubricating oils and aviation spirit from abroad would remain necessary, as in the past. All functions of distribution, previously carried out by the Rafidain, were to belong forthwith to the State, which would acquire, by purchase, that Company's plant, premises, and equipment. The price payable for these, with the Alwand refinery and all its properties and attachments, was fixed at £1,300,000.

These provisions took effect in July 1952, when the necessary legislation was passed. A five-member Refineries Board was set up to administer the refineries, storage, distribution, and prices. The Board proceeded to review country-wide distribution arrangements, and showed a tendency to take these from private into State or municipal hands. To meet the serious shortages which resulted in southern 'Iraq from the sudden cessation of supplies from Abadan, output of the Alwand refinery was increased to its maximum capacity (some 450,000 t/y) and help was invoked from the I.P.C. stabilization and topping-plants at Kirkuk, from which products were delivered by pipeline to the R.O.C. at K2 station. At the same time a small refinery of 150,000–200,000 t/y capacity was in 1952 erected with all speed by the K.O.C. on behalf of the Government, from improvised and hastily assembled materials, at Muftiya on the Shatt al-'Arab outside Basra. It came into production in September 1952 and provided valuable relief.

Two other projects would, if they materialized, claim Government intervention. One was the construction of a chemical factory near the Kirkuk oilfield for the production of fertilizers, sulphur, carbon black, and other products, a scheme recommended by the International Bank's mission of experts which visited 'Iraq in 1950. The other, far remoter and indeed highly imaginative, was the suggestion for a natural-gas pipeline, of large dimensions and some 2,500 miles in length, to take its throughput from Baba Gurgur by way of Turkey and the Balkans to supply power and light to the cities of western Europe.

### VIII. UNCERTAIN PROSPECT

Mid-century 'Iraq was an oil country of the first magnitude, ranking sixth among oil-producing territories. It had reached that position after twenty-five years of 'Iraq Petroleum's field operations, which followed a protracted period of evolution into an international company of unusual type and the reconciliation of diverse interests. The Company's development had itself been gravely interrupted by the Second War, by the adverse conditions —adverse to all non-dollar enterprises—which followed it, and by the loss, which proved permanent, of half its total export facilities in 1948; nevertheless, it had overcome the formidable difficulties of its pioneering days and had set an admirable example of skilful and economic oil development, as well as of political and social goodwill. 'Iraq itself by 1952 was, except in certain substances, self-sufficient in refined petroleum products, with a current internal demand of 700,000 t/y and the certainty of greatly increased future needs; and it was an exporter of crude oil at a rate already of 20 million t/y,[1] soon to be 30 million or more. For many years, perhaps for a century, its vast and accessible reserves would inspire full confidence that output need be limited only by market demands, by its means of export across neighbours' territories, and by the security given to the operators.

If its contribution to the world's oil wealth was so considerable, 'Iraq's own economic and, therefore, political importance must be correspondingly enhanced: it must inevitably occupy, without regard to its agricultural or other resources, an important and delicate place in world affairs and, with this, feel all the resulting stresses and anxieties. Not least in the field of strategy the country's position, as the time-honoured land-bridge between the continents and as the nearest of the Arab States to the Russian frontier, was the more significant through its abundant possession of petroleum.

Within the country, the direct employment by the Companies of 'Iraqi staff and labour ranging between 10,000 and 20,000 men, was, if locally a dominant factor, nationally less significant: its interest lay rather in the superiority of the conditions of employment given by the Companies over those provided by any or almost any other employer. A wider circle was affected by the diffused addition to purchasing power, the circulation of imported funds—some £6–£8 million a year—by the Companies' local expenditure, and, less visibly, by the force of example in standards of living and housing, the diffusion of higher skills, the creation of new tastes and demands, the contribution, in a word, to the Westernization and industrialization of society. That such a contribution to national life and culture would extend its effects far beyond the oil industry: that it was not less full of dangers than of advantages: that it would hasten breaches with the traditional and the familiar, with doubtfully foreseeable results: these were as certain in 'Iraq as elsewhere.

[1] In 1951, output was 7·99 million tons from I.P.C., 121 thousand from B.P.C., 5·5 thousand from M.P.C., 437 thousand from K.O.C.: total, 8·5 million. Corresponding figures for 1952 were: I.P.C. 15·55 million, B.P.C., 2·23 million, M.P.C. 270 thousand, K.O.C. 492 thousand: total for 'Iraq, 18·5 million.

In the field of progressive state activity 'Iraq must for many years count, it seemed, almost wholly on its oil revenues. With unlimited scope for development in its social services, its agriculture, irrigation, and its communications, the need for more copious funds had been acute for a full generation of narrow budgets and irksome restrictions. Oil revenues for the years 1946–9, though normally reserved for capital works, had not exceeded £2·7, 2·7, 2·14, and 3·12 million, sums useful (indeed indispensable) to the 'Iraq Treasury but inadequate even for urgent needs. But with the advent of greatly increased receipts from petroleum—£7 million in 1950, £15 million in 1951, £34 million in 1952, and, perhaps, £50 million or more in 1953—adequate funds could flow at last to the account of the Development Board, a statutory non-political body set up in 1950, which was entitled by law to 70 per cent. of oil receipts. Unless tragic accident or error were to prevent the production of oil or the revenues were to be diverted to other purposes (such as current administration, or army expenditure), there was good reason to hope that within a generation more and better schools and hospitals, planned townships and healthier villages, better houses and clothes and food, broader cornfields and secure irrigation, which the oil revenues would enable the Government to bring into existence, would, wisely used, produce immense benefit to, or would indeed transform, the 'Iraq nation. All its hopes of progress depended on the uninterrupted continuance of oil production.

This was realized by many 'Iraqis, and the more responsible confessed to viewing the Companies' efforts and successes with approval; but the comparative reticence of these suggested, as did much else in 'Iraqi public life, the chief danger that confronted the Companies. Enough has been said elsewhere to indicate the essential difficulty of the Government–Company relationship when the latter is foreign, Western, and non-Muslim: when the local Government feels, with resentment, that it has too little voice in the conduct of the greatest enterprise in its country: when emotional nationalistic politics can silence all industrial considerations: when many of the politicians who aspire to power are suspicious of, or frankly hostile to, the Companies: and when, as in 'Iraq, the general public knows little even of the basic requirements —financial, technical, commercial, or international—of the industry which is the mainstay of their economy. It followed that the

Companies in 'Iraq, a fair target for nationalist dislike, were habitually accused of self-interested slowness in development, of injustice to the Government in every controversial matter (such as the 'gold case'), of ill-treatment of their workers, of favouring minority communities, and of refusing higher appointments to 'Iraqis.

Though these charges, baseless or absurd or both, were not made by the more stable elements in public life, yet in such an atmosphere, in a society as unstable as the 'Iraqi, no observer could be sure how long the Companies, even on the now approved profit-sharing basis, would be allowed to continue their work in tolerable conditions. Young 'Iraqis, who tomorrow, if not today, would claim political leadership, were already heard to express fervid admiration of Dr. Musaddiq and to clamour for immediate nationalization of the oil industry, with little heed of its technical and material needs or of the necessity to transport the oil across other countries (which they could not nationalize), or of tanker fleets, distribution systems, or markets. Others would for a time reluctantly allow the Companies some form of existence, but one restricted or burdened to the point ultimately of bare ability to operate—and perhaps inability to continue to capitalize the industry. Few, save the group of responsible statesmen denounced by the young intelligentsia as anti-national, anti-progressive obstructionists and the more level-headed citizens, admitted the real services of the Companies and would have them supported as the authorized providers of national wealth.

How long, in spite of present appearances, which indeed were not easy to assess, the forces of stability and commercial morality and the clearly recognizable national interest would prevail, could not in mid-summer of 1953 be forecast. The gap in outlook between foreign industrial company and local nationalistic politician seemed hard to bridge; the latter was unlikely to change his standards of values, his methods, or his antipathies; the former, with the best of intentions, could do little more than to show all reasonable generosity in policy and in service, to staff the enterprise with 'Iraqi executives to the maximum that their capacity would permit, to keep sympathetic contact with the Government and the public, to adopt such local organization or nomenclature as was acceptable, and to maintain a competent information service for the enlightenment of the public; it could not change its essential foreignness or its Western respect for efficiency or its duty to shareholders.

## CHAPTER XII

# ARABIA, 1946–53: THE ALL-AMERICAN COMPANIES

## 1. THE PENINSULA, 1946–53

DEVELOPMENT in Arabia in the years 1946–53 could proceed without hindrance at the great speed and scale indicated by world demand and made possible by the abundant facilities for production of which the installation had already begun in 1945. As 1946 opened, one medium-scale field, that of Bahrain, was in full production and served by a large refinery; another, that of Dhahran on the mainland, had already an important output and vast prospects; three others in the same province had been discovered and a refinery of substantial capacity brought into being; at Kuwait and Qatar oilfields had been discovered but had not yet come into production. Arabian output did not at this stage exceed a rate of 6 million t/y with a refining capacity of 5–5·5 million. The position seven years later was one of four, instead of two producing territories, among which Sa'udi Arabia and Kuwait had reached a position of world eminence, while Qatar was destined to reach a high and Bahrain to retain a respectable place; one small and two very large refineries were in operation and another (at Aden) was planned and begun. To these striking achievements was due the immensely important position achieved by the Arabian territories in world economics as this period ends.

No finality had been reached, however, in a group of questions closely affecting the Arab States and their potential wealth: those, namely, of the land frontiers, which Arabian nomadism and age-long, mapless vagueness had left unsettled because, until the possession of mere desert surfaces could mean the right to buried millions, they were devoid of interest. Thus, the open western region of Oman, and in particular the Buraimi group of oases, was in 1952, for the first time in the present century, claimed and forcibly occupied by King ibn Sa'ud; the Sultan of Muscat's control over his inland mountains and his southern coast-lands grew no stronger; stretches of the Trucial Coast hinterland, and indeed that coast itself for a long stretch east of Qatar, were claimed also by the Sa'udi Kingdom, and the Qatar peninsula itself was entered at times by Sa'udi parties. No recognized boundaries *inter se* existed between the Trucial shaikhs or between them and Oman. A peaceful settlement of all these questions of topography and allegiance seemed a condition both of satisfactory future oil operation and of general security in south-eastern Arabia.

A different and more interesting problem was presented by the intrusion into the Arabian scene of the 'Continental Shelf' conception: that is, the claim, first advanced by the United States in 1945, that riparian states should exercise authority (including that over underlying oil deposits) over the inlying or 'continental' area of the ocean bed off their coasts. The novelty of the legal conception [1] does not here concern us; but authority over their 'Continental Shelf' was, in fact, claimed after 1945 by various governments to various seaward limits, and was, at the suggestion of the British Foreign Office, asserted by proclamation by the Persian Gulf rulers in 1949. The 'Continental Shelf' area of each of these would extend, it was assumed, outward from their coasts in the shallow Gulf waters (in much of which drilling would be practicable) to a median line between the Persian and Arabian shores. This action, questioned by none, had the effect of placing considerable new areas of 'submerged land' at the disposal of the rulers. The reaction of the oil companies was two-fold: the holders of concessional rights on the mainland, which included 'territorial waters and islands' or even 'the whole extent of the ruler's dominions', claimed the new territory as already theirs by the comprehensiveness of the original grant; while companies anxious to secure rights over unencumbered territory took the opposite view, with the cordial agreement of rulers convinced that they had something new to sell. In Qatar, where in 1949 the Shaikh granted a new and separate (but undelimited) concession for his 'Continental Shelf' lands to the Superior Oil Company,[2] his right to do so was challenged by the existing mainland concessionaire, Petroleum Development (Qatar); but he won his case as a result of arbitration proceedings conducted in Doha in

---

[1] Novel, because the sea and sea-bed beyond territorial-water limits (however defined) have been hitherto considered either as owned equally by all or as incapable of being owned.

[2] Associated with the Central Mining Corporation of London; joint operation in the Gulf was in the name of the International Marine Oil Company, formed *ad hoc* and registered in Canada.

January 1950 (with a force of eminent counsel from London ranged on both sides) and made good his grant to Superior. A similar concession for 'submerged lands' given by the Shaikh of Abu Dhabi, similarly disputed by Petroleum Development (Trucial Coast), led again to arbitration, which was held this time in Paris in July 1951. Its result reinforced the Qatar decision, which limited the mainland concession to lands under the authority of the ruler at the time of the first grant; and this ruling was likely, thereafter, to be treated for practical purposes as a precedent and to imply that the 'Continental Shelf' accretion could be everywhere considered as eligible for new concessions. Aramco obtained for itself the Sa'udi 'shelf' of al-Hasa, at the cost of surrendering their rights (acquired in 1939) in the Neutral Zone; the Shaikh of Kuwait and the Kuwait Oil Company arranged a similar issue between them in 1952 upon lines which were understood to include the delimitation of the sea areas to be treated as inside or outside the 1934 Concession; and the Bahrain waters and sea-bed had been allotted already by the Bapco Supplementary Agreement of 1940. In spite, therefore, of the rigours and embarrassments of sea-drilling, the future might well hold the development of submarine oil reserves in the Persian Gulf.

The political structure of Arabia changed little in these years. A murder and a revolution in the Yemen substituted one Imam for another. The balance of power between the rival Oman rulers continued. Minor changes occurred among the Trucial shaikhs. The aged Shaikh 'Abdullah of Qatar abdicated in favour of his son, Shaikh 'Ali. 'Iraqi claims to Kuwait, as having been a nominal appendage of Basra vilayet before 1914, were still heard but were not pressed. Signs of modernization in transport, in equipment, and, to some extent, in governmental procedure [1] were visible throughout the Arabian peninsula; new conceptions were gaining ground in considerable though restricted circles, the rigidity of ancient habits relaxing, accepted loyalties becoming liable to question, the outside world intruding. Concentrations of industrial labour, frequented by Arab skilled workers from other and less primitive countries, and equipped to receive by wireless the news and views of Russian, Egyptian, and European trans-

---

[1] For example, the Sa'udi Arabian Monetary Agency, with local directors and an American chairman, was set up at Jidda in 1952, and was entrusted with budgetary and currency functions.

mitting stations, could be breeding-grounds of strange and possibly subversive ideas wholly remote from the Arabia of yesterday. The United States Army Air Force base at Dhahran, completed with the agreement of the King in 1946, was maintained in operation throughout the period.

## II. PROGRESS OF ARAMCO

The strength of the position from which Aramco could view the future as 1946 opened has already been suggested; but since the need both for heavy expenditure and for widespread markets must evidently confront it, it was natural that, in the early months of peace, the Caltex Group should welcome approaches from quarters well able to supply these. By the end of 1946 agreement in principle had been reached, and in 1947 was fully elaborated and signed, with the New Jersey and Socony-Vacuum Companies. The former of these was to acquire 30 per cent. and the latter 10 per cent. of the shares of Aramco and simultaneously of those of the Trans-Arabian Pipeline (or Tapline), which had been registered in 1945, with equal California and Texas participation, to build from the Aramco oilfields to the Mediterranean the pipeline proposed (but rejected) as a United States Government enterprise in 1944. The 1947 Agreement, which promised to afford a co-ordinated supply of petroleum and its products to Asiatic and European markets,[1] could not, however, become effective as long as the restrictions on New Jersey and Socony freedom of action (by virtue of the Red Line Agreement) were still asserted by their I.P.C. partners; and, until late in 1948, their new partnership with Caltex took effect not by shareholding but by their guarantee of important bank-loans. These, exceeding $100 million to Aramco and $125 million to Tapline, were accompanied by detailed provisions for the New Jersey and Socony participation, both immediate and ultimate, in the Caltex projects; and the arrangements assumed their final form when, on resolution of the Red Line problem (p. 175), the two I.P.C. constituents could assume their intended shareholding. The ownership of Aramco and Tapline was thus, from December 1948, 30 per cent. in the hands of each

---

[1] It was in this connection that the Texas Company in January 1947 sold its European marketing outlets to the California-Texas Company; after which, the latter built refineries in Holland, Spain, and France and could supply them with Aramco crude.

of the Standard of California, the Texas Company, and the Standard (New Jersey), and 10 per cent. in those of Socony-Vacuum.

The area of the Aramco Concession underwent changes during these years. In 1947 its preferential right over lands west of the 46th meridian was surrendered; in 1948 those in the Kuwait· Neutral Zone were given up; and in 1949 some 33,000 square miles in the far south-west of the concession were handed back to ibn Sa'ud's Government.

But the vast spaces still at Aramco's disposal were not suffered to remain unvisited. The annual campaign of exploration, with its fleets of specialized vehicles, its self-sufficient teams of geologists, geophysicists, and structure-drillers, its escorts and attendant aircraft, its lavish and meticulous supply arrangements, visited, surveyed, assessed, and tested large and remote areas of Central Arabia, including much of the Ruba'al-Khali; and, apart from oil, accomplished a great work of geographical research and cartography. A later page (p. 296) will speak of the deep test well drilled in the Ruba'al-Khali in 1954–5.

These researches were richly rewarded. The wide, flattish, dome-like structures of Sa'udi Arabia, concealed from the eye and revealed only by structure-drilling or geophysics or both, came one by one to light, each with its huge reservoir of oil stored in the porous limestone. That of Dhahran had, by 1946, been in production for eight years; abu Hadriya, with its great depth and comparative remoteness, was not at present operating; Abqaiq, largest of these fields, stood ready for immediate production as the war ended, with a 12–14-inch pipeline to Dhahran completed in 1946, to be followed by a 14-inch the following year; the Qatif field was in process of equipment and further drilling. The first of major post-war discoveries was made in June 1948, that of the 'Ain Dar field, twenty-five miles south-west from Abqaiq. Production here was from the same element in the 'Arab Zone' as at Abqaiq, at depths from 6,500 to 7,250 feet, and the reservoir revealed itself as of high importance. It was followed six months later by two more successes, each one again in the productive 'Arab Zone' of the Jurassic limestone. One was at Fadhili, seventy miles north-west of Dhahran, where oil was found at the great depth of 10,100 feet; the other, at which the oil was heavier (30 degrees A.P.I.) but the 'Arab Zone' less deeply covered, was at

Haradh, 160 miles south-west of Dhahran. Meanwhile, oil dis-covered at Buqqa north of Abqaiq in 1947, and at first believed to represent a separate reservoir, was later proved to belong integrally to the Abqaiq structure. Each of the other structures, after dis-covery, was explored by further drilling and its proportions and characteristics were rapidly established.

Abqaiq was an obvious choice for early and intensive develop-ment, and sixty-two producing wells had been completed by the end of 1952. 'Ain Dar, scarcely inferior, had by the same date forty-four completed wells, Qatif ten, Dhahran thirty, Haradh (not yet in production) six; Fadhili and abu Hadriya had been left for later times. During most of the period Aramco was operating eight or more drilling-rigs, with the intention of expedit-ing production, for which—save for a brief recession in 1949-50—the world's markets were calling and which the Persian catastrophe rendered the more needful. In the spring of 1951, two years after the Haradh and Fadhili discoveries, another field was re-vealed by the drill at 'Uthmaniya, forty miles south of 'Ain Dar and directly west of the city of Hofuf; the oil was found in the now familiar limestone horizon at a depth of 7,000 feet and the field appeared to warrant an immediate campaign of further drilling. A month later, in the extreme north near the Neutral Zone border, the existence of a field below the waters of the Gulf itself, three miles from shore, was revealed by seismic exploration, followed by drilling through 20 feet of sea water. In this field, known as Safaniya, the oil reservoir was, unlike all others in Sa'udi Arabia, formed in sand instead of in limestone, and the oil was notably heavier than elsewhere.[1] Six further wells were drilled.

Late in 1952 Aramco announced that the 'Ain Dar and 'Uth-maniya were proved to form part of a single field, which included also a recent discovery at Shedgum, north-east of 'Uthmaniya. Seven wells had been completed at Shedgum by April 1953. The combined field, known henceforth as Ghawar, must take its place with Abqaiq, Burgan, Kirkuk, and Haft Kel as one of the dozen, or half-dozen, greatest fields in the world, and provided one-third of total Aramco output.

Of all these fields, astonishing in richness, concentrated in a

[1] The A.P.I. gravity-rating of the Sa'udi oil is: Dammam (Dhahran) 35, abu Hadriya 36, Abqaiq 38, Qatif 35, 'Ain Dar 35, Haradh 34, Fadhili 38, 'Uth-maniya 34, Safaniya 27.

single territory, and containing proved reserves perhaps not less than those of the United States, only four—Abqaiq, 'Ain Dar, Dammam, and Qatif in that order of output—were in production by the end of 1952, with 'Uthmaniya almost in readiness; [1] but the tale of discovery was still incomplete, and almost no limit appeared to future offtake, should market demand require it. Annual production in Sa'udi Arabia from 1945 to 1952 was 2·5, 8, 12, 19, 23, 26, 37, and 41 million tons. The latter figure made Aramco the greatest producing Company in the world, with the Kuwait Oil Company as its nearest rival.[2]

Producing wells [3] being valueless without full connected facilities for collecting, treating, storing, and transporting the oil, the period was one of intense activity in the provision of these. The task involved, undertaken simultaneously with exploration and drilling, included the construction of gathering and flow lines and pumps to serve them, and field tankage: the erection of gas-oil separation plant in every field, adequate in capacity to deal with its intended contribution: stabilization plants, in Abqaiq and Dammam fields and at Ras Tanura, for the removal of hydrogen sulphide: an

[1] 'Uthmaniya came into production in February 1953, giving 100,000 b/d from eight wells; a 30-inch pipeline brought the oil fifty-three miles to Abqaiq.

[2] The year in which Kuwaiti was to exceed Sa'udi production was in fact 1953, and this lead was not again to be lost; neither territory was, of course, producing quantities comparable with its full potential.

[3] Status of Aramco wells at the end of 1952 was

| Field | Producing wells | Shut-in or standing | Observation wells | Suspended |
|---|---|---|---|---|
| Abqaiq . . . | 56 | 7 | 3 | — |
| Ghawar | | | | |
| 'Ain Dar . . . | 41 | 5 | 2 | — |
| 'Uthmaniya . . . | — * | 19 | 2 | — |
| Shedgum . . . | — | 3 | — | — |
| Dammam . . . | 28 | 3 | — | — |
| Qatif . . . | 9 | — | 2 | 1 |
| Abu Hadriya . . . | — | 1 | — | 1 |
| Fadhili . . . | — | 1 | — | — |
| Haradh . . . | — | 6 | — | 1 |
| Safaniya . . . | — | 9 | 1 | — |
| 'Alat }<br>Jauf } . . .<br>Ma'qala } | Dry holes | | | |
| Total . . . | 134 | 54 | 10 | 3 |

* Produced in Feb. 1953.

important and costly project at the Abqaiq Field to allow for gas injection [1] into the structure for the maintenance of reservoir pressure: tankage at every stage for crude oil and for products en route for their next destination: and pipelines [2] to and from all Fields' installations, to the refinery at Ras Tanura, to Bahrain, to the crude loading-jetties, and to feed the great trans-desert tapline leading to the Mediterranean. A 'white products' line also was built to lead back from the refinery to the Dhahran bulk-storage plant and airport. The Dhahran–Bahrain half-submarine line was looped for increase in capacity in 1949 and duplicated in 1952. The construction of workshops, storesheds, yards, and industrial buildings of all kinds at Abqaiq, Dhahran, Ras Tanura, and other main locations was increased annually to attain the scale of considerable townships, in which water, sewerage, gas, and electric power systems were constructed and were constantly under extension. The Company's transport strength by 1952 exceeded 3,000 vehicles, with maintenance facilities adequate to this force. The marine fleet included some dozens of tugs, barges, and launches. Jetties at Ras Tanura, connected to the shore by long causeways, permitted the rapid loading of tankers with oil from the terminal tank-farm nearby. Communications were assured by ubiquitous telegraph and wireless installations, centred at Ras Tanura, Dhahran, and Abqaiq. Roads were greatly improved by the use of the asphalt which the Tanura plant produced from 1951 onwards. The air fleet operated by the Company was without equal in the annals of comparable industry.

The Tanura Refinery developed from the medium-scale plant of 50,000 b/d capacity, which began to operate in September 1945, to one of 150,000 b/d early in 1952, and this in turn was in process of being increased, late in that year, to a capacity of 200,000 or 210,000 b/d or some 10·5 million t/y. The variety and quality of its products had been extended and improved by the installation of

[1] The new plant, to cost $20 million, was designed for a capacity of 150 million cubic feet of gas a day.

[2] Such lines were, in order of construction: Dhahran–Tanura, 35 miles, 10-inch, 1939: Dhahran–Bahrain, 34 miles, 12-inch, 1945: Dhahran–Tanura (submarine), 23 miles, 12-inch, 1946: Abqaiq–Dhahran, 39 miles, 12–14-inch, 1946: Abqaiq–Dhahran, 40 miles, 14-inch, 1947: Abqaiq–Qatif, 45 miles, 30-inch, 1948: Qatif–Tanura, 24 miles, 20–22-inch, 1948: 'Ain Dar–Abqaiq, 28 miles, 22-inch, 1950: Qatif–Qaisuma, 270 miles, 30–31-inch, 1950: Abqaiq–Qatif, 45 miles, 29–22-inch, 1951: Qatif–Refinery, 18 miles, 12-inch, 1951: and 'Uthmaniya–Abqaiq, 45 miles, 30–31-inch, 1952.

thermal reforming, equipment for improved chemical treatment, and vacuum distillation. A catalytic polymerization plant was under erection in 1952, but neither lubricants nor aviation spirit were being manufactured. Quantities of crude treated were in 1946 nearly 4 million tons and thereafter yearly, to 1952 inclusive, amounted to 5·12, 6, 6·16, 5·1, 7·75 and 8·28 million tons, while annually increasing quantities of crude were piped or were ferried in barges and tankers to the Bapco refinery at Bahrain.

The refined products available for export from Ras Tanura were taken proportionally by each of the shareholding companies for the supply of their markets, primarily, though not exclusively, east of Suez; the shares of New Jersey and Socony were mainly consigned to their jointly-owned Standard Vacuum (p. 130). The crude exported from Ras Tanura was passed similarly by its owners to 'Stanvac' for the supply of its refineries in South Africa, India, Sumatra, and Australia, to refineries of the Caltex group east and west of Suez, and, by all the Aramco co-owners, by sale to non-affiliated companies in need of supplies.

### III. TAPLINE

The birth and infancy of the Trans-Arabian Pipeline project have been mentioned on an earlier page (p. 147). Once Arabian production was assured, the world's market insistent, and local security seemingly adequate, the 1,070-mile construction of such a line must evidently be justified by its potential service in reducing, by some 3,500 miles, the distance between the Aramco fields and Western Europe, by obviating the need to employ seventy to eighty tankers, by making less demand (as compared with that of tanker-construction) on the limited available stocks of steel, and by avoiding the payment of Suez Canal fees, amounting to some 18 cents per barrel or $15,000 to $30,000 per tanker-cargo. The cost of transport of oil by pipeline was assessed by Aramco economists and by Burt Hull, the veteran pipeline designer and constructor who became President of Tapline, at between one-third and one-half of the cost of tanker-transport.

The work, completed, must rank as among the greatest of all engineering achievements, by virtue of its formidable mass of material used, its organization and administration in adverse and extremely severe conditions, its solution of transport and supply problems, its innovations in method and design, the range of specialized equipment which it employed, and its cost. Its construction, moreover, coincided with disturbed political conditions and even with war itself in Palestine, due to the Arab–Jewish hostilities in 1948–9, which gravely delayed construction in the western sector: with a world-wide steel shortage so acute as to postpone by a year the arrival of steel materials and pipe from the United States: [1] and with revolutionary political events in Syria, where parliamentary ratification of the agreement for the necessary wayleaves was long withheld.

For the disadvantages of mid-Arabian climate and conditions there was no cure; difficulties of terrain—sand-dune country, featureless and waterless plain, hard or disintegrated limestone and lava-strewn desert—were overcome by the construction of roads (which became the public highways of Arabia) and by the use of specially designed vehicles in profusion. The problem of waterlessness was met by sea water distillation, by the drilling of fifty or more wells in mid-desert, and by transporting water from Tanura and from Jauf by convoys of lorries: the combined effect of which on the nomadic tribesmen and their migrations was immediate and profound. The problem of a supply of workers was solved by the recruitment, maintenance, and administration of a force of Sa'udi Arabs in numbers which at one period reached 15,000 and by helping these to acquire, as they did with great rapidity, skill in multifarious tasks under the supervision of, and side by side with, some 2,000 Americans. The unloading of materials, relatively easy on the coast of the Lebanon, was possible in Persian Gulf waters only by the construction of a deep-water wharf on an artificial island three miles seaward from Ras al-Misha'ab, 125 miles from any inhabited place and from potable water, and the joining of this to the mainland by an elevated cable-way—the 'sky hook'—along which pipe in ten-ton loads, to a total of 1,100 tons a day, could travel at a speed of twenty-five miles an hour. Materials from over 5,000 suppliers in the United States included 265,000 tons of steel pipe and 1,500 vehicles. The pipe, of 31- and 30-inch diameter, travelled 'nested' length within length, and was welded at Ras al-Misha'ab into three-pipe lengths before dispatch to the desert.

[1] The United States Office of International Trade refused for two successive quarters to grant export licences for steel pipe and limited the quantities licensed in other quarters.

Ras al-Misha'ab, where work began early in 1947, became the chief port and depot for the project and was for four years the scene of immense activity. From it radiated the transport, the workers, the supervisors, the materials, and supplies to accomplish the successive stages of the work—reconnaissance, road-making, water-finding, station-construction, and the stringing, welding, wrapping, and (in some areas but not all) burying of the pipe, and finally of testing it when completed. It served as a base for the pumping stations of Nariya (Nu'airiya), Qaisuma, Rafha, Badana, and Turaif, all of which lay in Sa'udi territory, spaced at intervals of 150–180 miles apart: stations at which, with their powerful pumping-plant and tankage, their secure water-supply, and their self-sufficiency in electric power and all normal services, communities of Americans and Sa'udis were to be installed (as they had been long since in the similar stations of the I.P.C. system, further north) to lead lives which, if remote, could be normal in their interests and occupations, as in their comforts and safety.

Shipments of pipe began to arrive at Ras al-Misha'ab in November 1947, when stringing and welding could begin; but work in the western sector, based on the Lebanon, could not be taken in hand until late in 1949. The last weld connecting the two sections was made in September 1950; the first oil reached Sidon in November and the first tanker was loaded on 2 December; the line had required fifteen days and almost 5 million barrels of oil to fill it, and a further 6 million barrels for storage in station and terminal tankage. The eastern one-third (or 315 miles) of the system, up to and including Qaisuma station, became by purchase the property of Aramco, with its two stations (in addition to the first, that of Abqaiq) took its place as part of that Company's gathering system as well as its westward trunkline; the western two-thirds (or 755 miles), with three stations, remained the property of Tapline, whose terminal works at Sidon will be mentioned elsewhere (p. 245). The cost of the completed work was assessed at $230 million. Its designed throughput with six stations was 15–15.5 million t/y, which could at any time be increased to 25 million by the construction of further stations. Tapline remained in uninterrupted operation from the end of 1950 onwards, a significant element in the economics of the western hemisphere, a contribution to its strategic potential—and a hostage to fortune.

## IV. ARAMCO, GOVERNMENT, AND PUBLIC

Aramco, operating under enlightened leadership in a territory which, with all its rigours and backwardness, was without the fervid politicians of the Fertile Crescent and Persia and enjoyed the only form of government suited to it, a patriarchal benevolent despotism, was, up to the time of writing, happy in its freedom from the troubles to which Anglo-Iranian succumbed and of which the I.P.C. had had sobering glimpses; and, at least for the time, it increased this advantage—which the passage of time, dynastic uncertainties, human frailties, and the development of politics of Middle Eastern type might well reduce—by the adoption of a policy of complacent liberality, of concession in preference to bargaining, in the face of successive and various government demands. This policy did not, indeed, save it at times from awkward and disturbing incidents with the local public and officialdom; [1] but it earned gratifying and no doubt sincere tributes from King ibn Sa'ud and his ministers. The Sa'udi Government, as long as it should wield unquestioned authority, and as long as it retained a form and spirit similar to those operative at the end of the mid-century, seemed in 1953 likely to accept Aramco 'partnership' as its authorized agency for oil-development for some years to come.

A controversy, reminiscent of those in 'Iraq and Syria, over the gold conversion-rate, as affecting dollar or sterling royalty payments, was solved after the war, not easily or soon, by a Company–Government agreement which equated '£1 gold' with $12; [2] but the vast success of the Aramco enterprise, the needs of the Sa'udi Government (and not least those of its ruling family), and the knowledge that royalty adjustments were under negotiation elsewhere, led in 1950 to Sa'udi pressure for an altogether higher scale of payments than those agreed in 1933. After talks lasting for some months and the Company's acceptance of the obligation to pay income tax (from which the 1933 and 1939 Agreements had specifically exempted it), an entirely new basis of agreement was

---

[1] The sudden prohibition on the import of all types of alcoholic drinks, even for the strictly controlled consumption by oil-company non-Muslim personnel, in Dec. 1952, was an example.

[2] The International Monetary Fund rate being $8.24, the $12 conversion had the effect of raising royalties from 22 to 34 cents a barrel. The royalty for 1950 was some $70 million, for 1951 royalty and taxation produced $140 million,

announced on 30 December 1950. The royalty remained at 4s. gold, to be calculated henceforth at official bank rates. Aramco's local requirements in Sa'udi riyals would in future be purchasable at that rate, in place of a highly disadvantageous premium rate as hitherto; and royalty payments would be made, not in gold or dollars, but in such currencies as the sale of products might have enabled the Company to earn. In return the Company would pay, in addition to royalty, an income tax calculated to bring Government's receipts up to one-half of the Company's operating profits after deduction of all exploration, development, and operational expenses, and depreciation and foreign taxes.

This half-and-half basis, though no stranger to Middle Eastern oil discussions,[1] was now agreed and published for the first time and was with little delay to become the next objective of every Middle Eastern oil-owning government; but while it greatly increased Sa'udi revenues,[2] it did not long satisfy their statesmen. Further demands were made in 1951 and in 1952 and led again to anxious negotiations. These dealt with the reckoning of the profit-share before, instead of after, United States taxation:[3] with the appointment of further Sa'udi directors to the Aramco board: with a more rapid surrender of unexploited territory: and with the demand that the Company should sell its oil to its constituent groups at world prices without discount, thus substantially increasing its divisible profits. The last of these questions and that of the relinquishment of territory were understood to be still under consideration in the mid-summer of 1953; on the rest, agreement was reached in June 1952. Two Sa'udi directors were to be appointed, and the Company's own headquarters, with its chairman and all chief executive officers, were to move, and in fact moved, from New York to Dhahran, thus setting an example which other Governments might or might not, in their turn, insist that their respective Companies should follow.

Such matters of high finance and policy apart, relations between the Company and the Government had covered by 1952 a wide

---

[1] A profit-sharing scheme on this basis had been examined by Anglo-Iranian and the Persian Government in 1948–9.

[2] The country's budget for 1952–3 included 570 million riyals (about £59 million) for direct oil revenues: the only other important item of revenue was 70 million riyals for customs, itself almost wholly due to oil expansion.

[3] The United States Treasury gives due credit to a tax payer who has paid income tax abroad: some other governments do not.

field of common endeavour. Not only had its royalty and tax payments made possible a vast extension of government services and armed forces—made possible, indeed, the very existence of Sa'udi Arabia as a state of the modern world—but Aramco experts had been able to assist in the planning or execution of many government works made possible by its new riches. Such were the piped water-supplies to towns, the new jetties and breakwaters at Jidda, the wireless network throughout the country, the construction of airports, mechanized irrigation projects wholly novel to Arabia, pilot schemes in modern farming (notably at al-Kharj), and successful water-drilling at a score of thirsty places. The Company had provided supplies of all petroleum products throughout the country, including bulk storage installations at principal centres. It had constructed on behalf the Government a 355-mile standard-gauge railway from Dammam by way of Abqaiq, Hofuf, and Haradh to the capital Riyadh, an arduous enterprise through difficult terrain which was begun in 1947 and finished late in 1951. It had completed important harbour works, including an eight-mile pier and causeway and fully equipped wharves at Dammam, the whole offering facilities for unloading, loading, and handling cargo unknown elsewhere in Arabia. These came into operation in 1950.

The Aramco labour force during these years varied in number, according to current construction programmes, from 16,000 to more than 20,000. The need for varied industrial skill and specialized experience, unknown to Sa'udi Arabs, prevented the local recruitment of more than three-fifths of this force, though all efforts were made, for every reason, to increase this proportion. The rest of the workers consisted of skilled Italians, who were recruited in Eritrea, first in 1945 and thereafter regularly: Indians and Pakistanis: and Arabs of Aden and the Sudan, and after 1948 also of Jordan and Palestine. Americans, in charge of all administration and technical and specialized ancillary operations, numbered from 2,500 to 3,500; their recruitment, accommodation, and administration, with wives and children not much less numerous, posed many problems. Indeed, the magnitude of the tasks involved in the creation, maintenance, and supply of a body of staff and labour on the scale of many thousands of men so diverse in race, habit, language, and character, from season to season and from year to year, in a far-off desert country lacking all resources useful to industry and almost all which could be of value for domestic purposes is not easy to exaggerate, even though the same or similar problems had been met before and solved in Persia and 'Iraq and were being solved in Kuwait.

Little need be said here of the carefully designed system of recruitment or day-by-day administration of the heterogeneous and fluctuating labour-force, of pay-rates and allowances, of discipline and awards, or of the yet heavier task of providing all with living quarters, food, water, light, and transport: or of the Company's meticulous instruction in safety measures, or its many 'welfare' activities. The desire to avoid an exclusively oil-town atmosphere, pervaded by the Company in all spheres of activity, and in general the wish to integrate the Company's social as well as industrial operations with the life of the country, led to two particular developments. One of these was the encouragement of Company-assisted house-building by workers themselves, the foundation by Sa'udi enterprise of satellite villages at suitable points, such as Nariya, 'Ain Dar, Thuqba, Ruhaima, and Abqaiq, and the development of new quarters at existing settlements—Khobar, Misha'ab, Dammam; a conception and programme which had, however, in 1952, still far to go and had as yet done little to solve a labour housing problem which Aramco were unwilling to meet by efforts such as those of Anglo-Iranian at Abadan, and which led to the formation of ugly 'shanty-towns' in the vicinity of their centres. The other development was the formation of a special department to promote industrial progress among the local public, not only by the allotment of contracts for the Company's works to Sa'udi business men, but also by the fostering, outside the Company, of such new-founded small businesses as those of electric power-provision, manufacture of cement-wares, ice plants, furniture making, machine shops, garages, and service stations. All these and suchlike enterprises depended on modern and reliable roads, and these it was the concern of the Company first to construct and then to keep free from the ever-invading enemy, sand.

Medical services were highly developed and comprehensive. Hospitals at Tanura, Damman, Abqaiq, and Misha'ab were fed by smaller clinics and dispensaries at many points: all specialized departments were represented, all installations the most modern and complete, and care was given to the families of workers and to thousands of the general public. The preventive organization directed against insanitary conditions, malaria, and fly-borne and water-borne diseases could not but affect favourably the safety of life and the standard of physique. The training of workers, and especially that of the Sa'udi majority of these, was carefully considered and developed. It covered general adult education, the three-month 'vestibule training' of new recruits, and the long and patient instruction—seven-eighths 'on the job', one-eighth in class—of established workers, whose skill and earning power were thus greatly improved. Beyond this lay the hope of scholarships, of higher training in the Advanced Trade Training unit, of study in the United States or the Lebanon, and ultimately of posts of high responsibility.

Whether the present and future life of an industrialized, modernized community in al-Hasa, with its back turned on the easy and primitive (but hungry and stagnant) ways of twelve years earlier, was or will be happier and fuller was not a certainty; industrialization has its own evils, too rapid social changes their danger; doors suddenly opened can admit moral disaster as well as physical blessing. But whatever the future might hold for the Company or for the Arabian public, it was fair to conclude that whatever goodwill and great resources and sympathetic intelligence could do to minimize these perils, to encourage the better and to diminish the more sinister elements in the new life, and to regard the Sa'udi people and their nation with friendly and respectful sympathy [1] was being done, or sincerely attempted, by Aramco. Meanwhile the Sa'udi Government, with revenues [2] thirty times larger than in 1940, gave priority in its expenditure to its armed forces, which were to be completely modernized and would cost 135 million riyals a year. Other principal heads of expenditure were: R. 55 million for the Hijaz Railway, R. 23 million for water improvements, R. 29 million for the new Ministry of Health, R. 28 million for mosques and facilities for pilgrims, R.13 million for education, R. 4 million for agriculture, R. 10 million for airports. It

---

[1] The Company's 'Foreign Service Training Centre', to teach American recruits something of the Arab and Islamic background, was started on Long Island in 1948 and moved to the Lebanon in 1951.

[2] Direct payments by Aramco to the Sa'udi Government are stated by the United Nations 'Review of Economic Conditions' to be: for 1940, $1.5 m.: for 1946, $13.3 m.: for 1948, $31.5 m.: for 1949, $66 m. (including the initial payment for the Neutral Zone by Pacific Western): for 1950, $112 m.: for 1951, $155 m.: and for 1952, $170 m.

was, however, characteristic of the still medieval and personal structure of the State, so ill-fitted and unaccustomed to the disposal of
great wealth, that over R. 150 million was absorbed by the town and
royal settlement of Riyadh, the capital. This allotment included
R. 36 million for the claims of the very large royal family and its
thousands of dependents, R. 66 million for the cost of the administration of the town, and R. 50 million for the payment of doles and
presents to tribes and irregulars. The tradition of lavish expenditure at the centre, the lack of any social conscience in many of the
chief direct recipients of the new wealth, and the dearth of trained
officials (partly corrected by recruitment from other Arab countries) were disturbing features of the time.

### V. NEUTRAL ZONE

The oil rights over the 2,000 uninhabited square miles of
Neutral Zone, squeezed between Sa'udi Arabia and Kuwait, had
long remained unallotted   Aramco, since acquiring its preferential
rights for ibn Sa'ud's half share of the Zone in 1933, had taken no
practical steps; the Shaikh of Kuwait, though more than once
approached (p. 112), had made no grant; and the organizational,
as well as the physical, difficulties which must confront any joint
concessionaire were an obvious deterrent.

Late in 1946, however, Shaikh Ahmad al-Subah of Kuwait
declared the lists open, and a number of British and American
companies—Gulf, Amerada (with Seaboard and Continental),
Superior, Sinclair, and Burmah and Shell interests—declared themselves candidates and sent representatives then or subsequently to
the spot. The I.P.C. inquired, hesitated, and withdrew. The
Shaikh proclaimed an auction, without fear or favour, to be his
method of award; and throughout 1947 interest in the unan-
nounced progress of this was sustained. In July of that year a new
group of American companies, all of whom lacked Middle Eastern
experience, had been formed as the American Independent Oil
Company,[1] or by abbreviation 'Aminoil', and, after a glance at
'Asir and the Yemen, had decided to apply for the Neutral Zone.
Their bid was successful; in June 1948 the Shaikh's half-rights
for a sixty-year term were bestowed on Aminoil.  In the agreement
finally approved, the ruler retained important rights of shareholding in producing and refining companies eventually to be formed,

---

[1] For the composition of this Company, see Appendix IV.

and an eighth share of locally-made profits. The royalty was fixed at $2.50 a ton (33 cents a barrel)—the highest, beyond compare, in the Middle East at the time. A payment on signature of $7·5 million and thereafter of $625,000 a year were due. These formidable terms, which the eventual right-holder from the Sa'udi side must necessarily match, made Aramco the more willing to abandon its agreed priority; and its surrender of all Neutral Zone pretensions, in return for rights over Sa'udi 'continental' waters, was announced in October 1948. The succession fell to the Pacific Western Oil Company [1] which, after negotiations, signed in January 1949 a sixty-year agreement with the Sa'udi Ministers at Jidda. The terms exceeded in their severity even those of Aminoil: Sa'udis were to have preference in subscribing up to 25 per cent. of publicly-issued shares, a refinery must be built, products (including aviation spirit) must be delivered without cost at Riyadh and Jidda; and meanwhile an initial payment of $9·5 million, an annual payment of $1 million, a royalty of 55 cents a barrel, a one-eighth share of production profits, and a quarter share of profits from refinery operation were due to the Sa'udi Government. All payments would be in dollars.

The two concessionaires lost no time in arranging a working organization—but not a joint company—for their enterprise, and engaged James MacPherson, an Aramco veteran, to direct their field operations, which began with the dispatch of a geophysical party into the territory to locate drillable structures. A 327-foot tank landing craft was acquired, converted, equipped, provisioned, and anchored off the Neutral coast, to act as base depot and floating camp; it arrived on site in the autumn of 1949. Drilling, so based, began in December at Wafra,[2] in the centre of the Zone, where a small drilling-camp was established; another, for the locally-improvised labour force, was formed near the base-ship's anchorage. Water for these and for all field parties was brought by tanker lorry from Kuwait.

The later career of the costly Neutral Zone Concession was a dramatic one. Drilling, well by well, continued through 1950, 1951, and 1952. Three wells were sited in the Wafra area, but were all

---

[1] See Appendix IV.
[2] Neither this name nor those of subsequent sites denote an inhabited place: the country was and is total steppe-desert, visited seasonally by a few nomadic parties. It is also waterless.

abandoned as dry holes at depths of 5,000–5,250 feet. The fourth well, at Fuwaris towards the western border, was taken equally in vain to 9,400 feet. The fifth well, sited at al-Hazani in the south of the Zone near the coast on evidence provided by seismic survey, was declared dry at 4,730 feet. This ill fortune, the more surprising in a tract immediately north and south of great oilfields, and granted under a concession for which unprecedented payments had been made, led now to a pause while further geophysical results were studied.

In spite, however, of persistent ill-success and of an expenditure already of not less than £10 to £12 million on concession dues and operations by the end of 1952, hope in the enterprise was not abandoned. Early in 1953 it was decided to drill two more wells, one at Wafra and one in the extreme south-west of the zone. The first of these, Wafra no. 4, was reported late in March 1953 to have found oil in the 'first Burgan sand' in volume of 2,500 b/d, and of 31 degrees A.P.I. gravity, at a depth of 3,800 feet. The importance of this strike, apparently considerable, would be established by further drilling and tests which would call for further heavy expenditure. The concession-holding companies were understood in May 1953 to be pressing on with further drilling and to be considering a pipeline to the coast and storage and other installations. The subsequent well no. 5 was completed in June 1953 as a small producer, leaving the potentiality of the field still uncertain though soon to be emphatically revealed.

A serious new contribution from the Neutral Zone to existing over-copious Middle Eastern production would have interesting and various effects. Such oil, it appeared, must make its way into markets against powerful established competition and would feel the handicap of its high royalty costs: must somewhere find refinery capacity and must, indeed, under the Pacific Western Agreement, itself construct a doubtless uneconomic refinery within the Zone: and must probably be imported into the United States against strong 'independent' pressure, if dollar-producing sales were to be forthcoming. At the same time, such a supply would bring a new and doubtless competitive element into the ownership and disposal of Middle Eastern oil, would increase the American commitment in Arabia, and would, for once, range forces of the 'independents' in the United States with those of much-decried Big Business.

## VI. BAPCO AND BAHRAIN

In the Bahrein [1] Petroleum Company (Bapco), owned by Caltex, and the oldest all-American enterprise in Arabia, no such changes as in Aramco were made in the Company's composition; it remained, with its Canadian registration, owned and controlled in equal halves as between the Texas Company and the Standard of California. The Company, under American direction and higher management,[2] was served in the field by predominantly British or British Empire supervisory personnel, with the objects both of conformity with British traditions in the Gulf and of reducing the 'dollar content' of Bapco oil. It maintained without difficulty excellent relations with the Shaikh and the public, and enjoyed the stable blessings of a well-governed island, to whose prosperity it was the outstanding, though not the only, contributor. Its payments to the Bahrain Treasury were until 1950 of the order of £400,000 a year, in 1950–1 of £1 million or more, and from the beginning of 1952 some £2·25 million. The rate of royalty was by agreement raised from Rs. 3 to Rs. 10 a ton in 1950, and, with effect from January 1952, a fluctuating income tax was imposed on the Company such as to realize the 'half-and-half' principle of profit-sharing already accepted in Sa'udi Arabia and elsewhere. At the same time payment was to be made, for the first time, in respect of Aramco oil entering Bahrain to be refined. Customs receipts of some £500,000 a year were the other chief state revenue. Of the oil revenues, one-third has traditionally been allotted to the Shaikh for his personal expenditure and for the fulfilment of his many obligations towards his family and entourage, one-third was for local expenditure, and one-third for investment. The direct payments by Bapco, expressed in dollars, were for 1946 $1·2 million, and for 1948–52 inclusive $1·4, 1·5, 3·3, 3·8, and 6·3 million.

These payments were additional to the many services which Bapco were able to render to the Bahrain community. Such were its support of medical institutions, missionary and governmental (apart from its own hospital for its Bahraini labour, at 'Awali), its

---

[1] The Company's name was changed from Bahrein to Bahrain in 1952.

[2] The leading figures in Bapco at Bahrain were in these years E. Skinner and R. M. Brown; in New York H. M. Herron and W. K. Pinckard were respectively President and Chairman.

willing help in the state's campaigns of preventive medicine and for better water supplies and improvement in agricultural methods, its precept and example in raising local housing standards from reed huts to permanent dwellings of modern type, its encouragement of education both general and technical, and its execution of public works on behalf of the state authorities.

For its own Bahraini or other non-European employees, who by great majority preferred to live in Manama, transport was provided morning and night and help given in the organization of their clubs and recreation. For these and all employees, clean and healthy working conditions, pay rates superior to prevailing levels, the best of health services, and a well-graduated system of vocational training were provided. Bahrainis employed ranged, according to work in progress, from 6,500 to 8,000, with Europeans and Americans in about one-tenth to one-eighth of these numbers.

In the exploration of the concession area, as extended in 1940, what needed still to be done was completed in 1946–52. Hawar Island and the outlying fringes and shoals of the archipelago were examined, submarine seismic work was carried out, possible extensions of the main Bahrain structure southward were investigated, and two deep test wells were drilled at 'Awali. One of these was abandoned at 11,085 feet and the other, which reached 11,080 feet, was kept as a gas well for gas-injection; they revealed no new possibilities below the existing 'fourth pay'.

Exploitation drilling was resumed in 1946 after a six-year pause, with a twelve-well programme. This was designed to improve the drainage pattern of the oilfield, to provide gas for re-injection and to replace wells which had in the course of time been captured by gas or water; substantially greater total production could not be expected. These wells, completed early in 1948, made a total of sixty-eight producers and four observation wells. They were in turn increased in 1951–2 by a further ten, of which eight were small or medium-scale producers mainly in the 'southern extension'. By the end of 1952 over one hundred wells in all had been completed, of which seventy-six were capable of producing by flow. The output of the Bahrain field, under careful and conservative control, amounted to 1·1 million tons in 1946, 1·25 million in 1947 and in the years following 1·5 million annually.

The Bapco refinery, on the other hand, which ended the war with a throughput of 65,000 b/d, was destined for great extension to take advantage of the availability of Sa'udi crude to supply it. Its growth after the war was continuous. The erection of an asphalt plant was completed in 1948 and attained an output of 50,000 t/y; in 1949 a 7,000 b/d re-forming unit was added; the drum factory and filling plant at Sitra were enlarged; more refinery tankage was provided: and the installation of new distillation units brought the output of oil products—except aviation spirit and lubricants, which were not made—to a rate of more than 100,000 b/d by mid-1947 and, with another unit added in 1949–51, to 155,000 b/d in the latter year. Modifications to the catalytic cracker and the addition of a fifth crude distillation unit succeeded late in 1951 in bringing output to 210,000 b/d, making Bahrain thereby in 1953 the greatest refining centre, with or after Ras Tanura, in the eastern hemisphere, since the closure of Abadan.

Arrangements for conveying Sa'udi Arabian crude to Bahrain (p. 205) were improved, first by 'looping' the line on the Arabian mainland in 1947, then by extending the barge and tanker services to convey additional supplies. By 1952 over 150,000 b/d was being moved to the island and it was decided to duplicate the submarine section of the line, so as to eliminate surface transport. To such processes and to the extension of refining at Bahrain in general, no limit could be set save that of ultimate market demand.

Products from the Bahrain refinery, which ranked as 'dollar oil' with a substantial sterling content, were since 1945 partly drawn by United States armed forces—at prices which were the subject of frequent criticism in American official circles, but which Caltex stoutly defended—and in part dispatched to Caltex markets both east of Suez and in southern and western Europe.

## CHAPTER XIII

# ARABIA, 1946–53: THE INTERNATIONAL COMPANIES

## I. KUWAIT

IF the reader of Middle Eastern oil history runs the risk of weariness at the repeated tale of discoveries, development, and rapid increases in output, the record of the Kuwait Oil Company, which without waste or disorder brought oil production in six years from nothing to a rate exceeding 3 million tons a month, and equipped a remote waterless desert with all the necessities and many of the luxuries of a civilized modern life, is sufficiently remarkable to interest the most jaded mind.

The structure of the Company, with headquarters in London, three Gulf and three Anglo-Iranian directors and a Managing Director—C. A. P. Southwell since 1946—remained simple and unchanged; the substitution in December 1951 of the two companies known as the Gulf Kuwait Company and the D'Arcy Kuwait Company as the twin shareholders had significance in connexion with the new profit-sharing agreement with the Shaikh, but did not affect the Company's control or organization. In the Kuwait shaikhdom the proportion of American to British supervisory staff diminished (as it had similarly in Bahrain) from 1949 onwards as a means of reducing the dollar content of the oil; Americans numbered on an average 170 in 1949,[1] 65 in 1950, 50 in 1951, and 45 in 1952, as against an average of 700 British in 1952; but at Kuwait they retained a predominant role in matters of oil production and handling, and an American, L. T. Jordan, became General Manager at Kuwait in 1948. The Company's Chief Representative for relations with the Shaikh and public, Lt.-Col. H. R. P. Dickson, had served continuously in that capacity since 1934.

It remained the function of the Kuwait Company, which, like the I.P.C., neither possessed nor was concerned with a world marketing organization, to hand its oil in equal shares to its two parent companies. Each of these in this period made arrangements with powerful outside purchasers for the disposal of its part

---

[1] These figures exclude contractors' staff.

of the output. The bargain made in 1947 between Anglo-Iranian and the New Jersey and Socony-Vacuum Companies for the sale of Persian and Kuwaiti crude—the latter of which oils was in effect chiefly intended—has been elsewhere mentioned (p. 147); this arrangement after the failure of M.E.P.L. to materialize became effective in January 1952, and ensured a considerable and reliable offtake from that date. A similar agreement between the Gulf Corporation and the Shell group had been arranged a few months earlier, in May 1947, and took immediate effect for the sale and purchase of annually increasing and, in total, extremely large quantities of Gulf's share of the Kuwaiti crude; at first a ten, later a twenty-two, year period was envisaged. The sale price was to be determined in relation to profits realized out of the oil sold, an arrangement which linked the interest of buyer and seller; and certain restrictions applied to the choice of areas where the purchased oil might be sold. The transaction was, in any case, favourable to rapid Kuwait development as well as to a controlled, as opposed to an anarchic, régime in the industry; it also made good a deficiency in Shell's ability conveniently to supply its eastern-hemisphere markets. At the same time neither the Anglo-Iranian's nor the Gulf's arrangement for disposing of a part of its crude precluded the adoption of other outlets for the rest; large quantities were drawn and dispatched by those companies themselves for the use of their refineries in Europe and Asia and, in the case of Gulf, in America also. But the Gulf-Shell pipeline planned in 1947, and at that time expected to take its place four years later with Tapline and M.E.P.L. as a Persian Gulf–Mediterranean trunk line, was never built, just as M.E.P.L. itself (in the use of whose capacity the American as well as the British partner at Kuwait might well have asked a share) came to nothing (p. 148). Kuwait oil, therefore, remained without pipeline outlets to the Mediterranean and must continue to face the familiar disadvantage of a long and costly sea passage to the west and the risks of irregularity and delay in tanker-liftings.

Shaikh Ahmad al-Subah died in the first days of 1950 and was succeeded by his cousin Shaikh 'Abdullah al-Salim, a mild and prudent ruler. The Company's relations with each of these were excellent; no clash of interest existed, no irritant 'politics' inflamed the population, who could not but be aware of their almost inconceivable good fortune and of whom five-sixths lived in Kuwait town. The transition to the new profit-sharing arrangement introduced by Aramco, involving the payment of taxation in addition to the tonnage royalty, was accomplished at Kuwait in an atmosphere of amity and took effect from 1 December 1951; the profits attributable to operations in Kuwait were divisible between the ruler and the Company, before the deduction of foreign taxation. The Shaikh's future income was popularly computed at £50 million or £60 million a year; in 1949 it had been less than £3 million. The Company bound itself at the same time to increase its contribution to the State for scholarships for Kuwaitis in Europe; and both parties agreed to give consideration to any change in conditions which might render unfair the basis for payments now agreed upon. Meanwhile, the period of the concession was extended by seventeen years, to 2026, and the seaward boundary of the area covered by it was amicably agreed, thus avoiding another 'continental shelf' dispute or arbitration.

The rehabilitation and completion of wells and buildings, which had been begun in 1945, made it possible to inaugurate the export of oil from the temporary marine terminal at Fahahil on the last day of June 1946. This occasion, made ceremonial by the formal attendance of the Shaikh, marked not the end but the beginning of the Company's post-war achievement. At that time nine wells were in production, with an output of some $1\frac{1}{2}$ million t/y; but the combined exploration and exploitation programme next initiated with twelve drilling-rigs was able, in the five following years, to complete more than a hundred more wells, which included no dry holes and only four specialized for observation purposes. The extraordinary scale and richness of the oil-bearing horizons in the Burgan sandstone, from 2,500 to 4,800 feet below the surface, was confirmed in every well, and these were so spaced, initially at intervals of one per 600 acres, as both to define and economically and scientifically to produce from the field. The drilling of these wells presented no unusual features, save for a technique which was developed as peculiarly suitable to the dead flatness of the terrain: that of 'skidding' entire derricks with their engine-houses from old to new locations, with a perfected procedure for rapid movement of the 'unitized' remainder of the rig and equipment. By the summer of 1950 ninety-five wells had been completed, nearly all producing from two horizons at once; two years later, with three drilling rigs still in continuous use, the figure exceeded 130, all on the Burgan structure. A deep test to 13,850 feet gave no significant result, and the well was completed as an ordinary producer.

Producing wells were grouped by pipelines to serve one of the nine gathering centres, where multi-stage gas-separation took place; thereafter the oil was pumped through large-diameter lines to the main tank-farm at Ahmadi, from which it could descend by gravity to the coast by 22-, 24-, and 30-inch lines. The Ahmadi tank-farm contained, by the middle of 1953, twenty-five 139,000- or 168,000-barrel tanks, with one more under erection.

In 1951, after further seismic survey, drilling operations were extended to indicated locations elsewhere in the principality. In the neighbourhood of Magwa a well completed in October of that year found oil at 4,300 feet, and later wells were drilled there in 1952–3, when three rigs were concentrated in the area and had completed a dozen wells by March 1953. The results of these tended to confirm the early suspicion that the Magwa field represented an extension of Burgan. A gathering-centre, a gas-separation plant and pumphouse was erected at Magwa, a pipeline laid from it to the tank-farm at Ahmadi, and from mid-February the Magwa field came into production, a considerable addition to Kuwait's wealth and reserves. On the Ahmadi ridge a few miles north-west and south-east respectively of the Burgan and the Magwa fields, and adjoining the Company's tank-farm, structure-drilling was carried out in the spring of 1952, and later in that year test drilling at a location there found oil, in similar oil-bearing sands, at a depth from 4,560 to 4,750 feet. It was apparent, indeed, that the Burgan field, with its satellites and extensions discovered and yet to be discovered, had not yet shown its limits; but already Kuwait's proved reserves might be placed at 2,500 million tons and upwards: that is, at more than double the estimates made in 1943—and then thought extraordinary.

Production in Kuwait amounted in 1946 to 800,000 tons, in 1947 and 1948 to 2·19 and 6·3 millions respectively. From 1949 to 1952 the yearly production was 12·2, 17, 27·8, and 37 million tons.[1] The need to make good the loss of Persian production was among the factors which expedited these increases, which

---

[1] Kuwait production for the first six months of 1953 was 20·4 million tons, as against 18·2 million tons for the corresponding period of 1952, Kuwait thus slightly surpassing Sa'udi Arabia as a producer.

called for the unremitting efforts of all branches of the organization and were made possible by the ability and willingness of the two parent companies to make available for the territory very large capital sums and vast technical resources.

In July 1950 the Company transferred its Fields headquarters from Magwa to the new town of Ahmadi, leaving the former both as an incipient production centre and as the site of the Company's main hospital and of its Training Centre. Lying athwart a low ridge fourteen miles south of Kuwait town, Ahmadi with its great tank-farm and chief concentration of industrial buildings of all kinds, its European, American, and other staff residential quarters, its mosque and Catholic and Protestant churches, its gardens and plantations, represented an extraordinary transformation of the desert tract. It took its place as a modern oil centre capable of unlimited development on model lines.

Excellent company-made roads ran through the whole system and joined it with the capital. The main electric power-station was at Mina al-Ahmadi, and there also had been erected the all-important water-distillation plant. This replaced a dependency for fresh water on cargoes brought in the earlier days by dhow and, later, by steamer from the Shatt al-'Arab, since Kuwait had virtually no fresh water of its own. An extensive search for water carried out by the Company had unfortunately shown that while indigenous supplies of subsoil water were considerable, they were mostly too brackish for human consumption. The distillation plant produced 600,000 gallons of fresh water a day, of which one-third was dispatched to serve the needs of Kuwait town, until a similar though larger plant, being built by the State, came into use. Mina al-Ahmadi, named after the late ruler, was designed as the Company's port and loading-terminal and, after 1949, took the place of the limited installations constructed in the same area then known as Fahahil, after the nearby village of that name. The port included tankage to serve terminal purposes and a dredged small-craft harbour which was protected by a sea-wall containing 130,000 cubic yards of stone quarried in the hinterland. The great pier, one of the largest of its type in the world, was begun in 1947 and finished two years later. The 'T' head, with eight tanker or cargo berths in forty feet of water, lay at the end of a 4,150-foot cause-way, carrying vehicles and pipe, and was itself 1,080 by 100 feet in size; a million barrels a day could be loaded from it. The construction of the pier involved driving 3,850 nine-foot steel pipes into the sea-bed and using 40,000 tons of steel and timber. Cathodic protection was provided to minimize corrosion. Air-conditioned offices and a recreation room were built on the pier-head. Loading facilities at Mina al-Ahmadi also included the use of five buoy moorings to which oil was brought by submarine pipeline.

Plans for a small or medium-scale refinery were made in 1946 and erection started next year. It came on stream in November 1949 with an intake of 25,000 b/d, or 1·25 million t/y. Like the power-plant and water-distillation plant, it used natural gas from Burgan as fuel. Steps were taken in 1952 to increase its throughput to 30,000 b/d. Of the products, the kerosene, gas oil, and gasoline (which was improved by chemical treatment to 70-octane) were used by the Company itself and by consumers in Kuwait town, while furnace oil and marine diesel oil were used to supply tankers visiting Mina al-Ahmadi. A bitumen processing plant was nearly complete in February 1953.

The Kuwaiti labour force reached 17,000 in 1949, the peak year of varied activity, diminished to 10,000 in 1950, and did not exceed 5,000 in late 1952. Some hundreds of Indians and Pakistanis helped to meet the abnormal demand for clerical staff and for men trained in the wide variety of trades and crafts required for oilfield operation. Much work was given by the Company to Kuwaiti contractors, for reasons both of policy and of convenience. Apart from one strike by Indian staff in 1948, industrial peace was unbroken. In the case of labour neither the Kuwaiti public nor its form of government had yet evolved to the point when formal labour organizations could become useful or desired. Pay and allowance rates were some five or more times in excess of 1939 levels and included a much larger proportion in the more highly skilled categories. Considerable attention was paid to safety measures and instructional campaigns on this subject. The proximity of the city, where the great majority of all Kuwaiti subjects live (and where many will doubtless prefer to live even though employed in the oilfield) lessened the need for housing construction by the Company, though it was the latter's policy to build residential quarters for a large proportion of its local workers. Houses for Indian and Pakistani workers were necessarily of a temporary nature to begin with, but the rapid replacement of these by permanent dwellings was the Company's objective. Some

700 permanent houses for Kuwaiti workmen had been built by the end of 1952; these were of high standard and with all modern amenities and services. Transport was provided at week-ends for workers to move to and from their homes in Kuwait. At Ahmadi coffee-shops, reading and recreation rooms, and clubs were provided for workers, and Kuwaitis in 'staff' positions enjoyed the use of social and recreational facilities of the highest standard. Instruction 'on the job' and at the Training Centre at Magwa, with its 300 pupils, was intended to increase the number of skilled Kuwaitis, to raise their status and earnings, and to fit them for more responsible posts in the Company. The medical care of the workers, entrusted until 1947 largely to the long-established American Mission at the Shaikh's capital, was thereafter secured by a comprehensive clinical and protective system installed by the Company. The 200-bed hospital at Magwa, with all its specialist departments and advantages, was supplemented by clinics at Ahmadi, Mina al-Ahmadi, and elsewhere, and by an ambulance service, dental clinics, and a 'desert rescue squad'.

The city and government of the Shaikh, brought in a day from a resourceless wilderness to the height of opulence, faced the task—a task probably without precedent in the world—of constructing both physically and morally a completely new city and state, with almost limitless resources with which to do so; indeed, the financial difficulty was one not of scarcity but of excess, with the immediate result of soaring land-values and speculation by the initiated. A completely new town-plan was adopted and would take fifteen years to realize. A distilled-water plant, to provide a million gallons a day (but capable of five-fold expansion beyond that), was among the first of the new works. The most modern of hospitals and sanitoria were, in 1952-3, under erection. Asphalted roads, imposing public buildings, shops of European type, boys' and girls' schools, a Technical Institute to serve the needs of the whole Middle East: all these appeared or were being planned.

From this single source of wealth which, without risk or trouble to them, has deluged a small backward remote community and its conscientious, pious, and conservative ruler, the dangers of popular demoralization and parasitism are clear. Undesirable elements might well be attracted from neighbouring countries to the State and, in it or from it, might plan movements disturbing to its tranquillity. Impatience with a patriarchal type of government, mixed with progressive personal ambition, seemed likely to appear among those whom its own wealth and goodwill have educated; and indeed the new age and responsibilities, so different from the slow-moving, simple, shaikhly régime of former years, must call for a form of administration adequate to them. Among its neighbours and the world at large, the position of the tiny state—no stranger already to international intrigue and ambition—became sensitive, envied, and possibly threatened. What action, if any, the Kuwait Government and its advisers would take towards helping less fortunate sister countries, restraining the vagaries of those of its subjects whom wealth might corrupt, and prudently providing for the day, certain if still remote, when the oil itself would be exhausted,[1] time would show.

## II. QATAR

Though ranking today as one of the major oilfields brought into production since 1945, Qatar was the least fortunate of the Persian Gulf group. The responsible Company was neither American nor half-American; Qatar development had had no place in wartime projects; and production from it must be less interesting to any of the I.P.C. shareholders (unless to the Compagnie Française) than rival and greater projects elsewhere.

Its wells and installations stripped or destroyed in 1942, the Dukhan field called after 1945 for more than rehabilitation and re-equipment; it called for all the required construction to be begun again upwards and downwards from ground level, the creation of all communications and services to and within a remote and water-less peninsula, and the assembly of all materials and supplies. With the best of goodwill, the fulfilment of these requirements needed time; and thanks to supply difficulties in the United Kingdom and competing priorities in other countries, no drilling at Qatar could begin until late in 1947, nor could export be secured until the last week of 1949. The Dukhan field, then, after three years of costly and well-directed effort, became the second oil-field, in the second country, from which the I.P.C. group enjoyed commercial production.

A General Manager of Petroleum Development (Qatar) and of

---

[1] An Investment Board was set up in London early in 1953, to invest funds as a provision against such an eventuality.

the other two companies [1] of the I.P.C. group in the Persian Gulf was appointed in 1950 in the person of G. Heseldine. His head-quarters was at Dukhan, but was likely to be moved in 1953 to the east coast loading point at Umm Sa'id, as soon as accommodation for it had been completed.

Exploration of the peninsula outside the productive Dukhan structure, discontinued during the war, was resumed by survey and geophysical parties from 1946 onwards. The southernmost zone of the concession, an area adjacent to the tract claimed by the Sa'udi Kingdom, was at least once invaded by Aramco reconnaissance parties under Sa'udi escort; and another in the north-west of Qatar, the Zubara district, continued intermittently to be claimed by the Shaikh of Bahrain as the property of his family: a *cause célèbre* between the two rulers which was happily settled in 1950. Elsewhere in the Shaikhdom exploration could be and was carried out in security and with full technical resources; it embraced also the search for potable water, rarest of Qatar blessings.

Production from the Jurassic limestone of the Dukhan structure was obtained by the completion of twenty-five wells, to depths around 6,000 feet. Three drilling rigs were habitually in use from 1947 onwards. Initial production at a rate of 1·5 million t/y was, after two years' work, secured from eight wells drawing from the 'no. 3 limestone'; but a comparatively rapid pressure-drop, following the beginning of production, led to the development of the underlying 'no. 4 limestone', and this horizon, to which all wells after 1950 were taken, was by the end of 1951 supplying three-quarters of Qatar production. The latter had by that date attained a rate of over 2 million t/y and by the end of 1952 one of 3·5 million, a rate which was to be progressively increased to at least double that output and probably within five years, if all went well, up to 10 million t/y. The probability that the whole Qatar peninsula formed a broad, flat anticline led, after an encouraging seismic survey, to the siting of a test well in the central area of the territory at Kharaib; but deep drilling in early 1953 showed, disappointingly, that the 'no. 4 limestone' was here oil-less and water-logged, and hopes were temporarily dashed. Meanwhile,

---

[1] Petroleum Development (Trucial Coast) and Petroleum Development (Oman and Dhofar): the Bahrain base and office was until 1952 conducted in the name of the parent company, Petroleum Concessions Limited.

Qatar reserves were provisionally assessed at 1,500–2,000 million barrels, or 200–270 million tons.

Multi-stage gas separation was carried out at the Khatiya de-gassing station and a second de-gassing plant added in 1952 at Fahahil. Brought to atmospheric pressure, the oil is stored in nearby tankage, then pumped through twenty miles of 12¾-inch and fifty three miles of 14-inch pipeline, constructed in 1949, by way of Umm Bab to the east coast at Umm Sa'id, twenty miles south of Doha. The pipeline is accompanied by a surfaced road and telegraph line. The addition of a second line of 24-inch diameter formed part of the extension programme established in 1952 for immediate execution, and the work was in hand in the winter of 1952–3. The same is true of further tankage at Umm Sa'id and sea-loading lines, additional to those provided in 1949–50, of 16-inch diameter and 4,200 feet in length. Operations at Umm Sa'id had included also the location and marking of a deep-water channel leading in-shore, the construction of a signal station, a jetty, a pumphouse and offices, and the provision of residential quarters for staff and labour of all nationalities. At Dukhan, equally an uninhabited waste and seashore before the advent of Petroleum Development (Qatar), a greater settlement had come into being, with jetties and transit yards, the main offices, a residential area with clubs and messes, an industrial area of store-sheds and yards, repair shops, and provision for all services. At both centres power-plants supply electric power and light, hospitals care for the sick, airfields are in hourly use for the Company's ubiquitous aircraft, and water-distillation plants provide drinking water, aided by such scanty well-water as the peninsula affords.

Among the population of Qatar, perhaps physically the least vigorous of any among whom oil development in the Middle East has been carried out, the recruitment and maintenance of labour for the Company's work have been full of problems. As everywhere in the I.P.C. group of companies, wise attention was paid to the provision of medical services, to the encouragement and training of Qatari artisans (who showed full Arab quickness and adaptability in acquiring new skills), to the provision of transport to and from the workers' homes in Doha on rest days and holidays, and to local prejudices and preferences. The standard of remuneration, impartial and sympathetic administration and discipline, and regular paid holidays, were features wholly new to

Qatari conceptions of employment; and the provision of food and good water, and of permanent or semi-permanent housing of good standard, while not free from the imperfections of pioneer days, nevertheless represented a move towards immensely higher material living standards than Qatar had ever known, and were not slow to produce a gratifying improvement in workers' physique. Setbacks against orderly progress were indeed not lacking: industrial life was uncongenial to many, idleness and thieving were widespread, and the work of trouble-makers made easy by avarice and credulity. In a labour force of some 3,000 all possible efforts were made by the Company to give pride of place to Qataris, but the importation of workers from outside—clerks from India and Pakistan, artisans from Jordan and Palestine (after 1948) and from 'Iraq, and labourers from Dhofar and elsewhere in Arabia—was indispensable even though leading at times to dissension and sometimes to strikes; nor could the Company's best efforts to satisfy the various communities in their living and messing arrangements be invariably successful. Nevertheless, the gradual establishment of a regularly employed, well-treated, and reasonably contented body of workers created an immensely important, indeed a dominating, element in Qatari life, which, for better or worse, can never return to its ancient ways and for which a progressively uplifted standard of material life, wealth, and opportunity is assured. It is to be hoped that in Qatar, as throughout the Arabian oilfields, the normal drawbacks of industrial life, the dangers of so sudden a break with tradition, and the brusque irruption of outside influences, not always beneficial, can be successfully met.

Good relations with both the outgoing and incoming rulers and their advisers were maintained by the Company, who installed a representative and rest-house in Doha and were able, on many occasions, to render services to the Shaikh. The latter, whose administration remained entirely patriarchal and almost unorganized, though strengthened by a British adviser since 1949, was nevertheless enabled by the payments he received from the Company to start a small police force under a British officer, to satisfy the needs of his many indigent relations—the first essential duty of every Arab ruler—and to initiate some public works. The village of Doha was to be developed, in part destroyed for replanning and rebuilding, and made adequate to its new status as a rich ruler's capital. Public works and new buildings began to appear,

the shops and markets began to reflect a new prosperity, plans
were made for new roads and jetties. The royalties paid by the
Company amounted in 1950 to £400,000 and in 1951, after the
tonnage royalty had been raised by the Company from Rs. 3 to
Rs. 10, to £1·75 million. In August 1952 a retrospective arrangement for a half-and-half profit-sharing, on the now accepted
pattern, was agreed by the Company with the ruler. This, with
the increasing scale of production, could be expected to lead to
annual payments of £4 or £5 million or more: fantastic wealth by
Qatari standards, and posing moral as well as material problems to
the population and their ruler.

Nor was it certain that Qatari wealth would end there. The
claim of the Shaikh in 1949 to the submarine 'Continental Shelf'
area off his coasts, his grant of oil rights over this to the Superior
Oil Company and its associates, and the arbitration award in his
favour when this grant was challenged by Petroleum Development
(Qatar), have been mentioned earlier (p. 199). Superior (or, more
strictly, the International Marine Oil Company) began operations
by carrying out geophysical research in the sea-bed for some
months, but retired from the scene when the prospects appeared
dubious and the expenses and difficulties all too certain. They
were succeeded in December 1952 as Qatar ocean-bed concessionaires, over an area assessed at 10,000 square miles, by a Company
formed by and to represent the Shell group, the Shell Overseas
Exploration Company. The latter acquired rights for seventy-five
years in return for an initial payment of £260,000 and bound
themselves to start active sea-bed operations within nine months
and drilling within twenty-four; they accepted the principle of
equal division of profits as governing their later development and
production, should this eventuate. This was the first concession
taken within the old Red Line area by an I.P.C. partner in isolation. Seismic survey was to start in the spring of 1953.

### III. SOUTHERN ARABIA

The great tracts of salt marsh and sandy desert, which form the
Trucial Coast, from the base of Qatar to the Oman ranges, were
unvisited by oil-seekers throughout the war. The shaikhs of the
seaside village kingdoms lived on their annual payments from the
concessionaire company, Petroleum Development (Trucial Coast),
pursued their normal domestic and neighbourly quarrels, and

could advance no step nearer to the establishment of territorial boundaries (p. 198). The claim to 'Continental Shelf' 'submerged lands' was put forward by each of the rulers in 1949 and their right to free disposal of the mineral rights in these was made good (p. 199). A change of rulers took place, by supersession or death, at Ras al Khaima, Kalba, and Sharja; loans, repayable from future royalties, were made by the Company to some of the shaikhs to help them in necessitous times; and personal contact was kept with them by the Company's representatives, based at Bahrain or Dibai. These maintained also such relations as were possible with the shaikhs of the hinterland oases and valleys, whose homes fell or seemed to fall within the Trucial Coast or the Oman Con- cessions—unless, indeed, their own claim to complete independ- ence and statelessness be accepted; but the infinitely complicated politics and pretentions of these hungry and threadbare chieftains cannot here be described.

The work of exploration for oil was re-started, after a six-year interruption, as soon as was practicable after the war, and a strong seismic party, sent by Petroleum Development (Trucial Coast)—in effect, by the I.P.C.—took the field early in 1949. Thereafter, seismic or gravity-meter teams were active in each season in one part or another of the tract, within limits imposed by current but inconclusive Anglo-Sa'udi conversations on frontier questions, by the exclusion of about half the abu Dhabi shaikhdom, as tem- porarily 'out of bounds' for oil explorers, and by insecurity and disputed claims to suzerainty in the foothills of western Oman. The Company's decision to test the more hopeful discovered structures by drilling was reached in 1949, beginning with one at Ras Sadr in abu Dhabi territory. Work began in that year on the preparation of a drilling site and involved the construction of a jetty, a passable road, a landing-ground, and a drilling-camp with all essential buildings and living quarters, distillation plant and services; and the recruitment of some hundreds of abu Dhabi subjects as workers.

The Ras Sadr well was spudded in in February 1950. Its history, that of a full year's work, included the mastery of excep- tional drilling difficulties, the successful organization and main- tenance of supplies, and labour troubles which could not be un- expected with so primitive and unaccustomed a body of workers, and a ruler so little qualified to guide them. In March 1951 the well was abandoned at the great depth of 13,000 feet, having shown no indications of the presence of oil. A second drilling-rig was then imported for a further attempt at Jabal 'Ali, a conspicuous hill some miles west of Dibai and situated, according to a recent delimitation made by the Political Resident, inside the latter shaikhdom. Dibai village, the most important and developed on this coast, now became the centre of operations, which involved further road-making, camp-erection, and the employment only of Dibai subjects. The Jabal 'Ali well was taken to a depth of 12,350 feet and then abandoned. The western half of abu Dhabi terri- tory being declared inaccessible, a third well-site was chosen at Murban, some miles west of Shaikh Shakhbut's capital and, after a repetition of the same costly and laborious preliminaries, a well there was spudded in late in 1952. Geophysical parties continued seasonally to examine other tracts of the coast up to the Oman ranges.

The history of these years of oil search on the Trucial Coast, a region of good promise by reason of its position in the Persian Gulf geosyncline and its proximity to heavily oil-bearing terri- tories, is one of toil and expense in arduous conditions, without thanks or reward: a sequence of events familiar in the oil industry (and one simultaneously exemplified in the Middle East in Syria, Lebanon, Turkey, and elsewhere) but rarely appreciated by the general public. The International Marine Oil Company, success- ful in the 'Continental Shelf' arbitration in Paris (p. 199), carried out few, if any practical, operations under the sea-bed concession which was granted to it by Shaikh Shakhbut and withdrew from the enterprise at abu Dhabi, as at Qatar, in the summer of 1952. A concession for the abu Dhabi 'Continental Shelf' and, separately, for that of Dibai was thereafter granted to Anglo- Iranian and the Compagnie Française des Pétroles, in the pro- portion of two-thirds and one-third. The possibility that the I.P.C. group itself, after one or more further unsuccessful wells, would follow Superior in the abandonment of Trucial Coast activities, seemed, early in 1953, not to be remote.

The same was true of the Oman Sultanate, where the long and friendly contact of the Company—in this case Petroleum Develop- ment (Oman and Dhofar)—with the Sultan could do little to solve the abiding problem of his country: that is, that the districts of probable oil-occurrence in the south-west hinterland and west of the main Oman mountains—districts the more tempting since their oil could be moved by pipeline southwards to a loading point on the south coast of Arabia—are the areas of maximum insecurity, where the rule of Sayid Sa'id is, at best, nominal and in practice habitually rejected. No practicable means could be discovered by the Company or its governmental advisers or the Sultan himself for introducing exploration parties, under reasonably secure and workable conditions, to examine these areas, in view of the complete instability of, and physical danger threatened by, the scanty but hostile tribal communities. In fact, exploration in Oman was confined in these years to a few weeks' work by a party in 1950 in a section of the central mountains, studying for general Arabian tectonic data, and that of another which briefly visited Dhofar early in 1948. The separate concession, covering the latter province, was handed back to the Sultan early in 1951 as of no further interest to the Company; and efforts were made, it was understood, by the ruler to interest others in its oil possibilities. The rights over Oman, other than Dhofar, were still held by Petroleum Development (Oman),[1] whose possibilities of future activity could not, however, be confidently foreseen.

Petroleum Concessions Limited continued in 1945–53 to hold its exploration rights over the Aden Protectorate, from which expeditions before 1939 had brought back discouraging reports from such areas as they could visit. After the war small and rapidly moving geological parties visited the territory on three occasions by permission of the authorities of the Protectorate: in the winter of 1946–7, again in 1947–8, and in the last weeks of 1949. The Company's geologists were escorted into and through the Mahra country, the Wadi Hadhramaut, and the hitherto inaccessible Beihan and Shabwa country; but an advance northward into the disputed zones claimed by the Yemen or Sa'udi Arabia, on the fringes of the Ruba'al-Khali, was not feasible. Early in 1953 exploration flights were made by the Company's aircraft over the eastern and north-eastern tracts of the Protectorate, south of the sands of the Ruba'al-Khali, and it was probable that these would be followed shortly by such ground-exploration as might be possible.

Simultaneously, an enterprise at Aden Colony itself made very different demands, and in a very different setting. This was the

---

[1] Dhofar was dropped from the registered name of the Company.

erection by Anglo-Iranian—through a subsidiary, Aden Refineries—of a large refinery covering 250 acres at Little Aden, the
barren peninsula opposite Aden town. The purpose of the installation, which was designed for a capacity of 5 million t/y,
was to supply the Red Sea and East and South Africa with
petroleum products. It would consist of two atmospheric distillation units, with stabilizers and caustic washers, a 'platforming'
unit, and a sulphur dioxide extraction unit. Nearly 100,000 tons
of steel would be required for the construction, with fully adequate
provision for power-generation, water-cooling, and the piping of
fresh water from Company-drilled wells on the mainland. A port
fifty acres in area, with four jetties and all facilities, was to be
constructed by dredging and reclamation: and the existing fishing-
village on Little Aden would be replaced by a new town, planned
and controlled by the Government of Aden. By the end of 1952
construction had well begun: at the peak period 12,000 men were
likely to be employed, from whatever races or communities could
provide the skills required. In subsequent operation, a staff of
250 British and 2,000 other skilled and unskilled workers would be
required. The significance of the enterprise to the economies of
Aden and, to some extent, of adjacent countries was clear. The
refinery was expected to start operation late in 1954. Its cost
would be of the order of £40 million.

Spokesmen of the Government of the Yemen made in these
years a number of efforts to interest British or American companies
in the oil exploration of the Imamate and, in vague terms, promised
favourable treatment; but the little promise revealed by previous
exploration (slight as this had been), the unfavourable inland
situation of the area of presumed interest east of the main igneous
massif, the wildness of the village and tribal population, and the
arbitrary and incalculable character of the Government itself,
were sufficient to deter applicants. There appeared in 1952-3
little immediate likelihood of the Yemen joining the ranks of oil-
producing countries.

## CHAPTER XIV

# THE LEVANT COUNTRIES
## SINCE 1945

### I. TURKEY

THE Mining Research Institute (M.T.A.) entered the post-war period disappointed of its high hopes of Raman Dagh (p. 139), doubtful where next to turn, and looking back, in spite of the country's wide and favourable sedimentary areas and its alluring seepages, at a record of ten years' search and effort under State monopoly, which had failed to discover commercial oil. The next seven years were not greatly to alter this situation but were to lead, at last, to a radical change of policy. Meanwhile, Turkey's need for petroleum products grew year by year and must be met by importing.

Exploration, entrusted to teams both of Turkish experts and of American geophysical contractors, covered again the sedimentary areas of southern Asiatic Turkey where, if anywhere, major oil accumulations must be expected to lie—the Mardin–Diyarbakr area, the Adana plain and the province (Syrian till 1938) of Alexandretta. To each of these the geophysicists and core-drillers devoted their efforts with varying degrees of concentration from 1947 onwards. A drilling campaign of some magnitude, with a dozen new American rigs, began later in the same year.

The first success was once again at Raman Dagh, where well no. 9, spudded in in 1947, was completed in March 1948 with a production of 300–400 b/d of heavy sulphurous oil. President Inünü hurried to the spot; for the second time Turkey rang with the news of a major discovery; and in fact the Raman Dagh field had this time made a humble, but not negligible, beginning. Subsequent wells sought to delimit the field and raised its production capacity to 5,000 b/d of which, for lack of refining capacity, only a part could at present be utilized. The oil was found in an Upper Cretaceous limestone reservoir, at an average depth of 4,500 feet; the structure measures twelve miles in length by one and a half in width and can claim 'proved reserves' of, perhaps, 15 million tons. The average gravity is of 20 degrees A.P.I. No wells flow, all are pumped. By 1952 a dozen wells had been equipped for production, out of twenty drilled on the structure, and quantities of the crude oil produced were used, untreated, as fuel on Turkish railways.

A second field in the same region, at Garzan, was located in 1951 after some months of drilling. Three wells were completed in 1951–2 and a potential production amounting to perhaps 900 b/d of oil of Raman Dagh type, but with gravity 26 degrees A.P.I., was assured. Meanwhile, drilling in the Adana Plain had been undertaken in 1950 at Hojali and at Adzikara; but technical difficulties were encountered and no favourable results were obtained from the first two wells. In Alexandretta district, at Ekber not far from Changan (Tchenguen, Çengen), after the first two wells had been abandoned at 4,500–5,000 feet, the drill located in the spring of 1951, if not production, at least shows of gas reported to be encouraging; work was in progress at the end of 1952.

A topping-plant, to permit some utilization of Raman Dagh oil, was erected in 1948 at Batman, with a capacity of 200 b/d, which was raised to 350 b/d in the next year, with a small output also of road asphalt and a drum plant. Late in 1952 a contract was awarded to an American company for the erection at Batman of another installation of 6250 b/d capacity, to serve the Raman Dagh and Garzan fields and to be on stream early in 1955; the new refinery, to cost some £2½ million, would be operated by American experts for the first years, and thereafter by the Turks. The scale of these installations, giving an output of refined products scarcely exceeding 300,000 t/y, was still in contrast to the actual needs of the Republic; these amounted currently to 750,000 t/y, or five times the requirement in 1938. The advantage to Turkish economy of adequate sources of native petroleum would, therefore, be important. Meanwhile the supply of the territory was assured by imports and distribution in the hands of a Government-controlled agency, the Petrol Ofis, which was founded during the war and supplied with products by Caltex, and in those of Socony-Vacuum, Shell, Anglo-Iranian and a Turkish Company, Turk Petrol. The products, which were principally those of the Haifa refinery until 1948 and thereafter those of Abadan, were after 1951 largely brought from Sa'udi Arabia and Bahrain.

Rumours were frequent during these years that the indifferent results of the long state monopoly of petroleum activity would lead soon to a reversal of this restrictive if politically acceptable method, which had been much admired by other Middle Eastern governments. A decision on the anticipated lines was reached in the latter weeks of 1952 and was announced as one of inviting, at last, the co-operation of the great foreign companies in establishing and developing the industry in Turkey. The terms of the law to regulate this were awaited. Meanwhile, Socony-Vacuum had in 1951 founded a Turkish-Socony Company, and Standard (New Jersey) announced in March 1953 that it intended to send geologists into Turkey forthwith, with the blessing of the Government. It was reported in May 1953 that similar steps were being taken by Shell and that Caltex would follow. The Mutual Security Agency announced in the same month that a large sum in dollars had been allotted to Turkey for the purchase of equipment, and the authorities at Ankara were busy with the organization of the industry on the new lines. In the period 1952–3, therefore, it remained to be seen whether the financial and technical resources now for the first time to be allowed to devote themselves to search and research in Turkey, could avail to create a considerable petroleum industry there.

## II. SYRIA–LEBANON

If the Levant States were in this period enabled, or indeed forced, by their geographical position to continue and enlarge their contribution to the world's oil supplies by providing transit-room and marine terminals for petroleum from farther east, they were not, in other respects, contributors; the search for sources of oil in these countries gave no positive results, drilling where it occurred was unsuccessful, and the refining industry expanded only within narrow limits. The story of achievement told for 'Iraq and Arabia, and until 1951 for Persia, cannot be told for Syria, Lebanon, Jordan, or Palestine-Israel; but the efforts of the oil companies, who were substantially identical with those operating in the more eastern States, were no less deserving, or the difficulties they had surmounted, or still faced, less formidable. The present section of this work will deal with Syria, the Lebanon and Cyprus in 1946–53, then with Palestine and Jordan, and finally with Israel in the same years.

The story of Cyprus is soon told. Under the still valid exploration licence given in 1938 and annually renewed, Petroleum

Development (Cyprus)—an I.P.C. subsidiary [1]—sent geophysicists to Cyprus in 1947 to explore limited areas selected by earlier study. Their efforts in the summer and autumn of that year and the next—gravity survey throughout the Mesauria plain and seismic in Nicosia area—failed, however, to reveal prospects such as to justify drilling, for which no suitable location offered itself; the party withdrew, and early in 1949 the Colonial Government was informed that Petroleum Development (Cyprus) would cease to operate or to ask for renewal of its licence. The closure of these operations did not, however, discourage Cypriot enterprise; a local company, Prospectors Limited, was in the early months of 1953 drilling near Limassol and was understood to have reached, without favourable results, a depth of more than 4,000 feet. The chances of a serious 'strike' of oil in Cyprus appeared, however, to be negligible.

In Syria the drilling programme of the Syria Petroleum Company, which the war had interrupted in 1940, was planned for renewal, partly in new and partly in the already tested areas, as soon as preparations could be made and supplies obtained. Construction of a fully equipped base and depot was begun in Aleppo in 1946 and camps were erected successively at the chosen sites. Water supplies were improvised, desert tracks improved, drilling equipment, and a sufficient labour force assembled. At Baflun, forty miles north of Aleppo, a first well was spudded in in May 1947, only to be abandoned as without hope fifteen months later at a depth of 8,650 feet. Another was begun at Dola'a (Dhal'a), sixty miles due north of Palmyra, in November of the same year and was left at 10,165 feet as a dry hole late in 1948. At 'Abba, in the upper Jazira, the thirteen months from August 1948 to September 1949 was spent in drilling to a depth of 10,250 feet, with no greater success. At Ghuna, between the middle Khabur and the 'Iraq border, where a site was prepared in 1948, the year from January to December 1949 was similarly passed in drilling to 8,600 feet, without recompense. Another well at Jibissa (where two dry holes had been completed before the war) was next undertaken in 1949–50, and abandoned at 8,610 feet in August.

---

[1] More strictly, all the 'Petroleum Development' companies, and those named from Syria, Lebanon and Jordan, are subsidiaries of Petroleum Concessions Limited (p. 113), a company parallel, not subsidiary, to the Iraq Petroleum Company.

In the Bec de Canard in the extreme north-east of Syria (covered at one time by the Lattakiya Asphalt Company's permit (p. 92)), all preparations were made for drilling and a rig was erected, but priority was given to a well at Qubaiba, near Ghuna, where 9,460 feet were drilled, without finding traces of oil, in the winter of 1950–1.

In these wells rock of all ages was penetrated, down in some cases to Palæozoic strata and almost to basement, passing through all series where oil accumulation could be expected. The effort and cost of the drilling campaign, in the conditions offered by the Syrian desert and far from the bases improvised *ad hoc* in a non-industrial country, was severe; nor was it assisted by the *idée fixe* of Syrian publicists that abundant oil was in fact present but the Company for its own reasons refused to bring it to light. Structures worth testing by the drill were, in fact, not lacking; on general grounds the presence of oil was probable; but, in the event, it appeared either not to exist or to be untraceable; and geophysical work, which continued in all parts of Syria from 1946 to 1952, revealed no prospects superior to those already tested and disproved. The Syria Petroleum Company, which in February 1949 surrendered one-third of its area as the 1938 Agreement prescribed, decided early in 1951 to notify the Government of the Republic of its intention to abandon the concession. This abandonment became effective in August, after which the Company's premises were progressively evacuated, its staff reduced, and its assets inspected and valued by the Government. The transfer of almost the whole of its movable property to the Syrian authorities during 1952 formed part of the settlement of the long-standing 'gold case', which had for some years been a cause of serious disagreement between Government and Company. The former had frequently restated its claim (p. 140) to receive payments under the concession in gold sovereigns, a claim denied, on the highest legal advice, by the Company; and the Government had refused the arbitration, for which the concession provided, and refused to accept payments calculated at Bank of England or International Monetary Fund conversion-rates. An amicable arrangement was made during 1952 in settlement of all claims.

A Syrian–American drilling contractor, J. W. Minhall, who visited Syria from the United States in 1948, claimed in March 1949 to have been granted a concession for the area of Syria recently surrendered by the S.P.C. and for the area south of Damascus which had never been granted to that Company. Some 21,000 square miles was covered, it appeared, by the alleged concession. Promises of remarkable future achievement by the new concessionaire alternated for a time with propaganda hostile to the S.P.C.; but, although a Syrian-American Oil and Gas Company was formed, the financial support sought in the United States was not forthcoming and it later appeared that no concession had in fact been awarded. No more was heard of Minhall or his venture.

The future of oil-search in the Syrian Republic was, in the period 1951-3, obscure. The lack of success and heavy expenses of the S.P.C. over nearly twenty years must, it seemed, deter others from entering the same field, even if a reasonable and confidence-inspiring agreement could be obtained from the existing dictatorial Government; nevertheless, the confidence of Syrian patriots in their own oil wealth was persistent, and, in fact, the territory could not at this stage be finally dismissed as without possibilities of petroleum deposits.

In the area covered in the Lebanon by the Jabal Terbol exploration licence, a well on the mountain side overlooking Tripoli, was spudded in by the Lebanon Petroleum Company in May 1947, and the next seventeen months were devoted to drilling it. A depth of 10,060 feet was reached without encountering traces of oil or gas, and the well—and with it the licence and the hopes of a Lebanese oilfield—was abandoned. Other locations in the Lebanon found favour with more than one local syndicate, who secured exploration licences to cover them. The Lebanese Oil Company, in association with Pacific Western (p. 213), drilled a well at Yohmor in the southern Beka'a plain, and, in general, Lebanese hopes were by no means at an end. The discovery of any major sources appeared, however, highly improbable.

In the absence of indigenous production, the oil interest of Syria–Lebanon could only be that of the transit and shipping, perhaps of the refining, of oil. The small refinery erected by the French at Tripoli in 1940, with its capacity of some 200,000 t/y, was transferred on 1 January 1946 to the Iraq Petroleum Company, by whom it was thereafter operated and improved. The enterprise, a war legacy in a branch of activity quite strange to I.P.C. theory or practice—but a valuable asset to the Lebanese and

Syrian States—showed, indeed, considerable profits, thanks to its low-price crude supply; but these profits were locally taxable at high rates, and the basis of such taxation, with connected matters, long remained the subjects of negotiation between the I.P.C. and the Government. Other such subjects were the prices of the re-fined products, the Government practice of manipulating the sterling–Lebanese exchange rates to its own profit but the severe detriment of the Company, and its desire to obtain for Lebanese marketers a share of the refinery output (which was otherwise the property of the already established marketing companies, who were I.P.C. constituents); all these became matters of controversy from 1947 onwards, but remained unsettled in the period of mid-1953. They were, indeed, largely covered by a provisional agreement reached in January 1951, but this was unratified: and were more precisely settled by another agreement concluded in June 1952, which, however, proved equally abortive through non-ratification. Under these agreements the Company was prepared to raise its payments for the transit of the 12- and 16-inch pipelines and further to increase refinery capacity at Tripoli (which it had meanwhile doubled in 1949 by the addition of a new distillation unit) from 500,000 to 700,000 t/y, so as to spare the Lebanese the necessity to import hard-currency products, and assist their balance of trade.

Questions of local refining both in the Lebanon and Syria were, in the course of these long-drawn negotiations, closely connected with those of the new and harder terms demanded from the companies by the Governments for pipeline transit. Rights for the latter were obtained from the Lebanese authorities by Tapline (p. 206) in August 1946 and were ratified in August 1947; they provided for a terminal at Sidon, a transit fee of 30s. per thousand tons and a loading-fee of 2d. per ton. Ratification of a similar agreement for Tapline in Syria was delayed from 1947 to 1949, then obtained in June from the short-lived dictator, Colonel Husni Za'im; the terms were similar to those obtained in the Lebanon, with the addition of an annual sum payable for protec-tion, the right for the Government to use Tapline for the trans-port of Syrian oil (if any), and the sale of 200,000 t/y of crude to Government, at a world price, on demand. In both countries the application of artificial exchange-rates was to be limited. These bases of agreement, in reliance upon which Tapline was constructed, were, nevertheless, frequently criticized by the parliamentarians of both countries; commissions were appointed to revise them, and successive governments disclaimed their predecessors' engagements. In May 1952 fresh agreements were signed by Tapline in both Damascus and Beirut. The new Agreement with Syria raised Tapline payments to the Government from the equivalent of $450,000 to $1,100,000, and increased the quantities of crude oil which the Government had the right to purchase; the agreement with the Lebanon increased annual payments to a level of some £500,000 sterling, raised the loading-tax at Sidon by 50 per cent., prescribed payments to local municipalities and for pipeline protection and road maintenance, and stressed the need for the employment of Lebanese in higher posts. In view, however, of the competitive use of 'the foreign oil companies' as a political issue in both countries, and the not unnatural desire to obtain maximum immediate benefits at all costs, the stability of these agreements, which required—and by March 1953 had not obtained—parliamentary ratification, was by no means certain.

The I.P.C., which in 1947 volunteered to pay *ex-gratia* transit fees of £45,000 a year in the Lebanon and £75,000 in Syria (and in 1950 increased the latter to £108,000), agreed later also with both Governments to make crude oil available, on lines similar to those accepted by Tapline, should the need arise. In the Lebanon, outstanding pipeline questions were to be adjusted in the abortive agreements of 1951 and 1952 above mentioned. The latter provided for raising I.P.C. transit dues in the Lebanon to £L. 4·5 million (about £450,000 sterling) a year; but later in the year, before the agreement was ratified, pressure declared itself in Beirut for yet higher demands. In Syria the I.P.C., before beginning work on its 30-inch pipeline to Banias, obtained the specific agreement of Government to the alignment and terms; but the completion of the work was closely followed by demands for increased payments and advantages on levels quite remote from those accepted two years before. Such were the construction of a refinery in Syria, preferably at Homs: the claim to half or nearly half of all profit from, or saving effected by, the transit of oil through Syria as against sea transport: and the delivery of free crude oil to Government. An I.P.C. negotiator spent much time in Damascus in 1952 and early 1953, seeking formulas which would compromise, upon acceptable principles, between the Company's desire for security and reasonable operating conditions and the Government's pressure for payments and privileges without precedent in similar circumstances. It remained to be seen to what length the Syrian and Lebanese Governments would go in turning to account the position of stranglehold with which their situation between the great 'Iraq oilfields and the sea had endowed them; neither Tapline nor the I.P.C., owners of the great trunk pipelines, could in the prevailing atmosphere feel secure of future untroubled operation or the permanence of any agreements which had been or might be concluded.

The same would, no doubt, have applied in due course to Middle East Pipelines (p. 147) which, after two years' delay, obtained its transit rights through Syria in June 1949, had not other reasons compelled the abandonment of this project. A concession to build a refinery on the Syrian coast, granted at the same time to Maritime Refineries Limited, a subsidiary of the Anglo-Iranian Oil Company, did not, for obvious reasons, lead to immediate operations of construction; whether it would ultimately do so, on a basis of I.P.C. crude drawn from Banias, had not by the end of 1952 been revealed.

No field activity between 1946 and 1952 had followed the grant of refinery concessions by the Lebanese Government to an I.P.C. constituent, the Compagnie Française des Pétroles in 1947, nor to Mediterranean Standard Oil Company (a subsidiary of New Jersey) in 1945. Whether these would in future build refineries in the Lebanon or not, was undisclosed; and the same was true of governmental projects of refinery-building mooted at times both in Damascus and Beirut in the hope of using profitably the crude oil supply which they could obtain from the Companies. The Mediterranean Refining Company, jointly owned by Caltex and Socony-Vacuum, applied successfully in 1945 for refinery rights in the Lebanon, and six years later announced its intention to build an installation, of 12,500 b/d capacity, at the Sidon (Zahrani) terminal of Tapline. Construction of this, which was to include a cracking-plant, began early in 1953.

Meanwhile, the great construction works of the period—the I.P.C. 16-inch and 30-inch lines with a new terminal at Banias and important extensions at Tripoli, and Tapline with its terminal and its future refinery at Sidon—had added considerable economic assets to the wealth of the two countries: wages and salaries, important contracts and local purchases, receipts from taxation, annual transit-payments, and profits on the sale of local currency for sterling or dollars at artificial rates, had all accrued to the public or the Government without loss or risk. The move of the I.P.C.'s Middle Eastern headquarters from Haifa to Tripoli in 1948 greatly increased its staff and its disbursements in the Lebanon—an increase likely, however, to be partly reduced by the devolutionary system of administration, territory by territory, introduced in 1952. The pipelines in operation at the end of that year were capable in their present form of bringing 22 million t/y of oil through the Lebanon and 14 million to the coast of Syria.

The Tapline terminal at Zahrani, four miles south of Sidon, with its great tank farm of 180,000-barrel tanks, was constructed on the low hills immediately inland, thus offering gravity loading. It included domestic and industrial buildings, a hospital, a signal station, six 30-inch sea-lines, and an L-shaped jetty running 1,000 feet from the shore into fifteen feet of water. The I.P.C. terminal at Banias, covering 1,200 acres, had similar essential constituents and similar functions, with equal or greater beauty of setting. The six loading berths, half a mile apart, were served by 24-inch submarine lines from the 25,000-ton tanks sited on high ground inland; a pleasant residential area flanked the river Jorbar; the 'industrial area' contained offices and a canteen, store sheds, workshops, and an electric power-house; a stone-built small-boat harbour provided for the safety of tugs and launches, and a signal station controlled marine traffic.

In both Syria and the Lebanon trade union organization, legalized by the local Labour Codes, gained ground after the war and was recognized and accepted by the Companies. The unions, though they lacked the deep roots and sense of responsibility of the better unions in Europe, made fair progress and largely avoided the ever-present threat of 'political' domination. The Companies kept, on the whole, cordial relations with these potentially valuable bodies and devoted the same care to the welfare of their workers as in other territories. Political circles in both States and the less responsible of the newspapers treated the Companies with varying degrees of suspicion or hostility, and wholly baseless charges were not infrequently made against them of defrauding the local treasury, illtreating their workers, trafficking with the

State of Israel, or concealing discovered oil deposits. Inevitable reductions in the labour-force after construction periods were resented by the local authorities and aroused angry outcry in the Press. This prevailing, though not universal, attitude of local publicists was not shared by such of the general public as could appreciate the important contribution which the industry was making to the well-being of the two territories.

### III. PALESTINE AND JORDAN

Work by the Iraq Petroleum Company in Palestine, preparatory to its intended 16-inch trans-desert pipeline, had already begun (p. 142) before the end of 1945; and in addition to various improvements and expansions to base services at Haifa, which were carried out continuously thereafter, specific provision for the greater quantities of crude soon to arrive by pipeline—7 million t/y instead of 2·25 million—was in hand between the early weeks of 1946 and the end of the Mandate in May 1948. These works were interrupted at times by labour demands and abstentions, organized by the powerful Histadruth organization of Jewish trade unionism, and faced the same post-war difficulties, restrictions, and shortages as elsewhere; but good progress was made in the provision of additional sea-loading lines, the adaptation of terminal pipe and valve systems, the erection of additional tankage, and in all the services ancillary to pipeline construction and operation. The unloading and forwarding of pipe and of station-construction requirements and machinery for the western sections of the pipe-line involved months of great activity at Haifa and Mafraq and on the roads and railways of Palestine and Jordan.

By the early weeks of 1948 with all pipe unloaded and station equipment forwarded inland and the laying of the line completed westward as far as the Jordan crossing, the end of the work seemed in sight: only forty miles of pipe, from the Jordan to the Haifa tank farm, remained to be welded and buried; and a Supplementary Agreement was made with the High Commissioner in April 1948 regulating such outstanding matters between the Company and the Government of Palestine as the free transit of Jordan oil (if such should prove to exist) through the territory, the assessment of municipal taxation, and an annual payment (£45,000) for security services. But the internal disorders of the country, marked for months past by continual attacks on property, robbery of transport vehicles, and spasmodic fighting, grew to a climax with the end of the British Mandate and the declaration of a State of Israel in May 1948; not only was work on pipeline construction perforce discontinued and the pipe strung in Palestine abandoned, but the whole organization of the I.P.C., save a small rear-party left as caretakers, was moved hurriedly to Tripoli with whatever stores and vehicles could be collected and loaded. The 16-inch pipeline was never completed and the 12-inch was, thereafter, to remain unused. How severe was this blow both to the Company and, by its self-inflicted loss of important royalties, to the 'Iraq Government, has been suggested elsewhere. I.P.C. activity in Palestine, eager and continuous since 1931, was at an end, most of its physical assets were deprived of their use and functions, its labour force and staff were reduced to a handful, and the considerable benefits of its presence in the country were lost.

This applied equally to the other main I.P.C. enterprise in Palestine—its quest for local sources of petroleum. The twenty-nine exploration licences acquired in 1939 were kept valid by a war-period moratorium and their obligations—those of drilling wells in each of the two main areas—remained to be fulfilled after 1946. Work to this end was begun by Petroleum Development (Palestine) in the latter year, with the formation of a camp and the assembly of a rig and all drilling necessaries at Hulaiqat; the structure was eight miles north-east of Gaza, where a headquarters and depot were organized. A well was spudded in in September 1947 and, in spite of drilling difficulties, had been deepened to 3,465 feet by 7 February 1948. The increasing anarchy of the countryside, however, with every phenomenon of violence and civil war compelled the closure of operations on that date and the withdrawal of personnel. The 'Judea limestone', in which oil accumulation had been considered possible, had proved dry.

A second drilling site was located in southern Palestine on a remarkable structure at Kurnub, fifty miles south-east of Gaza. A sixteen-mile road across hills was constructed from the Beersheba road and a camp built on a high point; water was provided from wells sunk in the neighbouring wadi bed. All this effort and expenditure was, however, destined to be futile; the conditions prevailing in the spring of 1948 compelled the abandonment of the enterprise before the test well could be spudded in. Movable stores and equipment were withdrawn from both Kurnub and

Hulaiqat to Gaza and there stored for later removal; a quantity was dispatched to Jordan and some by way of Haifa to Basra. Surviving vehicles were driven to 'Amman.

The experience of Consolidated Refineries Limited, in Haifa Bay, was scarcely happier. The expansion of this important plant between 1939 and 1945 has been described (p. 141); a further enlargement, with capacity to produce a wider range of products, was intended by its owners as their immediate programme after the war. Throughput was to be raised from 4 million to 7·5 million t/y by the addition of another distillation unit; plant was to be added for the production of various grades of bitumen, white spirit, and solvents, with a lubricating-oil plant of 120,000 t/y capacity. Additional boilers and cooling towers, tankage for products and various ancillary equipment were to be installed. These works were well in hand throughout 1946–8, in spite of persistent labour unrest and attempts at politically-inspired sabotage; but on the 17 April 1948 it was decided to yield to force and to discontinue not only construction work but also the current operation of the refinery, which had until then been continuous in face of dangerous and abnormal conditions. The stoppage of crude supplies from 'Iraq, enforced by the 'Iraq Government, thereafter deprived the refinery of all hopes of any but a partial and temporary re-starting. Nothing could have been more damaging to the economy of Palestine, which was entirely dependent on the output of this refinery; and the effect on the oil supplies of southern and western Europe, at a time of shortage in all countries and of Marshall Aid American assistance, was serious. The refinery was relegated to a régime of care and maintenance, its staff and workers reduced. Its status and future operation under the State of Israel remained for some months doubtful.

In Transjordan, which in April 1946 became the Hashimite Kingdom of the Jordan with the Amir 'Abdullah as King in treaty relations with Great Britain, the construction of the 16-inch line from 'Iraq gave employment and prosperity for two years, 1946–8 and was, except for work at stations, completed by the spring of 1948. The installation of new machinery and accommodation at H4 and H5 stations was finished later in that year; but, for reasons elsewhere made clear, no transit of oil could follow, and the I.P.C. 'southern lines' could be no more than maintained, useless and inactive until times should change: change of which there was still, in and after the early summer of 1953, no hopeful sign. Employment for numbers of Jordanian skilled workers was found by the I.P.C. in their Qatar operations.

Tapline, which obtained transit rights from the King of Jordan in August 1946 in return for an annual payment of £60,000, carried out its pipeline construction work in the Kingdom, as has been seen (p. 208), between 1949 and 1951, crossing the I.P.C. alignment in the lava country and swinging north therefrom to avoid the frontiers of Israel; none of its pumping stations was on Jordan soil. The transit agreement with Jordan was amended in June 1952 to equate it with those made or re-made by Tapline with the Syrians and Lebanese in that year. The Hashimite Kingdom was thereby to receive £215,000 a year, instead of £60,000; it was likely also to benefit by Tapline's local purchases (notably of garden produce for its Arabian workers), by tourist traffic, and by its receipts of hard-currency payments. It could expect a supply of Tapline crude at favourable prices in the event of a decision, which was foreshadowed from 1951 onwards, to erect a refinery in the country, probably at Mafraq. Meanwhile, the supply of the country's humble requirements in refined products, not exceeding 100,000 t/y, was with difficulty and expense assured by the marketing companies (Shell and Socony) from the Lebanon; it was for technical reasons not possible for the I.P.C. to repeat the assistance, which it gave once in 1948, of 'slugging' gasoline down the disused pipeline to H4.

The possibility of discovering native petroleum sources in the Kingdom itself had not been forgotten. The régime of exploration licences, which was on the point of coming into force before the war with the I.P.C. as the principal or only declared candidate for them, gave place in 1947 to a 'blanket concession' to cover the whole country. This was granted by the King to the I.P.C. on 10 May of that year: or, more strictly, to Petroleum Development (Transjordan) Limited, an affiliate formed in 1938, whose name was changed to Transjordan Petroleum Company in August 1947. The concession provided for an initial payment of £50,000 (gold), annual payments rising from £15,000 (gold) at first to £80,000 (gold) after twelve years, and a royalty of 4s. (gold) per ton or (as in the Syrian Concession) 3s. or 2s., if the oil should prove of inferior quality. 'Gold' was closely defined, and all royalty rates were subject to revision after twenty years.

The concession was doomed, however, to a short and valueless existence. Survey and geophysical work was carried out, but did not reveal structures of attractive promise; and the State of Israel repudiated the Agreement made in April 1948 with the Government of Palestine which had secured the passage of Jordan oil, if any, to the sea. The prospects of the territory appeared, after all, unattractive; and the Transjordan Petroleum Company did not proceed to the drilling stage of exploration. The Government at 'Amman was notified that it could, if it thought fit, look elsewhere for a more hopeful concessionaire; the burden of paying annual dead-rents for ten years, until 1956 (since the terms of the concession precluded voluntary surrender before that) remained incumbent on the existing concession-holder, unless and until released by agreement. This was the only consolation of the Hashimite Kingdom for its failure to realize hopes of oil wealth of its own, for the blocked communication between it and the Mediterranean, the dwindling traffic and employment on the I.P.C. pipelines and stations, and the difficulty of obtaining supplies of products for its own public.

### IV. ISRAEL

The State of Israel began its career in the field of petroleum with three grave disadvantages and three assets. The former were the absence of native crude oil sources in the territory, the refusal of the former supplier of crude oil, 'Iraq, to permit further stocks to reach Israel by the I.P.C. pipeline, and the consequent necessity of spending much of its scanty foreign exchange on the purchase of crude and products from overseas. The assets of the new State were, first, the presence of a fully equipped refinery at Haifa: secondly, the power which the new Government possessed, or assumed, to regard all previous commitments as null and void and to insist on better terms and higher payments from all locally-represented oil companies: and thirdly the high scientific and industrial qualities of Israeli subjects and their friends abroad, willing to undertake development work in the oil industry of the country.

No oil from 'Iraq reached Israel after April 1948. The I.P.C. pipeline terminal and tank farm were unused, the oil dock served only for the discharge of a trickle of imports. The Company remained constantly in touch with the officials of the State of Israel, its installations were borrowed, when needed, by the Government, and the loading-fees of £30,000 a year continued to be paid, though no loading occurred. The future operations of I.P.C., if any, were discussed in Haifa, Jerusalem, and London, and Israeli suggestions for increased immediate payments were received and rejected. The general question of the Company's rights in Israel, deriving from its 1931 and 1934 agreements with the Mandatory Government, the honouring of which the new state was far from accepting as an inherited obligation, was unsolved during this period. The exploration licences under which the Company had arranged to drill at Hulaiqat and Kurnub were pronounced invalid and the Mining Code of 1939 ineffective; and in any case the uncertainties of the present, the prohibitive cost of operations in Israel, and the unknown conditions of subsequent exploitation, if any, deterred the Company from seeking to undertake further work. The country ceased to be a scene of active I.P.C. operation, though the Company retained not only its close interest but its highly valuable (though now unwanted) assets in the territory.

Successful efforts were made, meanwhile, by the Israel Government to attract other concerns from outside—that is, from American and European Jewry—to the consideration of oil development in their country. Swiss, Canadian, American, and South African enterprises showed, singly or in groups, sufficient interest to lead in 1949–52 to visits by their experts to Israel, the discussion of terms, and the formation of syndicates in which Israeli shareholding—private or Governmental, or trade union through Solel Boneh, or all or any of these—appeared side by side with foreign. The United Petroleum Company, the New Continental Oil Company, the Israel Oil Prospecting Company, the Ampal Corporation, the Israel Fuel Corporation, and the American-Israel Petroleum Company were among those who awaited the preparation of a new Israeli petroleum law and the licences which would be obtainable under it. The Jordan Exploration Company, which had in 1944 acquired the two exploration permits held by the Palestine Mining Syndicate (and formerly by Sutherland), disputed in the courts the right of Government to dispossess it of its acquired rights, and won its case.

The new Israeli mining law, in supersession of all Mandatory regulations, appeared late in 1952. It provided for the grant of restricted areas to applicants, in the hope of competition and rapid returns. Rights could be granted in three forms: that of a general survey, that of a licence permitting geological research and test drilling, and that of an exploitation lease. The licence would be valid for three years, with the possibility of limited extension, and carried the obligation of early field work and drilling. Each licence could cover a maximum of 100,000 acres, but not more than three in any one district could be held by one grantee. A lease would be granted after oil had been struck; the term was for thirty years, extendable by twenty more; royalty at 12½ per cent. would be payable and an income tax of 50 per cent. imposed. A single lease could not cover more than 62,500 acres, nor could more than three in any one 'petroleum district' be granted to one holder. Application for licences was made late in 1952 by some of the companies mentioned above and others.[1] Much optimism was shown by Israeli officials and experts on the probabilities of the discovery of oil. Drilling was expected to begin late in 1953. The Government in June 1952 followed the example of others (p. 199) in announcing its ownership of mineral rights in its 'Continental Shelf' area of the Mediterranean.

But while future riches were awaited, no industrial or financial embarrassment of the new state was, meanwhile, more serious than that of its petroleum supply, the requirement for which amounted to nearly 1 million t/y, and upon which its industry and transport almost entirely depended. For the first year after May 1948 existing stocks were used and small quantities of products imported by the marketing companies from the Netherlands West Indies and elsewhere. In 1949 single cargoes of crude were imported from Venezuela and processed by one unit of the otherwise inactive Consolidated refinery; the latter was, however, never furnished, from 1949 to 1953, with crude sufficient to supply more than a quarter of its capacity. Such crude came necessarily from the western hemisphere, since no oil of Arab origin was allowed to reach Israel and the latter refused the offer of Rumanian crude. The cost in foreign exchange, in spite of efforts at economy in

---

[1] The Husky Oil Company of Delaware, Marigold Oils Limited, the New Continental Company of Canada, Barclay Oil Company, the Lapidot (or Israel) in association with Jordan Exploration Company, Trans-Era Oils Limited, Wilrich Petroleum Limited, Minerva Mining Corporation, and one or more private groups.

petrol consumption which included the institution of 'carless days', was some £15 million a year, part of which Israel tried, without success, to borrow from the British Treasury. The importation of oil, arranged initially by the Shell and Socony Companies, was from the summer of 1952 onwards handled in part also by the Israel Fuel Corporation, a body founded *ad hoc* with one-third public, one-third Government, and one-third Histadruth shareholding; the crude imported by it was treated, by arrangement, in the Consolidated refinery but remained the Corporation's property. The easier supply of Caribbean crude by the Shell Company, to an intended value of £800,000 a year, was a result of the Israeli–West German agreement of late 1952, which provided the sterling exchange required. No progress was made towards realization of the Israeli project of an 'Aqaba–Haifa pipeline, designed to avoid the Suez Canal and Egyptian scrutiny of cargoes.

Refining within these narrow limits continued to be carried out by Consolidated Refineries, which sought to supply all products required in the country (except aviation spirit) and to serve also the growing local petro-chemical industry. No serious talk of 'nationalization' was heard, but close Government supervision was to be expected and the near-monopoly of marketing, hitherto enjoyed by the Shell and Socony Companies, with unimportant smaller distributors, was to end: a proportion of the C.R.L. output, beginning at 15 and rising to 30 per cent., was by agreement with Shell and Socony to be reserved for the parastatal Fuel Corporation. After three years of negotiations, a settlement of the uncertain position of Consolidated under the new régime was reached in February 1953. It covered the products to be issued from the refinery, the rights of the Government Fuel Agency or its nominees both in refining and distribution, and the imposition of normal Israeli taxation on the Company which, under its previous (Mandatory) agreements, had been largely exempt.

A pipeline for refined products from Haifa to Tel Aviv was a probable project of the near future.

### V. EGYPT

The oil history of Egypt from 1946 to 1953 is one of the hopefulness and tenacity of the companies permitted by the Government to operate in that country, of their partial success in new discoveries and thereby in the production of national wealth, and of a Government attitude to the industry so restrictive and so discriminatory against foreign-owned enterprise as gravely to damage the Egyptian economy and to preclude, for five years, all hope of progress in the direction most necessary to Egyptian interest.

No Egyptian capitalist or company throughout the period—or at any other period—attempted to play a part in its oil development, discouraged not unnaturally by its long record of risks and limited successes. The three foreign companies—Anglo-Egyptian Oilfields, Socony-Vacuum, and Standard Oil of Egypt (that is, New Jersey)—who, in spite of costly and fruitless exploration and test drilling before and early in the war, decided to persevere after 1944, lost no time in launching a campaign of geological and geophysical search which year by year covered all parts of Egypt, and in drilling on sites selected within the licenced areas which they held, or proceeded to obtain, under the regulations and forms current in and since 1937. From 1945–8, Standard of Egypt drilled at abu Hamdh, Darag and Nakhl in Central Sinai, two wells at abu Ruwash close to the Pyramids, others at abu Rudeis and Wadi Baba on the west coast of Sinai, another (to a great depth) at Khabra in the north-eastern Sinai near the Palestine border, others at Wadi Firan on the west Sinai coast. All were dry, save the last-named, where—for the first time after fifteen years of work by New Jersey and an expenditure of $16 million—oil in appreciable quantities was discovered in Miocene sands at a depth of 6,500–6,570 feet; it was judged to amount to about 150 b/d, of 20–25 degrees A.P.I. gravity. This oil, for reasons which will appear, was not then developed.[1]

Anglo-Egyptian, meanwhile, spudded in a further exploration well to the north of Ras Gharib, another (on joint account with Socony) at 'Ain Musa at the top of the Gulf of Suez, another at Myos Hormus north of Hurghada, and another, on the joint account, in north-western Sinai. A well begun at 'Asl on the western Sinai coast was abandoned in 1946; but a second in the same area drilled by Socony in 1947 showed good results early in the following year and was confirmed by subsequent wells, as indicating an oilfield of useful capacity. This, and a similar field discovered at Sudr immediately north of 'Asl, was an important

---

[1] It was stated in May 1953 that a lease for Wadi Firan had been given to the Société Cooperative Egyptienne des Pétroles, in association with American and Swiss interests, who included the Southern California Petroleum Corporation.

gain for the shared enterprise of Anglo-Egyptian and Socony; the Sudr field was located in the spring of 1946 and justified immediate work in further drilling and equipment of the field. Other wells drilled for the joint account of Anglo-Egyptian and Socony at Misalla and Hamra on the same coast, and those of A.E.O. alone at Ataka and at abu Sultan in the Canal Zone west and north of Suez, were all unproductive; and a series of wells at Lagia and at Nebwi, both promising licence-areas, gave no results and were abandoned. At Ras Matarma, south-east of Sudr, a small field was located and three wells drilled. Leases for the exploitation of the 'Asl and Sudr fields were obtained in 1948 and provided terms on the whole similar to those of Ras Gharib; the royalty rate was 14 per cent., and 15 on the half of the output belonging to the Socony half-interest; the rate after renewal, thirty years hence, was to be that prevailing at the time.

These, however, were the last leases to be granted, in consequence of serious changes in the legal background, which were introduced by the Egyptian Government in 1947-8. A new Company Law provided that companies constituted in Egypt must be, at least, 51 per cent. Egyptian in their share-holding and control, and the new Mines and Quarries Law of 1948 laid down that only an Egyptian company, so constituted, could take out an oil mining lease and imposed a royalty rate of 15 per cent. on half, 25 per cent. on the other half, of an area held under exploration licence and qualifying for a mining-lease;[1] on renewal the rate for the whole would be 25 per cent. It followed that the foreign licence-holder, who had discovered an oilfield, would be entitled to develop it only at the cost of first becoming an Egyptian-controlled company. These terms, and others of an unduly restrictive character, were unacceptable to the operating companies, which were in any case unwilling to submit to an Egyptian majority control. It resulted that no leases of the new type were accepted, even for proved areas. At Ras Matarma, Anglo-Egyptian could claim in 1953 to hold a right to lease on terms which had been defined before the issue of the exploration licence, and tried in vain to secure the issue of such a lease on these or any other acceptable terms; for the semi-proved field of Wadi Firan no lease was

---

[1] That is, the licence-holder could obtain on mining-lease one-half of his permit area for a 15 per cent. royalty, but the other half only by paying 25 per cent.

issued. The New Jersey Company, indeed, rather than accept a lease or carry out any further operations on such terms, abandoned its enterprise and in 1949 withdrew definitely from all exploration and drilling in Egypt. Socony-Vacuum, like Anglo-Egyptian Oil-fields itself, decided in 1953 to suspend all further exploration operations until further notice.

Between 1948 and 1952 applications for exploration licences were made by Anglo-Egyptian Oilfields and Socony and by new-comers to the field—the Société Generale Française des Huiles de Pétrole, and the Société Nationale Egyptienne de Pétrole—rather in hope of a change in the law than with the intention of immediate operation. All drilling, in fact, except exploitation drilling on proved structures already held on lease, ceased in 1950, and the most vital of Egypt's needs—continued exploration with a view to new discovery, which was essential to its economy—was thus by its own policy frustrated. Conversations on this and connected matters between the Companies and the Government continued intermittently from 1948 to 1952, and late in the latter year the authorities so amended the law as to permit non-Egyptian com-panies to take up oil-mining leases; other conditions for licences and leases differed little from those of the 1948 law as regards the size of leaseable areas, periods, and renewals. But no move was made by the Companies towards restarting their suspended opera-tions: not only was the question of the internal selling-price of refined products still unsolved, but the Government announced also that the two major Companies—A.E.O. and Socony-Vacuum—and two inactive local companies (elsewhere mentioned) had all lost their priority rights to the prospecting licences, for which they had applied in 1948-9; these licences were to be put, under the new law, to public auction.

The same tendency towards a close regulation of the industry in Egypt was shown in other fields of its activity. The export of asphalt was restricted and thus prevented from earning, as it could well do, badly needed foreign exchange; authority to extend the land leased to the Anglo-Egyptian refinery at Suez was withheld; the selling-price of refined products in Egypt were fixed, in the interest of the local consumer, at arbitrary rates below world prices and seriously affected the business of the distributing companies; and an agreement made in 1951, in partial rectification of this position, was repudiated by Government next year. These defiances of economic law appeared to observers as unwise and unjust and highly discouraging to the sorely-tried foreign enterprises which had created and sustained the industry in Egypt. The prohibition of tankers passing through the Suez Canal *en route* for Israel had, of course, political motives. Politics, indeed, in the form of a nationalism ready to invade the field of industry, dominated Egyptian life at this period, and in the troubled winter of 1951–2, when anti-British violence was widespread in the Canal Zone and intimidation of Egyptian workers habitual, it was not easy for the Companies, in an atmosphere of Egyptian aggression and British restriction or reprisal, to provide transport and distribute the supplies upon which modern Egyptian life so largely depends. This task they successfully achieved, as in 1948 they had, under Government orders, made arrangements for the supply of petroleum products to the Egyptian forces during the campaign against Israel. The principle of dividing by 'half-and-half' the profits made locally from local production (as adopted in Sa'udi Arabia in January 1951 and later elsewhere) was at one time suggested by Government spokesmen, but proved on analysis to be unattractive to the local treasury and was abandoned. Cries for nationalization of the industry in Egypt, inevitable in the prevailing atmosphere, were discouraged by the Government.

Both for fiscal reasons and the better to confront prevailing conditions in Egypt, the decision was taken in mid-1951 to move the control and management of Anglo-Egyptian from London to Cairo, where, with a board of the Company's executives and eminent Egyptians, it was duly installed and thereafter resided. The General Manager, R. G. Searight (who had relieved D. R. Mackintosh in 1945) became Chairman and was succeeded, as such, by G. S. Taitt in 1952. The arrangement for management by Anglo-Saxon, which had been in force since 1911, was discontinued after 1951, though technical and other help from it was still forthcoming. In 1950 Sir R. Waley Cohen, after forty years connection with A.E.O. in London, vacated the chairmanship of the Company there in favour of Sir Frederick Godber. Socony-Vacuum early in 1952 followed the example of A.E.O., by moving the controlling management of their Egyptian interests to Cairo.

The demands of the Egyptian services and public for petroleum products grew rapidly after the war, reaching in 1951 nearly 2·5 million t/y against a local output of 1·75 million t/y of products:

and the deficiency, which, with the demand for foreign exchange to make it good from outside sources—amounting to some £13 million in 1952—must inevitably increase year by year until new supplies were forthcoming in Egypt, offered the strongest motive for encouraging local field-operations. The hard-won successes at Sudr and 'Asl, which came into production in December 1947 and January 1949 respectively, did indeed, for a time, materially diminish the gap; but the Ras Gharib field, in spite of continuous drilling—to the maximum, finally, which could be of further value to production—and the erection there of new dehydration and desalting plants and a new pier, new power-house and much ancillary building, could barely maintain its output of 1·2 to 1·3 million t/y from wells some flowing, some gas-lifted and some pumped; while the output of the Hurghada field, still carefully fostered from its dozens of feebly-producing pumped wells, varied between 65,000 and 40,000 t/y.

The new Sinai fields of Sudr–'Asl[1] belonging, with Matarma, to a single production area, gave half a million tons in 1948, a million in 1949, and a quantity close to 1·2 million in each of the years 1950–2, of which half belonged to each of the two partners. Egyptian production in all therefore amounted in successive years from 1945 to 1952 inclusive to 1·34, 1·25, 1·32, 1·90, 2·27, 2·32, 2·33 and 2·4 million tons and raised the country to the rank of the seventeenth among the world's producers.[2]  Its output had been approximately doubled by the Sinai accretion, a result secured by assiduous drilling (including deep tests) on those structures until, in 1952, no more exploitation drilling could profitably be done. The Sinai fields were equipped with all necessary installations including dehydration plant, a power-station, tankage, a pipeline to the sea at Sudr, and a loading wharf; loading conditions were as good at Sudr as they were perennially bad at Ras Gharib. The oil from 'Asl was brought by 10-inch pipeline to Sudr, and that of both fields there loaded for the refinery at Suez. Both fields afford flow-production by hydraulic drive and are without gas; the main Eocene reservoir being very permeable, the wells drilled in it are

---

[1] At Sudr the reservoir is in Miocene and Eocene limestone, its capacity limited by faults which delimit a capriciously tilted structure; at 'Asl oil is found in parts of a dipping upthrown mass of Eocene limestone.

[2] Egyptian production for January–June 1953 was 1·2 million tons, but was unlikely to be able to maintain this scale of output for long.

likely to continue to flow—but to produce increasingly, and in the end exclusively, water; the advance of the water-drive up the structure was already, in 1953, well established. In the minor Miocene structure pumping may be increasingly required. Thirty-two wells had been completed at Sudr by the end of 1952, twenty-eight at 'Asl; [1] but in general the early hopes inspired by the discoveries of 1947–8 on the Sinai coast had been shown to be exaggerated. In these fields and in Egyptian production as a whole the future, it seemed, could scarcely be other than one of fairly rapid decline, not long postponable. The direct payments of the producing Companies to the Egyptian Treasury rose from £1 million in 1946 to over £2 million in 1951 and 1952. [2]

The refining industry, in spite of the physical and legal difficulties of the time, more than held its own. Plans were made in 1948 to extend the Government refinery at Suez from its existing capacity of 1,750 b/d to one of 9,000 or more, and in 1949 a contract was given to erect new plant, including thermal cracking plant, designed to give a capacity of 25,000 b/d. This work was well begun during 1952, but no progress was made during the first half of 1953 and further delay was anticipated. Government's intention to exact a refinery from Tapline, should that enterprise be forced to adopt an Egyptian terminal for its line, was unrealized; but products for Caltex were prepared for their local market at the Government refinery from crude imported from Arabia. The Anglo-Egyptian refinery, also at Suez, overcame by patient improvement the many difficulties of corrosion due to the 'wet' and sulphurous oil, which it was called upon to treat; it increased its asphalt output [3] and enlarged its drum factory, extended the production of bottled-gas, and steadily raised its crude intake from 22,000 b/d at the end of the war to 28,000 in 1947, 33,000 in 1948, and 40,000 b/d or more in 1951. It erected a new power-house and gas de-sulphurization and sulphur-recovery plants, which permitted the local sale of sulphur as well as of sulphur-free gas (for

---

[1] Of the 32 at Sudr, 10 were in production, 3 were observation wells, 14 were dry holes, and the rest awaiting investigation, repair, etc. Of the 28 at 'Asl, 16 were dry, 4 observation, 6 producing, 2 awaiting further investigation.

[2] The figures, given in dollars by the U.N. 'Economic Survey for 1951–2' are, for 1946, $2·8 million: for 1948, $4·3 million: for 1949–52 respectively, $5·0, 4·9, 5·8, and 5·8 million.

[3] The restrictions on export of asphalt were made subsequently to the increase in output.

the local manufacture of fertilizers). The Sinai and Ras Gharib crudes, being of different properties,[1] were kept separate for distillation purposes. The oil due to Socony-Vacuum from the jointly-operated Sinai fields was by arrangement processed by A.E.O. on their behalf at the Suez refinery and passed thence to their distribution organization, as that of A.E.O. itself was passed to Shell. Products from the refinery were dispatched by the white-products pipeline [2] to Cairo, by road and rail to all parts and by sea to Port Said and Alexandria. The future of the plant, if Egyptian supplies decreased as was expected, must be largely one of processing imported crude, as it was before 1938.[3]

Every effort was made by the management of Anglo-Egyptian Oilfields, and in so far as it was incumbent upon them by the distributing companies in Egypt, to provide their Egyptian staff and labour with good working conditions and with the welfare services and amenities, which not only the Labour Code and current practice enjoined but their own habitual standards and policy of labour-treatment indicated. Pay rates and allowances were periodically revised, latterly by collective bargaining with the Staff and Labour Syndicates. A pension scheme for Egyptian staff was under active contemplation in 1952; a Provident Fund had been introduced to include all grades of labour, and periods of service prior to this were covered by retirement gratuities prescribed by law. Well-built accommodation was provided for both staff and labour and their families at the producing fields. Personal transport was arranged, where thought necessary; it included provision for school children and for workers' periodical leave journeys [4] with their families. Shops, a company commissary, canteens, bakeries, restaurants, and messes existed on varying scales and forms at the Company's locations both east and west of the Gulf of Suez. Clubs, recreation rooms, and cinemas for both staff and labour were much used, and sports encouraged and practised. Mosques and Coptic churches had been erected by the

[1] Mixed Ras Gharib and Hurghada crude had an A.P.I. gravity of 25 degrees, that of Sudr-'Asl of 19–22 degrees.

[2] The line, constructed by Shell for the British Army during the war, was acquired in 1953–4 by the Egyptian Government.

[3] Among projects current in Egyptian circles early in 1953 were those for the erection of refineries at Cairo and Alexandria, to be supplied with crude from Banias and Sidon; and for the development of internal pipelines.

[4] The bulk of the Ras Gharib workers' homes were at Kenna on the Nile, 250 miles distant.

Company or by company-assisted public subscription. Electric light and power and supplies of good water were available everywhere. Medical services included campaigns against fly-borne diseases, dental clinics, and the maintenance of women's and children's welfare centres. All safety precautions were taken and safety training was given. Close co-operation was offered to the Government in its anti-illiteracy work among adults.

Staff and labour syndicates have existed for some years in the producing fields and at Suez refinery and at other major centres, where oil workers are employed, such as Cairo, Port Said, and Alexandria. From time to time negotiations in respect of wages and other relevant conditions of service took place, but in 1948 for the first time the Companies and the various syndicates entered into formal agreements regulating wages and cost-of-living and other allowances over a definite period. The tariffs then established, with modifications in cost-of-living allowances, remained in force until mid-1951. Towards the end of 1950 a Confederation of Petroleum Syndicates came into being, with headquarters in Suez, and the syndicates, which existed at the different centres, became affiliated members. New agreements, providing for a considerable upward revision in rates of remuneration, were negotiated and concluded with the Federation to take the place of the 1948 expired agreements.

## CHAPTER XV
# 'IRAQ, 1953–60

THE present chapter and those following, each covering a defined region of our area, are to deal with the very important period of consolidation, re-establishment (in Iran) and progress in the years 1953 to mid-1960. These five chapters will in their turn be followed by six more (Chapters XX to XXV) to cover the subsequent fortunes of each group of territories in oil discovery and development during the years from mid-1960 to late 1966, and one more chapter will be added to provide a summary of some main aspects of the subject as seen in the autumn of the latter year.

We pass now, therefore, to the 'Iraq of 1953–60.

### I. GOVERNMENTAL AND GENERAL

If one outstanding requirement for successful industrial development, that of social and political tranquillity, was lacking in the Iraq of 1953–60, it cannot be said that its oil industry, of which nine-tenths[1] remained throughout in the same competent hands as before, those of the I.P.C. Group of companies, suffered otherwise than temporarily from the disturbed and disturbing events of the time. The more extreme utterances of Arab or 'Iraqi nationalism inevitably created at times an atmosphere of apprehension far from conducive to confidence (or maximum willing investment) by a foreign-owned industrial concern; but of an imminent passage from words to damaging action there was in 'Iraq fortunately no definite sign. The destruction of the I.P.C.'s mid-desert pipeline stations in November 1956, by the Syrian army, brought export of oil from northern 'Iraq to a standstill for some months, and severely limited it for more; but the position was, by great Company efforts, restored after eighteen months, and thereafter improved. Meanwhile the I.P.C. not merely bore

---

[1] The separate fortunes of the isolated Khaniqin Oil Company are mentioned on pp. 265-6.

its losses with patience, but provided the 'Iraq Government with a loan of £25 million to help it to maintain its development programme. The revolution of July 1958, which ended the monarchy and ushered in a nominal republic but actual military dictatorship, had, contrary to the fears of pessimists, no catastrophic effects on the operations of the industry. It led, seriously but not fatally, to an increase of supervision and 'security' measures, sometimes embarrassing: to delays and difficulties in obtaining decisions: to censorship and restricted movements: to critical querying of European employees' credentials: to the disappearance from Government service of most (or all) of the high officials experienced in the oil industry, and thereby added at least temporarily to the difficulty of friendly and fruitful Government-Company liaison: and to the dominance, even more than before, of political over economic considerations in the high councils of the State. But relations on the whole remained gratifyingly correct; revolutionary fervour and bitterness against the former governmental regime did not lead to a diminution of the Company's rights obtained therefrom, or of its ability to operate. Nevertheless, any prospect of future working without friction or controversy was precluded by such sudden, unilateral demands from Government as that, in midsummer 1960, for an additional five shillings per ton duty on crude exported from Basra—a duty immediately rendering this crude markedly less competitive, with resulting enforced cutback in production, no less promptly resented by the Government.

The Companies on their side were, within the limits of their own constituents' marketing potentials and policies, fully ready to co-operate with Government in increasing their output, including the extremely expensive provision of full facilities to this end. Their objectives were largely Government's, their successes (so conspicuous during this period) were welcome to both, and their changes in top-management administration, in the direction of more unity and more authority for and under their Baghdad office, were designed for better liaison with Government as well as greater efficiency in operation. The Companies repeatedly assisted Government's plans in practical matters: a piped water-supply from the Lesser Zab to Kirkuk and its inlying villages, the supply of oil and gas to the Dibis power station, the building of the K2-Daura pipeline for the Government refinery, the drilling of wells at Qaiyara to supply the Government bitumen factory, and friendly collaboration over a fair at Mosul, an exhibition at Kirkuk, athletic sports and the like. In a more controversial sphere, a long-standing dispute was settled in 1957 regarding discounts allowable against seaboard prices before settling the Companies' (divisible) profits for the year. (The Company ultimately agreed to a discount figure reduced to 1 per cent., and paid not only a lump-sum of £7 million in settlement of 1953-7 claims, but also half-profits thereafter based on the higher prices.)

Except in minor matters, to be later mentioned, no changes in the terms or interpretations of the I.P.C.-Group Companies' concessions were made during the period; but a clear reminder was given in September 1958, shortly after the revolution, first that Government would expect greater revenues resulting from accelerated production, and, secondly, that it reserved its right to invoke the terms of its letter of September 1951, to the effect that, in the event of a neighbouring country receiving a higher average revenue per ton of oil exported than was currently being received by 'Iraq, then Government would claim a similar amount.

To the existing Ministry of Economics and Directorate of Oil Affairs, the Republican Government added by law, in mid-1959, a new General Committee for Oil Affairs, with a comprehensive list of duties in all branches of the industry, covering policy, concessions, pipelines, research, production, refining, etc. Before this, in August 1958, another amending law had changed the constitution of the Government Refineries Administration in the direction of bringing its decisions 'in the interests of the public' more closely under the Ministry of Economics and the Cabinet. The Government showed also every sign of sharing fully the prevailing attitude of Middle Eastern authorities in the period, in demanding a greater governmental, and perhaps public, share in the industry: a view based partly on national *amour propre* and designed to minimize or destroy the spectacle of a great foreign monopolist, partly on hopes of direct profit, partly to aid industrialization—and possibly to provide non-political careers for a part of the under-employed intelligentsia; nor was the presence of numerous oil-technicians from the U.S.S.R., busy in the field and in the refineries from late 1958 onwards, likely to damp down such aspirations. Such had indeed been the spirit of at least part of the agreements signed on 3 February 1952 (p. 191) with the I.P.C. Group, and in July 1952 (pp. 193-4) with the Khaniqin Oil

Company, and such also could be a reasonable lesson to be drawn from the 1954 Consortium Agreement in Persia. The activities arising from these aspirations will be briefly reviewed.

They included, evidently, the control of all distribution and disposal of oil products within the territory, to an extent which had reached some $1\frac{1}{4}$ million t/y by 1959. The Rafidain Company had ceased entirely to operate after the agreement of 25 December 1951. The Khaniqin Oil Company handled the main distribution of products on behalf of Government until June 1959, when it handed over those functions to the 'Iraqi authorities; after which date, B.P. ('Iraq Agencies) Ltd., as the K.O.C. was now renamed, retained the distribution only of aviation spirit and special products. 'Iraq Government administration covered also, since 1952, the whole field of local refining, a sphere entrusted to the *ad hoc* Government Oil Refineries Administration (G.O.R.A.) which (until 1959) enjoyed considerable autonomy and was allowed to enjoy a £2 million loan, publicly subscribed. The refinery at Alwand had been bought from the Khaniqin Company in 1952: but the latter continued to administer it on behalf of G.O.R.A. until April 1959. The refinery, drawing its crude from Naftkhana, did not in the later years work to its full capacity of 0·5 million t/y. The small plant at Muftiya, near Basra (p. 194), worked under G.O.R.A. without incident; it was announced in July 1960 that G.O.R.A. intended to build a large refinery at Basra, with 2 million t/y throughput, to cost £20 million and be complete by 1965. The larger plant at Daura outside Baghdad (p. 193) came on stream early in 1955, using crude pumped by Government-owned but Company-constructed pipeline from K2. To the plant in its original form a lubricating oil factory was added in 1956–7, and a bitumen plant in the latter year. Its overall output was increased to $2\frac{1}{2}$ million t/y in 1958–9, and Soviet technicians replaced British in its operation from late 1958 onwards. Government-Company agreement was reached in 1959 to the effect that surplus products from Daura, which the enlarged capacity made available, were eligible for export; and further ambitions in that field were indicated by plans under discussion from the spring of 1958 onwards for a much larger ($6\frac{1}{2}$ million t/y) refinery at Basra, to use Rumaila (royalty) crude and to produce products for export. This had not, by mid-1960, eventuated. At Qaiyara, G.O.R.A. decided in 1954 to erect a bitumen factory, capable of a 60,000 t/y output, with some diesel and fuel oil. The Mosul Petroleum Company drilled a heavy-oil well, and later a second, to provide raw material for this. The plant began to operate in 1955. Two years later its output was reduced, then discontinued, and plans made in 1958 for its transformation into a refinery were not carried out. It was, in 1959–60, inactive.

Industrial enterprises on the fringe of the oil industry also attracted the interest of the Government. In June 1958 a contract was signed with an American company (Ralph M. Parsons) for the erection at Kirkuk of a 300-ton-per-day plant to derive sulphur from natural gas; the plant, intended for completion by midsummer 1960, would produce also gasoline and l.p.g., and at the same time 90 million cubic feet of gas a day would be pumped to Baghdad. A second Government scheme, also mooted in 1958, was for utilization of natural gas from the Basra fields for a power plant and fertilizer factory at that city. Other similar plans were not infrequently suggested, and seemed likely to play a major part in the future. The same might well apply to ambitions (encouraged by Arab inter-statal discussion) to own a governmental, or at least all-'Iraqi, tanker fleet, whose services the producing companies would be asked to use; an 'Iraqi Maritime Transportation Company already existed in 1958 when these plans came into the open.

More immediate was the first appearance of the 'Iraq Government in the role of oil producer. The agreement with the Khaniqin Company in 1952 had provided for the relinquishment of their concession in the event of their failing to reach a production from their Naftkhana field such as to justify export from the territory by February 1959; by late 1958, all efforts sufficiently to increase their production having failed,[1] the field passed into government occupation and operation, the crude being, as before, treated at the already-governmental Alwand refinery. Some Egyptian, and later some Russian, advisers were believed to be employed at Naftkhana, in substitution for K.O.C. personnel. The possibility of acquisition by the State of other crude supplies already existed, since a proportion of I.P.C.-Group royalties could, under the 1951 agreement, be taken in kind; and a further provision, to which the Company agreed in 1959, permitted

---

[1] Naftkhana production (in thousands of tons) was, for the years 1954–8 respectively, 539, 433, 217, 196, and 197.

Government so to request at shorter notice than had been envisaged before. In fact, however, such supplies in kind could in
existing conditions be of little benefit to the State, since they
would be saleable to outside buyers only at a discount: that is to
say, below the posted price at which the Company was bound to
buy all royalty oil offered to it by the Government. Nevertheless
the latter in 1959 announced (not for the first time) that it would
have nearly 6 million tons of royalty oil to sell in 1960, thus
envisaging a total output of 46 million tons, and hoping presumably
for outside sales (to Poland, or India?) which the current keenness
of world competition must render, in fact, unlikely.

The wish to regain possession of some of the territory already
conceded to one or other of the three I.P.C.-Group Companies,
in order to reconcede it (doubtless on revised terms) to newcomers,
or possibly as a sphere for direct Government development, was
clearly expressed. The Basrah Company was asked, and agreed,
in 1959 to give up its narrow frontage of territorial waters, and
Government not only proclaimed in November 1958 that these
were twelve miles in depth but emphasized also its full claim to
its outlying Continental Shelf waters, of which the delimitation
as against Kuwait and Persia was unlikely to prove easy. More
significant than this were conversations which began in 1958
between the Companies' management in 'Iraq and the Government regarding a more general surrender of territory, even
though the text of the concessions contained no provision for this.
The Companies early agreed in general terms to divest themselves
of some areas, and negotiations continued; the difficulty lay in
the question of what the areas should be, and who should select
them. As to future incoming concessionaires for such acreage,
there was naturally no present suggestion, nor as to the terms
likely to be demanded, be they traditional, revised, or revolutionary.
But it could be felt that, in a world already over-supplied with
oil, and with new sources in Libya and Algeria to come shortly
into the market, from areas far nearer than 'Iraq to main centres
of consumption, there might well be little enthusiasm among
applicants for areas discarded, after years of fruitless search, by
the pioneers of the industry.

Total production of oil from the fields of the three Companies
of the I.P.C. Group in 'Iraq during these years, 1953-9, was
respectively (in millions of tons) 27·2, 29·58, 32·71, 30·6, 21·36,

34.93, and 40·9. All of this,[1] except for amounts approximating to 1½ million t/y dispatched to Daura and Muftiya refineries, and for the Companies' own consumption, was exported by pipeline from northern 'Iraq, by tanker from southern. 'Iraqi proved reserves of oil were estimated in 1959 to be of the order of 3,570 million tons. Direct royalty-*cum*-taxation payments by the Companies to the Government amounted, in 1953–5, to £58 million, £68·3 million, and £64 million; and in 1956–9, to £68·8 million, £48·9 million, £79·9 million, and £86·6 million.

The policy of the three Companies *vis-à-vis* their employees and the local public was unchanged in these years, and, with due allowance for expansion and improvement year by year in the varied and comprehensive services and amenities offered, it continued on the lines already described for the immediately preceeding years (pp. 177–9, 184–5, 187). In the later years to, and including, 1959–60 further progress was made in the introduction of 'Iraqi personnel into positions of responsibility in the Companies, so that by the end of 1959 50 per cent. of the senior administrative and technical grades were 'Iraqi, as against 35 per cent. at the end of 1958. Of the total number of personnel (13,165) employed by the three Companies, 96 per cent. were nationals and 4 per cent. foreigners by mid-1960.

With the authorized formation of trade unions during 1959 the Companies could further develop their machinery of industrial relations, and a new pattern of labour relations was created. There were also considerable developments in the field of training. The Training Departments at Kirkuk and Basra continued their established courses, and in addition thirty-five 'Iraqi employees were sent abroad for special studies in the United Kingdom, the United States, and Holland. Subjects of study covered all aspects of the petroleum industry, as well as civil and electrical engineering, architectural design, and industrial management. The regular training programme for 'Iraqi drillers was also enlarged during the year to include training in Holland and the United Kingdom. The number of 'Iraqi staff sent abroad for training in 1959 amounted to fifty.

As chairman of the Board of the Companies in London, Lord Monckton assumed duty in place of Admiral Cunningham in 1959.

---

[1] For *total* 'Iraqi output in these years, the figures given in the footnote on p. 266 must, of course, be added.

As Managing Director, G. H. Herridge took over from H.S. (Sir Stephen) Gibson in 1958. The Companies' Chief Local Representative in 'Iraq was from 1952 to 1957 Sir Herbert Todd, thereafter till 1960 R. G. Searight, followed by F. Rylands. Successive General Managers of I.P.C. at Kirkuk were M. S. Mainland, L. J. F. Teyssot, E. E. Thorneloe, A. J. Perks; of M.P.C. at 'Ain Zala, J. Hopkinson; of B.P.C. at Basra, L. J. F. Teyssot, J. J. Page, and A. H. R. Grimsey.

## II. NORTHERN 'IRAQ

Of the Companies' clear, indeed obvious, objectives in their field activities, most were well achieved during this period of mainly satisfactory expansion and consolidation, with many visible and invisible improvements and additions to the scale, ease, and economy of operation, and considerable increased output; but one objective remained elusive. This was the discovery of further large-scale oil-bearing structures to take their place in lightening the burden on, and prolonging the life of, the present unique provider in northern 'Iraq, the Kirkuk structure. Year by year geologists and geophysicists with their varying equipment toured, camped, examined, and calculated, in widespread areas of all northern 'Iraq; year by year holes were drilled to test (or in some cases to retest) structures which offered promise. In the area of the Mosul Petroleum Company, no discovery of any significance was made; in that of the 'Iraq Petroleum Company, in spite of shows of oil at more than one new or old location, the only fair hopes were those which came to light at Bai Hasan in 1953 and at Jambur (p. 71) in 1954. At the former (pp. 72, 176), where high-pressure gas had long ago been discovered, the presence of oil in probably commercial quantities was confirmed, and development drilling proceeded. By the end of 1959 eight wells had been drilled on the structure capable of production (out of thirteen drilled in all), but the field, one of only limited importance, had not yet produced for export, though small quantities had been taken from it for local use. It was reported in August 1959 that well number 13 in this field had found oil in a new horizon, in promising quantity. At Jambur, thirty-five miles south-east of Kirkuk, four production wells were drilled in 1954–9, and the field was put on export production in August of the latter year, after which it produced at a rate of 0·66 million t/y. This oil, from 5,700-foot depth, was of 41° A.P.I. Both these fields were equipped, after discovery and during drilling, with gathering-lines, degassing stations, tankage, pipelines to K1 station, roads, and buildings: but, disappointing after all in performance, they appeared in neither case to offer anything remotely resembling another Kirkuk. Elsewhere, in M.P.C. territory, in spite of drilling on selected locations at Jabal Makhul, Sasan, 'Atshan, 'Alan, Gullar, Ibrahim, Milh Tharthar, Samarra, Falluja, 'Ana, and Khulaisiya, no hopeful signs could be announced; and the existing M.P.C. fields ('Ain Zala, Butma) sufficed, not without difficulty, to produce the minimal concessionary requirement of 1 million t/y—an unhappy situation. At the same time in the I.P.C. area seismic work followed by drilling at Palkhana, Khormor, Chamchamal, Injana, and Gilabat was no more fortunate. Of these, Khormor seemed at one stage to be a likely candidate, but failed to fulfil hopes. Areas in which geophysical work, but not drilling, was carried out need not here be specified. The total exploration effort of these years, however ill rewarded, was both considerable and costly.

As to current production, the situation in the Mosul Company's area has already been indicated. At both the producing fields development drilling was continuous. Wells in production in the midsummer of 1960 were at 'Ain Zala ten, and at Butma five. The aggregate production, dispatched by pipeline (134 miles) to K2, there to join I.P.C. oil on its seaward journey, was in the years 1953 to 1959, in thousands of tons, respectively 1,277, 1,283, 1,282, 1,081, 564 (both of these last under the effect of the damaged pipelines), 1,280, and 1,270. Without new discovery, so long and earnestly sought, little or no improvement in these figures could be expected; indeed only by applying a gas-lift system (with 'Ain Zala gas) could the Butma field, with its dropping pressure, be kept in useful action. The proportion of each field in the M.P.C. total was approximately 'Ain Zala five-sixths, Butma one-sixth. The output of Qaiyara, from two wells drilled *ad hoc*, was intended not for export but to serve the 'Iraq Government's bitumen factory during the latter's short life, and for local uses. M.P.C. annual drilling, largely exploratory, varied annually from 18,000 to 36,500 feet; cumulative drilling by the end of 1959 had amounted to 485,000 feet.

The operations of the I.P.C., its output from the giant Kirkuk field conditioned at all times by seaward pipeline capacity, passed in these years through three phases. The first, 1953–6, was one of only slowly increasing production, which in these years amounted respectively to 22·86 million, 23·73 million, 24·2 million, and (with a total interruption towards the end of the year) 21·08 million tons. The number of producing wells increased at a moderate pace; others were drilled for observation purposes, and one, in the Avana section, as a deep test. Two more units were added to the Stabilization Plant, more degassing stations were provided, and a group of wells tied in to each; more works of construction (training-centre expansion, a Club, workshops, improved water-supply) were carried out. Minor pipeline improvements were made, with a slight increase of potential throughput.

The second phase was one of sudden ruin followed by recovery; it began with the destruction of the pumping-station installations in the pipeline desert stations in Syria, T2, T3, and T4, in November 1956 by a force of the Syrian army, in a moment of anti-Western political excitement, and this was followed by total inaction on and along the line until repair and replacement could, with Government consent, be started. The position was restored by a series of temporary expedients, followed by improved permanent installations, at a reduced number of stations. A new high-pressure pump-house at K1 station was commissioned, and at T1 station (in 'Iraq) two more pumping sets were added to the existing 30-inch line pumping units; other steps were taken in the Syrian section of the line, notably a major development of T3 station with five new pumping sets, and the rapid construction of ninety miles of loop lines. By June 1958 the rate of pumping on the trunk lines had again reached their pre-1956 capacity of approximately 25 million t/y.

A plan conceived at this period, as an alternative or addition to transit through Syria, was that of a large-diameter pipeline to run from northern 'Iraq across southern Turkey to a Mediterranean port, Mersin or Alexandretta. A rough survey on the ground by I.P.C. personnel established at once the feasibility and the costliness of the plan, which was capable also of extension southward to the Persian Gulf and Kuwait for possible two-way operation. The plan in general commended itself to the Turks, and was taken seriously by conferences of oil-men in Europe; but the 'Iraq Government, from reasons of Arab solidarity, vetoed the project, and its execution became less and less probable.

The third phase in I.P.C. history began in mid-1958 and continued steadily thereafter. It was one of increased expansion, destined to be followed shortly by a much accelerated rate of the same. The Kirkuk structure gave in the years 1957–9 an output of 11·66, 22·63, and 27·33 million tons respectively, the last mentioned being the highest yet achieved. The field produced its 200-millionth ton of oil in 1958—a rare distinction among the world's oil-fields. The first target set after restoration of the 25-million t/y rate was 28 million t/y, which was achieved late in 1959 by completion of 125 miles of pipe-looping, accompanied by further production-drilling in Fields and by the construction of three more degassing stations as well as new units in the stabilization plant. A new target of 35 million t/y from Kirkuk (together with the modest M.P.C. contribution) was promptly set, and with the aid of a further programme of pipeline looping and duplication,[1] was to be achieved before the end of 1960.

A certain pressure decline in the structure seemed in 1957–8 to call for remedial measures; these were applied, and took the form of gas injection into the Avana section of the structure, using gas brought by pipe from Bai Hasan.[2] At the same time water-injection was initiated by pumping water from the Lesser Zab into wells on the southern, or Baba Gurgur, part of the structure, at an initial rate of some 40,000 b/d. Both these methods were capable of almost indefinite extension. The condition of the reservoir—the pressure maintained, its growing gas-cap, and its slow rise in water-level per million tons of oil produced—was kept under keen observation. Admirable as had been and was the performance of the Kirkuk structure, the annual and still rising figure of offtake from it suggested strongly the need (as we have said) of additional large-scale sources to support it; production from northern 'Iraq was, according to current plans, intended to reach 48 million t/y by 1962, and no help was in sight beyond the doubtful resources of the M.P.C., Jambur, and Bai Hasan.

[1] The I.P.C. Kirkuk–Mediterranean pipeline system, by the spring of 1960, consisted of the old 12-, 16-, and 32-inch lines, together with 66 miles of 32-inch under construction in 'Iraq (to be followed by a further 180 miles), 217 miles of 30/32-inch and 68 miles of 24-inch in Syria already completed, with 21 miles of 24-inch under construction, and 30 miles of 30-inch in Syria–Lebanon which were completed in May 1960. The K2–Daura pipeline took annually about 1·3 million t/y of Kirkuk oil to the Government's refinery.

[2] By early 1960 83,000 million cubic feet of gas had been injected, the equivalent of 40 million tons of crude.

### III. SOUTHERN 'IRAQ

The orientation, geology, and potential of the south-'Iraqi fields, the domain of the Basrah Petroleum Company, were in many ways different from those of the north. There were here no short-cuts to the Mediterranean, with their competitive advantages—and their vulnerability; there were, instead, long sea-miles to be faced en route to markets, side by side with powerful Persian Gulf oil rivals. No good natural loading-point existed from which to set out, and the Suez Canal (with its memories of 1956-7) had to be passed en route. And oil deposits occured only at, for the Middle East, exceptional depth.

In early 1953 Zubair (p. 186f.) was the Company's only producing field, with an output in that year of 3 million tons, and 4½ million in 1954. But, following a thorough geophysical survey, a second field was discovered by the drill late in the same year at Rumaila, twenty miles west of Zubair, at over 10,500 feet, in a structure which at once appeared important. All steps were taken to develop it; a gathering-centre and degassing station (later duplicated), a pumping plant and necessary buildings, and a 12-inch pipeline to Zubair, later increased by another 16-inch one. Production from Rumaila began late in 1954; by 1957 the offtake from it (4·88 million t/y), already exceeded that of Zubair, and its potential was evidently far in excess of the older field's; it was likely indeed by the middle 'sixties to be greater by six times, or more. By early 1960 the Zubair field had thirty-eight, the Rumaila field twenty wells capable of production, and for the exploitation of them all necessary installations had been provided and were under constant extension. The combined production of B.P.C. was, in each year of the period 1953-60, 3·07 million, 4·58 million, 7·23 million, 8·42 million, 9·14 million, 11·02 million, and (in 1959) 12·3 million tons. Of the last mentioned amount 12 million tons were actually shipped, in 661 tankers. The current target in the middle of 1960 was to raise this export to 22 million t/y within two years. This would involve a continuance of development measures already well begun in the Basra fields: the drilling (in part by contract) of further wells (to 12,000 feet if necessary),[1]

---

[1] Annual footage drilled by B.P.C. varied from 30,000 to 127,000 feet, thanks to the rapidity of expansion and the great depth of the wells. Total drilling by B.P.C., to the end of 1959, was 784,000 feet—more, by 150,000 feet, than that of I.P.C.

and the construction of three new degassing stations with pumping units and other works—all to be completed by mid-1961.

The increase in export of oil to a level of 12 million t/y in 1950 had called already for major works at, and pipelines to, the marine terminal at Fao (pp. 186–8). Here, by 1959, jetties and berths had been extended and strengthened, dredging carried out to admit ships of up to 26,000 (or, by early 1960, 30,000) tons; tankage had been much augmented—to a total of 22 164-foot-diameter tanks, [1] with a working capacity of 330,000 tons, by early 1960— and all loading facilities as well as domestic and office buildings had been provided. But for the further expansion of export by sea now planned, still more must be done; mere additional jetties, and further dredging to permit the handling of 32,000-ton tankers, would not suffice. The decision was therefore reached in 1958, in accord with the Government, to construct an off-shore, mid-sea loading terminal at the head of the Persian Gulf twenty-four miles from Fao (but within 'Iraqi waters). Preliminary work began in 1959; pile driving and the arrival of materials started early in 1960. The completed terminal was to permit the expansion of exports from 12 to 22 million t/y, and was intended to be in service before the end of 1961. Five platforms, [2] all interconnected, would stand in seventy-five feet of water, the central and largest platform to measure 400 by 240 feet. The smaller platforms, at the sides and ends of this, would serve for mooring lines and would provide living quarters for shift crews and a helicopter deck. Connexion with Fao, where a new pump house would be erected, would be by two 32-inch submarine pipelines. The Fao tank-farm itself would be fed by a new 30/32-inch pipeline from Zubair. Initially two 65,000-ton tankers would be able to berth and load simultaneously, with a combined loading rate of 8,000 tons an hour.

The discovery of Rumaila and its rich production did not render needless exploration elsewhere in the B.P.C. concession area. This was in fact undertaken by many fully equipped parties in various districts, from the vicinity of the existing fields to the

[1] Six units of the Fao tank-farm were struck by lightning in November 1954; but the efforts of the Company's staff and local authorities extinguished the blaze in three hours, without the loss of export. Another tank was similarly struck again in the same month.

[2] The first two pontoons, joined together, made the 7,000-mile trip from Tyneside to Fao in July-September 1959, via the Suez Canal.

middle Euphrates (Najf and Karbala area, and that of Musaiyib), and from the south and west of the concession area to the neighbourhood—and beneath the actual waters—of the Hammar Lake, and in 'Amara province on the Persian frontier. In spite of the generally good promise of the areas tested, no discoveries were made. In the summer of 1960 it was decided to drill further at Nahr 'Umar (pp. 185f.) where light oil had been found in 1948. In the spring of 1960 exploration drilling was in progress at Kifl, Shawiya, Turba, Dujaila, and Ghulaisan. Even if these, and other sites selected after them, failed to reveal commercial deposits, it would remain improbable that Rumaila and Zubair would prove to be the only oil-resources of southern 'Iraq; far more probably that region would yield other secrets and prove a major and continuous oil provider for the world.

## CHAPTER XVI

# PERSIA, 1953–60

## I. THE CONSORTIUM

THE situation of disastrous deadlock in Persia and its oil industry (pp. 172–3), as it appeared in the spring of 1953, had by the end of the year, thanks to the disappearance of Dr. Musaddiq, taken a turn towards possible solution. The Prime Minister, having rid himself by 'referendum' of both houses of Parliament, and refused the orders of the Shah for the appointment of a new Premier, witnessed the departure from Persia of the former and set up a Council of Regency. In mid-August, however, he and his now bewildered followers were themselves worsted by a revolt of loyal officers led by General Zahedi (the Shah's choice as Premier-elect), and he lost in a few hours both his office and his liberty. The Shah returned, Musaddiq was sentenced to three years' imprisonment, and the Zahedi Government, with the Shah's support, assumed power. Both reasonable policy and economic necessity now compelled the reaching of an agreement with somebody, whether the 'former Company' or another, capable of restoring to Persia its greatest industry and its indispensable revenues. The Treasury was empty, the currency debased, all credit gone; it was time for a return to reason and the resumption of progress in Persia. The incoming Finance Minister prescribed three conditions as basic to an oil settlement: regard for Persia's political prestige, recognition of its legislative rights, and 'reciprocal respect' between Persia and Great Britain. Visits to Teheran and London were paid by Mr. Herbert Hoover, President Eisenhower's oil adviser; understanding grew, preliminary talks were held between British, Dutch, United States, and French oil companies, and in December 1953 the bilateral decision to resume Anglo-Persian diplomatic relations was published.

Negotiations on the oil issue between British, American, and Persian spokesmen began early in 1954, and revealed practicable bases for agreement. This was reached by early summer, announced in August, and ratified by the Majlis on 21 October. This Agreement, substantially unmodified in the years following, became the cornerstone of the reborn Persian oil industry. Reached as between the Persian Government and a group (known loosely as 'the Consortium') of foreign oil companies, it aimed at combining the advantages of effective and fruitful field and refinery operation with the safeguarding of Persian *amour propre*, and avoidance of unpopular monopoly.

Two Operating Companies were to be formed, both incorporated in Holland and registered in Persia. One was the Iraanse Aardolie Exploratie en Productie Maatschappij (Iranian Oil Exploration and Producing Company), the other the Iraanse Aardolie Raffinage Maatschappij (Iranian Refining Company), each with the functions in Persia indicated by its name. Each Company was given two Persian and five Company directors, and all their documents were to be available for inspection by the National Iranian Oil Company (N.I.O.C.). The latter statal organization, representing the Persian Government, and operating in part through its own subsidiary, the older I.O.C., became the agreed owner of the properties in Persia of the A.I.O.C. and, under the present Agreement, authorized the Operating Companies to use (and add to) these without restriction, for their proper functions. The area covered by the Agreement was that of the A.I.O.C. Concession of 1933. The period of the Agreement was to be twenty-five years, with possible extensions for three five-year further periods, to cover lesser areas.

The Consortium Companies proceeded immediately to form two Companies in London: one, Iranian Oil Participants Ltd., to hold the shares in the two operating Companies; and the other, Iranian Oil Services Ltd., for the provision of supplies and personnel for their operations. At the same time each Company of the Consortium formed its own 'trading company' to receive and dispose of its share of the crude and products. The two Operating Companies in Persia were not themselves to buy or sell the oil, which was to be sold by N.I.O.C. to the trading companies; they were solely to produce and refine it, in return for a fee additional to their operating costs.

A division of profits on a fifty-fifty basis was to be secured by payments from the Companies annually to the N.I.O.C., and by the application of the fiscal laws of Persia. Up to $12\frac{1}{2}$ per cent. of crude oil produced could, on demand, be payable as part royalty. To secure vigorous operation, it was stipulated that certain agreed minimum quantities of crude must be produced in each of the years 1955 to 1957.[1] Refined products for consumption in Persia, via distribution by the N.I.O.C., were to be made available at low rates at Abadan and Masjid-i-Sulaiman, as well as from N.I.O.C.'s own small refinery at Kirmanshah. Important 'non-basic' services in the Consortium area, connected with housing, roads, medical and welfare organizations, transport, and the supply of food and clothing, all hitherto part of the normal functions of A.I.O.C., were to be gradually transferred to the A.I.O.C's successor, the N.I.O.C., for carrying out, largely at the cost of the Consortium.

An account remained to be settled as between, first, A.I.O.C. and the expropriating Persian Government: and, secondly, between A.I.O.C. and the incoming Consortium Companies. The Government was to pay £25 million, by ten instalments, to cover the Company's assets within the Concession area, its distribution equipment throughout Persia, the Naft-i-Shah field, and the Kirmanshah refinery. For the 60 per cent. of its former concessionary rights and future revenues, which under the inter-Consortium Agreement it was to sacrifice, A.I.O.C.'s new partners were to pay it as consideration an immediate sum of £32·4 million and 10 cents a barrel (or 5s. 4d. a ton) on all exports until a total sum equivalent to $510 million had been reached. Those terms were duly carried out during the ensuing years.

As has been indicated, the A.I.O.C. retained a 40 per cent. interest in this field of its half-century of immense success, that of the oil industry in Persia. The other 60 per cent. was divided, in proportions which emerged from inter-Company discussion, between the international 'majors' of the industry. Royal Dutch-Shell took 14 per cent., the Compagnie Française 6 per cent., with 8 per cent. each for the five American concerns obviously designated for such shares—New Jersey, Socony-Mobil, Standard of California, the Texas Company, and the Gulf Oil Corporation. This arrangement was modified in April 1955 when, with Persian Government agreement, each of the Americans sacrificed one-eighth of its holding so as to permit the division of the resulting 5 per cent. between a group of nine other American companies

---

[1] These amounts, respectively 15 million, 23 million, and 30 million t/y, were in the event easily exceeded.

which sought admission.[1] These formed the Iricon Agency, in which the constituents held varying shares.

The new phase which the industry was thus, in 1955, about to enter rested upon bases which appeared to satisfy at least a majority of Persian opinion; the spectre of a single giant monopolist had been exorcized, foreign help, tardily recognized as in fact indispensable, would be that of a composite and international body; and in carrying out the non-basic services, as well as in the free disposal of a considerable share of the crude produced, Persia would find scope for more direct participation in the industry, by more of her citizens and interests, than in the past. And all the rest of Persia, outside the 100,000 square miles of the Consortium holding, was available for any operations that the N.I.O.C. might undertake or delegate.

## II. THE OPERATING COMPANIES IN ACTION

From the effective date of the Consortium Agreement, 29 October 1954, the new operators in the south-west Persian oil industry took their tasks vigorously in hand. While intensive exchanges in Europe and the United States arranged the remoter background of organization of the Operating Companies and compliance with the highly complicated provisions of the Agreement, the necessary operational headquarters in Persia were quickly established. Relatively small numbers of Europeans (American, British, Dutch, French) were recruited and sent to Persia, including a number of valuable ex-A.I.O.C. specialists; the too-abundant Persian labour available in Fields and at Abadan was sifted, almost entirely re-engaged, redeployed, and prepared, with increased pay-rates, for more and better work than that of the last three wasted years. Plant at all locations (much of which, indeed, had been adequately maintained) was overhauled and reconditioned; domestic questions of housing, discipline, amenities, and the non-basic services (which N.I.O.C. showed no immediate desire to take over) were set in order and in motion. Two initial, and largely persisting, difficulties met the incoming Operating authorities. One was that the proportion of labour to output was remarkably high in Persia: but for political reasons the Operating

[1] These were American Independent (pp. 214 ff, 308 f.) with 16⅔ per cent.: Richfield Oil Corporation with 25 per cent.: and Standard of Ohio, Getty Oil Company, Signal Oil and Gas Company, Atlantic Refining, Hancock Oil Company, Tidewater Oil Company, and San Jacinto Petroleum Corporation, each with 8⅓ per cent.

Companies, forbidden to reduce it, were compelled to carry hundreds or thousands of unwanted men: a source of potential Company–Government friction. Another was the differing attitudes of British and American administrators to local labour; to the former a paternalistic attitude, offering many domestic and social benefits, was traditional, while Americans tended to prefer the 'high wage and low obligation' approach.

In the vital field operations of exploration, drilling, and production, the scientific search for new oilfields within the area, to meet future needs, began in 1956. Topographical (including air-photographic and triangulation) and stratigraphical surveys were carried out by a number of parties in various parts of the area, island, coastal, and hinterland; base camps, supply depots, and landing strips were created, aircraft (including helicopters) as well as all forms of land transport were in constant use; geophysical parties, using all appropriate methods, covered wide and scattered areas. Test-drilling, once sites had been selected, was carried out at various locations. At Ahwaz (drilled unsuccessfully, to shallow depths, before the First World War) oil was found at 7,755 feet, under strong pressure, in Ahwaz no. 6 (no. 5 having proved dry), but the accompanying gas ignited and the well burnt fiercely from 19 April 1958 till its extinction, by Myron Kinley, on 4 June. The Ahwaz field, still to be fully tested, seemed in 1959–60 secure of an interesting future, though its oil proved heavier and more sulphurous than in any of the Khuzistan fields. Oil in still uncertain quantities was found also at Kuh-i-Binak, 80 miles south-east of Gach Saran, opposite Kharg, during 1959, in a well which had presented various difficulties, and was then placed under further test. Promising exploration wells were begun in 1959 at Kuh-i-Mund, 75 miles south-east of Bushire, and in 1960 at Suru in the vicinity of Bandar Abbas, where a marine gravity survey was carried out.

Production in the existing fields was resumed in 1955, from five to nine rigs being simultaneously employed. The close of each year's work showed, in one field after another, an increased number of new well-completions, new wells drilling, and others worked over. By the end of 1959 a total of 428 wells [1] (dating from

---

[1] The distribution of these wells, and the average daily production of each field in 1956 and in 1959 (in thousands of barrels) were as follows: Masjid-i-Sulaiman 257 (39:45); Lali 15 (7:15); Haft Kel 48 (84:150); Naft Safid 29 (21:55); Agha Jari 48 (371:599); Gach Saran 24 (13:59); Ahwaz 27 (nil).

all periods of A.P.O.C., A.I.O.C. and Consortium history) existed (well over half at Masjid-i-Sulaiman) and included 129 active producers. Footage drilled in 1959 alone was 103,000 feet, of which 11,300 were exploratory; twelve completions were effected in that year, including seven producers with a total potential of 150,000 b/d; the corresponding figures for 1957 and 1958 were 8 and 9. It was confirmed that, with Lali as a lesser field, and Masjid-i-Sulaiman having doubtless passed its peak production, Haft Kel, though an old field and perhaps past its prime, remained highly productive and ranked second among the fields in output (150,000 b/d in 1959). Naft Safid was a more than useful contributor. The greatest part of future output seemed, however, to belong to the two very great fields of Gach Saran and Agha Jari. The latter averaged 450,000 b/d in 1957 and 500,000, from 33 producing wells, in 1959, and was by far the greatest contributor (over 60 per cent.) to total production in this period. Much work was done during these years towards the increase of pipeline capacity from Agha Jari to Bandar Mashhur, and of production drilling (10 new wells in 1958-9), installations and facilities in this remarkable field. At Gach Saran, where the oil is somewhat heavier and more sulphurous than elsewhere, but individual well production is remarkably high, a major programme of developing facilities, housing, stores, workshops, power station, etc., as well as new producing wells, was being completed early in 1960; an offtake of 450,000 b/d was being provided for. In all the fields actual production, which totalled 535,500 b/d in 1956, 716,000 in 1957, and 923,000 in 1959, was far below maximum capacity: the limiting factors being, as ever, pipeline and offtake capacity, and ultimately market demand. The production from Persia in millions of tons, was thus, in the years 1955-9 respectively, 15·8, 25·9, 34·8, 39·8, and 44·7; that of the years 1952 and 1953 had been negligible, that of 1954 was 3 million tons.

Crude oil, after dispatch by pipelines to the coast, was all (except for a very few cargoes from Abadan) exported from Bandar Mashhur, where, however, the considerable works of improvement carried out (new jetties, tankage, and loading-systems, new buildings and amenities) still did not permit access of ships of more than 40,000 tons. The numbers of tankers loaded there increased from 479 in 1955 to 958 in 1957 and 1953 in 1959, the last-given figure representing 213 million barrels of crude. An important new crude outlet development, planned in 1955–6 for completion in 1960, was the creation of a new oil-loading base on Kharg Island, twenty-three miles offshore in the Persian Gulf. Here crude-oil and bunker-fuel tank-farms were constructed, with initial capacity of 2·7 million and 0·34 million barrels respectively, with attached housing, water-distillation, and other facilities, and a four-berth jetty, breakwater, loading-lines, power house, airstrip, etc. Oil to be exported was brought to this base by 71·5 miles of land pipeline across the wildest of country from Gach Saran to Ganaveh on the coast, and twenty-five miles of line (also of 26-28-30-inch dimension) from Ganaveh to the Kharg terminal by way of Khargu Island. Capacity of the line was 330,000 b/d, flow was by gravity, controlled by remote control at Gach Saran. Twenty-two miles of the line were submarine—nineteen to Khargu, three beyond—and these gave it the status of the longest 30-inch submarine line in the world to be laid on the ocean bed by pulling. The first tanker was loaded from the Kharg terminal on 1 August 1960.

The destination of oil exported from Persia in 1959 was: to Europe 50 per cent., to North America 6 per cent., to Middle Eastern markets (including bunkers) 5 per cent., to Africa 17 per cent., to South-East Asia 13 per cent., to the Far East 3 per cent., and to Australia 6 per cent.

A recent (late 1958) estimate for Persian reserves, including N.I.O.C. areas, was 5,000 million tons.

### III. REFINING AND SERVICES

The re-establishment of the Abadan refinery, built up by A.I.O.C. since so many years ago as the greatest in the world, was the first care of the incoming Iranian Oil Refining Company. Using the modern aviation-spirit and lubricating-oil plants established by the 'former Company' as well as older units of all ages, the new proprietors were able to process 7½ million tons in 1955, and in the next four years respectively 11·7, 15·8 (a rapid increase due to the western world's post-Suez difficulties), 15·6 and 16·2 million tons.[1] Once the plants had been placed in full

---

[1] The break-up of these annual figures as between products for (a) export and for (b) local consumption is, starting with 1955, as follows (in millions of tons): 6·5 plus 1·0; 10·1 plus 1·6; 13·8 plus 1·9; 13·2 plus 2·4; and 13·4 plus 2·8. (The 'internal consumption' part represents the N.I.O.C. offtake.) The main constituents of the total products were, in a typical year, fuel oil 37·96 per cent.:

running order in 1954–6—a task of formidable magnitude: by the end of 1956 150 units, great and small, had been meticulously overhauled—main emphasis was placed on their maintenance in high efficiency, rather than on major extension. Refining programmes were arranged for maximum production of aviation spirit and the middle distillates. In February 1960 it was announced that the Refining Company was to build a 20,000 b/d catalytic reformer, to contribute to the production of higher octane gasolines; completion was expected in 1962. A steady but no rapid increase of refining throughput was visualized. Natural gas, received by pipeline from Agha Jari, was increasingly used as refinery fuel. Sulphur recovery from crude was increased. Increased power generation, from plant completed late in 1958, was in part placed at the disposal of the Government for power lines and for Abadan municipality. Loading of products for export was carried out entirely at Abadan, involving 392 cargoes in 1955, 554 in 1957, 752 in 1959. Rather over 12 million tons of products in all were exported in each of the years 1957–9. Plans were, late in 1957, under study by N.I.O.C. for a new products export terminal in the Khor Musa, near Bandar Shapur (the railway terminus), with multiple product pipelines to that point from Abadan; tenders were called for in July 1959, but the project was thereafter not pursued.

It was largely at Abadan that the transfer of the 'non-basic services' from Consortium administration to that of N.I.O.C., as provided in the 1954 Agreement, was to be made. This involved the reorientation of the very large and admirably conceived organization of the 'former Company' for care, housing, technical training, amenities, recreation, and shops. The N.I.O.C. was, in the event, unwilling to take charge of these services otherwise than very gradually. That of the health and medical organization was, however, transferred as from January 1956, under an arrangement for sharing all new capital expenses while the cost of maintenance of existing services devolved, under the Agreement, on the Operating Companies. Certain increases in medical installations and services in the fields and refinery area were planned; these, and others newly conceived, were progressively carried out in

motor gasoline, 15·51 per cent.: gas oil 14·76 per cent.: aviation spirit 4·2 per cent.: aviation turbine fuel 3·23 per cent.: and smaller percentages for vaporizing oil, bitumen, cracked gasoline, special solvents, luboils, insecticides, and l.p.g.

1957–60. The administration and maintenance of Company housing and related services at Abadan were transferred to N.I.O.C. on 1 January 1959, with the personnel employed therein. Work in this branch of activity continued: in 1959, for instance, some 250 houses for 'staff' and 650 for labour were erected in Fields and Abadan, together with improvements in lighting, fencing, drinking-water supplies, etc. A Home Procurement Loan Scheme, a joint enterprise between N.I.O.C. and the Operating Companies, was made effective late in 1959. The problems of housing, amenities, and social life in general among the overcrowded and under-employed public of Abadan city remained difficult, and awaited solution. The administration of the Companies' Abadan Institute of Technology (in which the curriculum was revised in 1956) was handed over to N.I.O.C. in November 1959. A large grant of funds was made by the Operating Companies for school-building purposes in Khuzistan province; they continued also to provide money for scholarships tenable by students in Iran and overseas. The comprehensive industrial and technical training operations of the Companies, including the Career Development programme, were in all their graded complexity further developed during the period; transfer of these to N.I.O.C. was carried out, but in Abadan only, early in 1960. The same applied to amenities and recreation facilities.

The processes of 'Iranization' of staffs in the industry proceeded in these years even further than in the pre-1951 period. In 1956 a total of 453 overseas staff was divided between Teheran (36), Fields (146) and Abadan (271) out of a total staff and labour force of 45,900; in 1959 the corresponding figures were 695[1] of total overseas staff (151, 240, and 304), out of a total of 39,840, a figure which excluded contract labour and N.I.O.C. personnel used on non-basic operations. Foreign staff was predominantly British and American.

Payments to N.I.O.C. and the Persian Government rose yearly with the increase in output and export of oil. For 1956, as between 'stated payments' and income tax, a sum of £54 million (as against £35 million in 1955) was paid by the Operating and Trading Companies, with an additional £772,000 in Customs dues, £17·9 million in wages and salaries, £2·5 million to con-

---

[1] The temporary increase was due to the growth of planning and technical staff for higher efficiency, and to current construction works.

tractors, and £1·5 million to the Social Insurance organization. In 1957 and 1958 payments to the Government were respectively £76·5 million and £88·3 million. In 1959, correspondingly, £93·745 million was paid, with Customs dues £900,000, wages and salaries £20·6 million, local purchases and contractors £6·3 million, and Social Insurance £1·78 million. These latter payments represented the bringing into Persia, in 1959, of some £27·6 million in foreign exchange. It is needless to insist here on the value of this to the country's balance of trade, or, more generally, on the immense importance of the contribution made by the industry within 'the defined area' to Treasury and public alike.

The fiftieth anniversary of the founding of the oil industry in Persia was celebrated in March 1958.

The General Managing Directors of the Operating Companies in Persia, 1954–60, were: L. E. J. Brouwer, October 1954 to March 1956; K. Scholtens, March 1956 to July 1959; E. W. Berlin, July 1959–.

### IV. N I.O.C.

Following the new orientation of the oil industry in 1954, and the strict limitation of the Consortium to its own inherited area, operations in all branches of the industry were carried out elsewhere throughout Persia by the National Iranian Oil Company, which was established by statute early in 1955, under the law of 2 May 1951—the famous Nationalization Law (p. 163): and by its adopted subsidiary, the Iranian Oil Company. The activities of the Company, above which stood the Oil High Council of three *ex-officio* members and four parliamentarians, included certain services within the Consortium area (p. 283), and, outside it, the control and administration of the industry as a whole throughout Persia, including (subject always to Cabinet approval) the grant of concessions: exploration on its own for new fields: the development of one existing field, Naft-i-Shah: refining if and where indicated, and particularly at the one existing refinery, the 3,500 b/d plant at Kirmanshah: country-wide distribution and sale of products: establishment, possibly, of a petrochemical industry, with utilization of natural gas: trading in crude oil (including deliveries from the Operating Companies as part-royalties) and/or in products: and transportation and shipping. These tasks were, from early 1955, progressively handled by N.I.O.C. The Company

was permitted by the Government to retain, for its own development purposes, a stated proportion of its receipts: a proportion
which, however, was halved in 1959, to diminish the Government's
own budget deficit. A possibly disturbing element was removed
from the Persian scene when, in 1956, the U.S.S.R. 'renounced
its rights' in the Soviet-Iranian Kavir-i-Khurian Company
(p. 130), set up in 1925.

Geological and geophysical exploration carried out by I.O.C.,
largely under contract with foreign expert concerns, began in mid-
1955. It was pressed particularly but not solely in Central Persia,
where exploration, including drilling by Swiss and Americans on
behalf of the Government and I.O.C., had been in progress
(uninterrupted by the Musaddiq troubles) since 1951 (p. 171). The
discovery of a field at Qum, seventy-five miles south-west of
Teheran, in August 1956, with good quality 32° A.P.I. oil at
7,000–8,000 feet, was indicated by a gusher, control of which was
only achieved after two weeks. Further drilling was at once put
in hand; the decision was taken to develop the area by direct
N.I.O.C. control, and grandiose refinery and pipeline plans were
conceived.[1] Early in 1959 the N.I.O.C. announced that its second
well at Sarajeh, thirty miles south-east of Qum, had, after a first
gas-well, found light oil as well as gas at 7,870 feet; further drilling
followed and supplies of light oil and gas were established. These
it was proposed early in 1960 to develop by the formation of a
public company; a gas line to Teheran, and a refinery there, were
envisaged in April 1960; the Italian concern S.N.A.M. Progetti
(of the E.N.I. Group) was to build the required 140-kilometre
20-inch gas line to the capital and create a distribution network
there. In the Gorgan area near the Caspian, 200 miles E.N.E.
from Teheran, gas and light oil were found at 6,600 feet early in
July 1960.

Subsequent wells at Qum, however, contrary to expectation,
did little at first to establish a commercial field: two wells were
dry, one yielded only high-pressure gas. In mid-1960 a further
well (Aborz no. 8) in the same area found a promising yield of oil
at 10,540 feet. The future remained uncertain, but rather hopeful

[1] In mid-1957 agreement in principle was reached between the Persian and
Turkish Governments for a pipeline from Qum to Iskenderun, some 1,000
miles. The Persian Government was to pay, but Turkey to share profits. A
more detailed formal agreement was signed by the two Governments late in
1958, but realization of the project appeared not less remote.

than hopeless; and the same applied to discovery and development
in general in the areas outside Consortium territory. The Qum-
Sarajeh discoveries were the first in Persia east of the Zagros
(p. 9 *ad fin.*). An exploratory well at Sorkheh, 100 miles east of
Teheran, was commenced also in 1959, but suspended pending
further geophysical work. French geologists were meanwhile
exploring Azerbaijan.

N.I.O.C.'s own production at the time was limited to the
resources of the small but useful Naft-i-Shah field, in and near
which drilling proceeded with interesting results, though outlets
were limited (p. 148); and its own refining was limited to the
miniature Kirmanshah refinery (p. 61). A large-scale refinery at
Teheran was among N.I.O.C.'s current projects. Distribution of
products in all Persia was among its major tasks, and all A.I.O.C.
facilities for that purpose had been taken over. These were now
increased by a series of product pipelines, which included a 10-inch
line laid from Ahwaz to Teheran (570 miles) by way of the Qum
area, a line of $1\frac{1}{4}$ million t/y capacity built by British and French
contractors in 1955-7. Its potential was later doubled (1959) by
the addition of seven more pump-stations to the existing six.
From this line forked a 146-mile 6-inch branch line from Azna to
Isfahan; another from Teheran to Resht on the Caspian was begun
(1959) but suspended. Late in the same year an 8-inch line from
Teheran to Shahrud (240 miles) was placed on order with American
contractors; the line, with an initial capacity of 500,000 t/y, was
to serve the Khurasan province. Persia's internal consumption
to be thus satisfied rose annually, to a total of almost 3 million
tons in 1959—an increase of nearly one-fifth since the previous
year; further increase to 5 million tons by 1964 was expected.

Another care of N.I.O.C. in these years was the formation of an
all-Persian tanker-fleet. Four units destined for this were ordered
from Netherlands shipyards, and delivered in and after 1958.
The first two were of 33,000 tons, the third and fourth of 47,000
and 73,000 respectively. The earliest two delivered were chartered
by Consortium members, and it was then understood that up to
ten further orders, on credit terms, would be placed. Disposal of
the later-delivered ships proved, however, to be difficult in view
of the American companies' other commitments. The fleet was
organized as a Persian company, Iranian Tankers Ltd.

Use of oilfield or refinery products, including natural gas, was undertaken during the period, for the first time in Persia, by the Plan Organization and other authorities of the central Government. At Ahwaz, in Khuzistan province, a chemical fertilizer plant, using natural gas, was announced in 1956 as to be erected by a Belgian concern for the Plan Organization; but this did not eventuate. In 1958 an Italian firm decided to build a plastics plant, also at Ahwaz, using natural gas from Agha Jari; this also did not appear. Gas from Gach Saran, it was stated late in the same year, was to be taken to Marvdasht, 25 miles north of Shiraz, to supply a fertilizer plant and for use as fuel in other industries; contractors of various nationalities were to be employed, on behalf of the Ministry of Mines and Industry. The basic contract was given to a French concern. The design provided for the production of ammonium nitrate and urea. The plant was expected to be under construction at Shiraz late in 1960, as a Government project. The S.N.A.M. Progetti gas line from Sarajeh to Teheran has been mentioned above.

### V. MORE FOREIGN ENTERPRISES, 1957–60

The direct activities of the N.I.O.C.—or, in effect, of the Persian Government—have been described: but, since that body could not competently at one time undertake all tasks of country-wide discovery, production, and the rest unaided (an error so expensively made in various countries, including Turkey in 1920 to 1955), it was decided by the Government to permit also a regulated delegation to outside bodies, with their rich experience and their essentially needed capital, without sacrificing the much-desired possibility of Persian participation. The Petroleum Law, issued in mid-1957, provided procedures for this.

The N.I.O.C. might under this Law (which at many points gave wide discretion as to the terms of each grant) give rights—for which the name 'Concessions' would be improper—within the eight defined Districts declared by it to be available[1] to suitable and fully qualified[2] outside concerns, without, or with only a minimum of, Persian shareholding; but in the latter cases (none of which had in fact arisen by mid-1960) the areas granted would be more restricted, the terms of operation more stringent, payments

[1] A considerable part of Persia was reserved as a 'national reserve', not eligible for grants, and Qum area was kept for direct N.I.O.C. exploitation.

[2] One qualification was reciprocal treatment by the foreign country to which the applicant belonged; this excluded Russia.

(including an initial bonus) and drilling obligations heavier, compulsory surrender of territory more rapid, and deliveries of royalty-oil in kind to N.I.O.C. more substantial. Such conditions, or some of them, were to apply to cases of foreign-controlled enterprise; but the possibility of, and procedures for, equal joint Government-*cum*-foreign-Company enterprises were the chief contribution of the Law. In such cases, three of which will be mentioned below, provision was made for normal taxation of the profits of the enterprise on the standard fifty-fifty basis, with division of what was left between the partners. Thus, if the State held half the shares, it would take first half-profits as governmental dues, and then half the rest as equal shareholder. Exploration expenses prior to the discovery of oil, including rentals (but these at lower rates than in an all-foreign concern), would be wholly borne by the foreign partner in lieu of an initial bonus-payment; amounts would be prescribed in terms of period and minimum amount. The terms of the agreement would be for not more than twenty-five years from the date of first commercial production, with three possible five-year renewals, such renewals to be, in certain cases, accompanied by a revision of terms in Government's interest. Failure to find oil within twelve years would involve abandonment; progressive relinquishment of non-producing territory would be enforced, and provisions were stringent in precluding the employment of all but a minimum of foreign staff. The Boards of Directors of such Companies would be equally Persian and non-Persian, with a Persian chairman. Successive districts of unallotted Persia were, by decree, made available for development, and by 1960 covered most of the country.

The provisions thus summarized, and the generally more enlightened and realistic Persian approach to foreign enterprises since 1954, seemed likely to lead to such initiatives in potentially fruitful forms. In effect three such grants were made, in the period 1957-9, within areas declared to be available. The first, in the autumn of 1957, was to a joint Company known as the Société Iran-Italienne des Pétroles (S.I.R.I.P.), formed by the Italian A.G.I.P. Mineraria jointly with N.I.O.C. S.I.R.I.P. was allotted three blocks totalling 23,000 square kilometres, one (5,600 sq. km.) in the Continental Shelf at the north-east corner of the Gulf; one (11,300 sq. km.) inland, on the east side of central Zagros; and one (6,100 sq. km.), on land and sea combined along the Makran coast of the Gulf of Oman. Detailed provisions followed the lines indicated above; all pre-discovery costs devolved upon A.G.I.P., whose first experience this was in such an orientation, and who undertook heavy exploration expenses in the early years. The second grant, on similar terms, was made in May 1958 to Pan American Petroleum Corporation (a subsidiary of Standard of Indiana, also a newcomer to the region); the joint Company became Iran Pan American Oil Company (or I.P.A.C.) to which was now granted 16,000 sq. km., entirely offshore, at the head of the Gulf in a location bisected by the first mentioned of S.I.R.I.P.'s blocks. In this case, perhaps because bidding had been keen, an initial bonus was payable in addition to annual rentals, and the exploration expenditure imposed was extremely high—$82 million within an initial twelve year period. The agreement was, in a number of ways, more exacting than S.I.R.I.P.'s; for example, preference in exporting oil was to be given to Persian tankers, and penalties for delay in honouring drilling obligations were heavy. The third grant was for an area of 1,000 sq. km. only, in the extreme south-east of Persia, both on and off-shore; it was made, on the same joint basis, to a minor Canadian Company, Sapphire Petroleum. The joint Perso-Canadian company formed was known as I.R.C.A.N. Sapphire undertook to spend $18 million on early exploration, unaided by its statal partner.

Each of the incoming companies pursued its enterprise. S.I.R.I.P., after a year of intensive surveying and geophysical (including marine seismic) work, selected locations in 1958. In 1959 it drilled one offshore well which had reached 6,250 feet by the year's end, and one at a high altitude (8,200 feet) in the Zagros portion of their holding. I.P.A.C. drilled a first well offshore, in 125 feet of water, and reached 13,150 feet with no oil show; its second, spudded in in May 1960, was in 144 feet of water, twenty-one miles south of Kharg island and twenty-two miles west of Bushire. I.R.C.A.N. appeared to its potential partner N.I.O.C. as the least satisfactory; a dispute arose, late in 1959, as to its accomplishment of its exploration obligations, but this was composed on the basis of exploration being commenced forthwith.

## CHAPTER XVII

# SA'UDI ARABIA, 1953–60

## I. KINGDOM AND COMPANY

THERE was throughout this period no change in the constitution, or the continuity, of the Sa'udi kingdom: from which, with all its implications of mediaevalism and strangeness to modern industrial conditions and demands, there could not but persist the now familiar difficulties (largely, in daily dealings, surmounted) which faced the operating Company in its local relations. Nevertheless some signs of a movement, sometimes willing, sometimes hesitant, towards the modern world and the Kingdom's own more developed neighbours were not lacking in these years.

The orientation and foreign policy of the Wahhabi State remained, indeed, strictly Islamic and dynastic, strongly anti-Communist, devoted (like most other governments) to its own immediate interests as conceived, suspicious of change, jealous of its status and 'face', and unversed in the proprieties of modern diplomacy as well as ignorant, or scornful, of the measure of compromise needed in dealings with foreign Powers. But by greater acquaintance with world events through foreign broadcasts and presses, by exchange of royal or statesmen's visits, by more American and European contacts at all levels and the employment of more non-Sa'udi officials, isolation grew less, and national self-confidence (if such can be claimed under a despotic theocratic monarchy) grew more. If Sa'udi interference in the internal politics of the Oman Sultanate was unfortunate as well as needless, and their persistent claim to the Buraimi Oases was accompanied by strange irregularities, at least the Anglo-French intervention at Suez in 1956 was greeted with suitable Arab indignation—directed naturally against British neighbours, at Bahrain, rather than at their own American concessionaires. Before that, an amicable interim agreement had been reached in 1954 with Great Britain regarding the Sa'udi–abu Dhabi and Sa'udi–Qatar boundaries, and another was made in 1958 with the Shaikh of Bahrain for the division of their offshore waters. Relations with the Kuwaiti shaikhdom, which the overlap of authority in the Neutral Zone might well have troubled, were in fact undisturbed, and with the Qatar ruler were friendly.

Internally, in spite of the survival of many of the ancient ways and the vagaries of arbitrary rule—and a financial near-crisis due to exuberant over-spending, later in part corrected—there were signs of improved administration, particularly after the wide delegation of royal powers, early in 1958, to the able and travelled Crown Prince Faisal. State budgets, of seemingly more value than in the past, were prepared and presented; executive power, under the King, was given to a Council of Ministers with defined functions; some real financial control and limitation of imports appeared to be exercised; grants to the royal family were limited, more of the state revenues spent on public services; and, with American help, a Sa'udi Monetary Agency had been established (p. 200) to perform the functions of Treasury and Central Bank. Relations with Aramco, contributor of almost the entirety of Sa'udi wealth, were well maintained, thanks not least to the ceaseless vigilance of the former and its specialized agencies for contact and assistance. But the essential and largely non-reasonable difficulties existing, or too easily created, in the relationship and day-by-day propinquity of a self-conscious, sensitive, oriental, and Islamic Government with a powerful and locally all-pervasive foreign (and Christian) industrial concern, could not but be present: and, passing from phase to phase, would probably continue and evolve the more dangerously as the host country grew more conscious, and then resentful, of the uneasy poise of the situation.

The presence, for the first time, of qualified petroleum experts among Sa'udi officials, fresh from their training in America, led the Government to stiffen its demands, not always prudently, from incoming concessionaires other than Aramco. It obtained unprecedented terms from its Neutral Zone concessionaire (pp. 214 ff.), but drove away one applicant (Standard of Indiana, acting here as Pan American International) for the 'Preferential Area', in which Aramco had the right to match any offer made. This was not the only move from outside to acquire new rights in Sa'udi Arabia; early in 1955 an American Company, International Development Services, took a fourteen-month option for the exclusive industrial use of surplus Sa'udi gas, for fifty years; a company was to be formed for the purpose, with considerable Sa'udi participation and a half-share of the profits. At the same time German experts studied the possibilities of founding a local petrochemical industry, to make fertilizers, synthetic rubber, carbon black, sulphur, etc. The fuller use of natural gas was indeed a constant preoccupation of both Company and Government, and the former in 1959 took the unusual step of circularizing potentially interested concerns throughout the world, to attract their attention to this unworked resource.

Although no Oil Law existed in Sa'udi Arabia, one was understood to be under drafting, with expert American help, from 1958 onwards. It was believed likely to include provision for a sixty-forty split of profits in Government's favour—profits deriving from operations in all phases of an integrated (perhaps world-wide) industry: a heavy refinery liability on future concessionaires, to cover perhaps 30 per cent. of all crude produced: the obligation to use natural gas in a petrochemical industry: and Arab nationality, or domicile, for the concessionary Company itself, which must commend itself in all respects to the Government. Concessions would be given only after fully competitive bidding. No law had, however, been announced by mid-1960.

The Aramco concession, in spite of some Government pressure for revision, underwent no major changes during the period. The Company, whose concession was held by Standard Oil of California (p. 107), was unwilling to constitute itself as a fully integrated operating concern—and thereby to compete with its own constituents. To the portions of the concession territory already relinquished in 1949 and 1952 (p. 202) was added in 1955 a further area of 33,000 square miles, in the south-west and north-west of the country; the concession thereafter, including the 'Preferential Area' around Riyadh and in the heart of the territory, still covered the whole of eastern Sa'udi Arabia, to a total of some 350,000 square miles, of which 33,000 were to be handed back in 1960. The Company held, but did not at present develop, the Sa'udi 'Continental Shelf'; over the Neutral Zone it had abandoned its rights in 1948 (p. 202). A large number of matters of lesser or greater importance, involving Aramco–Sa'udi consultation, within or on the fringes of the industry, were settled. A major controversy arose, however, from the grant by the Sa'udi Government in January 1954 of a near-monopoly for the shipping of oil from Sa'udi ports by a Sa'udi Arabian Maritime Company to be founded and owned by Mr Aristotle Onassis. The obvious flag-discrimination involved, the damage to Aramco as existing concessionaire (to whose constituent companies a minor and diminishing share in cargo-carrying was reserved), and the limitation of exports which might probably result, led Aramco (as well as British and other Governments) to protest, and to take the legitimacy of the new grant to arbitration. The tribunal charged with the case, at Geneva, decided late in 1958 that the grant was in fact inconsistent with Aramco's rights, and the project was dropped.

Direct receipts by the Sa'udi public from Aramco and its operations were considerable and increasing: they took the form, as elsewhere, of pay and salaries, local purchase, locally awarded contracts, scholarships and educational grants, loans, and gifts. The sums due and paid to the Government by the Company, roughly proportionate to its annual production, followed the latter upwards, and formed the mainstay—not less than three-quarters, excluding dues from Neutral Zone oil—of the State's revenues. The total of royalties and taxation amounted in the years 1953 to 1958 to $166 million, $180 million, $260 million, $280 million, $285 million, and $290 million. A sign of the inclination of the Sa'udi public towards modern ways was visible in the increase in their use of petroleum products,[1] for supplying and distributing which Aramco maintained an increasing country-wide machinery from bulk plants and some 225 service-stations; from a total figure of (approximately) 210,000 tons of products in 1953, local demand had risen in 1957, 1958, and (unchanged) 1959, to about 425,000 t/y.

It was significant, as elsewhere in Middle Eastern oil-rich countries, that the Aramco concessionaire, undeterred by world over-supply of oil, or by the obvious elements of insecurity in this politically incalculable area, was still willing to expend scores of millions of dollars in providing for future years of yet more development: indeed a giant 'hostage to fortune', yet judged to be in part a justifiable risk, in part an inevitable compliance with already accepted obligations. That these were years of great success and prosperity for the concessionaire and for the fortunate Kingdom alike was due, first and obviously, to the combined good

[1] Early in 1960 it was stated that a son of King Sa'ud, the Amir Sa'ab, intended to erect a 1 million-t/y refinery at Jidda, using the services of the Ralph M. Parsons Company of California.

fortune in finding and developing colossal resources of oil: 'proved reserves' in the territory were calculated in the last months of this period to amount to 7,000 million tons,[1] and discovery was still in mid-career. It was due also to the vision and the high technical and managerial capacity of the operating Company, and to the ability of the world's markets—notably those accessible to the marketing organizations of Aramco's great constituent Companies—to absorb the oil. Adverse factors lay, as ever, in the remoteness of the country from major markets, corrected but partially by trans-desert Tapline: its total lack of resources and amenities, involving heavy expenses to the concessionaire: the keenness of competition in the field of oil-disposal in general, and from other Middle Eastern States in particular, especially after the return of Persian supplies in 1955: the need, when some consuming territories were short of dollars, to minimize (by sterling-bought materials and staff) the 'dollar content' of the oil offered for sale: the restraints and inconveniences of life in Sa'udi Arabia for Americans and Europeans, which the Islamic strictness of Government policy in the social field rather increased than mitigated: and uncertainty regarding the Sa'udi Government's future demands and exigencies.

Two Sa'udi directors in 1959 joined the Board of the Company, the headquarters of which remained at Dhahran.

## II. EXPLORATION AND PRODUCTION

We return to the practical development of Aramco's field operations in this period, from the point which they had reached in the early months of 1953 (pp. 202–8). These operations were those of exploration, the drilling and equipment of fields, production, transport, refining, and export. Of work done in the sphere of research, technical innovation, and administrative adjustment, nothing can be said; and enough was given in previous pages (pp. 211–14) to suggest the constant efforts of the concessionaire to provide its staff and labour force with good physical conditions of work and life. These efforts, remarkable in extent as in goodwill, were for the benefit of (in 1959) 16,250 employees in the territory, of whom 11,682 (72 per cent.) were Sa'udis (usually

---

[1] A comparable contemporary estimate for the United States was 4,340 million tons. Sa'udi reserves were the greatest of any country in the world, except Kuwait.

with five or more years' service), with 2,464 Americans and 2,111 others. Sa'udi pay-rates more than doubled in the period 1953–9, while hours of work were reduced. A careful system of allowances and bonuses, and an Employee Thrift plan, gave further benefits. Progress in employee house ownership was rapid—two houses per day in 1959—and led to the establishment of interesting new communities. The training of Sa'udis abroad was on a formidable scale, and was pressed at all levels in the course of the Company's field operations; nor were educational opportunities confined to employees of the Company. The health organization was maintained and developed, and included important research. Fire and accident prevention procedures were highly developed, and notably successful. Aramco continued to emphasize its policy of fostering local industry, delegating all possible of its own operations to local hands, and maintaining practical and helpful liaison with Government's construction activities.

The work of exploring this extremely inhospitable and exacting territory in search of further oil-resources was unrelaxed. Year by year specialized parties, up to nine in a single season, with the appropriate instruments, equipment, transport, aircraft, and camps, were to be found in the nearer or remoter desert: seismic and gravity-magnetic surveyors and structure-drillers sought for structures or strata capable of oil storage. The discovery of a local water-source, which sometimes happened, would ease transport burdens; the air was, for some parties, the sole medium of transport; supply lines were on occasion up to 600 miles in length. A deep well was drilled in the Ruba'al-Khali in 1954–5, but revealed no oil-bearing horizons. Marine survey, off the Sa'udi coast, was undertaken more than once. In all, a remarkable and sustained effort in scientific exploration was carried out. Combined work in geologic-geographic mapping was carried out with the U.S. Geological Survey.

Important discoveries were made. Identity, in single greater fields, was established between fields thought separate, as with 'Ain Dar and Buqqa in former years; it appeared in 1954 that Shedgum and 'Ain Dar formed a single unit, or part of one, while Haradh and Hawiya areas, to the south of the great Ghawar complex, in fact belonged integrally to it, joining up with 'Uthmaniya and the fields mentioned above to form the gigantic whole of Ghawar, 220 km. long and the largest field in the world. 'Ain

Dar itself could be credited in 1957 with a major northern extension at Fazran, itself a field at least 20 × 3 km. in extent. Fields recently discovered—Safaniya, off the coast, in 1951 (p. 203)—were revalued and prepared for production. In mid-1956 a major discovery was made at Khursaniya, near the coast 80 miles north-west of Dhahran between the two earlier discovered but not yet developed fields of abu Hadriya and Fadhili. Oil of 32° A.P.I. was here found, in four distinct horizons of the Arab Zone, in a well drilled to 7,600 feet, and further drilling was at once put in hand to prove the field; two wells (one a producer) were completed in 1957–8, more in 1959–60, and a useful field some 11 × 7 km. in extent was established. It was brought into production of 2 million t/y in 1960. In 1957 drilling began at Khurais, a location some seventy-five miles west of Ghawar, not far from the western boundary of the concession and only ninety miles from Riyadh. In October the discovery of oil of 31° A.P.I. at 4,760 feet was announced, and later drilling showed its presence also in other horizons in the same system, where the oil varied from 33° to 37° A.P.I. The Khurais field was not less than 50 × 13 km. in area. In December 1957 yet another major discovery was made,[1] this time that of a second submarine field immediately south of the first (Safaniya).[2] The new field was offshore from Manifa, ten miles from land, and was so named. The first well, spudded in in September 1957 from the drilling barge *Queen Mary* (used previously at Safaniya), found some crude of 27–8° A.P.I. at 8,750 feet. A second well, seven miles from the first, also found oil.[3] Two more wells were drilled before the end of 1959. In the same year the discovery was made, in a deep well on Dammam structure, of a supply of natural gas not associated with production of crude. Drilling was resumed, after a long gap, at abu Hadriya.

In the fields already in production in 1953 (p. 204n.) as well as those (Safaniya, Khursaniya) brought to production in 1954–60, additional wells were drilled during this period, and production facilities increased. Twenty-two deep wells were completed in 1959; 1960 was expected to see another twelve. Gas-oil separation

---

[1] It was remarked at the time (November 1957) that all, except one, of the exploratory wells drilled by Aramco since the war had found oil, a highly unusual record.

[2] Safaniya came into production in 1957. It was considered the largest offshore field in the world.

[3] The Manifa field was thought to be at least 22 kilometres in length.

plant was erected where previously lacking; additional collecting and trunk pipelines were laid (including 22-inch lines from Safaniya to Ras Tanura, and from Abqaiq to Qatif); pumping plant was increased. An important residential and industrial centre was founded at 'Udhailiya, at mid-point in the Ghawar structure, between Hawiya and 'Uthmaniya. In 1958 a new mobile offshore drilling platform was delivered in Aramco waters from the United States, for use in conjunction with the existing drilling-barge; it was first used at Manifa no. 2, with the *Queen Mary*. Important gas-injection plant (p. 205) was installed in Abqaiq field in 1954, injecting initially an average of 150 million cubic feet of gas a day, a figure later increased to 205 million. A second gas-injection plant (the largest in the Middle East) was completed in 1959 for 'Ain Dar. This use of gas for maintaining reservoir pressure, in addition to industrial uses (power production, etc.), accounted for about two-thirds of the gas produced with the crude; this figure was to rise to 71 per cent. by 1961. Water-injection was adopted for the Abqaiq field in 1956 and increased in 1959, with good results in maintaining pressure; in 1957-8 additional injection was undertaken in new wells on the flanks of the structure. Tests relative to the injection of sea-water were put in hand. A plant was in 1960 under preparation for the injection of 37,000 b/d of l.p.g. into 'Ain Dar reservoir, its operation to start in 1961. The measures taken by Aramco for pressure-maintenance were reported as highly successful.

Production[1] as a whole rose substantially, if not (by Middle Eastern standards) sensationally, during the period; the territory was easily surpassed in output by Kuwait. In the four years 1953 to 1956, production amounted to 40·88 million, 46·13 million, 46·78 million, and 47·93 million tons respectively. In the years 1957 to 1959, it was 48·22 million, 49·35 million, and 53·30 million tons. The 3,000-millionth barrel of oil, since first discovery, was produced in December 1957. The years 1956 and 1957 were

[1] Fields in production, with the producing wells in each were, in 1953, Abqaiq (52), Ghawar (50, of which 39 in 'Ain Dar, 11 in 'Uthmaniya), Dammam (26), Qatif (9). In 1959 the corresponding position was: Abqaiq (56), Ghawar (91, 44 in 'Ain Dar, 14 in Shedgum, 33 in 'Uthmaniya), Dammam (27, including 2 gas wells), Qatif (8), Safaniya (21). Khursaniya came into production only in 1960. Production in Ghawar was in 1959 the greatest (702,000 b/d); Abqaiq gave 267,000 b/d, Safaniya 76,000, Dammam 34,000, Qatif 16,000. No production had yet been taken from abu Hadriya, Fadhili, Hawiya, Haradh, Khurais, or Manifa.

both affected by the Suez stoppage which involved the temporary cessation of pipeline shipments to Bahrain, and restriction of shipments to the British and French. Estimates of future Aramco production, 'all being well', were of the order of 350 million t/y by 1980—a sevenfold increase on 1959 figures.

### III. REFINING, TRANSPORTING, EXPORTING

The capacity of Tapline (p. 206–8), which stood in 1953 at 15·5 million t/y was raised by stages to 22·5 million t/y in 1959, notably by the installation, completed in 1958, of a series of intermediate and fully automatic pumping units; these units were 5,000 h.p. combustion-gas turbines, remotely controlled by radio from main pumping stations at Abqaiq and Nariya. Booster pumps were also added at existing stations. Nevertheless, the fullest use of this great 1,068-mile trunk oil-transporting system was, in a measure, discouraged during this period by the competitive cheapness of tanker freights (after a high peak in 1956–7), and by the uncertainty as to the demands—possibly to be retrospective— of the Governments of the transit territories, in the absence of a signed agreement (pp. 242f., 330, 340). It resulted that quantities of crude dispatched by Tapline from the Sa'udi Arabian fields was, in most or all years, well below the line's capacity. It took approximately one-third of total Aramco production. Throughput was in 1959 some 16·9 million tons, the lowest since 1956.

Apart from Tapline, two other more or less serious pipeline projects, of interest to Sa'udi Arabia, were proposed in these years. One was that of the Sa'udi oil-director 'Abdullah Tariqi; conceived as an inter-Arab enterprise, it would consist of two 32-inch lines running from the Gulf to the Mediterranean (with large-dimension feeder lines from Qatar and from northern and southern 'Iraq), with a capacity of 50 million t/y and to cost possibly £225 million. This plan, enunciated early in 1959, seemed to receive some, but not universal Arab support. The other project, that of a joint Sa'udi-German Company (Deutsche Arabian Oil Company, of Munich), was for a line to convey Sa'udi oil from the Mediterranean to Bavaria: a plan upon which no time, evidently, need be wasted at present.

The sea terminal at Ras Tanura with its equipment of tanks, pumping and loading facilities, piers and jetties, as well as normal industrial, office, residential, and institutional buildings, had a threefold function: to handle the export of refined products from the near-by refinery: to dispatch Sa'udi crude to Bahrain refinery by submarine line (p. 219): and the direct export of crude. The terminal, in all its operations, was under constant improvement and extension. The North Pier was adapted for super-tankers in 1954, the South Pier in 1955; further additions in length and berth capacity of both piers were completed in 1958–9, and gave a total of ten tanker berths, while at the same time conventional rubber loading-hoses were replaced by metal loading-arms, mechanically moved by hydraulic equipment. The average size of visiting tankers, as elsewhere, increased notably; the number loaded at Ras Tanura varied between 1,450 and 1,700 a year. The highest figure for a single day's loading was 1·36 million barrels, in December 1959.

The important refinery at Ras Tanura received almost yearly various improvements and/or extensions. In 1954 a new crude topping plant was added, and a catalytic polymerization plant to use refinery gases for the improvement of gasoline octane-ratings; in that year the total refinery throughput was 10·5 million tons. In 1955 a catalytic reforming unit was added, to produce high-octane gasoline, and a l.p.g. plant (mainly for the local market) went into operation. In 1956, total throughput (including asphalt and l.p.g.) amounted to 9·46 million tons, representing a slight decrease. A desulphurization plant was added in 1957 to improve the purity of diesel oil; throughput was 9·46 million tons. In 1958 an alkylation plant and other facilities for the production of aviation gasoline were begun; these were completed in 1959, in which year a further l.p.g. plant (to cost $6½ million) was also under construction, its production being intended for export, from early 1961 onwards. This was the first such plant in the world effecting its liquefaction by refrigeration instead of by compression, to make refrigerated l.p.g. available for tanker shipment, and calling for special refrigerated tankers for the purpose. Capacity was to be about 4,000 b/d.

Total crude oil refined at Ras Tanura was 80 million barrels in 1954, a figure not again attained; it approximated to 74·5 million barrels in 1955, 73 million in 1956, 70 million in 1957, 61 million in 1958, and 63·6 million in 1959. The quantity of each product produced was, in 1959, fuel oil 31·6 million barrels, diesel oil 10·5 million, gasoline (including aviation) 8·15 million, kerosene

4·9 million, jet fuel 3·12 million, l.p.g. 0·43 million, asphalt and miscellaneous 0·325 million. Some 50·8 million barrels were dispatched to Bahrain refinery in 1959. The failure of refinery throughput at Ras Tanura to increase was due principally to the growth of refining capacity in consuming areas.

Between crude and products, and by various routes, the distribution of Aramco's exports throughout the world was, in 1959, roughly as follows: to Europe 45·2 per cent., to Asia and Australia 36·9 per cent., to North America 11·5 per cent., to Africa and South America 3 per cent. each, and the rest to minor destinations.

## CHAPTER XVIII

# THE ARABIAN PRINCIPALITIES, 1953–60

T HE present chapter will attempt to cover the oil fortunes, during the seven years under study, of the whole of the Arabian peninsula, except Sa'udi Arabia. It includes, therefore, besides wide and desolate regions of south-eastern and southern Arabia still unblessed by oil-derived riches, the small but wealthy territories of Qatar, Bahrain Island, the Kuwaiti-Sa'udi Neutral Zone, and finally the fabulously enriched shaikhdom of Kuwait. To each of these a separate section of this chapter will be devoted.

## I. KUWAIT

The story during these seven years of the development of Kuwait's fantastic oil resources (pp. 220–7) is one of unvarying success and increase. The principality still faced, indeed, the commercial disadvantage of remote location, far from main markets and unaided by, because unprovided with, the short-cut of trans-desert pipelines. [1] The physical setting of the industry was featureless, unattractive, climatically harsh, and deficient in all industrial, or natural, resources—including water and food. The impact of sudden and immense wealth to a community and ruler of hitherto patriarchal simplicity, with an abrupt opening of medieval doors on to a troubled and complicated era of the modern world, must create social and political problems. The divisions, aspirations, and jealousies within the Arab world itself could not but be reflected in the cross-currents and potential discontents of a small weak country which had become suddenly enviable and conspicuous. But these troubles, actual or threatening, however familiar to students of current Arab affairs, did little to disturb the course of the industrial development here to be described. Rare acts of sabotage, without effect on production, indicated once or twice a political protest, usually by non-Kuwaiti personnel; and the stoppage of the Suez Canal for four months of 1956–7

[1] The distance from the head of the Persian Gulf to Marseilles is 4,850 miles, to Rotterdam 6,600: from the eastern Mediterranean coast it is 1,600 and 3,360 miles respectively.

had a temporarily serious effect on Kuwait's exports (normally 70 per cent. Canal-borne), reducing these for a time by half. But in general it appeared that, if spared by world upheaval or local disturbance, the Shaikhdom was assured of many decades of oil production on a truly remarkable scale.

Already by 1953 there were indications that the vast Burgan field was not to prove Kuwait's only resource. The proving of the Magwa field slightly to the north in 1951–2 was followed in 1953 by the establishment of that of Ahmadi, immediately south-east of Magwa; both these fields, in which drilling and equipment were thereafter actively pursued, were to become useful contributors. By the end of 1959 44 wells had been drilled at Magwa, 36 at Ahmadi, and 244 at Burgan. Later study indicated that the three fields were essentially a single reservoir, though diversified by subsidiary structures; the crude oils from each area were slightly different in specific gravity, with an average of 31·5° A.P.I.

In 1955 the first well drilled in a quite distinct area, at Raudha-tain in northern Kuwait, seventy-five miles by road from Ahmadi —but only twenty-five from the Rumaila field of southern 'Iraq —following promising seismic indications, found abundant oil in sands at 7,700 feet; the well was taken to 10,300 feet and the indications of a major accumulation, in a diversity of oil-bearing zones, with a formidable total thickness, were fully confirmed by subsequent drilling. All steps were taken thereafter to bring this seemingly important field, with its assessed reserves of perhaps 1,250 million tons, into production; by the end of 1959 twenty-five wells had been drilled, a gathering centre, gas-separator, power station, and pump-house had been erected, and a buried 30-inch pipeline, sixty-three miles long, to Ahmadi had been completed; and by the spring of 1960 oil was flowing from Raudhatain to main storage at Ahmadi, with an output designed shortly to reach 100,000 b/d, and the potentiality of large increase. The discovery and exploitation of the Raudhatain field, with twenty-three com-pleted wells, was the outstanding event of Kuwait history in 1954–60, and one of significance far beyond Kuwait. Locally, two innovations of interest may be mentioned. One was the inaugura-tion of a daily air service, Ahmadi–Raudhatain; the other was the installation of plant for the desalination of locally produced brackish water, rendering it drinkable, to a quantity of 4,000 gallons a day.

From 1956 onwards, further test drilling was carried out elsewhere in northern Kuwait, at Sabriya ten miles south-east of
Raudhatain, and at Bahra immediately north of Kuwait Bay—the
scene of the Company's earliest, and unsuccessful, drilling in
1936 (p. 112). At both these locations oil-bearing formations
were penetrated, that of Sabriya (considered to be possibly an
extension of the Raudhatain field) being thought worthy of serious
development. One well at each structure was, in April 1960,
produced into the Raudhatain gathering centre for evaluation
purposes. A test at Mutriba, thirty miles west of Raudhatain,
was spudded in in 1957 but encountered drilling troubles and
was abandoned at 11,500 feet; a second well there was commenced
in the summer of 1960. Other tests were unsuccessful at Umm
Gudair, immediately west of Burgan, in 1954, and at Dibdiba,
westward and far inland, in 1959; this well was abandoned at 9,440
feet. But at Minagish, twenty miles west of Burgan, a test well
found abundant oil, at a depth of nearly 10,000 feet, in May of that
year. A second well was spudded in late in 1959, a third early in
1960, and preliminary plans for commercial production were in
hand.

While exploration in, and enrichment of, the Kuwait Oil
Company's area thus proceeded, its main field of Burgan continued
to produce oil in extraordinary quantities for export. A cumulative
production of 3,000 million barrels was reached and passed in
September 1958. A regular programme of production drilling
was maintained, the total of producing wells standing at 319 at the
end of 1959. Drilling techniques were under constant study and
improvement; the towing of complete rigs for long distances to
new locations continued (p. 222). To maintain pressure (which,
indeed, showed little signs of falling) a gas compression plant was
to be put into operation during 1960, forcing some 100 million
cubic feet of gas per day into the oil-producing formations. Oil
from the Burgan structure was carried by pipelines to the fourteen
gathering stations, for gas separation and pressure reduction;
each centre served a group of twenty to thirty wells. Gas from
the separators was utilized in the power-station and refinery as
well as for industrial and domestic use, and was in addition
dispatched to Kuwait town. Electric generating capacity was
increased, notably in 1960. Degassed oil from the gathering
centres was pumped to tankage on Ahmadi Ridge, where a South

Tank Farm and a (later erected) North Tank Farm each provided storage on the required scale. The oil descended thence by gravity through a dozen or more pipelines of varying dimensions to the coastal loading installations. Tank-farm capacity by the end of 1959 was well in excess of a million tons.

The total production in Kuwait (all for export, except that required for the Company's own needs and for bunkering, and the small but not negligible local requirements, which were served by a dozen Company's filling-stations) continued to rise rapidly in these years from its pre-1953 levels (p. 223). In 1953 it amounted to 42·6 million tons, in 1954 to 46·9 million, and in the five years 1955-9 to 53·9, 54·1, 56·37, 69·1, and 68·4 million tons respectively. Production from each of the years 1958 and 1959 was therefore nearly five times that of 1949 (12·2 million tons), and over thirty times that of 1947, the first year of production. It had, moreover, become certain that an output of 70 million t/y could, at short notice, be increased by 50 or 100 per cent., if and when the market should expand to take it, while levels of ultimate production could be conceived as leaving those of today far behind. The proved oil reserves of the principality were in 1959 estimated at 8,800 million tons.

Meanwhile, crude oil was being exported to a score of countries, with the United Kingdom as by far the largest importer, taking some 20 million tons a year; major supplies were sent also to the United States, France, the Netherlands, Italy, Aden, Japan, Australia, and Argentina. The long-term contracts regulating the disposal of a large part of Kuwait crude (p. 221) remained in force; each of the two partners in K.O.C., paying the combined Company the bare cost of production plus 1 shilling per ton, disposed of its own share of oil. The Kuwait Treasury took a 50 per cent. share of profits, based (since 1955) strictly on posted prices without discounts.

For dealing with export on the current scale, the erection of the first great pier (later differentiated as the South Pier) was completed in 1949, and has been described (p. 224). This impressive loading-point, in full use ever since, witnessed the sailing from Kuwait of the ten-thousandth tanker in June 1954, the loading of the twenty-thousandth oil cargo in March 1958, and since then the visits of giant 80,000-ton (and once a 100,000-ton) tankers to the port. But with ever-increasing offtake the need of further facilities became evident, and in November 1957 a second (the North) pier was begun, and was completed with remarkable speed. It was commissioned in June 1959, and Kuwait became the largest oil-exporting port in the world. The North Pier, L-shaped, consisted of an approach leg one mile in length, with roadway and pipe tracks. The pier head, half a mile in length, offered 55 to 60 feet of water. The structure consisted of some 3,250 steel piles supporting a super-structure of 18,000 tons of steel. Oil reached it from the North Tank Farm by three 38/40-inch lines, and loading rates were up to 6,750 tons per hour per tanker. Buildings for the control of operations, and for the medical Quarantine Service, were provided on the pier, as well as offices, recreation rooms, fire pumps, industrial stores, and workshops. A boat harbour, with a jetty and lighter-quay, and a twenty-acre area of dredged water protected by breakwaters, was an added facility at Mina al-Ahmadi. Eight tankers could be accommodated simultaneously at South Pier, three at North. These, with the use of seven sea-loading berths, could give a total export capacity of some 2,145,000 b/d; in fact, however, two South Pier berths were set apart for cargo-handling, and the sea-lines were taken out of commission but could easily be recommissioned at need. The total of tankers loaded at the piers was in 1958 2,815, in 1959 2,488. The average size of cargoes loaded increased remarkably during the period, as it did elsewhere, with the changing fashion in tanker-construction; in 1952 it was 15,920 tons, in 1958 23,735. Kuwaiti-owned tankers were soon to join in the offtake from the oil port; two were ordered from Japan in 1957 by a locally formed Kuwait Tanker Company, and the first two to be launched were in 1959 chartered, flying the Kuwait flag, by the concerned subsidiaries of the K.O.C. constituent Companies.

The small refinery completed in 1949 and extended in 1952 (p. 225) soon proved inadequate to demands, especially those of bunkering; a major extension, therefore, was put in hand in 1956 with the addition of two new 80,000 b/d distillation units and other plant. Finished early in 1958, the enlarged refinery had a capacity of 190,000 (in place of the former 30,000) b/d, and besides its three atmospheric distillation units included new crude and products tankage, increased electric generating power, a 25,000 t/y bitumen plant for local roadwork, and a gasoline treating plant;

some aviation turbine kerosene, and l.p.g. for Kuwaiti use, were also produced. And signs that ex-refinery products, as also natural gas, were interesting the local public as a foundation for new industries, were not lacking; in 1958 a (Kuwaiti) National Gas Exploitation Company was formed by local merchants to deal in l.p.g.; another group early in 1959 were reported as considering the foundation of a chemical industry; and B.P. itself, early in 1960, contracted to supply l.p.g. in bulk to the Tokio Gas Company, from a new plant to be built in Kuwait. Quantities rising to 60,000 t/y by 1963 were envisaged.

The Company's employees in 1959–60 numbered some 8,000, by vast majority Kuwaitis. For these, comprehensive training schemes were in operation, both on the spot and abroad, and foreign personnel was being gradually replaced. Terms of employment were favourable, with good pay and allowances and generous recognition of long service. Other employee benefits included special allowances for shift workers, annual paid holidays, paid Pilgrimage leave, subsidized meals in the Company canteens, a Thrift Scheme, and free medical services. For freer and friendlier association, foreign staff were required to learn Arabic, and Kuwaitis given facilities for learning English.

Ahmadi, founded in 1946, had in 1960 a resident population of 7,000 and was still expanding. The administrative centre for all Company operations, it included the main offices, industrial installations, workshops and stores, mosques and churches, cinemas, restaurants, shops, playing fields, and schools. Buildings recently constructed by the Company included the headquarter offices, State Guest House, Display Centre, and the State Public Security Headquarters. Public and private gardens gave Ahmadi the appearance of an oasis in the desert. The Company had built more than 1,600 brick houses, equipped with all essential services, for Arab workers and their families; this housing was mainly located in South Ahmadi, where there were also some 1,300 houses for intermediate and senior staff, and another 300 dwellings were to be built for payroll employees, as well as 70 for staff. The health and welfare of employees were carefully supervised; the Company opened a new general hospital (the Southwell Hospital), with 200 beds and all modern medical facilities, in April 1960; there were also medical and dental clinics for the treatment of out-patients and a Preventive Medicine Division. Facilities for almost every kind of game and recreation were organized on a club basis; the Workers' Club with a fine swimming pool and restaurant, lounges and recreation hall, was the most up to date of the clubs in Ahmadi. The post of Managing Director of the Company, in London, passed in 1959 from Sir Phillip Southwell to the Hon. William Fraser. In the field, L. T. Jordan remained as General Manager throughout the period.

In early days, the Company had had to import nearly all the materials required for its operations: but it later became possible to order a wide range of items locally. The Company's Local Purchase Division was by 1959 in full operation and the scale of local purchase had steadily increased. Kuwaiti commercial enterprise had developed to a stage where local contractors could carry out major constructional and other functions for the Company. During the last years, 1949–59, virtually all constructional work was carried out by local contractors who worked in the happiest co-operation with the Company; and as a result of this economic integration policy some £16½ million was injected into the local economy in 1959, apart from payment to the State of royalty and tax on oil produced. The latter payments, calculated on the now standard fifty-fifty basis, are believed to have amounted, approximately, to the following sums in each of the years 1953 to 1958: £68·5 million, £70·5 million, £100 million, £100 million, £110·7 million, and £130 million. These figures exclude, of course, the Shaikh's receipts from the Neutral Zone.

## II. NEUTRAL ZONE

The circumstances in which oil rights over this constitutionally anomalous territory were granted to two American concerns, and the seemingly onerous terms of the grants by the two rulers, were indicated in earlier pages (pp. 214 ff.). The fortunes of the resulting joint enterprise had been, in the years 1950–2, unhappy; but the spring of 1953 brought discoveries which entirely altered the situation (p. 216), and the hopes cherished in those months soon became certainties. The Wafra field, some twenty miles south of Burgan, was proved in 1953 to contain major deposits of oil in middle-Cretaceous 'Burgan sands' at an average depth of 3,600 feet; a year later oil was found in the Eocene limestone at the shallow depth of 1,200 feet, and in 1955, at some 7,000 feet, the Ratawi limestone was proved also to be oil-bearing. The Burgan sands proved, however, to be the major producer, giving an oil heavier and more sulphurous than that of the great Kuwait field.

The active drilling programme of 1953 and succeeding years, which completed not less than 150 producing wells by 1959, both proved the Wafra field and made immediate export possible. A terminal erected by Aminoil in Kuwait territory, known as Mina 'Abdullah, was only thirty-four miles from Wafra, to which it was connected by 8-inch and 10-inch pipelines; and in 1955 the Getty interest—Mr Paul Getty being, in fact, the virtual (81 per cent.) owner of Pacific Western, the name of which was changed in April 1956 to Getty Oil Company—built a second terminal within the Zone itself at Ras al-Zur, known as Mina Sa'ud. This was initially connected with the field by a 10-inch pipeline; later a 16-inch was added, and terminal tankage increased. At both the terminals refineries (that is, crude stabilization and fuel oil plants) were erected in accordance with concession obligations, at Mina Sa'ud with 50,000 b/d capacity, at Mina 'Abdullah with 30,000; both terminals were equipped with long sea-lines to deep water. Export (from Mina 'Abdullah only) in 1954 amounted to nearly 1 million tons, in 1955 (from both terminals) to $1\frac{1}{4}$ million; it was held back, as had been anticipated (p. 216), by the initial difficulty of finding suitable markets. Combined production rose in 1957, 1958, and 1959 to figures of 3·3 million, 4·2 million, and 5·9 million t/y, and the full potential of the field was well in excess of this output. The main destinations of exported oil seemed to be Japan, America, the Netherlands, France, and Italy. Reserves were assessed at rather less than 950 million tons; Wafra was, therefore, a major field.

The administration of the joint, but far from integrated, enterprise was tackled on unusual lines. Both partners retained in the territory their own representatives and staff, as well as their own pipelines, tankage, terminals, and camps; and the crude which each produced was taken from a specific 'horizon' not used by the other. Many inconveniences, duplications, and potential frictions could not but arise from this system, which early in 1960 was said to be likely to be changed to unified management, and possibly a joint company. Meanwhile both concessionaires faced serious difficulties in marketing their offtake; entry into unfamiliar markets was difficult, especially after the imposition of import quotas into the United States, in which previously most Getty oil, and some Aminoil, had been marketed. The problem was not solved by the extreme lowness of the Neutral Zone posted prices. A dispute which arose in 1957 between the two co-concessionaires, regarding offshore islands, proved hard to settle.

The strange story of this unpeopled artificially created territory does not end here, with the richness of a single oilfield. The offshore, or Continental Shelf, rights, outside the six-mile territorial limit, had also, in the early 'fifties, become available for sale or bargain at the will of the two absentee Rulers. The successful offer for the Sa'udi half of these was made in 1957 by a group of Japanese industrialists[1] and companies (industrial, electrical, insurance, banking) formed *ad hoc* as the Japanese Petroleum Trading Company, with an operating subsidiary, the Arabian Oil Company. The same concern next, a few months later, in May 1958, obtained the Kuwait half-rights from the Shaikh, in face of considerable American and European competition. The terms agreed to by the Japanese were in both cases unprecedently rigorous. In the concession given by Kuwait the full concession period, including exploration, was $44\frac{1}{2}$ years only, and in the Sa'udi concession two years more: and in both the right of renewal was only partially assured, and not at all if a rival Kuwaiti or Sa'udi candidate were in the field. In each agreement, a heavy surface rental was payable from the date of signature, and was to increase with the passing years if oil was found; and in the Kuwaiti concession a bonus was payable not to, but by, the Company if a commercial strike occurred. In place of the fifty-fifty plan of dividing profits, current in other Middle Eastern territories, 56 per cent. to the Sa'udi Government and 57 per cent. to the Kuwaiti were to be payable; the Sa'udi text, moreover, prescribed that their proportion of profits would include those made at any stage of the industry and in any country. The Kuwaitis followed the same principle, adding that losses in one phase of operations could not be claimed by the Company as diminishing the divisible profits of another. More favourable terms given subsequently to any Arab Government by any Company must be matched by the Japanese signatories; no recourse might be had by the Company to its own Government for

[1] These included the important Mitsui and Mitsubishi groups, which possessed some oil interests in Japan; other participants included large-scale users of oil.

protection; no sales of oil might be made to 'enemies of the Arabs'. Stipulations for drilling and local refining were severe: the establishment of a local petro-chemical industry, added the Sa'udis, might be insisted upon. A part of the Company's shares must be offered to each of the granting countries, who would be entitled to name at least two directors to the Board, would assume a 10 per cent. shareholding if commercial oil were found, and would enjoy powers of close supervision of all operations. Areas of the territory covered, up to one-fifth every three or five years, must be surrendered to the Governments on demand.

Undeterred by these provisions, and driven forward by their country's known and serious need of oil under its own control, [1] the Arabian Oil Company arranged in 1958 for the carrying out of a geophysical survey by the (American) Geophysical Service International, and then for drilling by a Dutch concern, the International Drilling Company. A mobile drilling platform was towed from Texas through the Suez Canal to Neutral Zone waters, where, on shore at Khor al-Mufatta, a labour force with Japanese and foreign experts awaited it. Work began at a location twenty-eight miles from shore, in 104 feet of water. On 3 April the drill unexpectedly, at 1,500 feet, struck natural gas. This ignited and seriously damaged the platform and plant before being extinguished eleven days later. The contractors forthwith arranged for the dispatch of further materials from the United States, and the concessionaire company increased its capital to 10,000 million yen. With the new platform, oil of 26° A.P.I. was struck at 4,900 feet in January 1960, and flowed at about 6,000 b/d. This was a strike of the highest possible promise for its owners and their country, though likely to be acclaimed with less enthusiasm by the rest of an oil-surfeited world.

The second well, sited in 100 feet of water two and a half miles from the first, found oil at 5,250 feet in April 1960, with an estimated yield of 6,300 b/d; the third found 6,000 b/d of oil at 5,000 feet, in mid-June. The Arabian Oil Company had already ordered a second drilling platform and had arranged for five 15,000-ton tankers to serve as anchored storage for their oil. They intended to drill nine more wells in 1960, and established a permanent

---

[1] Japanese indigenous supplies of oil were negligible—some 7,000 b/d—against a usage of about 18 million t/y in 1959. Their refining industry was highly developed.

land-base at Ras al-Khafji on the coast of the Zone. A major effort in mid-sea oil production, probably destined to reach an output of some millions of tons a year, was thus launched by the newest and least expected of newcomers to the region and the industry. Marketing was likely to prove their major difficulty during the period of world surplus—and not least when they must expect the closest supervision, by the granting Governments, of all their operations.

### III. BAHRAIN

The composition, politics, and functions of Bapco, and the immensely important contribution made by the local oil industry to the island's prosperity, underwent no major change during the period under review, and have perhaps been sufficiently indicated in earlier pages (pp. 217ff.). The completion by the Shaikh's Government of an important women's hospital, increased allocations to education, a piped-water service, and a major enlargement of the island's electric-power plant, all belonged to 1959, and recent previous years had shown similar examples of wise spending. At the same time the revenues paid to the Ruler under the revised agreement (p. 217) formed but a part of Bahrain's direct gains from the industry; a rough total of Rs. 111 million (or £8,325,000) in 1958, and Rs. 135 million (or £10 million) in the year following, represented the Company's composite contribution to Bahrain in the form of royalties, pay and salaries, purchases, and contracts. Relations with the Ruler and public remained generally excellent; labour troubles which occurred late in 1954 were not in origin connected with Bapco's operations. The living of almost a quarter of the labour force of the island was ensured by Bapco, in excellent conditions; in 1959 about 6,000 Bahraini and Bahrain-resident Arabs were thus employed, a high proportion of whom were undergoing technical training courses to improve their prospects. Pay rates and working hours were under frequent review.

Further careful exploration of the island and adjacent seas by seismic means, by deep drilling, and by outside test drilling such as that (a dry hole) at Buri, north of the 'Awali structure, in 1958–9, and a mid-field deep test well in 1959, as well as previously and repeatedly in territorial waters, all failed during the period to reveal oil deposits other than those of 'Awali, a field of obviously limited capacity in which nearly 200 wells had been drilled by 1959. Nevertheless, production, which had halted at $1\frac{1}{2}$ million t/y for some years before 1957, was raised in that year to 1·64 million tons, in 1958 to 2 million, and in 1959 to 2·22 million. These increases were made possible by a rearrangement of the current production pattern, by a campaign of selective gas injection, and as a result of a major drilling programme instituted in 1955. 'Awali production appeared likely to find a new level at slightly over 2 million t/y. The island's proved reserves were some 30 to 35 million tons. Cumulative production, to the end of 1959, exceeded 30 million tons.

The Bahrain refinery, substantially increased in scale in 1951 (p. 219), and treating as usual large supplies of crude from Sa'udi Arabia as well as Bahrain's own production, was considerably enlarged in 1955-6, at heavy expense, by the construction of a second catalytic cracking unit, a polymer plant, and two vacuum units, with other associated additions; and it was further diversified in 1956-7 by the addition of a 11,000 b/d catalytic reforming unit for the production of high-octane gasoline. The refinery was in 1960 one of the largest in the Middle East, and offered a wide diversity of products. Its main units consisted in that year of five crude distillation units of varying (18,000–85,000 b/d) capacity, two thermal cracking units each of 7,000 b/d capacity, a fluid catalytic cracker (30,000 b/d), three thermal reformers (7,000 b/d each), a catalytic reforming unit (11,000 b/d), and two polymerization units, with chemical treating plant. Refinery output was at a rate of 103,000 b/d in 1958, and 189,000 in 1959: a peak figure of 204,000 b/d, reached in 1955, was not again attained. The 1957 figure was diminished by the temporary cessation of crude imports from the Sa'udi kingdom, as an Arab patriotic gesture connected with the Suez crisis of November 1956. Market demand, though largely secured by Bapco's membership of the Caltex group, was the main factor affecting refinery output; this was, in the period 1957-60, working below full capacity. Bahrain's own demand for products was about 170,000 t/y.

About 72 per cent. of the crude processed was Sa'udi,[1] brought to the Island by two 12-inch submarine lines. No crude was exported from Bahrain. Facilities at the point of export, Sitra, were steadily improved; further work on the wharves there, for the reception of larger tankers, was in progress in 1959-60. Construction of a new island wharf was begun, to provide two berths

[1] In 1959, of crude processed, 50·5 million barrels was Sa'udi, 16·4 million Bahraini, 2 million from outside sources.

for ships up to 45,000 tons dw., and to supersede the existing island wharf. The present No. 2 wharf was to be modified and strengthened. The three-berth wharf, built in 1946, and sited at the end of a three-mile causeway, could accommodate vessels up to 35-foot draught. A new mile-wide, 34-mile-long sea approach to Sitra was marked and lighted.

### IV. QATAR

The desolate, scantily populated, and almost waterless peninsula and shaikhdom of Qatar (pp. 227–31) maintained during these years its position as a major oil-producing and exporting territory. The operations of the industry in Qatar, confined (except for a small topping-plant) to exploration and the production and loading of crude oil, were pursued without interruption from the beginning of production, in the last days of 1949, to the close of our period. Important local disbursements by the Qatar Petroleum Company[1] (and by the marine-operating Shell Company of Qatar) in the form of salaries, wages, and payments for purchases and contracts raised the Qatari standard of wealth beyond anything previously imagined, while annual payments to the Ruler's treasury amounted, in the last years of the period, to some £20 million a year.[2] One-half of this source of state revenue was devoted immediately to works of building and town-planning at Doha, and to the (previously non-existent) public services; these included the planning and construction of a virtually new capital, a magnificent hospital, a variety of schools, a water-distillation plant and piped water, a power station, housing estates with modern amenities, an airport, a jetty, and sheds. An immensely higher material standard of life was thus placed at the immediate disposal of the Qataris. It was accompanied by no fundamental change in the local form of government—shaikhly absolutism, tempered now by European advice—but by a large measure of physical and mental opening-up of the region, with a new status, new air and sea communications, and closer links with the Arab world in and beyond the Gulf.

The 'proved reserves' of the shaikhdom could not at present be

[1] The name was changed from Petroleum Development (Qatar) Ltd. in June 1953.

[2] An assessment of annual payments to the Shaikh, for each year 1953 to 1959, was: £4 million, £7·4 million, £13·1 million, £16 million, £20·3 million, and £20 million.

re-estimated upwards to any important extent, and remained at some 300 to 350 million tons. Investigation of the territory by seismic means was completed early in mid-1959. A deep test at Dukhan, taken to 13,260 feet and completed early in 1960, failed to reveal under-lying productive strata; tests previously made in 1952–3 in the centre of the peninsula (Kharaib nos. 1 and 2) had been dry, and a final attempt at Fuwairat, in the extreme north-east of the peninsula, was spudded in only in the early summer of 1960. The Dukhan field was still, therefore, in 1960 the only source of oil. Within it, more than sixty wells had been drilled, five-sixths of these being capable of production and two-thirds actually producing at any one time, the rest serving for observation purposes. Cumulative drilled footage exceeded 450,000 feet at the end of 1959. Production was from an average depth of 6,550 feet, from no. 3 and no. 4 zone in the Middle Jurassic 'Zekrit' limestone—the greater part from no. 4. The crude was light and of excellent quality, rating 41·5° A.P.I. Production from Dukhan had reached, by the end of 1959, some 50 million tons since its inception and had amounted in 1959 to 7·87 million.[1] It appeared probable from the discovered size and characteristics of the reservoir, that this figure would not be much exceeded in subsequent years; but it showed a gratifying rise in scale since the earliest production in 1950.

The Dukhan field was continuously equipped with all necessary and improved installations. These included domestic buildings, messes, and clubs, as well as a hospital, offices, workshops, stores, a fire-station, power houses, a Qatari Training Centre (with another at Umm Sa'id), etc. Comprehensive transport (including air) facilities and telecommunications were provided. Oil produced in the Dukhan field was de-gassed at three stations (Khatiya, Fahahil, and Jaliha, constructed in 1949, 1954, and 1955 respectively). At each of these, pumps were installed to dispatch the oil to the east-side terminal at Umm Sa'id, by way of Umm Bab in the centre of the field. For 14 miles of the 49-mile journey to Umm Sa'id two 14½-inch lines were used, and thereafter one 20-inch. At the terminal, sixteen storage tanks, with a total capacity of some 265,000 tons, held the oil in readiness for loading, which

[1] Production in each of the years 1953 to 1958 had been, respectively, 3·99 million, 4·7 million, 5·36 million, 5·78 million, 6·5 million, and 8·09 million tons.

was carried out at three loading-points at sea, served by sea-bottom pipelines with flexible ends. An average of almost one tanker a day called for the oil. The 36-mile buoyed channel leading to Umm Sa'id was served by Company pilots. The sea-loading berths offered nine fathoms of water. The port facilities of Umm Sa'id included launches, tugs and landing-craft, fire-fighting equipment, inland communications, housing, drinking water, etc., and attracted progressively more general shipping, to an extent of some twenty cargo ships a month. A topping plant of some 30,000 t/y capacity, intended for local and the Company's needs, was constructed. Good roads connected Umm Sa'id with both Dukhan and the capital, Doha, and a secondary network of passable roads was created. The headquarters of Q.P.C. was moved to Umm Sa'id in 1956. The Company's facilities and resources were used during 1954–60, to an important extent, as those of a base for other I.P.C.-Group operations in south-eastern Arabia. About 4,000 Qataris, including Arabs from neighbouring territories, were employed. The Company's General Manager at Umm Sa'id was from 1954 P. R. A. Ensor, followed in 1959 by G. J. R. Tod.

The Shell enterprise in an area of some 10,000 square miles of Qatar offshore waters has been already mentioned (p. 231). The Shell Group formed, for these operations, a Shell Company of Qatar in October 1953, established a headquarters and depot at Doha, put in hand a programme of submarine surveys, and ordered a drilling-platform, costing some £900,000, from the Netherlands. With this, their first well was drilled to 6,700 feet in 1954–5 at Matbakh, north-east of Doha; a second in 1955–6 at Id al-Sharqi, forty miles farther east, was drilled to 13,000 feet. Neither hole offered promise of oil. A third location was then selected, but the drilling-platform, while under tow to this late in 1956, was wrecked by a sudden and violent storm, with loss of life. Shell were understood to have spent, thus far, nearly £8 million in their Qatar enterprise. A new platform, the 'Seashell', measuring 210 × 105 feet and provided with retractable 220-foot legs and with quarters for a staff of seventy and a helicopter deck, was at once ordered from the Netherlands. It was launched early in 1958, and towed to Qatar. Capable of withstanding 100-mile-an-hour gales and thirty-foot waves, it arrived in its destined waters late in 1959. Drilling of Id al-Sharqi no. 2, fifty miles offshore, began in December some sixty miles north-east of Doha, and proceeded normally; but, after a show of oil there, the rig was moved at mid-summer 1960 to Hadat Shabib, half-way between Id al-Sharqi and Doha.

Thus, assured of an abundant income from operations on dry land, the tiny Qatar principality could still hope for further revenues from the sea bed—a hope doubtless encouraged by the promising news from Das Island (p. 320), not far off. Meanwhile the *per capita* income of its population was probably, with the single exception of Kuwait, the highest in the world.

### V. SOUTH-EASTERN ARABIA

The area thus designated includes the territory of Dhofar—a separately governed province of the dominions of H. H. the Sultan of Oman—the main block of the Sultanate, and the Trucial Coast with its offshore waters. No commercial production of oil was achieved in this region during our present period; but the persistent efforts made to locate it, by arduous and costly fieldwork in the face of every natural difficulty and some political embarrassments, were not unenlightened by some moments of hope—and even of premature rejoicing; and, as will be seen, a decision was taken, early in 1960, to set on foot preparations for commercial production at a single sea-girt location.

In the Dhofar province the Sultan was successful, after the abandonment in 1951 of concessionary rights by the I.P.C. interests (p. 234), in attracting other aspirants. The Cities Service Company obtained a blanket concession for the area in 1952, forming an *ad hoc* subsidiary, Dhofar-Cities Service Petroleum Corporation, for its operations, and soon afterwards accepting the Richfield Oil Corporation (then active also in Egypt with the Sahara Company (p. 342) ) as an equal but non-operating partner. Cities Service early began field exploration, and showed itself able to overcome the truly formidable difficulties of climate, terrain, and transport. A drilling location was established in 1953, and the first well at Dauka, 140 miles inland from Salala (the capital of Dhofar), was spudded in early in 1954. The well, taken to nearly 12,000 feet, proved dry, as did the next two drilled in the vicinity. At Marmul, however, only forty miles from the coast, the second well drilled on the site, in the summer of 1957, produced a flow of some 2,000 b/d of oil of 22° A.P.I., from the shallow depth of 320 feet: an occasion of rejoicing and the highest hopes in the Sultanate. Output, however, fell rapidly, and subsequent drilling was unrewarded except by occasional shows of oil sufficient to maintain interest and optimism. By mid-1960 a full dozen wells had been drilled, mostly to depths exceeding 8,000 feet, and two were still drilling, while geological and seismic work proceeded. While hope was not, for a period of six months or a year, abandoned, the prospect of a major strike could not but be decreasingly probable; the I.P.C. had had, thus far, no cause to regret its withdrawal (p. 234).

In the main body of the Oman Sultanate, and more particularly in the open, undulating, wholly desertic country west of the great mountain massif (pp. 233–4), it proved possible in these years at last for Petroleum Development (Oman), the concerned Company of the I.P.C. Group, partially to explore and test-drill the area: an area presenting extreme difficulties of access, supply, and living conditions, and one, actually ungoverned, in which sovereign authority was claimed by the soi-disant ruler (or Imam) of hinterland Oman as against his internationally recognized overlord, Sayid Sa'id bin Taimur—a circumstance of little comfort to the concession-holding Company. In 1958 the promising Jabal Fahud structure, 200 miles from the Arabian Sea at Ras Duqn, was first selected for drilling. Communications to this desolate spot were organized from Duqn, from the north-east across the mountains from a depot at Asaiba near Muscat, and by air from Dukhan (Qatar) and Bahrain: by the last-mentioned of these routes lifts of up to sixteen tons were conveyed. The Jabal Fahud well was spudded in in January 1956, only to be abandoned as a dry hole at 12,250 feet in May 1957. The next site chosen was at Ghaba, eighty-five miles to the south-east, and a well spudded in in March 1958: this in its turn was abandoned as dry at 12,660 feet a year later. The third well, at Haima, spudded in in May 1959, was taken to 11,255 feet before abandonment in February 1960, and a fourth was spudded in at Afar in that month, only to be given up at 4,750 feet in April 1960. These so far wholly negative results were the more disappointing in view of the successful conquest of the exceptional difficulties of the enterprise, and of the generally high promise of the region on tectonic grounds. Meanwhile, in the spring of 1960, a gravity and two seismic parties were still operating in the territory. The Company's main depot, originally at Ras Duqn, was moved early in 1957 to Asaiba. In 1960 three of the major I.P.C.-Group constituents withdrew from the Oman Company (B.P., Near East Development, and the C.F.P.), leaving Shell with 82·6 per cent. and Partex (the Gulbenkian interest) with 17·4 per cent.—shares which were susceptible of later modification.

On the Trucial Coast, with its multiplicity of small rulers, its unmarked boundaries, Sa'udi menaces, and general desolation and poverty, the post-war exploratory operations already in part described (pp. 232-3) continued, those on land and in the sea being, as before, in separate hands. On land (where the concession for the small Sharja shaikhdom was surrendered in 1959, and that of Ras al-Khaima late in 1960), Petroleum Development (Trucial Coast), drilling in 1953-4 their first well at Murban (but third on the Trucial Coast as a whole) in the shaikhdom of abu Dhabi, found hopeful but not convincingly commercial traces of oil; it was abandoned in October 1954 at 12,590 feet. A fourth well was commenced in January 1955 at Jazira, ninety-five miles west and twenty south of Murban, but was in turn relinquished in March 1956 at 12,360 feet. The next site to be tested in 1956-7, at Shuwaihat on the coast, lay half-way between Murban and Jazira; it was abandoned at 12,360 feet in November 1957. The subsequent choice of location at Juwaisa in the shaikhdom of Sharja, was drilled in 1957 to 12,915 feet, but proved no less unrewarding. A second well was next spudded in at Murban, in October 1958, and completed in July 1959; taken to 10,600 feet, it revealed some gas but not oil. Murban no. 3, spudded in in December 1959, reached 10,250 feet in April 1960 and showed below 8,400 feet an oil-flow which would be tested. Geophysical work had meanwhile continued in other regions, including a seismic marine survey in abu Dhabi coastal waters in 1959-60. The headquarters for P.D. (T.C.)'s field operations moved from time to time, as necessitated by the wide distances between drilling locations: in the spring of 1960 it was at Tarif. Supply and liaison offices were maintained also at Dibai and at Abu Dhabi.

The formation in 1953 of abu Dhabi Marine Areas Ltd. as a joint operating company, as between A.I.O.C. (later B.P.) with a two-thirds and the Compagnie Française with a one-third interest, for the exploration and development of the abu Dhabi offshore (or Continental Shelf) waters, has been indicated above (p. 233).

The Company was granted by the Shaikh in 1954 a sixty-five-year concession over some 12,000 square miles of sea-covered area, while a corresponding but much smaller (1,200 square miles) grant was made simultaneously by the Shaikh of Dibai to an identically constituted Dubai Marine Areas Ltd. The staff of A.D.M.A. proceeded forthwith to submarine exploration by geophysical means, carried to the spot and serviced by specialized craft which included the *Calypso* of the renowned underwater operator Jacques Cousteau, the *Sonic* of the Geomarine Service International, and the specially adapted *Astrid Sven*. Sufficient indications of submarine structures having been obtained, a 4,000-ton drilling-barge christened *Adma Enterprise* was brought to the site from Western Germany. Costing £1·5 million, and fitted with retractable legs, it was designed for work in waters up to eight fathoms deep, and could attain a drilling depth of 15,000 feet. The first well was sited at Umm Shaif in the sea-bed not far from Das Island, which itself, lying eighty miles out, belongs to the abu Dhabi shaikhdom. The island was equipped with stores and domestic buildings, a jetty and protected area, separators and tankage, and a landing-ground. Oil of 40° A.P.I. was struck at some 5,500 feet, in quantity (2,400 b/d) considered to be probably commercial. A second well, spudded in in November 1958, proved oil-less; a third, Umm Shaif no. 3, produced oil from over 9,600 feet in depth, and turned the scale in favour of production. Other wells were sited and a programme of production drilling undertaken. Plans were made early in 1960 for a twenty-mile 18-inch submarine pipeline to convey the oil to Das Island, where it would be gas-separated and stored for loading into tankers, for which purpose a suitable jetty would be constructed. A new type of craft for A.D.M.A. was launched on the Tyne in July 1960, carrying a large flow-tank and 28-foot separator on deck, for use in testing the flow of wells. Production was planned to begin in 1962—the first from any of the Trucial Coast shaikhdoms, and the forerunner, perhaps, of new ways of life, with new complications and temptations, for the Ruler and people of abu Dhabi.

## VI. SOUTH-WESTERN ARABIA

In this largely desolate yet highly interesting area of the Arabian peninsula no sources of petroleum were brought to light during this period, in spite of persistent efforts by foreign companies and the natural eagerness of the local potentates. The opening of a major refinery at Aden, intended for the supply of products overseas and for bunkering, was the outstanding event of the time.

In the Yemen, the extreme political unattractiveness of this little-visited and mediaevally governed or ungoverned territory (p. 235) did not prevent renewed efforts to examine its oil possibilities, under the encouragement, possibly, of some intermittent signs given by the Imam's Government of a desire to emerge into the twentieth century. In 1953 an agreement covering most of the territory was made with the Imam by the German firm of C. Deilmann Bergbau G. m. b. H., for the carrying out of geophysical and geological exploration. A surprising feature of the agreement was the alleged provision by the Government of 75 per cent. of the capital required, with the hope of a similar proportion of ultimate profits; Bergbau would operate the expected oilfields for twenty years, but must withdraw from the territory after five years if these did not exist. The Company, under the name of Yemen Deilmann Petrol, conducted aerial and other exploration of a coastal area north of Hudaida; but its work was thereafter cut short by the surprising grant in 1955 of exploration rights over 40,000 square kilometres of substantially the same area to a United States concern, the Yemen Development Corporation, owned mainly by Oil and Gas Property Management Inc. of Texas. The Germans ceased work and appealed, with results never made public, for arbitration on their rights. The Development Corporation is believed to have carried out some surveys, but it withdrew when faced with the insurmountable difficulty of raising funds for exploration and meeting dead-rent payments. In 1959 a further concession over 10,000 square miles was reported to have been given to an American Overseas Investment Corporation, made up of private investors in the Southern States. No drilling has been reported. The discovery of an oilfield in the Yemen, in the present or perhaps any circumstances, would on existing indications be surprising. The probability that Russian or Rumanian technicians, known to be present in the territory, were assisting in the search could not be excluded. Rumours of Italian or Japanese interest in the territory were at times in circulation.

In the tiny Crown Colony of Aden, the A.I.O.C. (British Petroleum) refinery, built at Little Aden in 1952–4 (p. 235), came on stream, with a throughput of some 5 million t/y, in the last days of the latter year. On crude received mainly from Kuwait, it operated subsequently with no greater interruptions than those caused by some acts of sabotage and the not infrequent labour disturbances in the Colony (political in origin rather than due to any faults or omissions by the Company), and by a temporary reduction of output in 1956–7 due to the Suez Canal stoppage and consequent diversion of shipping. Since its completion, improvements but no major expansion were carried out. The refinery contained, in 1959–60, two crude distillation units of 60,000-b/d capacity each, equipped with electronic control instruments; a sulphur extraction plant treated 8,800 b/d of raw kerosene; an 'autofining' process was used to desulphurize 3,000 b/d of tractor vaporizing oil; a 12,000 b/d catalytic refining unit (or 'platformer') was used to improve the octane rating of gasoline. In 1956 an l.p.g. plant was installed to meet an interesting new demand for this product within the refinery's orbit of supply. Total refinery throughput was 3·7 million tons in 1958, 4·1 million in 1959. Distribution of ex-refinery products was mainly to the territory itself, to the Red Sea ports and, more substantially, to East and South Africa; bunkering was, naturally, in so important a supply-point, of outstanding importance, and 2 million tons a year of fuel oil, out of the refinery's annual production of 3½ million tons thereof, were in 1959 supplied to the 4,500 ships per year which call at Aden. A twenty-mile gas line was laid, early in 1959, from the refinery to supply the electric generating station in Aden city. The economic benefits to Aden and its vicinity of the local expenditure of, and the well-paid employment given by, the refinery needed little emphasis; it was, of course, by far the greatest industrial enterprise in southern Arabia. Every care was taken, in many directions, by the responsible Company for the welfare of its labour force.

In the Aden Protectorate, the Petroleum Concessions exploration parties in 1954 (p. 234), operating by air and on land, could bring back no hopeful indications; and the frontier regions of the territory remained insecure from Yemeni incursions as well as by nature inhospitable. The Company, however, still in possession of its 1938 'blanket' exploration permit (p. 115), put further expeditions into the northern Hadhramaut in 1956–9 and carried out geophysical studies. In the early winter of 1959 some seismic work was done in the Thamud area some 180 miles inland, and discussion of a concession in the protected sultanates of the Qu'aiti and Kathiri was initiated with the two rulers. The latter, advised by an Arab oil-expert from elsewhere, proved to be exacting bargainers, and, demanding terms which the Company could not accept, witnessed the withdrawal of the latter and all its operations from their territories. This marked, early in 1960, the end of Petroleum Concessions' efforts in the Protectorate, and the surrender of their exploration licence. No drilling had been carried out, and a long-drawn expenditure of money and effort in exploration had proved fruitless. The Qu'aiti and Kathiri Governments proceeded to invite tenders for a concession over 5,000 square miles in the district of Thamud.

In 1956 the Governor of Aden granted to British Petroleum exploration rights over Kamaran Island, which, a part of the Protectorate, lies in the Red Sea off the Yemen coast. A geophysical party visited the island in 1956 and 1957 but, after seismic exploration, were unable to report any hopeful indications.

## CHAPTER XIX

# THE LEVANT COUNTRIES, 1953-60

THIS chapter will cover the territories of Turkey, Cyprus, the Lebanon, Jordan, Israel, the United Arab Republic (as it became in February 1958) of Egypt and Syria, and the Sudan. It will be found that, in spite of energetic and costly searches for new oil sources in each of these countries, often by new entrants to the field, no major discovery was made in the region; minor finds, but of limited international interest, occurred in Syria and Egypt only. At the close of the period it became yearly less probable, though never impossible, that the region would be found to contain internationally important deposits.

No large-scale refinery was completed, though new small- or medium-scale plants came on stream in Syria, Lebanon, and Jordan; three more were in hand or planned in Turkey and one in Syria, while two in Egypt were destined for early expansion. No major trans-territory trunk pipelines were built, though those existing were enlarged in capacity—and, in one case, partially destroyed, restored, and duplicated. The local demand for petroleum products rose year by year in all territories. In the field of distribution to meet this, and in that of refining and, in certain interesting cases, that of the search for and production of oil, it will be found that a feature of the period was the increased part played by governmental or para-statal enterprises.

## I. TURKEY

Signs of a radical change in the policy of the Turkish Republic, in the matter of permitting foreign assistance in the search for oil in its territory, after a full generation of ill success by its own governmental Mining Research Institute (the M.T.A.), were already perceptible in 1952–3 (pp. 237–8); the full realization of the new policy, that of attracting to Turkey the capital, skill, and tenacity of fully competent international oil concerns—a policy far better calculated to secure Turkish objectives and advantage— was the main feature of the period following 1953.

The first stage was the passage in 1954 of a basic Foreign

Investments Law, whereunder foreign investment, for the first time in republican Turkey, was welcomed without limit of time or amount, with due regard only to the avoidance of any eventual disadvantage to the Turkish economy by monopoly or otherwise; both the capital invested and the subsequent profits could in due course be repatriated, and no adverse discrimination against such enterprises would be made. In the Petroleum Law issued in the same year, and amended in 1955, provision was made for six-year exploration licences over each of (at most) eight blocks, in any region declared to be 'open'; no block was to exceed 50,000 hectares. (Two areas in east-central Turkey remained closed on security grounds.) Exploitation leases could run for forty (extendable to sixty) years, over areas up to 25,000 hectares, and such leases could be claimed as of right by a successful explorer. A royalty of 12½ per cent. was included in the total prescribed government receipts from such enterprises, which taxation arrangements would bring up to 50 per cent. of profits in all. Depletion allowances were provided for; possible delivery to Government of oil in kind, for military purposes, was envisaged; oil, once discovered, must be effectively produced, unless proved clearly uneconomic. Normal provisions were made for the use of local labour, the import of foreign specialists, and other matters.

In the new climate thus created, a large number of companies outside Turkey showed immediate interest, and eager applications for blocks of territory were handed in even before the new legal position was established. All over the seven 'open' zones of the Republic geological and geophysical parties appeared as soon as, mostly in 1955, the various overlaps and uncertainties as between competing block-applications had been resolved by the Petroleum Commissioner; final Cabinet authority for each grant had, as the Law demanded, been obtained; and the detailed Regulations under the Law had been issued and put into effect. During the following six years not less than 200 exploration licences were issued, covering, it was said, up to 25 million acres. The licencees included companies representing, as subsidiaries, both the 'major' and a host of other important or obscure American, British, Canadian, and German concerns. They included subsidiaries of Esso (New Jersey), Shell, Mobil, Caltex (through American Overseas), and Gulf, and also Cities Service, Sinclair, Seaboard, Tidewater,

Gilliland, Richfield, Feldmann, Bolsa Chica, Deilmann Bergbau, Parsons, Canada Southern Oils, Kern Oil, and Conorada and others up to a total of at least a score. The operations of each concern cannot, for reasons of space as well as lack of definite information, be here given in detail; some, including the last three named, did not long remain in the field, while others proceeded to long and costly campaigns of investigation. But the list of those who moved on from geophysics to test drilling is impressive. American Overseas drilled six wells at Kahta near Gaziantep, and one more in the same locality. In the same zone Shell drilled three wells, Esso two, Tidewater (in partnership with Atlantic Refining and Texas Seaboard) one well. In the area of the Raman Dagh field, Bolsa Chica drilled four wells, Esso and Tidewater three each, Gilliland and Mobil one each. In Iskenderun area, Gilliland, Mobil, and Esso each drilled one well. In Europe (Thrace) Esso drilled three wells, Shell and Deilmann jointly two, Gulf one; it was reported in July 1960 that the Deilmann-Shell enterprise had found oil and gas in their well Kuleli no. 1, thirty-five miles east of Edirne. No drilling, up to early 1960, was carried out by Deutsche Erdöl (who were active in Syria), nor by the local companies Etta, Istanbul Gas, and Marmara Petroleum, nor by Pan American Land and Oil Royalty. In all, nine rigs were at work, at the end of 1959, on behalf of foreign concerns, and six for the statal Turkish Petroleum Corporation, successor to the Mining Research Institute.

From all this widespread effort the only discovery reported in these years was one, of doubtful value by reason of its low quantity and quality (11° A.P.I.), at Kahta, by American Overseas late in 1957. For the rest, results were uniformly disappointing, even though wide sedimentary areas of the Republic still remained ill explored and hope could well persist, notably in European Turkey (Thrace) and in the Siirt region nearest to (or indeed within) the rich Persian Gulf geosyncline. Up to the end of 1959 thirty-six exploration wells had been drilled within the 100,000 square kilometres held under licence; 222 such licences had been issued, to twenty foreign and one local concern. Nearly $70 million were spent on these efforts from 1955 to 1959. The use of drilling contractors was widespread. Helicopters were widely used. No drilling was carried out in the south-west, or west, or north-central districts of Turkey.

Meanwhile the existing small fields in the south-east, those of Raman Dagh and Garzan, continued in production, giving 328,000 tons in 1958 and 372,000 in 1959; indeed, an extension of the Garzan field, at Germik, was discovered by the Turkish Petroleum Corporation, and gave a very small output by pumping. These fields contain forty-five wells, all pumping; their reserves are estimated at 10 million tons.

The Raman Dagh–Garzan production was limited by the local refining capacity (p. 237), even though the exiguous topping-plant erected at Batman in 1948 to serve the two fields was replaced in 1955 by the completion of a small American-erected refinery of rather over 6,000 b/d capacity, about one-quarter of Turkey's current needs. Plans were made in 1959 for an extension of the Batman refinery from a capacity of 350,000 t/y to 650,000, but no dates were assigned. The balance of the country's requirements, with a substantial surplus of products for export, was, under arrangements made in 1957–8 between the Government and the foreign 'majors' active in Turkey, to be secured by the erection of a medium-scale ($3\frac{1}{4}$ million-t/y) refinery to be erected at Mersin. A Turkish Company, the Anatolia Refining Company (Atas), was formed early in 1959, with shareholding as follows: Mobil 56 per cent., Shell 27 per cent., and B.P. 17 per cent. Mobil was to act as agent for the others, and Foster Wheeler to undertake erection. This was to be completed late in 1961, and would cost some £16 million; it would include a catalytic reforming unit and a kerosene desulphurizer, and was designed to treat Middle Eastern (or, later, Turkish) crude. Two jetties and a barge wharf would form part of the plan. The foundation-stone was laid by the Prime Minister early in 1960. Part of the Mobil shareholding was to be passed to the local distributor, Turk Petrol.

Pending the operation of this refinery, Turkey's needs, now amounting to some $1\frac{1}{2}$ million t/y—a modest figure, due to an embarrassed economy and to the wide use of local coal and hydro-electricity—were met by imports made by the distributing Companies named above. All of these had had to agree in 1959 to payment, through a long-drawn instalment plan, of the debts still due to them for products imported in previous years; the sums thus recovered would be available for the construction of the Mersin refinery. It was announced late in 1959 that a refinery

(Ipras) jointly owned by the Turkish Petroleum Corporation (51 per cent.) and Caltex (49 per cent.), with capacity of 1 million t/y, would be erected, for completion in 1962, at Tutuncifligi near Izmit in the Istanbul area; Caltex would be liable, after ten years' operation, to expropriation of its share. The plant was estimated to cost $26 million, and would be built by American contractors. Another project, for completion in 1961, was that of a 800,000-ton refinery at Buyukcekmece (west of Istanbul) to be erected by a private Turkish group, Maper.

## II. CYPRUS

From the island of Cyprus, distracted by its political troubles, no progress was reported during the period. After the failure of both the I.P.C. Group and the Cypriot company, Prospectors Ltd., to discover oil (p. 239), and their withdrawal, a four-year interval occurred before a Prospecting Licence covering most of the island and its territorial waters was issued in May 1957 to a further aspirant, the Forest Oil Corporation of Pennsylvania. Geologists arrived within a few weeks, but no drilling was undertaken and three years later the island remained as oil-less as ever. Cypriot enterprise was active in other branches of the industry; no refinery could be justified, but an all-Cypriot concern, Petrolina, began in mid-1959 the erection of a terminal and tankage at Larnaca, for the import and distribution of products.

## III. THE LEBANON

The scale and nature of operations in the Lebanon changed little in the period under review.

After the cessation of I.P.C. exploration and its Terbol test well, the activities of the Lebanese-American Compagnie Libanaise des Pétroles (p. 241), the surviving long-term concessionaire, fared no better, and its test in the Beka'a (Baqa') ended in similar unsuccess; in spite of some show of asphalt and natural gas the well was abandoned at 8,850 feet. The Company, however, undeterred by the slender prospects of success in this heavily faulted and deeply eroded terrain, and successful in arranging for an extension of the period allowed it for exploration, announced in February 1959 an arrangement with the Gewerkschaft Elwerath Erdölwerke of Hanover, a leading German producer, for further exploration by the latter, while itself assured a 50 per cent.

participation in the Concession: and for the formation of a joint concern in case of success. In April 1960, following geophysical work by another German firm, Deutsche Schachtbau und Tiefbohr, a well-location was established in the northern Beka'a, and the Compagnie Libanaise prepared to drill. The Company continued to be hampered by lack of finance, though politically well supported.

The interest of the Republic as a transit and loading territory remained, and in the closing months of the period a new 30-inch pipeline of the I.P.C., additional to the older 12- and 16-inch lines, was completed from the Syrian frontier to Tripoli, increasing the rate of 'Iraqi oil transiting the Lebanon to a potential 23 million t/y. The capacity of the Tapline trunk service (p. 299), with its 30/31-inch line to Sidon, was raised to some 23–24 million t/y. The important tank farms and loading facilities of both Companies remained in constant operation. The two I.P.C. lines terminating at Tripoli were inactive only during the period from November 1956 to the early spring of 1957, by reason of the destruction of pipeline stations in Syria in the former month; they were again interrupted, for a few days only, by civil disturbance in May 1958. Neither of the pipeline-owning companies had main pumping stations in the Lebanon. Loading of crude at Tripoli amounted in 1958 to 7·3 million tons, in 1959 to the same, carried by 351 and 333 tankers respectively: some 18 million tons of Sa'udi Arabian crude left Aramco's Sidon terminal in 1958, 16·5 million tons in 1959.

The vexed question of the transit dues payable by I.P.C. to the Lebanese Government for the right of pipeline transit and for loading yielded in these years but reluctantly to treatment. The improved arrangement offered by I.P.C. in 1952 (p. 243) was never ratified by the Lebanese Parliament which, unlike Syria, declined to base payment rates on any ton-mile calculation; and this was true also of a further increased offer made in 1955 which, with an annual rate of payment of £380,000, took only provisional effect. Not until June 1959 did the long-drawn discussions result in a new agreement, this time ratified. Annual payments by the Company would amount (on a basis of the then current 7·5 million t/y transit) to £1·235 million, or £L.11 million, compared with the previous £L.3·25 million. A lump-sum equal to £L.51 million was paid to settle all outstanding claims from 1952 onwards; in addition, a Trade School was to be established and paid for by the Company, and certain grants in cash would be made to local municipalities.

Tapline, with a similar problem of transit-payment calculations, failed during the period to reach agreement, and continued to pay no more than £L.1·25 million a year, a rate far from satisfactory to the Government.

The small refineries of both concerns, situated at Tripoli and near Sidon respectively, and in their expanded form capable of throughputs (which did not include lubricants or aviation spirit) of 575,000 and 450,000 t/y, worked continuously and provided for Lebanese needs in most main products as well as contributing to those of Syria and Jordan pending completion of the Homs and Zerka (Zarqa) plants in mid-1959 and late 1960. In respect of Tripoli, it was a provision of the pipeline transit agreement of June 1959 that 20 per cent. of the refinery's output of products should be made available for local marketeers. In the case of neither installation, Tripoli or Sidon, could a profit be expected as long as local control, price-fixing, and taxation remained at existing levels, and the erection of Syrian and Jordanian plants raised questions of finding outlets for the disposal of products[1] excessive to Lebanese needs. The latter amounted in 1959 to slightly more than half a million tons a year, including products imported because not produced locally. The Sidon (or, more accurately, Zahrani) refinery, owned equally by Caltex and Mobil Overseas in the guise of Medrico (Mediterranean Refining Company), was erected in 1954–5 with an initial capacity of 6,000 b/d, later increased to 9,000. It produced *inter alia* a high-octane gasoline, and supplies for locally needed ocean bunkers.

#### IV. ISRAEL

The main features of oil activity in Israel in the period 1953–60 were the increasing part played therein directly by the Government: the keen and prolonged search for, and a minor discovery of, crude oil supplies: the attraction of considerable and varied foreign capital to these operations: and the expedients adopted to ensure supplies for the truncated refining industry, in a territory surrounded by enemies of the Jewish state.

---

[1] Actual throughput of Tripoli refinery was only 305,000 tons in 1958, 181,000 in 1959.

A notable outburst of popular and governmental interest in exploration and test drilling followed the issue in 1952 of the Mining Law (pp. 251–2). Exploration rights over blocks of the approved sizes were obtained by a wide variety of new, or newly interested, concerns and the work of exploration was pressed forward from 1953 onwards in a dozen localities. Israel Oil Prospectors, containing an Israeli trade-union element, as well as American and Swiss participants, operated in places singly, and in places jointly with the Lapidoth Company, itself including Israeli para-statal shareholding as well as American. The Jordan Exploration Company continued to explore Dead Sea areas, where it already held licences. Drilling in the Negev was carried out by concerns which represented a mixture of Israeli and Canadian capital: Tri-Continental Drilling, Pan-Israel Oil, and Israel Mediterranean Petroleum. A similarly constituted company, Israel-Continental Oil, drilled near Tiberias. Others conducting field operations were the Sharon Oil Company (behind which stood the Israeli-American Oil Corporation), the (Canadian) Yellow Knife Power Company, and the local (but American-aided) Palestine Economic Corporation. To these was added in 1958 a Government-sponsored National Oil Company, which itself commenced field exploration.

Of all these, a joint effort of Lapidoth and Israel Oil Prospectors, who later formed a joint operating Company, Matsada, succeeded in September 1955 in finding oil at the location near Gaza where drilling by the I.P.C. had already well begun in 1948 (p. 247). The unfinished well, renamed Heletz no. 1, was deepened and oil was struck in Lower Cretaceous sand at a depth between 4,000 and 4,900 feet. The evidence was, and has remained, that of a strictly limited supply, which, five years later, amounted to some 2,000 b/d of 31° A.P.I. oil, obtained from twenty-five wells of which three-quarters required pumping. In May 1960 some further hopes were based on the better performance of Heletz no. 25, which indicated an oil-bearing porous limestone.

The Heletz discovery, which assured less than 10 per cent. of Israel's own requirements[1] was followed by widespread geophysical

[1] Israeli domestic production was, in the four years 1956–9, respectively, 30,000, 70,000, 89,000, and 130,000 t/y. Both Heletz and Bror were fully drilled by 1959, and were unlikely to increase their yields.

and drilling efforts by the Companies above-named. Drilling was carried out in the Haifa neighbourhood, in the desert south of Beersheba (p. 247, *ad fin.*) and in the Gaza vicinity, and early in 1960 further specific plans for a £3 million two-year concerted drilling programme were made known by the two Companies developing Heletz, while the National Company, holding numerous block concessions, was raising money for its operations. In spite of surviving but diminishing hopes—and some not unpromising 'shows', notably at Bror-Hayil, close to Heletz, in June 1957—no further commercial oil was located, probable though it still remained that such existed in small and scattered accumulations somewhere on this perimeter of the Arabian Shield; meanwhile less and less enthusiasm was being shown by most interested concerns, from mid-1958 onwards, for spending more money in so disappointing a quest, and a number of active licence-holders withdrew.

A gas field of some interest was discovered by a part-local part-foreign concern, Naptha Israel Petroleum, early in 1959, at Zohar in the Negev, thirty-five miles south-east of Beersheba; this was energetically developed with more wells, one of which, at Kidod five miles from Zohar, yielded 7 million cubic feet of gas a day. The potential reserve was already reckoned as 5,000 million cubic feet. For its utilization, outside experts were invoked for consultation, and the decision was reached in January 1960 to pipe gas by a twenty-mile 6-inch line to the Dead Sea Potash works at Sodom.

The refinery at Haifa, originally built and operated by Consolidated Refineries (pp. 89f., 141) continued to work with a diminished throughput supplying local needs with, as from March 1960, a small surplus of products for export shipments to Western Europe, and of asphalt for Turkey; this export business was handled by a United Petroleum Export concern, composed of Israeli marketing companies. The refinery itself, while working normally, changed owners in 1958, when it was acquired from Consolidated by the Paz Oil Company, an Israeli distributing company controlled in its turn by Mr. Isaac Wolfson in the guise of Iwol Investments Ltd. Throughput was in the range of $1\frac{1}{4}$ to $1\frac{3}{4}$ million t/y. The main Western distributors withdrew during this period from Israel, owing to their trade being rendered profitless by governmental measures. Esso in March 1955, Mobil

late in 1956 sold their assets and departed, and in 1957 they were
followed by B.P. and Shell, who sold their marketing installations
to the Paz (or Wolfson) concern. The difficulty of alimenting
the plant with crude oil (pp. 252f.) at times severe, diminished in
these years. The withholding of crude supplies of Arab origin,
or from sources sensitive to Arab displeasure, led temporarily to
the use of Western sources, including Venezuelan, Rumanian,
and Russian, until those from the two last-named ceased abruptly
early in 1957. Thereafter supplies reached Haifa by pipeline (see
below) from Eilat, of Indonesian, but far more of Persian (that is,
N.I.O.C.), origin.

A small Israeli-owned tanker fleet was also acquired during
these years, and in the summer of 1960 the first petrochemical
plant in Israel, to produce polyethylene, was announced as due
for construction at Haifa, the first step towards larger developments later.

In 1957 a 150-mile 8-inch crude line was constructed from
the port of Eilat to Beersheba, and extended thence to Ashdod
Yam and Haifa by a 16-inch line. The Eilat–Beersheba section
was later replaced by a 16-inch, with the aid of foreign
(Rothschild and other) capital; a concession was signed with
the Israeli Government whereunder the international investment group concerned (known as Tri-Continental Pipelines)
would own and operate the whole 257-mile Red Sea to Haifa
16-inch line, of which the capacity would be 35,000 b/d,
capable of increase to three times that figure if an export
demand for Haifa refinery products could be found on that
scale. The work was completed in mid-1960, when its operation was assumed by the Group who had constructed it. The
concession, of forty-nine-year duration, gave guarantees of
throughput and of remuneration which would ensure a reasonable profit for the operators. The latter's investment was
reported as £24 million.

Israeli requirements in refined products, rising steadily,
amounted in 1959 to some 1½ million t/y, the highest *per capita*
consumption of any Middle Eastern State. Distribution of these
ex-refinery supplies passed, with the progressive withdrawal of
the former marketers, to local, and in large part para-statal,
concerns. A 6-inch products line was laid in 1955 from Haifa to
Tel Aviv.

### V. JORDAN

No indigenous supplies of petroleum were discovered in Jordan during this period; but steps, to be complete only by late 1960, were taken to remedy a pressing immediate difficulty, that of ensuring the supply of the territory with its still humble requirements in petroleum products. The Jordan Petroleum Company of the I.P.C. Group (pp. 249–50) abandoned its 1947 blanket concession in November 1954, without having found structures worthy of test drilling. In 1955 the American independent, Edwin Pauley, with Phillips Petroleum participation, obtained a concession covering about 8 million acres, and after some geophysical work began drilling in July 1957. Wells at Mashash, twenty-six miles south-east of 'Amman, were abandoned dry at 8,500 feet, and another at Ramallah north of Jerusalem, taken to 10,400 feet, was no less disappointing; whereupon Pauley disposed of most of his interest to the Phillips Company in 1958. The latter concern proceeded to drill a well at Halhul near Hebron in 1958, which was abandoned at 6,000 feet; two more at Suwaila, ten miles north-west of 'Amman, and in the Jordan Valley, twenty miles south-west of 'Amman, were abandoned at 7,600 feet and 3,600 feet respectively. No drilling was in progress in late 1959, but a fresh start could be expected as the Government had in September agreed to an extension of the exploration period allowed. Meanwhile a second semi-blanket concession, for an approximate third of the country in areas not granted to Pauley, was allocated in 1957 to George Zimiri (or Izmiri), a Central American of Arab origin; its terms included a fifty-five-year term (with cancellation in six years if no oil had been discovered), a fifty-fifty division of profits, considerable interim annual rental payments, and serious geophysical and drilling obligations. This concession, announced as made over to an American company to operate, was reported early in 1959 as cancelled by the Government for non-fulfilment of obligations. Reports appeared from time to time in 1958–60 of other grants by the Jordan Government to, or applications from, Italian, West German, or American candidates for territory not covered by the Phillips grant.

The I.P.C. 12-inch and the (never used) 16-inch pipelines traversing the territory remained, with their pumping stations (H4, H5, and the Jordan Valley Relief Station) totally inactive throughout the period (pp. 248-9). Occasional rumours of, or proposals for, the disinterment and re-alignment of these to a Lebanese port led to no action, though the 16-inch line at last was doubtless capable of such service. Benefits to the country from the passage of Tapline (p. 249) were minimal, and constant pressure was exercised by the Jordan Government for a rate of transit-payment in excess of the low rate which was provisionally established in 1952; but, mainly owing to the failure of the other Arab States concerned to agree *inter se*, no conclusion had been reached with Tapline by mid-1960.

The difficulty for the Jordan public and army of obtaining petroleum products (p. 249), to the required quantities of some 150,000 t/y, did not diminish, and became acute in periods when relations with Syria (and, after July 1958, 'Iraq) were bitter. It became necessary for Jordan to obtain its products from the Red Sea port of 'Aqaba. These were provided (with great initial difficulty, due to absence of storage at the port) by the distributing companies, with (notably in December 1958) American Government help. Tankage at 'Aqaba was thereafter augmented, and an adequate ocean installation erected, to be operated by the locally constituted Jordan Petroleum Storage Company. Products were supplied after June 1959 to the latter under competitive contract, and were drawn from storage by the agents (or jobbers) of the established distributors. The situation would be greatly eased in October 1960 by the completion of the small refinery of 350,000 t/y capacity, constructed by the Italian contractors S.N.A.M. Progetti for the (largely but not wholly statal) Jordan Petroleum Refineries, at Zerka (Zarqa) fifteen miles north of 'Amman. This would draw its crude from Tapline, by a thirty-mile 8-inch pipeline, at preferential rates. Distribution of products from the refinery (which, however, were unlikely exactly to fit the pattern and scale of local demand) would probably be, wholly or largely, a function of the Petroleum Storage Company.

## VI. THE UNITED ARAB REPUBLIC: SYRIA

In this territory, which early in 1958 lost its sovereign status and became the northern province of the United Arab Republic (of Egypt and Syria, with capital at Cairo), exploration for indigenous oil resources, for which the regional geology could *a priori* afford good hopes, came to a pause in the period 1952 to 1956, when no companies ventured into a field in which the I.P.C. had already (pp. 239–40) expended so much money and effort. The latter year, however, was marked by a reappearance of J. W. Minhall (pp. 240–1), who, in association with Atlantic Refining, Portsmouth Steel Corporation, and (it is believed) other American companies, obtained new exploration rights in north-eastern Syria from the Government, and began field operations. He located a supply—some 1,000 b/d—of heavy (22° A.P.I.) and highly sulphurous oil at 6,500 feet in Upper Cretaceous fractured limestone in the Qarachauk (Karachok) area, at a drilling site already selected by I.P.C. before its withdrawal. Five subsequent wells confirmed the presence of a doubtfully commercial field of small or moderate proportions, and of low quality oil. In 1958 Minhall, accused by Government of having acquired un-authorized (American) participants, was despite his protests deprived of his rights, under a compensation arrangement, not made public; and the field reverted to Government, in which by now the General Petroleum Authority, with headquarters at Cairo, was charged with all oil affairs. These tasks included co-ordination as between the two regions of the U.A.R., super-vision of imports and distribution, and control of licences, leases and agreements, and of product prices. This authority, through its Damascus office, declared early in 1959 that it would itself undertake the development of the Qarachauk field, the reserves of which were calculated to be 150 million tons, and from which the G.P.A. expected to produce as much as 2 million t/y of crude and to justify, at a cost of some £10 million, a 470-mile 12-inch pipe-line to Tartus on the Mediterranean coast. Russian experts, of whom a team became available in the territory under the Syro-Russian Economic Aid Agreement of 1957, would no doubt assist in this as in all other petroleum projects. The latter were stated to include mapping and, in an exclusive area of 50,000 square kilometres, geophysical work, the drilling of not less than eighteen test wells, the training of Syrians, and the provision (on credit) of materials. But the difficulties and the economic un-certainties of pipelining this viscous and sulphurous oil appeared considerable, and work on the line was slow to start.

The Qarachauk field, whatever its value, did not long stand alone. Late in 1956 exploration rights were granted over 15,000 square kilometres, also in north-east Syria, to the West German concern Deutsche Erdöl A. G., taking here the form of a local subsidiary formed *ad hoc*, the Société des Pétroles Concordia. This Company, after a brief geophysical (seismic) season, began to drill in the area between Hasaja (Hassaché) and Qamishli, in August 1957. At al-Buwab, fifteen miles north-east of Hasaja, their first well was abandoned at 10,700 feet; a second was drilled without success in the same locality, and a third at Shaikh Sullakh (near an old I.P.C. location at al-Ghaiba), twenty miles south-east of al-Buwab. In August 1959, with the sixth well to be drilled, an encouraging strike was made at Suwaidiya, later (March 1960) confirmed as a smallish producer (700 b/d) from a depth of 5,620–6,450 feet. The drilling of further wells proceeded, and the field, in which a second producer was soon completed, appeared likely to be commercial. A joint Company as between Concordia and the U.A.R. authorities was in March suggested for the exploitation of the field; Concordia would at the same time maintain its own exploration operations independently.

These minor discoveries seemed to confirm rather than diminish the view that Syria, in spite of its abundant sediments and its location on the flank of the Persian Gulf geosyncline, was unlikely to be revealed as a producer upon any scale approaching that of an 'Iraq or a Kuwait; but useful supplies might, all the same, become available to assist the local economy.

The same purpose lay behind the decision, made late in 1955, to arrange the erection of a small (750,000 t/y throughput) refinery at Homs. This work, intended as a governmental enterprise, was financed from funds provided on favourable terms by the U.S.S.R. It was early in 1957 entrusted to a Czech Company, Technoexport, at a cost of £5½ million, and on completion in mid-1959 commenced operation. This put an end to a period (1957–9) during which the supply of products to Syria had been a matter of extreme difficulty, and had involved imports by the G.P.A. from the Black Sea and from Egypt as well as from Tripoli, and the requisitioning of units of I.P.C. terminal tankage at Banias. For the new refinery, after August 1959, crude supplies were taken, under the I.P.C.-Syrian agreement of 1953, at a price substantially below 'posted price', from the I.P.C. pipelines passing near Homs—with the provision that Tapline (whose transit of Syria carried a similar obligation) should reimburse I.P.C. for the latter's sole assumption of this duty, by supplying it with corresponding quantities of crude at Sidon. The construction of two 6-inch products-lines from the refinery to Aleppo (110 miles) and to Damascus (95 miles) was put in hand. These operations would suffice to meet Syria's principal needs in products, some 750,000 t/y, and the necessity to import products from the two Lebanese refineries no longer existed. Allocation of supplies from Homs were made to distributors by the G.P.A., the former importing directly, as hitherto, such products (lubricating oils, aviation spirit, gas oil) as the refinery could not, or not sufficiently, produce. It was decided before the end of 1959 to add an l.p.g. plant at Homs, with the probable later addition of a lubricants and (possibly) a fertilizer plant. Five Syrian technicians went to Russia in 1959 for a course of instruction. In the north-east of Syria, simultaneously, a small refinery was projected to supply local needs by the processing of crude from Qarachauk; the plant would be provided by moving a unit of 200,000 t/y from the Government refinery at Suez. These projects all formed part of an integrated development plan drawn up by the G.P.A. in 1958. The Lattakiya Asphalt enterprise (p. 92 n.) continued to operate, as a bitumen-producer of local importance; it was sold as a going concern in 1960 by its I.P.C.-Group owners to Syrian industrialists, under pressure of current Syrian (U.A.R.) law, restrictive to foreign-owned enterprises.

With a view to further works of oil development, a National Company, with substantial Government shareholding, was announced as under formation late in 1959; it would participate with outside concerns in any venture considered attractive. Meanwhile the current Syrian law governing petroleum provided for the grant of exploration licences with a four-year term, with a possible single-year extension. If oil were discovered, but not otherwise, a long-term exploitation concession was to replace the licence. The principle of fifty-fifty division of profits was to be achieved by adjusted taxation. Special provisions would no doubt be devised if and when the G.P.A., or the National Company, took a direct share in operations.

Production and refining apart, the Syrian public and Government continued to benefit substantially from the transit of 'Iraqi and Sa'udi Arabian oil, and the export of the former at Banias (pp. 244–5). I.P.C. pipeline capacity through Syria, before 1956, was 25 million t/y, raised from an original (1952) 22 million with terminal capacity at Banias to match. The thoroughly executed destruction of the I.P.C. mid-desert pumping stations T2, T3, and T4 in November 1956, by Syrian troops involved a serious immediate loss of throughput for the I.P.C., as well as of important transit dues for Syria (one-third of their total revenues) and of employment for members of the public; and it illustrated, once more, the type of risk to which Western companies, operating in politically unstable countries, were and would doubtless remain exposed. The lines with improvised pumping plant were in part reopened in April 1957, passing oil at a rate first of 10 million, then 14 million, then by mid-summer 1958 25 million t/y, the rate prevailing before November 1956. This was achieved, as we have seen (p. 271), by the rebuilding and extension of T3 station, with a combination of additional 30-inch and other pipe-loops and the use of temporary, and later improved and permanent, pumping sets. The throughput, which amounted to 27·2 million tons in 1959, was intended to reach 35 million tons late in 1960. By the end of 1959, 217 miles of new 30-inch and 68 miles of 24-inch line had been completed in Syria, parallel to the existing 12-, 16-, and 30-inch lines, and a further 21 miles of 24-inch were nearly complete. Another 30-inch spur, taking off the main line in Syria, but with destination Tripoli, was finished in the spring of 1960 (p. 329). A system of remote control of unattended stations was under contemplation. The tank-farm at Banias had, before November 1956, a capacity of 500,000 tons, giving a week's reserve storage for loading; loading rates were at 3,000 tons per hour, at six berths. These capacities were, however, under constant revision and extensions were made from 1959 onwards to cope with increased and still increasing pipeline throughput. Tankers loaded at Banias numbered 697 in 1958, 831 in 1959.

As to transit and loading dues payable by I.P.C. to the Syrian Government, the agreement of May 1952 (p. 243) did not long satisfy the latter and was never ratified. Discussions continued intermittently from 1953 to 1955; late in the latter year the Company agreed to increase its payment (based on the throughput expected in 1956) to £6 million a year, with a further half-million as port dues and payments for 'security'. It paid also a sum of £8½ million in settlement of past claims. This agreement, still in force in mid-1960, was based on the figure of 1s. 4d. sterling per ton/hundred miles through Syria, and 1s. 10d. per ton for use of the Banias terminal, these figures purporting to represent 'half the profit' made by I.P.C. from its adoption of the trans-desert route. The arrangement secured for Syria an important proportion of its total State revenues, while the public, as in other transit countries, continued to enjoy the pay, salaries, local purchases, and locally given contracts deriving from the Company's activities.

The Tapline 31/30-inch trunk line, traversing a corner of Syria but with no pumping stations located within it, had long encountered a similar problem of transit payment. The 1952 agreement (p. 243) proved unsatisfying, and the subsequent Tapline offer, to divide between all the transit countries (including Sa'udi Arabia itself) half of the Company's saving due to the use of the pipeline as against sea transport, could never be reduced to figures satisfying to the various Governments. The question, in spite of firm pronouncements made by the Syrian authorities from time to time, remained unsettled in mid-1960. The capacity of the Tapline system was raised by improvements and additions during the period from an original 14 million t/y in 1950 to 21–2 million t/y in 1959; actual throughput in 1958 was 18 million, in 1959 16·9 million, and in 1960 at a still lower rate.

## VII. THE UNITED ARAB REPUBLIC: EGYPT AND THE CANAL

Former pages (p. 253f.) have described the vigorous exploration and drilling campaigns in Egypt by certain foreign companies in the period 1946–8, their failure in Western Egypt, their limited success in the Sinai Peninsula, and the general decline or even stoppage of such efforts between 1948 and 1952: a check due to restrictive legislation (p. 255), a generally anti-foreign Government oil-policy, and an insecure political atmosphere discouraging to investment.

In 1953, however, other councils prevailed in Cairo. A new law which became effective in that year, and under which many and various licences have since been granted, allowed a wide discretion to the executive in arranging with applicants the diverse exploration and exploitation conditions to govern their operations. Concessions provided normally for a thirty-year term, extendable to forty-five years; surface rentals, excused during the initial six years, were of the order of £E.25,000 per block per year thereafter, by which time much of the original territory would have been compulsorily surrendered; the minimum sums which licence-holders must expend on their operations were to be exactly prescribed, and would be considerable. Other provisions dealt with the obligation to contribute, from oil produced, to the country's internal needs before export would be permitted: with free share-holding in an operating Company (up to 16 per cent.) to be allotted to the Egyptian Treasury: with the Government's right to buy local oil at a preferential price: and with the payment by the Company to Government of one-half of the net locally accruing profits, by a combined machinery of royalty plus taxation. The conditions thus summarized, which were amended by legislation in 1956 in a sense permitting greater elasticity in Government–Company arrangements, proved sufficiently attractive to foreign enterprise at a time when much of this was eagerly awaiting opportunities in the field of oil development, and the difficulties of Egypt's own foreign-exchange position rendered the large-scale import of oil as undesirable as it was inevitable.

The present narrative cannot provide full particulars of all candidates, numerous and varied as they were, for oil rights in this period of sudden activity. Some local and some foreign concerns failed to obtain licences, or having obtained them failed to operate; some started but rapidly abandoned their efforts in the field; some merged their capital and enterprise, and many embarrassed the observer (and the historian) by changes of name or the appointment of each other, or an outsider, as their operating contractors. It must suffice to mention those concerns which in fact undertook serious, even if unsuccessful, exploration: with the comment that certain new features of considerable interest appeared in these years on the Egyptian scene. One of these was the increasing participation of local capital in such enterprise; another was the direct, including the financial, interest of the Egyptian (later the U.A.R.) Government and of its operating oil Company founded *ad hoc*; and another, the closeness of governmental control exercised by the General Petroleum Authority over all branches of the industry in both territories of the United Republic (p. 336).

In the desert western areas of Egypt, mainly near or nearish to the sea, serious exploration was carried out between 1955 and late 1958, over a total area of 88,000 square miles, by the Sahara Petroleum Company, a concern earlier known as the Egyptian-American Oil Company and itself a subsidiary of the Continental Oil Corporation of Delaware. Sahara acted also in concession blocks held by Cities Service Mideast Corporation,

Richfield Mediterranean Oil Company, Amerada (who later withdrew), and Oasis Oil Company (representing Ohio Oil Company). The Sahara Company (undeterred by the presence of war-time land-mines) drilled in all nine wells in the Western area, eight of them between 10,000 and 15,000 feet in depth, but all dry holes. It then abandoned its efforts and retired from Egypt in October 1958. Sahara had spent some $26½ million. The same western region, certain to be re-examined before long in consequence of the 1958–60 discoveries in adjoining Libya, was the subject of new regulations issued by the General Petroleum Authority in May 1960. Under these the region was divided into thirteen areas, and each of these into Permit blocks of 400 square kilometres each. The acreage which a concessionaire might hold in any one, or in all, of the concession areas was to be limited, and a quarter and a half of acreage held was to be surrendered after respectively three and six years. No surface rentals would be charged, but royalty rates would rise from an initial 15 to a later 25 per cent. and would be combined with taxation to secure half-profits—or even more, if Government did not become a share-holder—from the enterprise. After discovery of oil, a local Company was to be formed. Strong inducement was offered to persuade applicants to admit Government participation; and priority would be given to those who offered to erect refineries.

In the area between the Nile and Sinai, the State-owned General Petroleum Company, set up in 1957 by the General Petroleum Authority, explored from its inception onwards within the sixty-three blocks allotted to it, upon the terms provided by the 1954 law; the blocks included territory for which Anglo-Egyptian Oilfields had unsuccessfully applied from ten to five years earlier. In April 1958 General Petroleum announced its discovery of a small but promising field at Ras Bakr near the entrance to the Gulf of Suez, and in August another at Karim on the same coast. The Company thereupon increased its capital, acquired a small marketing company, and hired a German geo-physical firm for further exploration; drilling was to be extended (using Russian turbodrills), and production, to begin in 1960, was expected to reach 10,000 b/d; twelve wells had been completed at Ras Bakr by the end of 1959, and five at Karim. General Petroleum was reported in June 1960 as beginning a wildcat in the Rahmi area, fifty miles north of Ras Gharib, again using

Russian equipment. In the same area Anglo-Egyptian Oilfields continued to produce an important share of Egypt's indigenous oil from its long-established fields of Hurghada and Ras Gharib; these fields were, however, accepted as in decline, in spite of intensive drilling, and could not be expected to increase their output. Gemsa gave no further production.

In the Sinai peninsula, Anglo-Egyptian continued in 1953–60 to produce from their fields (p. 258), on leases held, in this case, jointly with Mobil through its subsidiary Mobil Oil Egypt. These fields—Ras Sadr, Ras Matarma, and 'Asl—proved largely disappointing; nor was much improvement probable. The difficulties of production from the small and low-quality Egyptian fields, experienced over so many years and in such exacting conditions by Anglo-Egyptian, were not lessened by the sequestration by Government of the Company and its entire operations and plant, for political reasons, in November 1956, whereafter it was held and operated under direct Egyptian-Government control, through a Custodianship. Following, however, first a Company–Government (December 1958) and later an inter-Government (March 1959) agreement, control was thereafter restored to the Company: such control, that is, as rigorous supervision by the General Petroleum Authority still permitted. During the three-year period of sequestration the Anglo-Egyptian fields and all connected services and installations were kept in normal operation. A limited amount of new tankage and other facilities was completed. The output of each field approximated fairly closely[1] to both pre- and post-sequestration output, a tribute to successful operation by Egyptian personnel trained, over the years, by Anglo-Egyptian.

[1] The output of fields in Egypt, 1953–9, was as follows, in thousands of metric tons. (Figures immediately following the names of the fields represent the A.P.I. rating of the crude.)

|                   | 1953  | 1954  | 1955  | 1956  | 1957  | 1958  | 1959  |
|-------------------|-------|-------|-------|-------|-------|-------|-------|
| Ras Gharib (26·5) | 1,213 | 1,261 | 1,201 | 1,025 | 1,002 | 1,008 | 993   |
| Hurghada (23·5)   | 38    | 38    | 36    | 38    | 32    | 32    | 33    |
| Ras Sadr (22·5)   | 315   | 311   | 313   | 236   | 295   | 187   | 160   |
| 'Asl (22·5)       | 783   | 344   | 164   | 143   | 158   | 152   | 152   |
| Ras Matarma (16·5)| —     | 16    | 18    | 17    | 15    | 12    | 14    |
| Firan (25)        | —     | —     | 20    | 30    | 19    | 16    |       |
| Balayim (22)      | —     | —     | 55    | 224   | 680   | 1,387 | 2,248 |
| Abu Rudais (25)   | —     | —     | —     | —     | 61    | 390   |       |
| TOTAL             | 2,349 | 1,970 | 1,807 | 1,713 | 2,262 | 3,184 | 3,600 |

The output of Sadr, 'Asl, and Matarma was divided equally between Shell and Mobil. Abu Rudais output includes that of Sidri.

Military operations stopped production from the Sinai fields for a time in 1956–7, and affected that of Ras Gharib. Drilling for the most part continued normally during those years, no non-Egyptian personnel being employed; but outside exploration was largely halted. All activities were resumed when sequestration ended, with, however, a much reduced employment of expatriate staff. Chairmen of A.E.O. (in Egypt) were G. S. Taitt 1953–4, H. M. Jones 1954–6, F. H. Frangenheim 1959–. General Managers of Shell Company of Egypt were H. M. Jones 1953–4, E. E. Hudson 1954–6, F. H. Frangenheim 1959–.

The most promising of the newer developments in Egyptian production remains to be mentioned. This was associated with the Compagnie Orientale des Pétroles, a composite body established in 1957 whose shareholding was held in respect of 51 per cent. by International Egyptian Oil Company (and its associate, and sometimes operating agent, the National Petroleum Company), and in respect of the rest by the State-owned General Petroleum (29 per cent.) and the Société Co-opérative des Pétroles (20 per cent.), which contributed the licences from which production was obtained. (International Egyptian had itself various participants, notably the Italian E.N.I. (40 per cent.), the Belgian Petrofina (40 per cent.), and American and other independents (20 per cent.).) The producing fields inherited by the Compagnie Orientale, which drilled nine wells in its first year of life, were at the first-discovered but smallest, Wadi Firan (pp. 254f.), and more importantly at Balayim[1] (discovered early in 1955), and Abu Rudais with Sidri (early 1957). The oil is in all cases of low quality, with a heavy content of sulphur and other impurities, but is, by Egyptian standards, abundant. For details of production see the footnote on p. 343.

Total Egyptian crude production was in 1958, 3·18 million tons, and in 1959, 3·6 million. These figures indicated an approximation to overall self-sufficiency in crude for Egypt; but the country's pattern of consumption, with high kerosene and low gasoline and fuel-oil demand, did not fit the output of its refineries, and much of its domestic crude was dangerously sulphurous. It resulted that a fair proportion of the crude was exported as such, mainly to Italy. Gasoline was exported by the G.P.A. to Syria, and it was still necessary to import kerosene. At the same time, a sub-

[1] More properly, Bala‘im.

stantial increase in Egyptian internal demand for products of all kinds was foreseen—up to 6 million t/y by 1965 and possibly 8·5 million by 1975; the territory had no present alternative to oil as a fuel. Bunkering needs were considerable (about 1 million t/y), though they failed to recover fully after the Canal closure in 1956–7, and the influence of the Aden refinery (pp. 321 f.) was felt. The principal hopes for improvement of Egyptian production seemed in 1960 to lie with the Balayim field, with its five producing horizons and (already) fifty wells; reserves were believed to be of the order of 200 million tons—or more, given success in the use of secondary recovery methods—and the field was thought to extend westwards under the sea. A production of 6 million t/y, or more, was in 1960 believed to be a future possibility. Meanwhile the Compagnie Orientale obtained early in 1959 a further series of concession-blocks in Sinai, including offshore areas.

The refining industry in Egypt developed appreciably in the period 1953–60. The Anglo-Egyptian plant at Suez, while under constant improvement and modernization in detail, did not, in deference to the markedly unfavourable circumstances of the period, aim at a throughput exceeding significantly the 45,000 b/d (p. 259) attained in 1951, a capacity raised somewhat before and during the sequestration period, to about 55,000 b/d. The Government refinery at Suez, taken over in 1957 by the statal General Petroleum Company, was from time to time increased in capacity and in the variety and quality of its products. The extensions made in 1949–53 raised output to 25,000 b/d capacity and added a cracking-plant, and an increase to 35,000 b/d capacity was planned late in 1959, with the aid of credits and technicians provided by the U.S.S.R. It was announced in July 1960 that two distillation plants were to be delivered, from Czech sources, to Alexandria and Suez. A small refinery of 200,000 t/y capacity was erected at Alexandria in 1956 by the Société Égyptienne de Pétrole, in which French interests were prominent and Caltex owned a minority share. This was in 1960 expected to be shortly enlarged to more than double, or perhaps three times, that capacity. A considerable development of active statal participation in the industry in general, and the refining and distributing branches in particular, was under contemplation in 1958–60. These projects, as designed by the G.P.A. and intended to be carried out in due course with the aid of Russian credits, included exploration, drilling, and oil-field equipment: the extension (as already mentioned) of the Suez refinery: construction of new pipelines to link producing fields to it: the addition of oil jetties at Suez and on the Nile: the building of tankers: the erection of tanks; the initiation of a petrochemical industry; the construction of a coking-plant: and the establishment of a carbon-block industry.

Orders were placed by Government with a German firm in 1959 for products lines—Alexandria–Tantah, Agrud–Cairo, and Alexandria–Kafr al-Davar—with a view to economy in distribution as against road and rail transport. Internal products-lines built by the British during the Second World War were taken over by the Egyptian authorities in 1955, and later increased—notably by a 14-inch fuel-oil line from Suez to Cairo, constructed by an Italian firm. A proposal by Mr A. Onassis late in 1956, immediately before the Suez episode, to build a large-diameter crude pipeline or pipelines from Port Taufiq to Port Said, with throughput capacity of 45–55 million t/y—a possible solution for the Canal's future congestion problems—was at first favourably regarded by the authorities of the U.A.R.; but on further consideration it was, late in 1957, rejected as undesirable.

The Canal itself had obviously, as the sixties began, lost nothing of its immense importance to the oil industry. In 1955, before the long-drawn and economically disastrous stoppage of November 1956 to April 1957, north-bound tanker traffic through the Canal amounted to 66·9 million tons out of a total traffic for that year of 87·4 million tons. In 1956, it was 65·8 million tons out of 82·8 million: in 1957, 54 million out of 67·2 million: in 1958, 94·4 million out of 114·4 million: and in 1959, 98·7 million tons out of 121·7 million. The percentage of oil cargoes in the total (north-bound) Canal traffic varied, therefore, between 76 and 82 per cent. The main destinations of north-bound oil were, in 1959, the United Kingdom (25·7 million tons), France (15·3 million), Italy (14·9 million), and the Netherlands (11 million). Of the 1959 total of 98·7 million tons, products represented 11·3 million: these were from Bahrain, Abadan, Kuwait, Dhahran, and Aden. South-bound shipments of oil in 1959 amounted to 2·6 million tons, chiefly of Russian and Rumanian origin, and about half crude, half products: these were destined for the U.A.R., China, Siberia, and Japan. Not only the number of tankers but their average size increased during our period; the oil cargoes were being carried through the Canal by a total tanker-tonnage of 12–15 million tons, or one-quarter of total world sea-going tonnage. Service in the Canal was well maintained, both before and after its nationalization by the Egyptian Government in the summer of 1956; there were in 1960 some 225 pilots at work, about half Egyptian and the rest from any of sixteen nationalities; a training programme was established in 1959 to make possible the replacement of the remaining foreign pilots. The Canal Authority after nationalization proceeded with an amended version of the old Canal Company's Plan no. 8; this provided for a deepening of the waterway so as to permit passage of ships with 37 (instead of 35) feet draught, and for a widening by 30 metres, with relining of banks throughout. For above-surface operations, involving the removal of 5 million cubic metres of earth, local hand-labour was mainly used, to an extent of 30,000 workers. For under-water work, which began late in 1958, three American contractors were employed; 30 million cubic metres were to be dredged. Completion of the work, for which the World Bank late in 1958 agreed to lend $56 million, and which would make possible the passage of fully loaded tankers of 45,000 tons dw. (instead of 35,000 as before), was announced for late 1960. A further and more grandiose scheme, the 'Nasser Project', was understood to be under study; it would provide for ships of 45 feet draught and up to 70,000 tons dw., with possible duplication of the Canal for two-way traffic. In such calculations, or any others affecting this most important of oil arteries, the possibility of new trans-desert pipelines: the doubtful rate of future increases in world oil demand: the likelihood of increased exports from the U.S.S.R.: and the imminent competition of North African oil, were elements obviously relevant. The possibility that Canal operation would in future be 'insulated' from Egyptian political factors (anti-Israeli, anti-Western, inter-Arab, and others) must realistically be regarded as a remote one; the waterway remained international in its interest and value but, short of overwhelming and successful international pressures, could scarcely be other than national, that is, Egyptian, in its control and operation.

### VIII. THE SUDAN

This territory of the Upper Nile, whose political vicissitudes during the period—Anglo-Egyptian Condominium till 1956, republic till 1958, military dictatorship thereafter—do not here concern us, continued to attract little attention from oil-seekers: a position due to the scarcity, within its spacious boundaries, of interesting sedimentary areas, which are almost confined to a narrow coastal belt. An expedition for exploration was, indeed, announced by British Petroleum as imminent in 1954, but this was not in fact dispatched. Late in 1958 the Sudan Government prepared a Petroleum Resources Development Law; this pre-scribed the normal processes of four- or six-year exploration licences, initial fees, and rentals, and subsequent exploitation leases of thirty years' duration, extendable to sixty years. The Government share of profits would be 50 per cent., but this might be raised later to 70 per cent. In this and other respects the Law appeared to contain dubious and discouraging features.

It was, nevertheless, announced in August 1959 that the Italian para-statal concern E.N.I., through its usual executive subsidiary A.G.I.P., hoped to form, equally with the Sudan Government, a joint company for exploration and development; the Government, however, was to pay its half share of expenses only in case of a discovery of commercial oil. Profits would be equally divided. Initial Italian investment was to be not less than £5 million. Eleven four-year licences were obtained, covering 8,500 square kilometres of coastal (including some territorial-water) acreage. The conditions of operation imposed were likely to be less stringent than those prescribed in the 1958 Law.

A month later it was reported that Shell was to launch a geo-logical reconnaissance in the north-west of the territory, covering nearly half a million square kilometres; and a further permit, for coastal lands near the E.N.I. area, was granted to a Californian concern, the General Exploration Company.

Both E.N.I., through its new local distributing company A.G.I.P. Sudan, and the Shell Group in association with B.P., Mobil, and Esso, were understood to have made overtures to the Government in 1959 regarding the erection of a small refinery, hitherto lacking in the country; the latter group was already active in the local distribution of products, and A.G.I.P. prepared now to enter the same field. Sudanese consumption of products had by 1960 reached a level of somewhat less than 500,000 t/y, having almost doubled in the last five years.

## CHAPTER XX

# 'IRAQ, 1960–6

## I. MIDDLE EAST AND O.P.E.C.

THE last chapter of the present edition of this book will deal with some general aspects and expectations of the Middle Eastern oil industry as these appeared in the later months of 1966; but, since the present chapter and the five immediately following are to cover oil-development matters of the region in some detail country by country, it will be well, to avoid repetition, to give at the outset an indication of certain trends and phenomena which will be seen to concern every territory.

Such features can for our present purposes be limited to five. The first was the continuance of over-supply of oil in the world, due to the immense investments and the consequent development and production made by the great companies. This surplus availability had, of course, an adverse effect on prices and created an even keener atmosphere of competition among sellers. At the same time a number of hitherto importing countries had achieved their own at least partial self-sufficiency. It resulted that the companies in almost every exporting area, notably the Middle East, produced substantially less oil than they would have done in a seller's market.

The second feature to be noted is the appearance in the Middle East of a considerable number of newcomers among the operating or concession-seeking companies: companies sometimes of major or near-major status, sometimes relatively small, but all encouraged by host governments to hurry on with production (to which their own economics also impelled them), heedless of the existing glut. At the same time the 'cheaper oil' which might have been of great value to consumers (and not least to emerging but oil-less nations) was denied to these by the host-governments' resolute refusal to allow the 'posted prices' of the producing companies to be lowered after 1960, unrealistically excessive as they were.

Thirdly, political conditions prevailing in the region varied, from the foreign-owned oil-producing companies' viewpoint, from mainly satisfactory to precarious, or less. There were few countries in which the sanctity of negotiated and confirmed agreements was sure to be respected; there were more in which (as notably in 'Iraq, or in the Persia of 1950–3) they were likely to be flouted at will. Feeling among the political class or the governmental clique was (though they might deny it) as a rule more or less xenophobic or specifically anti-western, and it visibly created at times and places an atmosphere sadly inimical to confidence or even to efficiency. And, as we shall see, the stability of the Governments themselves was often highly uncertain, as was the politico-economic direction towards which territories were likely to evolve, or to slide, or to be thrust in the near or less near future.

Meanwhile, and fourthly, while the longest-standing and repeatedly amended concession agreements in the area might be still (but by no means always integrally) in force, new forms of government–company agreement took an increasing place. These were notably those of partnership—to be actualized, however, only after the discovery of commercial oil—between the concessionary company and the host government; they followed, that is, one of the patterns of joint government-*cum*-foreign-company enterprise evolved in Egypt (as in C.O.P.E., established in 1957 —p. 344), or in Iran (as in S.I.R.I.P., established in the same year, or in I.P.A.C. a year later—pp. 289f.). Some such arrangement, no doubt with local modifications, seemed likely to be that of the future, and was increasingly adopted in 1960–6. It seemed probable that the original type of 'blanket concession' for a whole territory would be used hereafter only in regions of maximum backwardness and lowest promise, if anywhere at all; elsewhere the techniques of granting and acquiring rights of exploration and exploitation were inevitably becoming more guarded and sophisticated. Examples of this abounded in Egypt, Turkey, and Persia, and were likely soon to be seen in the 'relinquished areas' of 'Iraq, Sa'udi Arabia, abu Dhabi, and others.

Fifthly, the appearance in almost every major territory of a National Company, intended to take a varying but substantial part in oil operations within the State, and possibly outside it, was another feature of the times, though it had been more than foreshadowed by the pre-1960 statal organizations in Turkey (pp. 85 and 236ff.), in Egypt (pp. 341ff.), in Syria (p. 336), and in Persia (pp. 163ff.). The functions undertaken by such corporations in future would, as they did in 1960–6, vary from country to country, but they were sure, at least in the more chauvinistic or state-socialist policies of some, to increase fairly rapidly and absorb a large part of the country's oil industry—as was the case already in Egypt and in Syria.

An intervention belonging specifically to the years here under review was that of O.P.E.C.—the Organization of Petroleum Exporting Countries. In the Middle East, where petroleum exports and their prices were all-important to half a dozen States and interesting to more, and where the added bargaining strength which effective unity among such States must bestow would be appreciable, a common organization on these lines could have been foreseen. The Organization was in fact conceived at Baghdad in 1960, was then formulated and agreed, met at Caracas in January 1961, and registered Venezuela, Indonesia, and Libya as non-Middle Eastern members. The founder-members were 'Iraq, Persia, Sa'udi Arabia, Kuwait, and Venezuela, with Qatar added a little later; Algeria and Nigeria might probably join in the future. O.P.E.C.'s headquarters and permanent paid secretariat were located at Geneva until 1965, thereafter at Vienna. Plenary meetings were held twice a year at various of the members' capitals, those at ministerial level quarterly, while standing and *ad hoc* committee meetings were or could be more frequent. Unanimity among members was, in theory, a *sine qua non*, with full mutual support. Foreign experts were regularly called in as consultants, and the Secretary-General—successively a Persian, an 'Iraqi, and a Kuwaiti—was in each case an instructed and distinguished figure.

O.P.E.C., the tone of whose discussions and recommendations rose markedly in seriousness and sophistication during its early years of life, had by 1966 perceptible achievements to its credit. It had since 1960 successfully resisted any lowering of the (actually unrealistic) 'posted prices' upon which the State's 50 per cent. was calculated; had on occasion taken over from individual governments the task of bargaining with Companies—to the dismay of the latter, whose own basic agreements were with a single host-country and not with an international committee; had obtained the reluctant agreement of most (not all) of the Companies to the 'expensing'[1] of the royalty portion of the Government's share; had

---

[1] This involved the treatment of royalty payments (usually $12\frac{1}{2}$ per cent.) as a working expense (of which, therefore, only half would be deductible ultimately from the State's share) instead of, as theretofore, its treatment as deductible *in toto* from the 50 per cent. The advantage of the new arrangement (one, however, entirely unknown to existing government-company agreements in the Middle East) is obvious. In partial compensation to the Companies, the new

obtained the lowering and standardization of the Companies' (deductible) 'marketing allowances', from $1\frac{1}{2}$ or 2 cents per barrel to $\frac{1}{2}$ cent. O.P.E.C. had ranged also in discussion and aspiration over a wide field of allegedly relevant topics, which included a higher standard 'government share' than 50 per cent., more and quicker relinquishments of concession-held territory, government's acquisition (by unspecified procedures) of equity shares in the grantee Companies, enjoyment of a share in 'downstream' post-export profits, and a scheme for controlling crude prices by regulating the percentage by which each member country's production should be allowed to rise year by year,[1] and thus limiting the total crude to be placed upon the market. O.P.E.C. had indeed by 1966 become a fairly strong and (so far) united force for pressing governmental aspirations, even though it must be felt that its interstatal unity, however clearly indispensable, might not be reliable in conditions (which could well arise) of a divisive nature; that its extreme but inevitable pro-government partisanship might be finally self-defeating if it reached the point of damaging too seriously the operations or economics of the industry; and that (not possessing, after all, a world monopoly) it tended to ignore outside, non-O.P.E.C. supplies or alternative sources of oil or other fuels, and ignored also the hopes of consuming publics abroad for cheaper oil. Some objective observers felt that rather more signs of a constructive, co-operative attitude to the industry, acknowledging the true interdependence and common interest of States and producing companies, might in the long run better serve countries for whom a physical interruption of the Companies'

---

arrangement permitted rebates off posted prices of $8\frac{1}{2}$ cents a barrel in the first year, $7\frac{1}{2}$ cents in the second, $6\frac{1}{2}$ cents in the third and (subject to prevailing price-levels) later years. The net immediate effect was a rise of $3\frac{1}{2}$ cents per barrel in government's 'take' in 1964, 4 cents in 1965, $4\frac{1}{2}$ cents in 1966, and possibly more thereafter. The cost to companies was estimated as some $125 million in 1964, and 160 million in 1966. During the latter year O.P.E.C. began efforts to eliminate all the rebates (regardless of current prices or conditions) and, with this backing, the Sa'udi Government was pressing Aramco accordingly; other companies would doubtless be obliged to follow.

[1] This scheme was evolved in 1965 for an experimental period of six months; there was, however, little sign of conformity by countries to the figures provided, and the plan was rejected by two (Sa'udi Arabia and Libya) and heavily queried by two more (Persia and Qatar). There seemed to observers to be a variety of difficulties in operating such a scheme, and in particular the ambitions and needs of developing countries, by whom an abnormal degree of self-discipline would have to be shown.

producing-exporting operations in their territory must have immediate and dire results.

All this having been said, however, about the Middle Eastern background conditions in 1960–6, including this new institution of a unified pressure group of the host-governments, it should be added with candour that these years formed a period of general moderate prosperity in this, incomparably the greatest industry and source of wealth in the region. Its profitability was certainly less than it had been in earlier years, the era of over-production was not visibly near its end (in spite of the continuous rise in world demand), the attitudes of governments and publics were a great deal less cordial or co-operative than could be desired; but none the less the discovery of new resources went on, oil wealth became or was shortly to become the happy lot of more and more territories, the vast procedures of extraction, treatment, and export of oil continued with full efficiency, to the benefit of the free world, of the producing countries, and of the foreign corporations whose capital had been so profusely invested (or, originally, risked) in them. The visible threats to this happy state of affairs were in 1966 mainly such that a greater measure of governmental self-restraint, and a greater distinction drawn between local political enthusiasms and (foreign) industrial exigencies, and perhaps also more objective study of the realities of the international oil world, present and future, could greatly diminish them.

One more general aspect or effect of Middle Eastern oil development—that of its consequences among the public and on living standards—has been mentioned on a number of previous pages; it will be treated further, if briefly, in the last chapter of this book (pp. 471–2).

We turn now to the States concerned, starting with that one, 'Iraq, in which, thanks mainly to the unhelpful policies of its Government, progress was in these years the least rapid.

## II. THE 'IRAQ GOVERNMENT AND I.N.O.C.

The three Companies of the 'Iraq Petroleum Group—I.P.C., M.P.C., B.P.C.—enjoying an almost total, though latterly a threatened, monopoly[1] of oil production in 'Iraq in this period, passed the six years 1960–6 without serious interruption of their

---

[1] Total, except for the now Government-administered Naftkhana oilfield (pp. 193, 265f.).

producing operation; this is attested by the figures of their drilling, production, and export, and by the large sums passed into the 'Iraqi Treasury. Nevertheless the period, and especially the first three years of it which ended in February 1963, must rank as perhaps the least happy in the Companies' history, if account be taken of the sinister political atmosphere created by the strangely unbalanced military dictator of the country (p. 263), together with the disappearance from the higher ranks of government of almost all personnel acquainted with the industry, the multifarious officially-imposed restrictions and delays, and above all the course of the 'negotiations' conducted with the Companies in person by General 'Abdul Karim Qasim—with the intention, on his part, of achieving objectives which ever receded, yet ever increased in scale. The releases made by him to the local Press on these 'discussions' were no more than crudely distorted propaganda documents, suppressing half of the relevant material; the dictator's demands appeared inconstant, often unrealistic, and rarely related to existing and fully binding agreements. He desired, somehow, a generous equity interest in the Companies;[1] somehow, an 'Iraqi tanker fleet; somehow, a complete and immediate utilization of all natural gas produced.[2] The General, specifying continually increasing figures and diminishing periods of time, pressed for wholesale relinquishment of the Companies' concessionary areas (p. 267), and gave abrupt orders early in 1961 that all exploration operations, outside actual producing fields, should cease forthwith. The Companies, of necessity, complied: one geological, five geophysical, and four drilling parties were withdrawn and disbanded, and some 1,000 'Iraqis were thrown out of work. Qasim next objected to annual deduction from profits of the hitherto agreed percentage of the repayable 'dead rents' which had been paid to government before commercial oil had been discovered in the Basra or Mosul areas;[3] the Companies, under protest, complied with his wishes, contrary as these were to concession provisions and established procedure. Recourse to arbitration, also prescribed

[1] Under the concessions the 'Iraq Government or public was entitled to take up to a 20 per cent. interest in the event of a call for public subscription of new capital. This had never occurred, the whole capital of the three Companies being provided by their parent companies, who were the only shareholders.

[2] The Company had already offered to supply to government, free of charge, all the gas which it could not itself use.

[3] The deductions in the case of I.P.C. had been completed without objection in 1955.

in the concession, was refused. In two other matters raised during the dictator's 'discussions', agreement was easy: the Companies' spokesman warmly favoured (as their past record showed) ever-increasing 'Iraqization of their personnel, a process which by now was far advanced at all levels; he offered a welcome also to the appointment of an 'Iraqi Executive Director on the Companies' Boards (on each of which, indeed, an 'Iraqi director had sat from the beginning) if and when Government should propose one, which it failed to do. No progress was made until mid-1963 in the matter of the export surcharge at Fao which, by curtailing cargoes, was highly damaging to the Government (p. 263) as well as to B.P.C.

It became apparent by mid-1961 that the dictator, whatever his true intentions, had no desire to settle his claims on the lines of normal business, but rather to keep them alive by constant refusals and fresh demands.[1] By the end of that year his threats of unilateral action became more explicit in the matter of relinquishment of territory. The Companies, far from obstructive, progressed from offering to surrender almost half their total acreage to proposing a total of some 90 per cent., to be handed over in three stages within ten years. This was refused as insufficient. The Companies offered also, in lieu of an equity share in the existing companies, an opening for the Government or public to take up to 20 per cent. of equity shares in any new company which might be founded thereafter for operation in any part of the relinquished area.

On 12 December 1961 was published, without more ado, the now famous Law 80. Depriving the three Companies immediately of some 99·5 per cent. of their concessionary area, in flattest defiance of fully binding agreements, the Law provided that they should retain 47 parcels[2] containing 1,938 square kilometres (out of the concession's 435,780), these being the closely confined areas of present producing oilfields; it was allowed as possible that

---

[1] It was widely believed in 'Iraq and outside that Qasim, who accepted no advice from any quarter on these matters, was moving towards actual 'nationalization' of the industry, involving no doubt total dispossession of the three Companies upon terms which he would dictate; a draft law for the purpose had, it is said, been prepared. This, however, cannot be regarded as certain, since even the dictator was aware of what must be the financial results of such a step.

[2] Twelve at Kirkuk, 6 at Bai Hasan, 4 at Jambur; in the M.P.C., 4 at 'Ain Zala, 4 at Butma; in B.P.C., 7 at Rumaila, 10 at Zubair. This gave the three Companies respectively 748, 62, and 1,128 square kilometres.

this area could be eventually doubled. No statesman, however, after the violent removal of Qasim by his fellow countrymen on 8 February 1963,[1] had the temerity to press for such an increase, since this could be represented as pro-foreigner;[2] and late in 1966 the Companies' areas remained as stated, and exploration has been totally halted for five years. It was reported that in reply to invitations some offers were received from foreign companies to take up the acreage thus seized from its concessionaires, but no grants were made. Indeed 'Iraq's small offshore area opposite Fao, of which the rights were offered by Government in August 1960 to anyone interested (after B.P.C. had voluntarily surrendered it—p. 267) had likewise attracted no bids.

The I.P.C. group were compelled, when deprived of their territory, to hand over to Government all their exploration and geological data accumulated over years of research and test-drilling. Meanwhile their request for arbitration and their nomination of their own arbitrator fell on the deafest of ears.

Simultaneously with the issue of Law 80 the establishment of an 'Iraq National Oil Company was announced, with a draft law and regulations shortly to follow. It was to be administered by a nine-man board of directors, would deal in all producing branches of the industry,[3] and especially would develop the ex-I.P.C. areas. I.N.O.C. would enjoy borrowing powers, could set up subsidiaries, and would be exempt from taxation for ten years. The I.N.O.C. Law, modified in 1965, was to be superseded by a new draft in the summer of 1966. Under the latter the Corporation was authorized (as were the other Middle Eastern National Oil Companies)

[1] According to *The Times*, the book found beside the dead dictator's bed was, surprisingly, the second edition of the present work.

[2] Agreement was reported as reached with the Oil Minister and the Cabinet early in 1966 but these were unwilling to risk submission of the agreed terms to Parliament, and in autumn 1966 the matter was still unsettled. The unratified agreement was to the effect that the Companies' acreage provided by Law 80 would be doubled; any I.P.C.-group company or companies could be allotted up to 7 per cent. of the 'relinquished' area, to operate there by an *ad hoc* joint company, with I.N.O.C. taking up to a 33 per cent. interest; elsewhere in 'Iraq, I.N.O.C. would, if it could, form partnership companies with selected foreign concerns—American independents, E.N.I., and French interests being visualized. Terms would be on the usual fifty-fifty basis, but with the use of posted prices and the expensing of the royalty share. The alternative of I.N.O.C. proceeding alone to exploration and development seemed to be ruled out as financially unpractical.

[3] Refining and distribution were already under their own departments of the Oil Ministry, as fully statal organizations.

to take over refining and distribution functions. Moreover, its powers were extended, its board of directors reconstituted, its authority to borrow increased. But the hesitations of Government *vis-à-vis* the I.P.C. and outside companies still inhibited I.N.O.C. from any freedom, or indeed possibility, of effective action. In the autumn of 1966 the establishment of a National Committee of Oil Experts with advisory functions was announced; it was to cover, apparently, all 'Iraq's oil interests including I.N.O.C. The nine members included two Ministers, the Governor of the Central Bank, and the Chairman of I.N.O.C.

The disappearance of General Qasim in February 1963 raised hopes of a less unfavourable atmosphere, and these were in part fulfilled. A capable Minister of Oil was appointed, and indicated what areas of ex-I.P.C. territory would be chosen by I.N.O.C. for exploitation with foreign partners or contractors. He also set up a new planning section in his ministry, and a new Oil Law was said to be under drafting, while the text of an O.P.E.C. draft law, believed to be in preparation, was awaited. The abnormal Port Authority charges on B.P.C. oil at Fao were, by a provisional compromise which the Company was forced to accept, to be limited to the first 8 million tons of each year's exports; thus confident use could at last be made of the new deep-water loading terminal (pp. 274 and 363).

Improvements and extensions, including a new lubricants plant and added storage, in the major Government refinery at Daura (capacity 48,000 b/d) were carried out. This and the other State-owned refineries (p. 265) were, as we have seen, not at once placed under N.I.O.C. but remained under G.O.R.A.;[1] they now included the ex-I.P.C. topping plant at Haditha, and would include also a proposed 20,000 b/d plant at Mosul, if this were built. Similarly, local distribution and marketing remained until 1966 under the Oil Minister. (Demand in 'Iraq for products was by 1966 running at more than 2·5 million tons a year.) Plans

---

[1] In 1965 crude supplied to Government refineries by I.P.C. and its sister companies was as follows: to Daura 2·05 million tons (Daura received also nearly 200,000 tons from Naftkhana); to Muftiya, 178,000 tons from B.P.C.; to Alwand, 361,700 tons (all from Naftkhana); at Qaiyara, 21,000 tons from M.P.C.; at K3 (Haditha, topping plant), 58,500 tons from I.P.C.

Production at these State-owned refineries in 1965 was: at Daura 2·5 million tons; at Muftiya 178,000 tons; at Alwand 340,000 tons (including 50,000 tons pumped back to Naftkhana); at Qaiyara, 195,000 tons; at K3 (for half-year) 48,000 tons.

already made for an important Russian- or Czech-designed refinery at Basra were still under study, but no action had followed by late 1966. The small State-owned refinery at Muftiya near Basra (4,500 b/d) supplied by B.P.C., and the earliest of 'Iraqi refineries, at Alwand (12,500 b/d), supplied from Naftkhana, continued in operation. The Naftkhana field, re-investigated by a Russian mission (and the subject of an agreement with Persia as to its relations with their Naft-i-Shah field immediately adjoining), continued to supply Alwand refinery, and in 1963 a 12-inch pipeline linked it also with Daura.[1]

Other plans formulated by the Oil Ministry, or agreed by outside firms with it, included an improved gas-treatment and sulphur-recovery plant near Kirkuk, which was under construction in 1965–6. Part of its sulphur output was to be used by a fertilizer plant near Basra,[2] soon to be initiated and expected to take its gas supplies from the Rumaila field. This plant would both supply the local market and find export outlets. De-sulphurized gas from Kirkuk would, in a connected project, be piped for industrial use in Baghdad 185 miles away, and at the same time natural gasoline and l.p.g. would be sent by pipeline to the capital.

The loan of £25 million made by I.P.C. to the Government after Suez (p. 263) was repaid in full by the end of 1961. Reduction from 70 per cent. to 50 per cent. of the share allotted to capital development from the Companies' payments to the 'Iraqi Treasury dates from the spring of that year; the change was due mainly to the heavy military expenditure favoured by the Government. Amounts received by the 'Iraq Treasury from the Companies as royalty and taxation for the years 1960 through 1965 were, in millions of pounds, 95·35, 95·08, 95·11, 110·04, 126·00, and 131·5. (The corresponding figure in 1950 had been £7 million.) In the Government budgets for 1966–7 total expectations from oil were I.D. 140 million; of this, 70 million would contribute to the ordinary (non-project) budget, which was to balance at I.D. 170 million; the other half would pass to the Economic Planning estimates.

---

[1] In 1965 Naftkhana production was: 555,770 tons, of which 362,000 were dispatched to Alwand and 194,000 to Daura. The 12-inch line was used in 1965 and since to convey fuel oil from Alwand to Daura.

[2] Tenders for the construction of this plant were being called for in October 1966. Japanese and French concerns were expected to secure the most important contracts.

### III. 'IRAQ PETROLEUM AND M.P.C.

Within each and all of the three I.P.C.-group Companies these were years of full activity except in the one field of exploration where all progress was vetoed by the Government. The total tonnage of crude exported from the territory in the years 1960 to 1965 was, in millions of long tons, respectively 44·5, 45·9, 45·9, 53·23, 58·24, and 60·7. The figures for the Companies' total production, including internal outlets and use, were 46·5, 48·0, 48·2, 55·57, 60·35, and 63·2 million tons; detail of this export and other disposal will be given under the account of each of the three Companies separately. The indications during the first half of 1966 were that the production figures of 1965 would be exceeded in the current year.

Lord Monckton continued as Chairman of the I.P.C. Group until his death in January 1965, when he was succeeded by G. H. Herridge, who had been Deputy Chairman since July 1963. As Managing Director of the Group Mr Herridge was succeeded in that month by C. M. Dalley. As the I.P.C. Group's Chief Representative in 'Iraq, F. C. Ryland handed over to W. W. Stewart in June 1962. The General Manager of I.P.C. and M.P.C. in 'Iraq in this period was G. J. R. Tod until May 1962, thereafter A. J. Perks until September 1964, and thereafter A. H. R. Grimsey.

Throughout the period the training of 'Iraqi staff and employees was pursued at all levels, with the intention of fitting a full sufficiency of these to fill the most senior as well as medium-grade positions. The full development of industrial centres, apprentice training, bench and workshop tuition, and 'on the job' instruction continued, with a highly satisfactory output. Dozens or scores of 'Iraqis continued to be sent by the Companies annually to western Europe or America to complete their studies in drilling, petroleum engineering, accountancy, materials, mechanical engineering, etc. (p. 268). Total personnel in 'Iraq employed by the three Companies varied from 12,900 in 1960 to 11,056 in 1965, of whom the overwhelming majority were 'Iraqis; in 1965 on the staff (that is, in senior positions) of the Companies were found 618 'Iraqis (85 per cent. of the total staff) and 116 foreigners (15 per cent.); the corresponding figures for 1960 had been 564 (54 per cent.) and 482 (46 per cent.); for 1950 they had been 486 (30 per cent.) and 1,122 (70 per cent.). This is to say that 'Iraqization of senior personnel advanced materially in the last decade; it was, of course, already complete in all unskilled and semi-skilled employments. Emphasis continued to be laid at all locations on good conditions of work, pleasant amenities, safety, and adequate housing, which included a great expansion of home ownership.

The 'Iraq Petroleum Company itself, within its concession-given area east of Tigris and north of the thirty-third degree of latitude, continued to produce oil from its world-famous Kirkuk structure and from its two small fields at Jambur (in production since 1959—p. 269) and Bai Hasan (in production since June 1960). The Company was throughout 1960 and the first quarter of 1961 active also in seismic exploration in many areas and with test-drilling to locate other fields,[1] until by Government order of April 1961 all such activity ceased. Drilling for production and reservoir observation at the producing locations was, however, carried on continuously, between two and a dozen wells being completed annually by 'Iraqi crews.[2] The water-injection scheme on the Kirkuk structure (p. 272) was, after 1961, in continuous operation, tens of millions of tons being injected annually—more in volume, indeed, than the oil simultaneously extracted. The effect on pressure maintenance was satisfactory. Water for the purpose was taken by a system of pumps from the Lesser Zab and dispatched, via a clarification plant, to the injection pumps and the wells reserved for the purpose. The system, made fully automatic, was worked from a central control room.

Large quantities of natural gas were supplied from the Company's degassing stations to the Government power-house at Dibis, to the main trans-desert pipeline stations, and to the water-injection and processing plants. The latter dealt with the 'sweetening' of up to 40 million tons (in 1965) of crude, preparatory to its dispatch to the Mediterranean terminals. Important extensions and modifications in the various units of the processing plant were made during the period. New gas lines were provided as necessary, including one to the process plant from Bai Hasan; pipe from the long disused 16-inch 'south line' served this purpose.

Pipeline capacity for main exports westward to the coast, which

[1] In 1960–1 test-wells were drilled at Gilabat, Chamchamal (deepened), Palkhana, Demir Dagh, Qarachauq, Taqtaq, and in the Jabal Hamrin. The two latter were left unfinished.
[2] By the end of 1965, 173 wells in all had been drilled on the Kirkuk structure since 1927.

had by mid-1960 (p. 272, footnote 1) reached 28 million t/y, was progressively increased in and after 1960 by a looping and duplication of the lines and by modernization and rebuilding of the stations in 'Iraq and in Syria (p. 445). Of the latter, two in Syria (T2 and T4) were worked by remote control, gas for their turbines being supplied from the Kirkuk field; the same procedure was followed in K1 and K3 stations within 'Iraq. A potential throughput of 35 million t/y was reached early in 1961 and, with the completion of the new 30/32-inch line Kirkuk–Tripoli, capacity was raised to 48 million t/y. Terminal capacity and loading arrangements on the coast had kept pace with these increases (pp. 339, 441).

Production in I.P.C. territory from Kirkuk and the two minor fields[1] amounted in 1960-5 to 33·84, 36·99, 38·07, 41·62, 41·71, and 43·9 million long tons. Of these amounts a small proportion were delivered to the Government refinery at Daura[2] and the greater part[3] exported from the territory for shipment, or for refinery use in Syria-Lebanon.

No more was heard in this period of the trans-Turkey pipeline considered in the late 'fifties as a possible outlet for northern 'Iraqi oil (p. 271).

In the Mosul Petroleum Company's area, west of Tigris, a seismic party was busy in 1960 and until April 1961 in investigating little-explored territory, and exploration drilling was carried on at Samarra and 'Alan, without success. Thereafter two or three development or observation wells per year continued to be drilled at 'Ain Zala and Butma, since these remained the sole, and unhappily meagre, producing fields in this, the weakest in production and reserves of all the I.P.C.-group enterprises. Gas injection in 1960-1, and later water-injection, were practised continuously at Butma, with a slight improvement of pressure. The two fields' combined output was, in the six years 1960-5: 1·29, 1·28, 1·30, 1·27, 1·3, and 1·3 million tons.[4] This was all exported with the I.P.C. crude to Tripoli terminal or refinery. (It is to be noted that

---

[1] Bai Hasan production in 1960-5 was in successive years: 1·11, 2·22, 2·25, 2·05, 2·05, and 2·3 million long tons. Jambur production was 0·62, 0·81, 0·82, 0·78, 0·63, and 0·60 million tons.

[2] 1·56, 1·78, 1·85, 1·87, 1·88, and 2·05 million tons.

[3] 32·38, 35·17, 36·06, 39·21, 39·75, and 41·6 million tons.

[4] In this output 'Ain Zala crude greatly predominated, since Butma never exceeded 300,000 t/y and sank to as little as 150,000.

the original B.O.D. provision granting the 'Iraq Government 20 per cent. of all B.O.D. oil 'free of cost at well-head' was extinguished under the 1952 agreement with the 'Iraq Government, which provided also for the fifty-fifty division of profit (p. 191). The same applied at the same time to future B.P.C. oil.)

IV. BASRA

Much of the B.P.C.'s activity in its southern-'Iraqi concessionary area came to an end with the stoppage of exploration in 1961, prior to which three seismic parties in 1960 and four in 1961 had been working in outlying areas—Salman, Kifl, Ur, and Shatra—as well as in the environs of Rumaila, and exploratory drilling was or had been in full swing at eight new locations; these were Kifl, Turba, Dujaila, and 'Afaq (all deep-drilled), and Shawiya, Ghulaisan, Safawi, and 'Ubaid. These costly efforts had, in their entirety, to cease.

Development drilling at the two producing fields, Zubair and Rumaila, continued in the years 1960 and 1961, after which drilling for production was suspended. Extensive oilfield operations, however, designed to provide for increased export, were carried out after June 1963 when, as mentioned earlier (p. 357) the Port surcharge on Basra oil exports was provisionally modified. These operations included, year by year, new or expanded installations for degassing, pumping, storage, etc., in the two fields and at Fao. Degassing stations in Rumaila field were both enlarged and remote-controlled. A new 30/32-inch line linked fields to Fao. Large quantities of natural gas were supplied to the Government power-station at Najibiya, as well as to the Company's own installations.

Production from B.P.C. fields amounted in 1960 through 1965, year by year, to 11·39, 9·78, 8·84, 12·67, 17·34, and 17·97 million long tons. Of these totals Rumaila supplied the greater part, varying from nearly double to four times the Zubair contribution.[1] All was exported from Fao (after mid-1963) from the new ocean terminal, except annual amounts varying from 160,000 to 200,000 tons which were dispatched to Muftiya refinery. (To all Basra oil the normal fifty-fifty arrangement applied in sharing profits with the Government, and the original '20 per cent. of oil free at well-

[1] Figures for these fields each year in millions of tons, starting with 1960 and placing Rumaila first, are: 7·71 and 3·68, 6·03 and 3·74, 5·46 and 3·37, 9·33 and 3·34, 13·89 and 3·45, 14·48 and 3·49.

head' arrangement, as in the 1938 concession, had ceased to apply since 1952.)

The outstanding achievement of B.P.C. in the period was the completion and successful use of the giant deep-water loading base, Khor al-Amaya. The work (p. 274) was begun in 1959, completed and commissioned in April 1963. Situated twelve miles from the mouth of the Shatt al-'Arab and costing some £22 million, it could carry out loading without tidal or draught limitations up to any foreseeable demand. Two tankers could load simultaneously at high speeds. Crude from Fao tank-farm was dispatched to Khor al-Amaya by two 32-inch concrete-cased lines laid on the sea bed, loading into tankers being carried out by 12-inch flexible hoses suspended from loading booms. Operations were directed from a control room connected by radio links with Fao, as well as by the full telephonic intercommunication which was installed. The terminal had its own electricity-generating plant, fire-fighting equipment, fresh-water storage, air conditioning, and accommodation for seventy-five people. Personnel normally resident did not exceed thirty-five, and were frequently relieved; the 'Iraq Government was represented by some twenty persons. Amenities included a recreation room and a cinema. A regular service of launches and a helicopter provided communication with the mainland. Navigational and berthing needs at night were met by well adapted lighting systems. Meteorological conditions were closely watched, and as far as possible foreseen.

The Khor al-Amaya terminal, from the date of completion of its equipment and testing in 1962, handled by far the greater part of B.P.C. exports: its throughput in and after 1963, year by year, was 8·48, 17·20, and 17·59 million tons, while that of Fao sank to 3·93, 1·27, and a mere 0·19 million.

As General Manager of B.P.C., A. H. R. Grimsey was succeeded in May 1962 by S. M. Sims, but was reappointed to serve again in March 1963 until July 1964, when the post fell to M. A. R. Gardiner.

## CHAPTER XXI

# IRAN (PERSIA), 1960–6

## I. NATIONAL IRANIAN

THE six years of oil development in Iran (Persia) to be next reviewed were years of high significance in that they witnessed the consolidation, after the nightmare of 1951–3, of a governmental régime rendering industrial progress and security once more possible; and they were years also of exceptional good fortune, thanks to remarkable success in the search, by those entrusted with this task, for new oil resources in the country by land and sea, as well as in the fruitful development of those already productive. With only brief interruptions—a frontier dispute with 'Iraq, political demonstrations by students and mobs—conditions for the industry remained favourable. The National Iranian Oil Company increased and widened its activities. Not only the Consortium (pp. 277 ff.) but the Italian, the American, and later also the multi-racial partner-companies with N.I.O.C. put forth laudable and hopeful efforts towards the development of the country's outstanding resource.

With these foreign concerns, headed as *facile princeps* by the Consortium, governmental relations—a nightmare during the Musaddiq régime—were maintained at a normally happy and co-operative level. This, an indispensable condition of the wellbeing of the industry and of the Iranian Treasury, applied both to contacts with the Central Government and Ministries—and the Throne—and to the provincial and local authorities of Khuzistan and the adjacent provinces. To these, and indeed to the local public, it was a pleasure to the foreign Companies to show goodwill and to offer many types of helpfulness, while the wealth accruing from the industry could be seen fertilizing and diversifying the country's economy in town, countryside, and the public services.

On the higher level, the fact of so much *joint* enterprise affected everywhere the tone of relationships, and penetrated the innermost workings of even the Consortium; formal visits of the Royal Family, unknown in earlier periods, were significant; and a typical manifestation of constructive goodwill on the Companies' side was the foundation in 1966 of the Iranian Investment Corporation, with a capital of £2 million subscribed (in foreign currency) by the Consortium member-companies. Its object was to assist the establishment of small or middle-sized industrial enterprises in the country.

None of this meant, of course, that the Treasury and Government of Iran were less eager than before to increase their oil revenues: on the contrary, they were firm upholders of O.P.E.C. and—for instance, in the matter of discounts allowable against posted prices (pp. 351f.)—certain to support, or outdistance, all O.P.E.C. demands. This was a field, inevitably, of pointed non-identity of company and official attitudes. And, among much of the Iranian public, and particularly the politically-conscious class, a general, sometimes a rancorous, antipathy to all visible, prosperous foreign enterprise, especially in the emotion-charged sphere of oil-development, was often all too obvious; its existence, with its background in the bad days of 1951–3, must remain a constant concern of the foreign oil-developers.

N.I.O.C., whose effective existence dated from 1955, was already by 1960 occupied with overall planning and the supervision of Iran's oil interests, with exploration and oilfield development, with distribution of products, and allied activities (pp. 285–8). Administratively it exercised wide powers under ministers of the Central Government; financially, it depended for its first half-dozen years on State aid and a percentage of the value of Consortium exports, but by mid-1963 it could stand firmly on its own feet. It conducted its business with competence and imagination, the latter quality being exemplified by its excursions, actual and proposed, into the international field.

We turn first to N.I.O.C.'s tasks and achievements in fields other than that of collaborating with foreign partners, which later pages (pp. 380ff.) will describe. That the National Company was already by 1960 active in oil exploration and development on its own account has been shown on earlier pages (pp. 285–7). This activity continued, though with a degree of success unequal to that of the Consortium, throughout 1960–6. Maintenance of the small Naft-i-Shah field led to no major development; its annual output did not exceed 420,000 t/y, all of which was refined locally or at Kirmanshah.[1] A steady effort in development and well-

[1] N.I.O.C.'s figures for output of the Naft-i-Shah topping plant and the Kirmanshah refinery in 1965, are 1·58 million bbl and 1·48 million respectively.

improvement continued year by year, and the field was still the main supplier of oil to Iran, other than the Consortium. Geophysical (seismic, magnetometer, and gravity meter) exploration and wildcat well-drilling in other areas were pursued, but were regrettably unproductive in these years. Areas tested were those immediately south and south-west of the Caspian, where some wells were drilled but abandoned; the same was true of three exploratory wells near Kirmanshah, and another on the fringes of the Salt Lake east of Qum. Survey was conducted also in the Azerbaijan province and in those of the north-east. Of the six exploratory wells drilled by N.I.O.C. in 1961, that at Gorgan, a few miles east of Bandar Shah on the Caspian (p. 286), was in July temporarily suspended by a fire, but it confirmed the presence of gas and some oil in unascertained quantities. A later well, No. 3a, found gas in considerable volume at some 6,700 feet. At Sarajeh (p. 286), twenty-five miles south-east of Alborz (Qum), plans were studied for the utilization in Teheran area of the discovered gas and condensate, of which the supplies were assessed at a high figure in 1962. This, it seemed, could be a valuable national asset. The potentially greater field of Alborz, discovered in 1956 (p. 286), though the next stage of its history was interesting, did not lead to the important development enterprise at first envisaged. By mid-1960 the field had been confirmed as probably rich, but it remained unexploited, and perhaps—owing to excessive pressure —not easily exploitable. Well no. 8, however, showed a high yield of some 20,000 b/d, nos. 9 and 10 were potential producers, and the field was passed as commercial in spite of its dry holes (nos. 1, 2, 4, 6, and 7) and uncertainties. No. 11, with oil at around 8,800 feet as in nos. 9 and 10,was of high potential, and some 75,000 b/d was already in prospect from the field if only production problems could be mastered. The planned Teheran refinery could provide an immediate outlet for its already feasible production. This is recorded for 1961 as 31,500 tons, for 1962 as 300,000, for 1963 as the same, and for 1964 as 345,000. Two rigs were maintained at and near Alborz on development drilling in 1961 and subsequent years; but the field could not be described as yet, in 1966, in effective production, and its problems remained largely unsolved.

Other interesting outside tests were made at Imam Hasan, 120 miles north-west of Kirmanshah; a well spudded in here in 1962 was abandoned dry the next year. In one of two subsequent wells, traces of oil and gas were found. Work proceeded continuously at Gorgan, five wells being drilled; in three of them slight indications of gas and/or oil were detected. A well at Talkheh was begun in 1961 and completed in 1962 but oil traces were non-commercial; wells in Mazanderan and at Yort-i-Shah were abandoned as dry. Geophysical survey was extended to some offshore areas in the Gulf (1963) and in north central Iran. In 1964 another well at Gorgan found only gas, one at Mileh Sorkh was dry, two more trials at Imam Hasan the same, and one at South Siah Kuh fared no better. Two more wildcats were drilled in 1965, and one deep test-well at Alborz.

N.I.O.C. had during this period other responsibilities than those of the search for and production of oil. Of one of these, the assumption from the Consortium under the 1954 Agreement of all the 'non-basic services' throughout their area, something has already been said (pp. 283-4) and little need be added. The Consortium employees thus to be served in housing, health services, roads, welfare, schools and technical training, recreation, etc. varied in this period from 25,000 to 18,000, all Iranians except a tiny minority of expatriates (p. 379). N.I.O.C. employees busy with these tasks numbered about half the Consortium's labour-force. The time was awaited when the development of the local municipalities could enable them adequately to assume the duty.

Another direct concern of N.I.O.C. was that of catering, by its own refineries (so far as these yet existed) and by a distribution network covering all products, for the needs of Iran itself. The country's consumption—more than half concentrated in Teheran city—was rising rapidly during these years, from 24·5 million bbl in 1960 to 28 million in 1962, 33·8 million in 1964, and 36·9 million in 1965. Due provision for all this was made difficult by the size and arduous nature of the terrain and the inadequacy of local refineries.[1] The number of roadside service stations was increased some twentyfold in these years and they were supplied, with difficulty and expense, by additions made to the products pipeline Abadan–Azna–Qum–Teheran which was already operating by

[1] Pending completion of the Teheran or other refinery there were (outside the Consortium) only the very small and simple plants at Naft-i-Shah and Kirmanshah, and a topping plant at Alborz erected in 1962-3.

1960 (p. 287). Additional lines were now constructed from Teheran to Shahrud and on to Meshhed and to Qazvin, with a later (1965) extension to Resht. The main trunk lines Abadan–Teheran were being enlarged, with new pumps, to a capacity of 44,000 b/d. Late in 1961 a line designed to carry gas from Sarajeh to Teheran (112 miles) was projected, largely to minimize the difficult transport of fuel oil or liquefied gas from fields. Early in 1965 plans were finalized, with the aid of French consultants, for a 475-mile 16/20-inch products pipeline for this purpose from Ahwaz to Teheran; it could be used later for crude, when Teheran should have its own refinery. The latter had long been a favourite project and was in May 1963 the subject of an agreement with a Franco-German-American group who would provide credit for the enterprise. The plant was to have initial capacity of 50,000 b/d, or possibly more, later to be raised to 100,000; crude would, it was hoped, be brought from the Alborz field, and/or, failing that, from the Consortium. Construction at a site south of Teheran began late in 1965 for completion in 1968. The cost was estimated at £25 million, to which the Central Bank and the Plan Organization would contribute. A smaller refinery at Shiraz was also considered.

A consideration of particular interest to and study by N.I.O.C. in these years was the increased use of natural gas—a problem never, so far, fully solved in the Middle East—and the connected establishment of a petrochemical industry (pp. 287–8). The subsidiary established by N.I.O.C. in 1961 for gas-based industrial development, with French and Swiss participation, seems to have achieved little, though gas was supplied from Consortium or N.I.O.C. fields to small fertilizer and cement factories, and other similar enterprises could well be expected. The Company invited suggestions and offers during 1962 but little was forthcoming. A major project for taking gas from the Consortium area to Isfahan, Kashan, and Teheran for industrial use was studied. Inquiries were also received from the U.S.S.R. as to possible export of gas to that country, and agreement was reached in principle late in 1965 for the construction of a trans-frontier gas-line for the purpose. The plan was part of a large project to include construction by the Russians of a steelworks and machine-tool plant. The gas-line would serve Persian towns *en route*. Costs would be met in part by a low-interest loan by the U.S.S.R., repayable in kind by natural gas. The gas supply was to last for fifteen years, rising from 6,000 million cubic metres in 1970 to 10,000 later. Gas would be brought mainly from the Consortium's 'central area' fields.

In the new petrochemical field, for which N.I.O.C. formed a separate subsidiary, the National Petrochemical Company, projects for possible fertilizer, plastics, and/or rubber industries were studied, as was the extraction of sulphur. The National Company, empowered to enter into partnerships with foreign or other companies, agreed in October 1965 to join with the (American) Allied Chemical Corporation to construct a large petrochemical complex. This with other major projects was referred to the Plan Organization at Teheran, and in mid-1966 the formation of a joint company, Shapur Chemical, was announced as imminent; a £30 million plant was planned.

The continuing progress of Iranian Tankers Limited (p. 287), of which the tonnage rose from 120,000 in 1960 to 300,000 in 1964, needs no detailed description; it was a source of interest and pride to its Iranian owners. Other foreign enterprises were more significant. They included the many negotiations with European and American companies leading to leases and partnerships, as will be described later (pp. 380 ff.); they included not only the international structure and officials of the Consortium, deep in Iran itself, but also the visits and the resulting local enterprises, planned or realized, of western industrialists in this awakened and enriched Kingdom. Of the ever closer contacts with the oil authorities of other Middle Eastern States and Venezuela in O.P.E.C., something has been said elsewhere (pp. 351 f.); these played their part in widening the Iranian outlook. Other symptoms of interest in the industrial and especially the petroleum world outside can be seen in N.I.O.C.'s participation in an Indian-built refinery at Madras, to which Iranian (specifically I.P.A.C.) crude would be supplied; a barter deal with Argentina, to supply crude oil in exchange for wheat and mutton; and the mission, by invitation, of Iranian oil experts to Libya. Some Iranian share in refineries planned in the countries of Centö colleagues (Turkey and Pakistan) was also discussed, as well as a proposal that a selected area in northwestern Iran should be explored jointly by the three Powers. Barter deals with East European countries were also conceived as possible, perhaps immediately.

## II. THE CONSORTIUM

If the period 1955–66 had shown (pp. 279–90) the triumphant resuscitation of the Iranian oil industry from the abysmal level to which the events of 1951–4 had reduced it, the succeeding years, 1960–6, here under review, delighted the friends of Iran by the remarkable further advances in this great wealth-producing industrial complex. The complicated arrangements provided by the Agreement, as ratified by the Majlis in October 1954, both gave reasonable (not, of course, universal) satisfaction to Persian *amour-propre*, and proved less embarrassing to the ease and efficiency of oil-enterprise administration than might well have been expected. The Consortium, operating with unity, competence, and high technological wisdom, could look back in the autumn of 1966 upon six years of comprehensively satisfactory achievement, not the least part of which was both to have increased materially the country's immediately available wealth and to have discovered large additions to its ultimately exploitable reserves. The oil-wealth of Iran, known since 1908 to be great, showed in these years, by new-found productive structures and greater off-take from the old, ever greater potentialities. Nor was there any sign or likelihood that the upward spiral was near its end. Total production of Iranian crude, which had reached 34 million tons in 1955 and 51 million in 1960, amounted in 1965 to 88·5 million tons; the figures for the intermediate years were 57·1 million, 63·5 million, 70·5 million, and 81·1 million. Rates of increase each year exceeded 10 per cent. (in 1963–4, 14·6 per cent.). Even so, these increases were far from satisfying Persian opinion at ministerial (and, more particularly, at Royal) level; demands that exports, and therefore revenues, should be early and substantially augmented, to provide more revenue for Iran's urgent needs and large population, were being pressed late in 1966, not unaccompanied by threats of drastic unilateral action if such demands were not met.

Before the period now reviewed, in the year 1959, nearly 45 million tons of oil was produced by the combined offtake from the Agha Jari field, that of Gach Saran (or Gachsaran), and the older fields grouped together as the Central Area—that is, Masjid-i-Sulaiman, Lali, Haft Kel, and Naft Safid (p. 280, footnote). In 1959 Agha Jari had 33, Gach Saran 13, and the Central fields a total of 73 producing wells. Another productive structure had lately been discovered at Ahwaz, but was not yet in production. The tasks of the six years following were manifold but inter-connected. There was the need or duty to seek yet more sources of crude oil, which involved year by year the use of topographical, geological, and geophysical parties operating over wide areas; upon their results, wherever not flatly negative, could be based the decision whether to test-drill the discovered structures. Such drilling was in fact undertaken in a diversity of districts—with, as we shall see, a diversity of results. Test-drilling, often necessarily repeated in the same area if it revealed the presence of commercial quantities of hydrocarbons, would lead next to drilling for delinea-tion, for development, for production, for gas-oil level observation: in fact, for the establishment of a defined, producible oilfield. In this event production units for collecting and processing the crude for onward transit were necessary; these, whether temporary or permanent, could be of various patterns and on any scale indicated. Pipelines to further collecting points or to shipment terminals or to the Abadan refinery were the next stage, with pumping units and tankage everywhere on the required scale. The many other industrial as well as human and domestic needs, which had to be and were supplied, can be easily imagined by readers of this work.

Meanwhile, the longest-established fields, some of which were by now half a century old, had to be maintained, improved, and repressured to keep them efficiently (if of necessity less abundantly) in production. This was the case in Masjid-i-Sulaiman, Lali, Naft Safid, and even the once record-breaking Haft Kel. A deep test in 1963-4 in the first and oldest of these, a test taken to the Lower Jurassic, 15,000 feet down (the deepest in Persia), recorded a powerful gas pressure at a depth of 15,000-15,500 feet, so powerful as not only to disrupt the drill pipe and casing but actually to re-pressure the oil-holding horizon throughout the field. The well was with difficulty killed and plugged. In general, the Central Area fields were kept, not without constant effort, at the best level of which they were still capable; they gave in 1959 at a rate of 265,000 b/d and in 1960 at 263,000, but by 1964 output had fallen to 187,000 b/d and in 1965 to 167,000 in spite of a temporary rally produced by 'remedial action', repairs, work-overs, etc. The main 'drop' was at Haft Kel.

The great Agha Jari field, drawing on the Asmari limestone, maintained its primacy, raising its output from 599,000 b/d in

1959 to 863,000 in 1964 and 833,000 (slightly less) in 1965. Its producing wells numbered fifty-one in 1960, seventy in 1965. Producing wells yielded an average of 20,000 b/d each, an almost uniquely high figure and, even so, the limits and potential of the field could not be taken as finally determined. Observation wells were provided as required and some of the producers were acidized to increase production. On 9 November 1962 the field yielded its two-billionth barrel of oil: the first billion had taken fourteen years to produce, the second only four. It passed three billion bbl in March 1966. Agha Jari oil was all exported from Bandar Mashhur until the link with Kharg terminal was established in 1965 (pp. 376 f.).

Gach Saran, with the aid of persistent production-drilling and a discovered extension of the structure at its north-western end, took second place only to Agha Jari, though with a heavier oil (31·0 degrees–31·9 degrees A.P.I., to Agha Jari's 34 degrees–34·9 degrees). The field, with its structural secrets perhaps not yet all revealed, and likely to be even more productive in further years, was studied, delineated, and fully equipped with production facilities. Its producing wells in 1961 were twelve (out of a total of thirty-eight drilled there); in 1965 they were twenty-two (out of fifty). It included wells of extraordinary output: from one, for instance, 80,000 b/d were produced. The oil column in the Gach Saran field exceeded 7,000 feet in thickness in the Asmari limestone, and extensions of the field in more than one direction were ascertained during this period. The field gave an average of 110,000 b/d in 1960 but in 1964 averaged 448,000 b/d and in 1965 reached a capacity of 615,000 b/d, which would become 725,000 when the expansion of one of its Production Units had been completed.

The important Ahwaz field, fifty miles long, came into first production in 1960 from its well no. 6 in the Asmari, at a rate of 6,000 b/d. Its history thereafter was one of the further drilling of producing and observation wells, and the full equipment of the field with permanent production facilities. Its output in 1965 averaged 166,000 b/d from twenty producing wells, and this figure would doubtless soon be exceeded. The crude was exported from Abadan. The potential of the Ahwaz field was by many equated to that of Gach Saran.

The oilfields above described had all been in production (as we saw) in 1960; by 1965 the list of producing fields had grown by five more, and certainly one, probably three or more, discoveries made in 1964 or 1965 would later take their place on the list; on others, where exploratory drilling continued in 1965–6, no definite verdict could yet be passed, while a number of exploration wells, even though they had revealed the presence of some, doubtfully commercial, hydrocarbon deposits, were abandoned or suspended *sine die*. Such were those at Binak, eighty miles south-east of Gach Saran, at Mund seventy-five miles south-east of Bushire, and one on the Suru structure near Bandar 'Abbas, a dry well which cost nearly £1·5 million; these had all been spudded in during 1960 (p. 280). Such also were the wells drilled on geophysical evidence at Shaikh Shu'aib Island, off the coast west of Qishm Island, and an uncompleted well on Qishm itself, the scene of costly but abortive drilling many years earlier (pp. 37, 53). At Khalafabad,[1] on the Agha Jari–Bandar Mashhur road, three wells were drilled in 1961–3 on a favourable anticline, and oil in appreciable quantities was encountered; Khalafabad could rank therefore as a minor discovery, its future performance still uncertain.[2] At three sites, located and prepared for drilling in 1961 and drilled in 1962–3, fortune was still variable. At Mushtaq, north-west of Ahwaz, a trial well found no oil but was retained as a water-pressure observation well. At Mansuri, thirty-five miles south-east of Ahwaz, some deep and almost certainly non-commercial oil was discovered. At Bushgan, 110 miles south-east of Gach Saran and sixty south-west of Shiraz—a long way, therefore, from the main complex of Iranian fields—traces not without interest were found, but the well was suspended. At Sabzpushan, sixteen miles south of Shiraz, the drill met only water. At Gulkhari, forty-five miles south of Gach Saran, a little heavy oil was met in 1963 but the well was abandoned.

The destiny of a number of wells drilled in 1964 and 1965 was less foreseeable. Such were those at Faris, a structure north-east of Agha Jari and parallel to it, and at Rag-i-Safid, south-west of Gach Saran and near the sea; in both of these some crude was found and tested, and commercial prospects were fair. At Rag-i-Safid, dangerously high gas pressure, met with in April 1964, called for the urgent summoning of an expert from the U.S.A. The gas did not ignite. The field might later prove to have been

---

[1] Also, or later, known as Ramshir.
[2] The field came into production in July 1966.

a valuable discovery. At Darqain, due north of Khoramshahr, there were found in 1965 some hydrocarbon traces, but these appeared non-commercial. In the same year a well on the Garagan structure, south-west of Gach Saran, produced only water.

On a different level of immediate importance, however, were those fields which were both discovered and brought into production during these years. The case of Pazanun (or Pazanan) (pp. 128, 149) is unusual in that, known for years as a powerful gasfield and exploited till 1945 as such, the structure was proved by further drilling in 1960–1 both to possess a long south-eastern extension and, as appeared by further work in 1963–5, to be also an oilfield with a respectable depth of oil-column. As such it was delineated, developed, and equipped: it contributed initially some 1,400 b/d in 1964 and 20,000 in 1965, and by the summer of that year had been equipped with productive facilities for an offtake of 70,000 b/d. As a gasfield Pazanun may be among the largest in the world; it is in extent some fifty by four miles. The case of Kharg Island has also its unusual aspects. An exploratory well was spudded in close to this busy and growing export terminal in October 1961; it revealed the presence of oil, which further drilling confirmed, in the same limestone and indeed in the same structure as that already tapped by the Darius well of I.P.A.C. (p. 381). Production from the first half-dozen wells was unimpressive in quantity, but enough oil had appeared by 1964 to justify tentative production, and this began in that year at an average of 20,000 b/d, increased to a much higher figure in 1965. I.P.A.C. was simultaneously producing from elsewhere in the structure (pp. 381 f.).

The Bibi Hakima field, south-west of Gach Saran, was the scene of preparatory work in 1960; drilling and a highly promising discovery (at 6,750 feet in the ever-bountiful Asmari limestone) in 1961; and delineation, deepening, and outstep drilling in 1962, which revealed the exceptionally high promise of the field. Its features are an extensive gas-cap and a 3,500-foot oil-column in the Asmari and neighbouring structures which are inter-connected. Successive wells, which included three major producers, gave production of over a million barrels in 1964 and 14 million in the following year, during which five more wells of various categories were drilled. The anticline at Karanj, north-east of Agha Jari and on the same alignment, was first drilled in 1962, and was recognized in 1963 as containing a notably promising reservoir: if limited in size, it possessed a thick oil-column, and the usual phases of oilfield work preparatory to production brought it to an output of 5,000 b/d in 1964 and almost 70,000 b/d in 1965. The crude was stabilized, pending other facilities, in one of the Agha Jari production units. Drilling in 1964 had indicated a structure bigger than at first appeared, and field development continued in 1965.

North of Marun and north-west of the Karanj structure, and on the same trend, yet another discovery was made in 1964 at Kupal. In a first test-well strong gas pressure was met; the well reached the Asmari limestone at 10,925 feet and was completed at 12,000 feet, revealing an oil-column of over a thousand feet in this formation. High hopes were aroused. In the same period, westward of but parallel to the Agha Jari structure, two wells drilled at Marun in 1963 showed the presence of high-pressure gas in the Asmari limestone at 7,585 feet. Drilling, continued in 1964, indicated with certainty a major discovery: the Consortium reported in 1964 that it 'may rank among the larger Iranian fields', a prophecy soundly based on the field's extent and 1,300-foot oil-column. Marun came into production, at an initial 27,000 b/d, in March 1966; three wells had then been completed, a number later increased to seven. If current indications were correctly interpreted the Marun structure might be of phenomenal length, perhaps seventy miles.

The last newly discovered field to be recorded here is that of Mulla Sani', situated some twenty miles north-west of Marun and twenty-four miles north-east of Ahwaz. The first well reached the Asmari limestone at 12,500 feet. On test it gave 1,000 b/d of 33·6 degrees A.P.I. crude, similar to that of Marun, and clearly represented an extension of that field.[1]

We have now seen that after 1960, when the Ahwaz field came into production, no other joined the already producing seven fields during 1961, 1962, and 1963. In 1964 Pazanun made a substantial, Karanj a slighter, Bibi Hakima and Kharg each a small contribution, and Khalafabad (Ramshir) did the same in 1966. The rapid increase of all these appeared certain: and it was not less so that they would be joined shortly—within two or three years— by Marun and Kupal, possibly Raj-i-Safid, probably Mulla Sani', imaginably Faris, and not impossibly Mansuri, Bushgan, or

---

[1] The field was later renamed Marun Karun; it extended under and across that river.

Gulkhari. The decision as to whether or when to bring a marginal or even a proved field into production would depend obviously upon its location and accessibility as well as on the quantity and quality of oil available.

The movement of annually produced crude—88·5 million long tons in 1965—once collected and stabilized in or near its field of origin, followed a regular but evolving pattern. Of the 1965 output (in thousands of b/d) 826,000 b/d were sent to Bandar Mashhur[1] for loading as crude, 568,000 in the same form to Kharg Island terminal, 376,000 b/d to Abadan refinery, and 27,000 to N.I.O.C. (at Ahwaz) as fuel oil from Masjid-i-Sulaiman topping plant. This suggests, as was the case, that the important project described earlier (p. 282) was far advanced towards completion: that is, the development of Kharg to be the main or sole ultimate crude loading-point, and the cessation of loading at Abadan as being both unapproachable by deep-draught tankers and also exposed to the malice of 'Iraqi politicians. For the loading of refined products Bandar Mashhur was destined to replace Abadan. (The N.I.O.C. plan to develop Khor Musa (p. 283) was dropped.) The first tanker carrying Gach Saran crude left Kharg in August 1960; by December 190,000 b/d were being loaded there. The need to handle that oilfield's increasing output or potential, and its increasing richness in facilities, in production units, and in additional pipeline pumps, led year by year to the necessity for rapid increase of accommodation, tankage, loading-lines, pumps, etc. at Kharg. In 1962 a second 30-inch pipeline from Ganaveh (p. 282) to Kharg was planned, and it was completed in 1964: it raised the terminal's throughput capacity from 380,000 to 540,000 b/d and was the herald of still more expansion in tankage, pipelines, berthing, loading equipment, etc. By 1966 eleven new tanks, each designed to hold 500,000 bbl, were complete; the main jetty was under conversion from an L to a T-shape, so as to provide ten deep-water berths for the heavy tankers of the future. New pipelines serving the terminal were to include a 106-mile 42-inch line from Agha Jari, Pazanun, and Karanj—and later, possibly, Marun and Faris—to Ganaveh, and two more 30-inch lines thence to Kharg. The loading of the lighter Agha Jari crude, first carried out there in November 1965, was a significant event. Lines connecting Gach Saran and Bibi Hakima to Ganaveh were duplicated, and a

---

[1] Its name was changed lately to Bandar Mahshahr.

powerful pumping plant was to be installed at the point of junction at Gurreh. Still further expansion in process of fulfilment in 1966 would establish Kharg as one of the greatest crude oil terminals in the world, with jetty accommodation running to 6,000 feet and a potential throughput of 2·5 million b/d. Domestic accommodation, institutions, and amenities were correspondingly expanded. The whole Kharg project was understood to have cost, by early 1966, over £33 million. The port in its developed form was officially inaugurated by H.I.M. the Shah on 15 March 1966, by which time export therefrom had reached the level of 1·32 million b/d—a figure surpassed, however, in later months.

No such development befell the already mature loading-base at Bandar Mashhur (p. 281). In 1959 this port had transmitted 213 million bbl of crude to the Consortium's Trading Companies (p. 277) before Kharg was yet in commission; the corresponding figures were 299 million in 1964 and 300 million in 1965, while Kharg's throughput had climbed to 161 million in 1964 and 207 million in 1965. The great days of the Island as an exporting base still lay ahead, but Mashhur was fully holding its own; it would, according to plan, so continue as the export-terminal for refined products, while cargoes from Abadan would diminish or cease.

The quantities of crude and products respectively delivered at these bases to the Trading Companies were, in 1962–5, in millions of long tons: crude—45·3, 52·1, 61·6, 68·2; refined products—11·1, 11·2, 10·8, and 10·5. The main recipients of crude were Western Europe and Japan, with lesser quantities going to non-Japanese Asia, Africa, North America, and less to South America and Australasia. Refined products exported from Abadan went, in order of quantities, to non-Japanese Asia, Africa, Japan, Western Europe, and Australasia. Bunkering at Iranian ports in these years took amounts of fuel-oil varying from 2·4 to 3·1 million tons. Total exports, in millions of long tons, amounted in 1962–5 to 56·4, 63·3, 72·4, and 78·7.

Direct payments to Iran, excluding amounts distributed as wages and salaries or as payments to the public, in the years 1961–5, were respectively £107·5 million, £119·2 million, £137·4 million, £171·5 million, and £183·3 million.[1] These sums were made up of the 'stated payment' from the Companies, varying from £30·7

[1] Total Iranian State revenues amounted in 1965 to some £340 million—of which, therefore, the Consortium provided nearly 55 per cent.

to £47·2 million,[1] the income tax from the same which ranged upwards from £74·4 to £132·6 million,[2] and the income tax from the Operating Companies, from £2·4 to £3·5 million.[3] In terms of cents per barrel of the Trading Companies' offtake, the figures are 75·6, 74·4, 79·6, 81·7, and 82·2 cents. Salaries and wages (plus 'employee benefits') paid locally by the Operating Companies came, in the years 1961–5 to amounts varying from £30·1 million down to £25·6 million. Payments to contractors and for local purchase ranged from £4·7 to £8·1 million.

At Abadan Refinery, domain of the Iranian Oil Refinery component of the Consortium, the objective in this period was not to restore the huge throughput of the A.I.O.C. pre-1951 period, which in 1950 had been more than 24 million t/y (p. 151), the greatest of all such plants in the world. By 1959, after the calamities and stagnation of 1951–4, throughput had recovered to 16·2 million t/y; during 1960 to 1966 in any one year it barely exceeded 18 million tons, to which level it gradually crept up; the figure includes products exported by the Trading Companies, amounts handled for local distribution to N.I.O.C.,[4] and refinery use and losses. Abadan, its non-basic services and amenities being now, under the Agreement, the concern of a specialized branch of N.I.O.C. (p. 283)—though at the Consortium's expense—remained a very great and important refinery, still by far the largest in the Middle East, and, after the comprehensive modernization, streamlining, and computer-aided automation of these years, outstandingly efficient and flexible. The severe handicap of Abadan's inability to accommodate tankers of more than 20,000 tons, and its vulnerability to politically-inspired interruptions to its traffic, such as occurred in 1961, led, as we have seen, to the decision to move progressively the loading of refined products to Mashhur. Steps in this direction were already well advanced before 1965, in which year a 26-inch 65-mile black oil line from Abadan to Mashhur was completed, and awaited only its pumps and heaters.

Though the overall capacity of the refinery was not extended,

---

[1] In successive years: £30·7 million, £34·5 million, £38·3 million, £43·5 million, £47·2 million.

[2] £74·4 million, £82 million, £96·2 million, £124·7 million, £132·6 million.

[3] £2·4 million, £2·7 million, £2·9 million, £3·3 million, £3·5 million.

[4] Fuel oil for local distribution was obtained by N.I.O.C., also from the Masjid-i-Sulaiman topping plant, and with other products from its own two small refineries (p. 367).

the plant was far from standing still. Steps were taken by new methods and expensive new installations to make possible still higher grades of gasoline; these included a large naphtha thermal reforming unit commissioned in 1960, and a naphtha catalytic reforming unit commissioned in 1963. The main distillation units were all overhauled and modernized. Tankage received important additions. Facilities for the manufacture and blending of l.p.g. were completed. Jetties and loading facilities were improved. New kerosene-treating units were commissioned. Bitumen production was extended. The manufacture of both aviation gasoline and jet fuel was improved and extended, as was that of lubricants. More natural gas (and therefore less liquid fuel) was used in refinery processes. Out-of-date plant was demolished. Electric power production was increased. These items, far from exhaustive, give the barest suggestion of the constructive activities of the I.O.R.C. at Abadan. The plant and its administration also afforded excellent examples of two welcome features: one, the visibly close co-operation of the technical and non-technical services, those of the Consortium and N.I.O.C. respectively; the other, the maintenance of an extraordinarily high level of industrial safety. The latter record was marred only by one serious accident (not on Consortium premises)—that of an explosion and fire on board a loading tanker at Bandar Mashhur in 1965, with the loss of thirty-two lives, including one Company employee.

As to the body of staff and labour employed in the Consortium's 'basic' operations—those described in the present chapter—it was possible materially to reduce the scale of this during these years. In 1961, 14,962 Iranians and 263 overseas personnel were employed in production: 22,634 and 346 respectively in refining, 428 and 186 at headquarters in Teheran. In 1965 the corresponding figures were: in production—11,388 and 169; in refining—17,353 and 112; at Teheran—544 and 91. Thus the total of all employees for each of these two years was respectively 24,939 and 18,054; and the overseas element had dropped in four years by more than 50 per cent., even though before 1961 it had already been much reduced. N.I.O.C. employees in the associated 'non-basic' operations numbered 138 in 1961; 11,603 in 1965.

E. W. Berlin (p. 285) remained as the Consortium's General Manager till 1963, and was succeeded by J. A. Warder, who was still in office at the end of 1966.

### III. THE PARTNERSHIPS

The granting of oil-rights to, and the formation with N.I.O.C. of joint companies with, an Italian statal concern (A.G.I.P. Mineraria) and an American (Pan American International, an affiliate of Standard Oil of Indiana),[1] which resulted in the establishment of S.I.R.I.P. and I.P.A.C. respectively, have already been recorded (pp. 289–90), as have the field operations of these which by mid-1960 had made a promising but not yet a rewarded start. I.R.C.A.N., a similar Canadian-Iranian partnership, retired from the scene in 1961. The other two were before 1965, with astonishing promptitude, to discover, develop, and export from important mid-sea oilfields.

I.P.A.C., busy each year with marine seismic survey, and working with one fixed platform and one mobile barge, and supporting its drilling crews from a shore base at Khosrawabad, had had the honour of the first discovery (p. 290), close to Kharg Island, after its first two wells numbered A and B had been abandoned at depths of 13,150 and 12,500 feet. Darius no. 1, in 1961 located three and a half miles south-west of the Island, and drilled in 158 feet of water, gave the remarkable yield of 25,000 b/d of 27 degrees A.P.I. oil, from 11,000 to 11,750 feet in Lower Cretaceous limestone—certainly among the richest offshore wells in existence. Cyrus no. 1, on a different structure some sixty miles south-west of Kharg, was next to be drilled, but was abandoned at 11,800 feet. In 1962 Cyrus no. 2 blew out, 2A was an effective producer of 27 degrees A.P.I. oil at 14,000 b/d from 7,250 feet in Burgan sand, no. 3 the same, and no. 4 was a non-commercial producer. Darius no. 2, two miles from no. 1, came in as a producer at 12,000 feet, and no. 3 nearby was the same. Next year Darius nos. 4 and 5 were similar Lower Cretaceous producers, both from 11,750 feet. No. 6, aimed at greater depth in the Jurassic, went awry. Cyrus no. 5, immediately east of 2A, was a producer at 10,700 feet, and subsequently nos. 7, 8, 9, 11, 12, 13 were all drilled as Middle Cretaceous producers, of depths around 7,500 feet. In 1964 one rig only was maintained on development work, but regular export of oil could begin from the Darius field (which had already pro-

---

[1] Pan American International was founded by Standard Oil of Indiana in June 1959; its name was changed to the American International Oil Company in July 1962.

duced and disposed of an appreciable quantity[1] while testing, but was not yet recognized as commercial.[2]

The Darius field, conveniently placed adjoining Kharg, and indeed extending well under the Island itself (p. 374), was in fact fully commercial and certainly important, with a potential offtake of upwards of 5 million t/y of light crude, and probably far more. Permanent shore installations had by this time been erected by I.P.A.C. on the Island, after a suggestion for joint use of those belonging to the Consortium had been made but rejected; they include gas-separators, de-sulphurizing plant, sea-lines, tankage, and pumps as well as buildings for offices, communications, and domestic use. I.P.A.C. produced 2·5 million tons in 1965, all from Darius.

The Company announced another discovery early in 1966, that of 30 degrees A.P.I. oil testing about 3,000 b/d, at some 9,000 feet: the location, known as Esfandiar, was given as twelve miles south of the Cyrus field. The field was almost certainly important.

To S.I.R.I.P., no less active in surveys both on sea and land, success was denied in its drilled wildcats in the mainland (Zagros) region of its concession area, and also in its Makran area of extreme south-eastern Iran (p. 289). The Zagros well, Sequta no. 1, had to be abandoned, and no good news came up from Makran; but the offshore drilling on Bahrgansar (p. 290) was, after two initial failures, handsomely rewarded by a strong producing well which came late in 1961 only six miles from the shore, and was followed by another. Drilling with two rigs in this more than hopeful field continued in 1961–2. In the course of tests to establish commercial status 175,000 tons of oil were produced and a variety of well locations in the vicinity and elsewhere were tested. The Bahrgansar field was pronounced commercial in 1962, in which year two more producing wells were completed and over 300,000 tons of oil were produced, soon to be followed by another two wells and double the quantity of oil. Six producers from an average depth of 11,000 feet stood ready by the end of 1963, in which year 325,000 tons were produced; this represented a considerable offtake potential, for which a newly constructed sixty-acre export terminal, seventy-five miles south-east of Bandar Dailam, stood nearly ready. With

[1] Given as 94,000 tons in 1962, 100,000 in 1963, 170,000 in 1964.
[2] On recognition of a field as 'commercial' N.I.O.C. was bound to subscribe its half of all expenses.

an initial capacity of 2 million t/y the terminal was fed by a 36-mile 16-inch submarine line, bringing Bahrgansar oil to be degassed and stored. The gas was utilized for sea water distillation and power production. Other installations included generating plant, pumps, five-mile sea-loading lines, access roads, an airstrip, offices, and residential quarters and amenities. S.I.R.I.P. produced and exported some 1·3 million tons in 1964 and 1·2 in 1965, from their Bahrgansar field.

In 1964 two more wildcats in the Zagros were tried in vain, a mid-sea exploration well was drilled, and another producer was brought in in the Bahrgansar field. The export terminal for the latter was inaugurated and 1·25 million tons loaded from it, both in that year and in 1965: a figure, however, certain to be formidably greater in future years. Three more exploratory wells were drilled by S.I.R.I.P. in 1965, including one in their Zagros concession.

Following the precedent established by the N.I.O.C.-E.N.I. and N.I.O.C.-Indiana partnerships, S.I.R.I.P., and I.P.A.C., the Iranian Government was far from unwilling to lease other territories in other districts to deserving applicants. Such areas could be found in district VIII (Fars), XIV (Isfahan), and XVIII (southern Khorasan). Blocks of territory there were in fact opened for bidding without attracting any offers; indeed, no new leases were granted in the period 1960–3, during which both Kuwait and Sa'udi Arabia raised queries as to the boundaries claimed by Iran in the mid-Gulf area. It was at the same time understood that there would thereafter be little hope of success for any company which had not shared in the expenses of the wide-reaching seismic survey which had been carried out under N.I.O.C. direction in the Gulf offshore districts.

In the summer of 1963 it was announced that offers for offshore areas in District 1, including relinquished territory, were shortly to be invited; these were to be submitted by N.I.O.C.-approved candidates by the end of October 1964.

The first awards were, after a period of intense negotiating activity, announced in November 1964. Five groups had been successful. One, which in due course was to form its joint company with N.I.O.C. entitled Iranian Marine International Oil Company or I.M.I.N.O.C.O., represented a combination of the Italian A.G.I.P. with Phillips Petroleum Company and the Indian Government's Oil and Natural Gas Commission. The second, which later formed the Lavan Petroleum Company (L.A.P.C.O.), included Atlantic Richfield,[1] Sun Oil, Union of California, and Murphy Oil Corporation. The third group, which with N.I.O.C. was to form I.R.O.P.C.O. (the Iranian Offshore Petroleum Company), included Tidewater, Superior, Skelly, Sunray DX, Kerr McGee, Cities Service, and Atlantic Richfield. These two, I.R.O.P.C.O. and L.A.P.C.O., thus represented an American independent element. The other two successful grantees were Royal Dutch Shell, which (the only major company to be chosen —doubtless by virtue of its marketing potential) was to form the Dashtestan Offshore Petroleum Company (D.O.P.C.O.); and French interests which included not the C.F.P. but the B.R.P. (Bureau de Recherche des Pétroles), and R.A.P. (Régie Autonome des Pétroles), and S.N.P.A.,[2] all state-owned; these, as Sofiran, would combine with N.I.O.C. as the Farsi Petroleum Company.

The terms under which these grants were made and the joint companies established were not identical *inter se*, but were closely similar. D.O.P.C.O. paid an initial bonus of $59 million for 6,075 square kilometres; I.R.O.P.C.O., $40 million for 2,250 square kilometres; F.P.C., $27 million for 5,800 square kilometres; L.A.P.C.O., $25 million for 8,000 square kilometres; and I.M.I.N.O.C.O., $34 million for 7,960 square kilometres. The immediate receipts to the Iranian Government from these grants were some $185 million or £66 million; the total acreage concerned stretched from a line south-west from Bushire to run due south from Lingeh seawards as far as the (imperfectly established) Median Line of the Gulf. Bonuses payable at later stages by each Company, or rather by the foreign participant in it, varied in number, amount, and dates of payment. In all cases a minimum amount was to be spent on exploration within a stated period, four years from signature. Unpromising areas could be relinquished without penalty, providing they had been explored and drilled; retained areas were subject to rental payment, such rents being treated as part of costs. Crude oil and also natural gas must be supplied to N.I.O.C. for internal consumption at little more than cost price, but in amounts not to exceed 10 per cent of production. Each party (foreign group and N.I.O.C.) was entitled to half the

---

[1] The name was changed from Atlantic Refining Company in May 1966.

[2] Société Nationale des Pétroles d'Aquitaine. Three French private companies had been included in the group but later withdrew.

production, with the right to buy any part of its partner's un-wanted half; all crude won would be sold at posted prices to be approved by the Board. Reasonable treatment on discounts was guaranteed by the Iranian Government; this and connected matters were governed by detailed provisions. N.I.O.C. was not to share directly, either initially or later, in exploration or pre-production costs (onerous as these would certainly be), but both these and the paid-up bonuses were amortizable from profits, the latter being calculated on a basis of posted prices with agreed dis-counts. The period of the agreement was in all cases one of twenty-five years production, with the right to three extensions up to a total of forty years. Total profits were (as already with S.I.R.I.P. and I.P.A.C.) to accrue first as to one half to N.I.O.C., and then one quarter to each of N.I.O.C. (as 50 per cent. shareholder) and the foreign group, on a basis of equal sharing of costs. The areas allotted are shown in a map at the end of this book.

A sixth, all-German group was added to the joint Companies' number in June 1965, on similar lines.[1] To this group was granted an area of 5,150 square kilometres, the initial bonus payable being $5 million. A joint company was quickly formed, with the name of the Persian Gulf Petroleum Company, or P.E.G.U.P.C.O. It was announced at the same time that the Spanish concern C.E.P.S.A. was, if N.I.O.C. agreed, to buy a 10 per cent. share in the Tidewater Group, which was now wearing the colours of I.R.O.P.C.O.

These Groups, who had thus appeared on the stage of Middle Eastern oil, presented a number of significant aspects. One was that of the variety of nationalities represented—British and American, Dutch and Italian, German and French, Spanish and Indian—and (it was said) the satisfaction of the Iranian authorities in this feature. Another lay in the newness of some of the partici-pants to the Iranian or indeed the Middle Eastern scene; and another, that the terms exacted, with their stipulation of thorough-going governmental partnership, failed to deter either such un-accustomed giants as Shell or companies such as E.N.I. which had already, since 1958, been taking part with the Iranians in similar enterprises which they had evidently found tolerable.

[1] It included six companies: Deutsche Erdöl (D.E.A.), Deutsche Schachtbau, Gelsenberg, Gewerkschaft Elverath, Preussag, Scholven-Chemie, and Winters-hall.

Finally, the terms exacted by N.I.O.C. were, it was clear, of a severity which only the high promise of the area, based on its regional tectonics and the enormous production already found in other parts of it—and perhaps on the structures revealed by the recent seismic survey—could justify. The Iranian authorities, who ended the negotiations with a large bird in the hand and many more in the bush, appeared to conduct the affair with great dexterity.

During 1965 D.O.P.C.O. spudded in its first well, C1, 8 miles offshore and 75 miles south-south-west of Bushire, in 60 feet of water, and took it by December to 9,100 feet. Farsi spudded in their B1, in 180 feet of water near Farsi Island, and took it to 8,033 feet. I.M.I.N.O.C.O. began their first, D1, in May 1965, 15 miles offshore and 100 miles south-east of Bushire in 80 feet of water. The well was abandoned at almost 12,000 feet, having shown minor traces of oil. A second well early in 1966 found light oil of 36 degrees A.P.I. from a depth of some 5,000 feet, testing at rates of 2,400 b/d. It was indicated, however, later in the year, that the find was probably non-commercial.

L.A.P.C.O. began well no. S1 in August 1965 in 60 feet of water, 90 miles offshore and only about 20 from Umm Shaif (p. 320). This proved an important discovery well, yielding some 7,500 b/d of 32 degrees A.P.I. oil from 9,900 feet in Thamama limestone. In May 1966 the Company completed a second well, testing 9,350 b/d, in the same Sassan field. The German P.E.G.U.P.C.O. began drilling early in 1966 from their drilling vessel, but in July abandoned the well at 11,750 feet as a dry hole; it had shown only slight traces of oil. Another well was spudded in at a new site. Early in 1966 the all-American group I.R.O.P.C.O. had completed their shore installations—offices, living quarters, a wharf, etc.— at Bushire and spudded in their first well from a four-legged platform located some 60 miles offshore, in 200 feet of water.

## CHAPTER XXII

# SA'UDI ARABIA, 1960–6

## I. THE SA'UDI GOVERNMENT

THE social structure of contemporary Sa'udi Arabia and its form of government having been described in previous pages of this book (pp. 290 f.), little on the subject need here be added. In the quinquennium now under review the tribal and village characteristics of the country remained almost unaltered, unless for a slowly growing habituation to the presence, with all its stark contrasts, of a great western and technologically advanced industrial complex; the spectacle, isolated though it was from the eyes of the vast majority of Sa'udis, of ways of life utterly different from their own, and new conceptions of the power—for good or ill, for themselves or others—of sheer wealth and all that it could accomplish, now invading the vast penniless spaces of Arabia. It was clear to observers that the deep, if still largely invisible, ferments created by the phenomena of the oil age in the Sa'udi world, indeed in that of all Arabia and much elsewhere of the Middle East and Africa, must one day produce profound, perhaps catastrophic changes in society and in the forms of government. In our present period there were certainly signs of restlessness in the small circles of evolved Sa'udis as well as among the imported other-Arab technicians; and the feeling grew that the age-long, desert, theocratic autocracy of the dynasty of Al Sa'ud, with its very minimum of compromise with the demands of the mid-twentieth century for representation, for shared authority, for evolved forms of law and justice, for the means to public welfare, could perhaps not survive unmodified for many more decades, or even years, to come. The upward and outward striving and ambitions for personal fulfilment of increasing numbers of the young awakened Sa'udis were likely, one day, to produce stresses which old dynastic authority and Islamic loyalty would be unable to contain.

From 1960 to 1966 the changes made in the structure of the Kingdom were not profound. With the final passage of supreme power from King Sa'ud to the Amir Faisal, his younger brother, the forms of government, though still despotic—and to any

western victim or participant highly dilatory and inefficient—
showed a movement towards decentralization, more specialization
of function, and more awareness of the rights (if any) of the public.
King Faisal, who finally assumed the Royal title and functions in
November 1964, presided over a government which could at least
show a Cabinet and a Prime Minister, a constitution of sorts,
advisory (non-elected) Councils in the main districts and tribe-
groups, and Municipal Councils in the towns, even though his own
Royal power remained absolute and Law was still represented
solely by the Shari'a code administered by old-type judges of
varied attainments. Archaic or not, the régime gave currently—
not least to the eyes of concerned oil-men—the appearance of
greater day-by-day stability than that of three-fifths of other
Middle Eastern states. The finances, in which oil-revenues played
a part equivalent to some 85 or 90 per cent., were the subject of
published budgets and suitable control, and the revenues were
spent more than ever before with an eye to the public benefit.[1]

The statal Development Committee was replaced at Riyadh in
1961 by a Supreme Council for Economic Planning, and an Oil
Ministry was created. The Sa'udi Arabian Monetary Agency (p.
292) was allowed to continue its functions, which were largely
those of account-keeping not of policy. In November 1962 a
General Petroleum and Mineral Organization (Petromin) was
created, with a chairman and a responsible board representing
finance, industry, etc., and available oil-experts; its field was that
of oil affairs in their widest range, including oil-based industries,
as well as that of other minerals. An Oil Law for the territory was
understood to be intermittently under study or drafting between
1961 and 1966: late in 1965 it was expected to be fairly flexible,
likely to favour 'joint companies' formed by foreigners with
Petromin, but doubtless thorough-going in its demands.

[1] The budget for the year 1961 to June 1962 showed total revenues of Sa'udi
riyals 2,166 million, of which oil was to be responsible for S.R. 1,682 (or, as
elsewhere reported, $375 million for the year 1961—S.R. 4·5 equals $1.00). In
1962-3 total revenues were budgeted at S.R. 2,452, of which Aramco was to
contribute S.R. 1,732. The budget for 1963-4, balancing at S.R. 2,452, showed
revenues from Aramco as S.R. 2,103. (Actual oil revenues in 1962 were $409
million, and in 1963, $608 million.) In 1965 the budget anticipated S.R. 3,112
of total revenue, of which Aramco oil would bring S.R. 2,392. That of 1965-6
foresaw revenues of S.R. 3,614, of which Aramco's part was S.R. 3,180. Other
oil receipts—from the Neutral Zone and Tapline—are specified elsewhere. For
1966-7, oil revenues were budgeted to contribute 88 per cent of current statal
revenues.

Apart from the Saʻudi interest in Aramco and in the Neutral Zone (both to be examined hereinafter), the Government had dealings in this period with various other foreign concerns. One of these was the Italian E.N.I., now an applicant for a concession in the (relinquished) central area of the Kingdom; terms were likely to be agreed as soon as a geophysical survey of the region, undertaken by American contractors, was completed later in 1966. Further interest in exploration by, or in partnership with, foreign concerns was shown in 1963 by a contract given by the Ministry of Oil to an American firm, for geophysical exploration of areas in the Saʻudi Continental Shelf in the Red Sea. Yet another enterprise was an arrangement, finalized in 1965, with the French Government-owned concern Auxirap (that is, the Société Auxiliaire de la Régie Autonome des Pétroles), whereunder Petromin would take a 40 per cent. share (but with a 50 per cent. voting right) in an area offshore in the Red Sea—by no means the most attractive of districts. Government's revenues from the enterprise would take the composite form of surface rentals and royalties (both 'expensible'), and an apparently ceilingless income tax. Auxirap would conduct the marketing for both partners, if and when there was something to market; it was in mid-1966 expected to specify exactly its desired areas of operation and to start drilling before the year's end. The concession agreement included provision that, at some time in the future, the Saʻudi Government would be admitted to a share in 'downstream' as well as in the producing operations. It was understood that other foreign concerns, including one British, some American, and one Spanish, were interested in inland or Red Sea areas; preference was likely to be given to applicants with assured entry to markets. Meanwhile the Government had in 1961 spent $7 million on acquiring, as the original concession permitted, a 10 per cent. interest in the (Japanese) Arabian Oil Company (p. 310) operating offshore of the Neutral Zone. Another plan formed in 1960 and finalized in 1961 was that of a refinery to be built in the Hijaz province, with a comprehensive permit to undertake the traffic in, and transport of, oil products in western Saʻudi Arabia. (The project owed its existence apparently to a son of the King himself (p. 294); the Saʻudi Arabian Refinery Company (Sarco) thus formed was, however, in due course taken over, to the extent of a 75 per cent. interest, by Petromin when the latter took up marketing activities.)

Apart from more general or political international affairs, which do not here concern us, and frontier questions with Qatar (p. 228), Neutral Zone concession adjustments (p. 410), and abortive mid-sea boundary demarcations with Kuwait and Iran (p. 408), the main foreign contacts of Sa'udi oil were in these years by way of O.P.E.C. The Sa'udi Kingdom, a founder member and supporter of this body, contributed some interesting personalities to its councils and supported its demands on the Companies concerned (including Aramco), but did not always follow its guidance; the Sa'udis accepted the 'expensing of royalties' agreement (p. 351), which indeed was worth some S.R. 215 million ($48 million) a year to them, but they rejected the plan for strengthening price-levels by limiting the percentage by which the annual production of O.P.E.C. members would be allowed to rise (p. 352).

The statal oil corporation, Petromin, was, from its creation onwards, active and ambitious. During 1965 it set in motion a number of surveys for the allegedly considerable mineral resources of the country other than oil; it arranged for independent assess-ments of Sa'udi oil reserves, both in individual fields and in general; and it reconsidered (as did Aramco continuously) the old problem of fuller natural gas utilization. A gratifying new institu-tion was that of the Petroleum and Minerals College opened at Dhahran late in 1964, with the financial support of the Govern-ment and of Aramco, and with French technical help. With a company of the E.N.I. Group, Petromin studied a joint petro-chemical (plastic) project to be located at Dammam, and aided the foundation of a Sa'udi Arabian Fertilizer Company (Safco) in which it had a 52 per cent. and the Sa'udi public a 48 per cent. shareholding. The factory at Dammam was to produce sulphur and ammonia to a total of nearly 250,000 t/y; de-sulphurized gas would be returned to structure at Abqaiq by re-injection. Other plants in the same industrial field were planned in these years, with American help in construction and in marketing. One of these, conceived jointly with Allied Chemicals, would be for the manu-facture of a complex of petrochemical products, including plastic pipe, synthetic rubber, carbon black, and detergents; other schemes under study and negotiation in mid-1966 were for a sulphuric acid plant, and another for carbon black.

In the field of refining and local distribution Petromin late in 1963 acquired a majority holding in Sarco (p. 388), and effectively superseded Aramco as supplier of products in the Hijaz in 1964. It would ultimately do the same elsewhere. Products for consumption in western Arabia (which afforded half the total Sa'udi market) were taken there by tanker from the Gulf coast, pending completion of the refinery near Jidda. Petromin in 1964 bought from Aramco all the latter's installations and facilities at and around Jidda, where the refinery, its scale now settled as 12,500 b/d, was to be definitely started in mid-1966, for completion in 1968. It had been decided to undertake also, as another Petromin project at Jidda, the erection of a rolling mill, using imported steel, and perhaps other works consequent on the development of local iron-ore resources, if such should come to light. The Corporation also reached agreement in 1963–4 with two French firms (Forex and Languedocienne-Forenco) on the formation of an Arabian Drilling Company to bore for water and/or oil; Petromin would have a 51 per cent. interest.

Physical room to manœuvre, for both the Government and its offspring, Petromin, was provided by the wide unallotted areas of Sa'udi Arabia, by the surrendered Hijaz province (an ex-I.P.C. concession area—p. 138), and by the abundant acreage progressively relinquished by Aramco itself (p. 293). As to the latter, the 33,700 square miles given up in 1960 brought the total of relinquished territory to 306,000; a further surrender took place early in 1963, leaving this time only 125,000 square miles of the original area, with the agreed prospect that this too would be reduced to 20,000 square miles within the next three decades. One may compare this severe yet peacefully arranged surrender of territory to the methods adopted in the same years in 'Iraq.

A controversial issue, produced by a governmental 'asking for more', was that of the Sa'udi demand, made in 1965, that crude sales made by Aramco to outside (non-constituent) parties at market prices should nevertheless be treated, for statal revenue purposes, as being sold at (much higher) posted prices. This affected latterly about 12 per cent. of the Company's sales. To this *prima facie* unreasonable demand Aramco was constrained to agree, and to make it retrospective to 1961; a payment of some $55 million resulted. The State's demand persisted also that, despite the provision in O.P.E.C.'s accepted formula for the allowances against posted prices (pp. 351–2), no such allowances at all should be payable after 1966. This was, late in that year, still being resisted by Aramco; if granted, it would doubtless affect equally all other companies operating in the Middle East.

In other fields, relations with the Sa'udi Government, in spite of its rigidity in social matters and a conscious puritanism in directions unfamiliar to Americans, remained never less than satisfactory, and generally cordial. The long-vexed question of the rates of payment for the transit of oil by way of Tapline across Sa'udi territory (p. 299) was settled, as was the price at which such oil should be reckoned for taxation purposes: in quantity, the total thus dispatched varied annually from 15·2 million tons in 1961 to almost 22 million in 1965. The transfer from company to government of distribution and marketing functions in much of the territory was peacefully completed. In joint operations, of survey or otherwise, there was frequent and cordial co-operation. The interest taken by the King and his Ministers in Company affairs was greater and more enlightened than in former periods. Important help was given in many directions by Aramco to the local and central Governments—and to the public; this could be in the field of potable or non-potable water discovery and production; the fostering of viable agriculture in highly adverse conditions; the provision within the Eastern province of accessible electric power for the public; and, one can add, the construction for the Government of between two and three dozen new schools for Sa'udi children, and payment for their maintenance and operation; the grant of scholarships for the higher university and professional education of Sa'udis; a health service of comprehensive scale and high efficiency; much assistance on practical lines to local industry; and expert guidance in town-planning and soil conservation. Amounts of money distributed to the public in return for local purchases of goods and services (apart from those paid directly to the Treasury, and excluding salaries and wages) reached some $37 million in 1964, and $66 million in 1965. The stimulus thereby given to local enterprise of every kind was immense, and must uplift and diversify the way and standard of life for many thousands of households.

## II. ARAMCO

The six years ending in the late summer of 1966 were for the Arabian American Oil Company a period of great activity and almost unbroken success. As the pages here following will show, new productive structures were discovered, new reserves brought to light, increasing yearly production achieved, and all the operations of processing, transporting, storing, refining, loading, and export of oil were excellently accomplished; and all this in an atmosphere of amity with both the Government and public of the territory.

The physical and domestic environment of the great enterprise was by constant and costly effort made as tolerable as the climate and surroundings, and the strict regulations imposed for socio-religious reasons by the Government, permitted.[1] Every care was taken of the housing and equipment of the Sa'udi staff and labour force in every branch and grade, aided by interest-free loans for house building, by the encouragement of indoor and outdoor sport, provision of TV facilities by the Company's own station, as well as of steadily increased pay-rates, living and family allowances, facilities for saving, and bonuses on suitable occasions. The safety and medical arrangements built up throughout the Company's system were of a high order and by no means confined to company personnel: they included preventive medicine, instruction at various levels, child care, medical treatment, and financial and other assistance to non-Company institutions. In 1965 the average length of service with the Company among Sa'udi employees was fourteen years, a striking figure; Sa'udis were by then found in numbers of highly responsible positions in the fields of geology, engineering, and medicine, drilling, refining, laboratory study, and others.

The immense change represented by this state of affairs as against the conditions of thirty or even twenty years earlier, was due in general to the Company's policy, and in particular to the great educational effort which had gathered force and scale with the years. A higher proportion of Sa'udi and other non-Western employees benefited directly from the Company's Industrial Training Centres, Industrial Training Shops, classes of instruction, professional and managerial training, and many forms of personal development. Training in management techniques as well as in the higher scientific and technological skills was made

[1] Notably, the absolute prohibition of the import or use of alcoholic drinks; an equal prohibition on ministers of the Christian religion; and limitations on freedom of movement outside camps or work-sites. By the end of the period, however, these restrictions on movement, and on the practice of religion, had been relaxed.

available at Beirut and elsewhere in the Middle East, and in the United States.

We pass now to Aramco's operations in the discovery and development of oil in 1960-6.

In the field of exploration for new oil deposits, the least showy but among the most exacting and costly of allied operations, the Company was in full activity. Exploration parties, using one or more of the recognized geophysical methods, were busy most of each year in some area of the dry-land portions of the concession territory, and also in its offshore waters. Communication and supply were maintained by specialized vehicles and by aircraft, including helicopters. Research, with structure drilling when appropriate, was carried out everywhere from the Sa'udi-'Iraqi Neutral Zone to the farthest reaches (unless already relinquished) of the Ruba'al-Khali. All results, in whatever form, were meticulously studied in the Company's laboratories, and also communicated to the Sa'udi Government. A number of deep dry holes were drilled and abandoned: such were Lihaba in the spring of 1963, Niban and Jiham in 1965, and others. Stratigraphic drilling up to 11,000 feet in depth was also practised. The joint survey work undertaken in 1959 with the U.S. Geological Survey was in due course completed.

Apart from the revelation of deeper producing horizons in existing fields—notably at Qatif in 1963—discoveries of new productive structures were made in three places during this period. The first was at abu Sa'fa, in mid-sea twenty-seven miles north-east of Ras Tanura, in June 1963; the second at Barri in 1964, three miles north of the village of Jubail, on the coast south-east of Khursaniya; the third at Zuluf in 1965 in the Gulf some forty miles from shore, east of the southern boundary of the Neutral Zone and fifteen miles north-east of the nearest Safaniya well. Abu Sa'fa, which lay in the marine area now shared with Bahrain (p. 416), was at once prepared by delineation, production-drilling, and necessary connexions and installations, for tying-in to the main productive system in 1966: a task duly completed, with an initial production of 30,000 b/d from six wells, and a 28-mile 18-inch pipeline to Ras Tanura. The Barri field was found by all indications to extend well out to sea and was to be brought into service as soon as practicable.

These discoveries and the further knowledge gained in the

course of production-drilling on known structures, raised the estimates for Sa'udi proved reserves from a figure of 45·6 billion bbl (say, 6,100 million tons) to one of 67·7 billion bbl (say, 8,500 million tons) by the end of 1965. If the single exception of tiny Kuwait be, rather doubtfully, allowed, the vast Sa'udi territory must take at least second place as the greatest oil-repository in the world; and the future was likely to hold considerable, perhaps immense, further discoveries.

From these stores, the annual offtake from Aramco oilfields in the years 1960 through 1965 was one of 56·5, 68·1, 74·5, 79·7, 84·5, and 99·4 million long tons. And production in the first eight months of 1966 exceeded that of the same period of 1965 by 18 per cent. In 1960 the aggregate production since 1939 had exceeded 4 billion bbl; in the course of 1965 it exceeded 7 billion. Such rates of annual increase speak for themselves. Production in 1960 was from six fields of varying productivity (p. 298, footnote);[1] in 1965 it was, with the same proviso, from ten. Production from abu Hadriya (1962), Khurais (1963), Fadhili (1963), and Manifa (1964) had in the meanwhile been added, and already discovered but hitherto untapped areas of Ghawar (southern 'Uthmaniya, Haradh, and Fazran) had been, or were on the point of being, made to contribute; from these another 120,000 b/d could be expected. The contributors in 1965 were, in thousands of b/d, the Ghawar complex (890), Safaniya (472), Abqaiq (409), Khursaniya (129), abu Hadriya (45); smaller quantities came from Qatif (32), Dammam (25), and Fadhili (19), while output from Khurais and (in 1964 only) Manifa was still minimal.

In almost every case the longer-standing fields showed during this period considerable increases in their revealed reserves— notably at Ghawar, Qatif, and Safaniya, but also at Khurais, abu Hadriya, and Manifa. The Qatif field was found to extend seaward, and in 1963–4 a beginning was made at underwater drilling to delineate it; its production would be much increased. In Ghawar and Abqaiq use was made on a very large scale of non-potable water-injection, mostly by gravity, and of natural gas injection, to secure reservoir pressure maintenance. This requirement led, as it must, to a complex of operations of injection-well drilling, and pipeline and gas-compressor construction. At Abqaiq and in the

---

[1] That is, Ghawar (including 'Ain Dar, Shedgum, and 'Uthmaniya), Abqaiq, Dammam, Qatif, Safaniya, and Khursaniya.

'Ain Dar area of Ghawar gaseous by-products of the l.p.g. plant at Abqaiq (which primarily served export needs) were injected into the structures. The l.p.g. compression and manufacturing plant itself was modified and enlarged in these years and represented an important asset.

The field whose output grew fastest—from 241,000 to 472,000 b/d—and was confirmed in its rank as world-leader among off-shore oilfields, was Safaniya. It was aided in this career by the particular value of its relatively heavy crude, being of 27–27·9 degrees A.P.I. as against other Sa'udi crudes with 31–34·9 degrees A.P.I. To this merit, as the present-day demand-pattern in products has made it, was due the rapid development of the field and the trebled pipelines conveying the crude past Khursaniya to Ras Tanura. The giant 42-inch pipeline installed in 1965 released the earlier 30/32-inch line to serve Manifa, which was destined for serious production from 1966 onwards. (Marine drilling at Safaniya was interrupted by the sinking in a storm of the drilling barge *Queen Mary* in December 1960.) It appeared to be established that Safaniya and the A.O.C.'s Neutral Zone field of Khafji formed a single reservoir. The Khursaniya field came into production in October 1960, and by 1965 was producing 130,000 b/d; abu Hadriya, the oil of which after stabilization was destined for Tapline, was in production in and after 1962 and had reached a rate of 50,000 b/d by 1965. Fadhili took its place as a 20,000 b/d producer in 1964: its oil would join that of abu Hadriya to be pumped westward.

In all main fields the increased number of producing wells and/or deepening of existing wells, resulting from an unceasing development-drilling programme, called for increased gathering and forwarding stations, oil-gas separators, stabilizing plant, tankage, and duplicated or triplicated pipelines to the main point of export, Ras Tanura. The main pipeline system, especially on the line Safaniya–Manifa–Khursaniya–Ras Tanura, and Abqaiq–Ras Tanura grew to a formidable capacity by the addition of further 30/34-inch or (in one case) 40/42-inch lines; only Khurais, which after 1963 specialized in supplying a few hundred tons of sweetened crude to a power-station in Riyadh (only ninety miles distant), was unlinked by pipeline.[1] The only main pipelines which failed to

---

[1] Khurais was also, however, destined to be linked to main production, via Abqaiq in 1966.

serve the Ras Tanura export jetties or refinery were those conveying crude to the first of the Tapline stations leading westward,
and those supplying the refinery at Bahrain.

The great refinery at Ras Tanura (p. 300) worked throughout
the period with annual though not impressive increases in throughput. This had been 63·6 million bbl in 1959, having been decreasing year by year since a peak of 80 million in 1954; in 1960,
however, 82·3 million of crude, already degassed and stabilized
*en route* from its producing wells, was processed, and in subsequent
years 1961–5 this became respectively 90·8, 90·8, 97·4, 100·4, and
110·0 million bbl; or, in millions of long tons, 12·1, 12·1, 13·0, 13·4,
and 14·7. The products manufactured included not only gasoline,
asphalt, diesel oil, fuel oil, kerosene, and turbo fuel, but also
aviation gasoline, with a surplus for export, and l.p.g., obtained
from the important plant begun in 1960 (p. 300). This plant, completed in 1961 at its location adjoining the North Pier and seven
miles from the main refinery, had an initial capacity of 3,400 b/d,
but by additions to its insulated tanks, compressors, pumps, etc.,
was increased in 1963–4 to one of 12,000 b/d. Unsaleable naphtha
was in certain years injected for storage into special wells on the
Qatif structure, to be later withdrawn as needed. Steps were taken
to improve the quality of products and the flexibility of the
refinery units, so as to conform to altered market demand; this
applied especially to naphtha and fuel oil.

At the main terminal of Ras Tanura (pp. 299f.), from which both
refined products and crude were shipped and exported, as well
as dispatched by submarine line to Bahrain, capacity was increased
by additional tankage (including that of l.p.g.) and pipelines serving it. An installation for blending crudes to any demanded
specification was erected and later duplicated. A serious fire at the
l.p.g. plant in August 1962 was survived with moderate damage.
The south wing of the North Pier was extended in 1963–4.

The outstanding terminal work undertaken in this period, however, was the construction of the 'sea island'. This was studied in
1963, begun in 1964, and commissioned in 1965. It was located
one mile north-east of the North Pier and was capable of handling
the largest tankers known or planned; it would add some 500,000
b/d to the terminal's capacity. The central barge was towed
from England, modified and equipped at Bahrain, moved to its
final location in eighty-five feet of water, posed upon its own

(retractable) legs, and finally connected to its walkways, dolphins, etc. It was later to be served by four pipelines from the mainland, three for crude and one for bunker fuel. The cost of the Island exceeded $10 million. Two more islands were planned for early construction.

Crude and products at the terminal were loaded into 1,800 ships in 1960, 2,242 in 1962, 2,154 in both 1963 and 1964, and 2,389 in 1965. As elsewhere the tonnage of tankers steadily increased.

Aramco's exports in 1965 went to Europe (43·7 per cent.), Asia (32·8 per cent.), North America (9·7 per cent.), South America (6·0 per cent.), Australia (4·6 per cent.), and Africa (3·2 per cent.). Sales of the Company's products within Sa'udi Arabia amounted to a million tons in 1965; five years earlier the figure was some 600,000 tons. Gasoline was the locally most demanded product, followed by diesel oil and kerosene.

## CHAPTER XXIII

# KUWAIT AND THE NEUTRAL ZONE, 1960–6

## I. GOVERNMENT, PUBLIC, AND K.N.P.C.

THE most striking episode of an otherwise less eventful six years of Kuwaiti history in this period was, beyond doubt, that of the claim in 1961 by General 'Abdul Karim Qasim, military dictator of 'Iraq, to ownership of the whole principality as an integral part of his country. The claim was made a few days after the Amir of Kuwait had thrown off the last traces of dependence on Great Britain, becoming fully sovereign and independent: but he had wisely made, at the same time, a treaty providing for his right to immediate aid from the latter in the event of need. This provision, hastily invoked in face of the imminent 'Iraqi threat, produced a small but sufficient British force to protect him, soon followed by its supersession by some scanty and unco-ordinated detachments from the Arab League. The danger receded, and the subsequent death of Qasim permitted the restoration of normal, indeed cordial, Kuwaiti-'Iraqi relations. The crisis of July 1961 did not materially interrupt oil operations—though it may well have reminded all concerned of the fragility of Arabian Gulf political structures; it probably did something also to encourage realism and some conformity to world opinion in Kuwaiti patriarchal ruling circles. A regretted blow to the latter occurred with the death in November 1965 of the Ruler, H.H. Shaikh 'Abdullah al Salim al Subah. He was succeeded by his younger brother, Shaikh Subah al Salim al Subah.

The principality advanced during these years in international status both by its new membership of the United Nations Organization, of the Arab League, of O.P.E.C. (p. 351), and of the International Monetary Fund and the World Bank and their associated bodies, and also by its cautious advance towards modern-type governmental institutions—a Constitution (1962), an elected National Assembly (1963),[1] a responsible Cabinet, an increasingly specialized administration, and a new sterling-based

[1] The Assembly was elected only by authentic Kuwaiti citizens of at least ten years' standing; these were a minority of the so largely immigrant population.

currency with a Currency Board and Currency Reserve Fund. The well-endowed Kuwait Fund for Arab Economic Development, founded in 1962, made many loans on favourable terms to other Arab States, and its sterling investments in London (and those of its profusely enriched sons in Egypt and Lebanon) were by any standards important.[1] The budgeting and financial control within the State were on approved lines; the estimates for 1966-7 balanced at Kuwait dinars (that is, pounds sterling) 248 million, of which 93·7 per cent. represented oil-revenues.

In spite of the formation of the Kuwait National Petroleum Company in 1960 and its active life, major decisions affecting Kuwait oil rested naturally with the central Government. The latter was aided in this regard by foreign consultants, by a Higher Council for Supervising Oil Affairs (under the Ministry of Finance and Industry), by an Oil Directorate, by its access to O.P.E.C. experts and draft regulations and specific recommendations (the latter, however, being not always accepted by the National Assembly), and by its own Petroleum Law announced as under drafting in 1963.

It would be beyond the scope of this work to inquire in detail how far or how long the administrative reforms of the period—which did not exclude the retention of most of the important posts by the Shaikh's own near relations, his own dominant position, and the probable absence of any effective sharing or democratization of real power in the foreseeable future—could be expected to withstand the aspirations, often unrealistic as these might be, of the Nasirite or Ba'thite or merely ambitious intelligentsia within the principality. The answer, which may be 'Not for long!' or less probably may be 'For ever', must appear in time, and the succession of events will doubtless be aided by those in other territories of the region where socio-political conditions and problems are not dissimilar.

Meanwhile industrial activity, concerted directly with the country's giant oil-wealth, was much and healthily alive. The formation of viable local companies dated back to 1957. Of these, the Kuwait Oil Tanker Company (p. 306) increased its fleet in 1965 by two large units, from Japanese shipyards, and found abundant cargoes for them. The Kuwait Petrochemical Company, founded

---

[1] The capital of the Fund, originally £50 million, was in mid-1966 to be raised by progressive annual allotments to K.D. 200 million.

in 1961 with governmental and public participation, planned to produce saleable hydrocarbon chemicals, and particularly to utilize local natural gas; a major Italian participation in it fell through. It shared, however, as did B.P. and Gulf, in the Kuwait Chemical Fertilizer Company, whose important plant for the production of ammonia, urea, sulphuric acid, and ammonium sulphate was completed in the late summer of 1966. Other similar enterprises were understood to be under study. The Kuwait National Industries Company, with a Government half-interest, proposed a wider range. An Asbestos Manufacturing Company, and a Kuwaiti Insurance Company, are self-explanatory. This is true also of the Kuwait Drilling Company, a public company with a substantial American shareholding; it secured from K.O.C. good drilling contracts within the territory and was prepared to operate abroad also. B.P. (Kuwait) became a partner in a locally operating Aviation Fuelling Company.

The Kuwait National Petroleum Company (K.N.P.C.), one of the most enterprising and competent of the similar and mainly State-financed national corporations in the Middle East, was established in 1960, with a 60 per cent. statal shareholding. It first took over in 1961 all local distribution of petroleum products, which it acquired at cost from K.O.C., and purchased the necessary installations. It ventured abroad by becoming a minor (5 per cent.) shareholder in the new Rhodesian refinery (1962). It planned to undertake the search for oil, alone or with (presumably foreign) partners, in the Kuwaiti territories relinquished in May 1962 by K.O.C.[1] After studies begun in 1963, K.N.P.C. undertook in 1966 (perhaps surprisingly)[2] the construction of a large export refinery located at the Government's Industrial Area[3] adjoining Kuwait city, with a 95,000 b/d capacity. Completion was due in mid-1967.

[1] Some 2,700 square miles (out of a total of 5,800) all on dry land. Further relinquishments, including the islands and some sea-covered area, were expected to be carried out within a few years.

[2] Major refinery construction at a location remote from markets is at variance with present-day usage. There were in Kuwait territory already the 12·5 million t/y K.O.C. refinery at Mina al-Ahmadi, and the Aminoil 5 million t/y plant at Mina 'Abdullah.

[3] This estate represented an important governmental enterprise including a harbour, power plant, supply (from K.O.C.) of natural gas, housing, water distillation, etc. It was the location also of the Fertilizer Company's plant; other enterprises were expected, for which ample local capital existed. An agreement was made by the Government in 1963 whereby it could buy at cost all natural gas available as surplus from Gulf and B.P.

A loan of £25 million would be provided by the Kuwait Treasury for this work. Crude would be provided, in part at least, by the (Japanese) Arabian Oil Company, and in part also, probably, by B.P. and Gulf. K.N.P.C. would require for its refinery the cheapest possible crude, while their Government, for calculating its revenue-share, preferred a crude fictitiously costly.

In exploring and developing the relinquished areas K.N.P.C. was negotiating for the collaboration of a newcomer to the area, the Spanish group Hispanoil,[1] in spite of some xenophobic murmurs by over-exclusive Kuwaitis. K.N.P.C. would take a 51 per cent. interest, and Hispanoil (itself a consortium of Spanish refining concerns[2] and bankers) the rest, in a development partnership in which the Spanish concern would play a part similar to that of the foreign elements joined with N.I.O.C. in Persia. In return for the privilege, the Spaniards guaranteed, for any oil which might be found by the joint company, entry into the Spanish market to the extent of a quarter of the latter's total intake, for fifteen years. This was a novel inducement to be offered to an oil-producing country with concessions to bestow, and one upon which marketers and consumers might well have comments to make. Hispanoil meanwhile was reported to be making similar proposals in 'Iraq and Libya.

## II. K.O.C.

Kuwait Oil Company, the locally operating joint offspring of B.P. Exploration Company (Associated Holdings) and Gulf Kuwait Company, continued on behalf of its parents to handle the production, processing, storage, and loading of crude and products within Kuwait territory; it left to the parent companies or their immediate associates all the tasks of shipping and marketing throughout the world—the latter a business in which the keenness of competition between oil suppliers grew in the period even faster than world demand, and was inevitably a restraining influence on Kuwaiti production. Nevertheless, annual increases of tonnage produced and loaded showed the effective vitality of the concern, and the immensity of Kuwait's resources. The period 1960–6 in Kuwait was one of almost uniform prosperity and progress.

[1] The Cia. Hispanica de Petroleos S.A.
[2] The constituents are C.E.P.E.S.A. (that is I.N.I., the Spanish state corporation, with C.E.P.S.A. and Caltex), Petrol Iba (Marathon, with Spanish interests), and a wholly-owned I.N.I. concern, Calvo Sotelo.

Relations with the Government of the Amirate, which was itself significantly modified (p. 398) in these years, remained generally excellent, even though the attitude of high-placed Kuwaitis, especially after the formation of an active and critical National Assembly, was one of keen advocacy of the State's interests rather than of mere conformity with the Company's, or even O.P.E.C.'s, recommendations. Scarcely one of the other major foreign oil-producing concerns in the Middle East was so fortunate, probably, in its governmental relations as the K.O.C., thanks to mutual confidence and cordiality.

The latter quality extended to the Kuwaiti public of the time, with the exception of limited (and often non-Kuwaiti) 'advanced' political circles. With the rest, at all levels relations were helped by visible signs of the Company's enlightened policies, apart from its basic rôle—now of twenty years' duration—of universal provider. They were helped by its pay-scales and the attractive careers it could offer; by its comprehensive personnel-training systems, at every level up to that of European and American universities; by its constant regard for safety procedures and for housing for every type of employee. Other notable features were its co-operative attitude to the Trade Union formed within its labour-force late in 1964, its constant favouring of Kuwaiti, as distinct from imported—Indian, Pakistani, or Persian—employees, its heavy expenditure on medical services, sports, clubs, and social advantages, its attractive public-relations phenomena of the Display Centre, tours of the installations, and production of films and publications. In the field of commercial relations the policy steadily pursued was that of increasing local purchase and contract-giving to the practicable limit, so that millions of pounds annually were disbursed in Kuwait under these headings. In 1965 some £3·5 million was spent on local purchase, £5 million in contracts, and £8 million in pay and salaries. At the same time surplus natural gas from Burgan was supplied to the Government free of charge (p. 400), and refined products, to an extent of some 320,000 tons in 1965, were sold to K.N.P.C. at cost price (p. 400). The Company was well represented at successive Arab Petroleum Congresses, held in Cairo or elsewhere, as well as at O.P.E.C.

The Company's Managing Director in 1959–62 was still the Hon. W. Fraser, in 1962–5 D. E. L. Steel, and from 1965 K. A. Henshaw. Its senior executives in Kuwait (General Manager in the earlier years of this period, and Joint Managing Director in the later ones) were L. T. Jordan from 1948 to October 1961, followed by E. Boaden till April 1962, H. L. Scott till August 1966, and then J. E. Lee.

Development drilling within the Amirate continued during the whole of our present period. At the end of 1961, 378 producing wells had been completed and connected;[1] by the end of 1965 the corresponding figure was 487.[2] The difference represented years of steady drilling, carried out latterly by contract save in exceptional cases, and in some cases by rapid-drilling techniques which were perfected during the period. One, two, or three rigs were in regular use for development-drilling, a number of the wells being sited not only for production but also for purposes of appraisal of the reservoir concerned and of defining its limits. During the process, the potential of already discovered fields was confirmed, or indeed notably reassessed upwards; Minagish, discovered in 1959, was proved as an excellent producing field; Umm Gudair was not only discovered but developed with four producing and four non-producing wells. In other fields, whose combined production though more than respectable anywhere but in Kuwait still did not equal half that of Burgan, oil was discovered in new or deeper horizons. A few wells drilled for production were used for gas injection, others were sited for oil-water level observation. A number of wells were drilled deep for exploratory purposes, but later completed as producers at a shallower level.

Oilfield development included the provision, or where already provided the improvement or extension, of gathering, gas-separating, and forwarding stations, pipelines, pumping installations, and tankage. It included the regular working-over of producing wells, a close watch on pressures and levels by the scientists of the petroleum-engineering branch, the laboratory analysis of crudes, and the application of plans for more perfect recovery by gas injection, fracturing, acid treatment, etc., and overall reservoir study and control. Gas injection was used on an important scale at Burgan and steps were taken in 1965 to erect similar plant at Raudhatain and Minagish.

[1] 268 in Burgan, 44 in Magwa, 35 in Ahmadi, 25 in Raudhatain, 4 in Minagish, and 1 each in Sabriya and Bahra.

[2] 320 at Burgan, 60 at Magwa, 42 at Ahmadi, 34 at Raudhatain, 13 at Minagish (one being in latterly relinquished territory), 14 at Sabriya, 1 (unused) at Bahra, 4 at Umm Gudair.

The production of crude oil in Kuwait, predominantly of 31–31·9 degrees A.P.I., rose rapidly between 1960 and the end of 1965, and it showed in 1966, in spite of north-African and other intrusive competition, every sign of continuing the same trend. The production figure (in long tons) had been 0·79 million in 1946, 17 million in 1950, and 53·9 million in 1955; in 1960 it was 80·5 million, and in the next five years successively 81·4, 90·7, 95·7, 105·0, and 107·3 million. A total offtake of 4,000 million barrels produced since 1946 was reached and exceeded in the course of 1961, and one of 1,000 million tons in 1965. In 1965, for the first time, a single year's production exceeded 100 million tons; output doubled in the ten years ending in 1965, and the forty-thousandth cargo of oil sailed from Mina al-Ahmadi during the latter year, while in 1966 occurred the twentieth anniversary of the first shipment.

Even so, it was felt that the future must be safeguarded, and higher-quality oil, if it existed, must be brought to light. Exploration, therefore, outside the established fields, continued without interruption while current production went on. It took the normal forms of geophysical survey, shallow or deeper pool-tests, and the drilling of wildcat wells. The first of these, handled in part by expert contractors, covered not only inland areas but also the islands of Bubiyan and Failaka and the submerged acreage in Kuwait Bay. In 1960–1 three structure holes were drilled at Mityaha, in the south-west of the territory, without favourable result, and a second well was sunk at Mutriba, in the north-west. In 1962, after the decision had been reached to drill offshore near Kuwait City, an artificial island in the bay was constructed to carry the drill. More test-wells were drilled in the Dibdiba and Mityaha area, and in that of Mutriba. In 1963, during which the relinquishment of part of the concessionary territory (p. 400) was arranged, work in West Kuwait was abandoned, but further studies were made of the marine area and the islands. The Mutriba well was abandoned, but at Umm Gudair (p. 304) in the extreme south, oil was located, as has been already noted (p. 403), and the field was placed under development. At Khashman, south-west of Kuwait City, a test-well was begun but suspended. The offshore well drilled from the artificial island was followed by two more, but no commercial discovery resulted; the same was true of wells on Failaka and Bubiyan Islands. More tests in the Bahra area were equally unrewarded. During 1964 wildcat wells were drilled at

Liyah, due west of Bahra, and at Jirfan in the extreme north, and yet another on the south-west fringe of the Burgan field. These were all unproductive. Deep pool-tests were drilled to various horizons at Sabriya and Raudhatain, and shallower tests made at Minagish, Umm Gudair, Ahmadi, and Raudhatain. In 1965 further seismic studies were made in the south of the Amirate, on a line Burgan–Minagish. A wildcat at Mutla (west of the western end of the Kuwait Bay) was abandoned. Mutriba was further tested, to be abandoned, however, early in 1966. A well was spudded in at Dahr and was still under drilling in 1966.

The Company's activity directed to the discovery of new fields and appraisal of prospects and indications was thus continuous and costly—and intermittently rewarded.

Of the oil produced year by year by the Company, by far the greater quantity was exported as crude. Nevertheless K.O.C.'s local refinery dealt—mainly of course for bunkering and export—with quantities varying from 177,000 b/d (8·8 million t/y) to 220,000 b/d (11 million t/y), of which in 1965 some 3·6 million tons were used for bunkering. The refinery at Mina al-Ahmadi (pp. 306–7) was throughout the period a scene of great activity, with modifications and enlargements of capacity which always, as was intended, kept ahead of demand. It could, in and after 1961, produce the aviation gasoline for which the important international airport then called, and from 1963 increased quantities also of aviation turbine kerosene. It satisfied all demands for bitumen, widely used on the roads of the Amirate. It maintained, by its Platformer, the needed supply of high-octane blending component. The overall potential of the refinery was raised, by alterations in 1962–3 to two out of the three distillation units, from a level of 180,000 to one of 250,000 b/d, or 12·5 million t/y, though the highest output in any year was in fact 220,000 b/d in 1965. Tankage for every type of product was progressively increased. Laboratory work was extended in new premises. An important feature was the growth of demand for and production of liquid petroleum gas, of which the initial stages dated back to 1957–60 (p. 307). The first ocean shipment of this product was made in 1962. Increased accommodation was provided for it in 1962–4 in the form of added condensation, fractionation, and refrigeration plant, and tankage for the liquefied butane or propane; compression units for tank-gas recovery at gathering-centres in the Burgan field and at Magwa were multiplied. L.p.g. was regularly exported in its specially constructed tank-ships to Japan.

The export of crude and reconstituted crude continued to occupy the South and North Piers at Mina al-Ahmadi (pp. 305–6).[1] These giant structures were kept in operation by periodical re-decking, improvements in equipment, and endless repainting. Quantities of oil loaded, handled at increasing speeds and taking fewer and fewer hours for the turn-round, increased from 76 million tons in 1960 (excluding bunkers), to 102·9 million in 1965. The even course of these processes was marred only by a single but serious fire, aboard a tanker at the North Pier in September 1964. It was noteworthy that, against the striking rise in tonnage loaded, the number of tankers employed actually diminished during the period, from 2,766 in 1960 to 2,568 in 1965; average cargoes in the former year were of 27,500 tons (and had been 15,000 in 1955), and 41,900 tons in 1965. This increase in tanker capacity was significant as well as economical, and the future trend was indicated by the eighty-five shipments of over 75,000 tons each in 1964, and thirty-one of over 100,000 each in 1965. Products used locally for bunkering averaged some 3·5 million tons per year.

The destinations of shipments from Kuwait, crude and refined —but 90 per cent. or more the former—while they varied under diverse market and alternative-supply pressures, showed a general overall continuity. In 1961, for example, the main recipients were, in this order: Great Britain, Japan, Italy, France, U.S.A., Holland, Aden, and nine others who took less than 2 million tons each; in 1965 the recipients of a much increased total were in order: Italy, Japan, Great Britain, France, Holland, U.S.A., Australia, Aden, Belgium, Sardinia, West Germany, Singapore, and a dozen more with amounts of less than 1·5 million tons each. The first five of those listed took in 1965 respectively 23·9, 17·2, 14·1, 8·1, and 5·4 million tons; and even these considerable amounts would certainly have been exceeded but for North African supplies.

A product of Kuwait's oilfields less easy to indicate in figures, but the subject of anxious company and Government consideration, was the natural gas produced necessarily and concurrently with the oil—a product of high value whenever it can make contact, as

---

[1] 'Reconstituted' implies a blend of crude with any of the following: butane, natural gasoline, light distillates, gas oil, or fuel oils. These formed a 'blended cargo', to suit the needs of buyers.

in industrial areas, with a market. In Kuwait the problem of gas-disposal was in these years solved to an extent of perhaps 75 per cent. Gas was used on a large scale for pressure-maintenance by way of reinjection into structures; by serving as fuel in oilfield and refinery processes, where this was feasible; in water distillation and electric-power generation; in the production of l.p.g.; by cheap supply to the Government for its Industrial Area at Shaiba, and for the purposes of the Chemical Fertilizer Company (p. 400).

### III. SHELL IN THE KUWAITI SEAS

The grant in January 1961 by the Ruler of Kuwait to a company of the Royal Dutch Shell group, for a forty-five-year term, of rights for the exploration and production of oil over some 1,500 square miles[1] of sea-covered territory[2] off his coasts (that is, six miles and upwards removed from them), created much interest in international oil and other circles. The terms of the concessions were severe and unusual, and the implicit partnership of a Middle Eastern host government with a vast international company such as Shell was a striking feature. (The Iranian agreements with E.N.I. and Pan American (pp. 298 f.), and that of Kuwait with the Japanese (p. 310) were smaller-scale precedents.) The initial bonus payable was £7 million, and subsequent bonus and dead rent payments due on specified occasions totalled £23 million more. The Ruler could choose, after the discovery of oil, to exercise an option to acquire 'at cost' (that is, presumably, by paying his share of all oil-finding expenses up to then) a 20 per cent. share in the local Shell Company to be formed to operate the concession, and could claim 20 per cent. of all oil produced. Otherwise Shell would handle (as it was abundantly qualified to do) all oil produced, unless and until Kuwait had its own commercial facilities for this. Co-operation between Shell and the Government in the fields of oil transportation and other branches was envisaged, perhaps including refining. Acceptance of these provisions appeared justified by the quite exceptional promise of the territory covered, surrounded as it was on north, west, and south by great oilfields already in production.

[1] The area of the concession was defined by co-ordinates given in the concession, but the practical application of these gave rise to difficulties with Iran and Sa'udi Arabia.

[2] Including reefs and small islands but excluding the islands of Warba, Bubiyan, Failaka, Mashjan, Auha, and Kubr.

To operate the concession Shell formed the Kuwait Shell Petroleum Development Company, opened a local office and base depot, conducted a marine seismic survey, and by the early spring of 1962 was ready for under-water drilling. The history of the enterprise thereafter was to be one of unrelieved disappointment.

In March 1962 the first test-well, Riqah no. 1, was spudded in eleven miles south of Failaka Island. In the course of drilling throughout the summer, traces of gas and of light oil were encountered. A drilling vessel, *Nola III*, was used by arrangement with operating contractors. The well was taken, in spite of drilling complications, to a depth of 12,250 feet, then temporarily abandoned. A second test-well, Hamur no. 1, was then spudded in, from the drilling barge *Panimoil 2*, chartered from Pan American; the location was seventeen miles east of Riqah no. 1. Intercommunication was arranged by helicopter, and special arrangements were made for a resident meteorologist to forecast possible hazards of the weather. The well reached a depth of 14,600 feet, but proved dry and was abandoned. The third and so far the last attempt was made at Zubaidi in 1963 in the southernmost waters of the concession, but a depth of 13,350 feet was reached without meeting commercially interesting signs of oil. The hole was abandoned. Riqah no. 1 was then deepened to 13,620 feet, without significant result.

At this stage Kuwait Shell's marine operations were discontinued in order to enable a comprehensive study and reassessment of the area to be made while awaiting the settlement of mid-sea boundary problems which were now created by Iranian and Sa'udi claims. In 1964–6 the concession and its operations were thus in a state of suspended animation. Rarely had acreage of such superlative promise—and such cost—proved so frustrating. In July 1966 it was announced that meetings of Persian, Sa'udi, and Kuwaiti representatives, ending with a conference at Copenhagen, had failed so far to resolve their difficulties. Further talks were to be held.

### IV. THE NEUTRAL ZONE

Oil operations in this curiously-constituted political unit (if such it is) continued with vigour throughout this period, by land and sea; a slight drop in production, however, in 1965 in the mainland field was not compensated by an increase from the mid-sea Khafji field—where rather higher hopes had been entertained—and the Neutral Zone as a whole showed a slight production drop of 2·5 per cent. as against 1964—a rare phenomenon in the Middle East. Gross combined production for the Zone in 1960-6 amounted to 7·2, 9·4, 12·5, 16·4, 19·2, and 18·8 million long tons.[1]

The two all-American Companies—that of Getty Oil being effectively a one-man enterprise, while Aminoil was an *ad hoc* consortium[2]—operating in the dry-land-*cum*-territorial-waters part of the Zone (pp. 214–16 and 308–10), continued profitably their combined but non-united activity throughout 1960–6 in spite of a slight decline in production. The steady exploitation of the Wafra field, without untoward incident, gave the two concessionaires each a half of a production amounting in and after 1960, in successive years, to 7·25, 7·5, 7·45, 9·4, 8·8, and 8·4 million tons. For the handling and export of this each company made its own arrangements at one or other of the two terminals (p. 309).

The Wafra reservoir was in the course of these years almost completely explored, its limits and limitations established. The development drilling leading to this result was on a scale represented by sixty-six producing wells (with seven more dry) in 1960, ninety-six in 1961, and ninety-three in 1962. Survey and wildcat drilling elsewhere in the Zone was active at the same time, with one deep and three exploration wells in 1960 and seven in 1961, while geophysical (seismic) survey covered most of the territory, and in 1962 its territorial waters also. Little success rewarded all these efforts until 1962, when a relatively important-seeming discovery was made a dozen miles south of Wafra, at so-called South Fuwaris. This structure, with further completed wells, came into production in mid-1964, by way of a pipeline connexion of 20,000 b/d capacity to Wafra. The Fuwaris oil was markedly lighter than that of any horizon in Wafra,[3] but production in subsequent years was disappointing; the wells did not sustain their promise.

---

[1] These figures are given by different reporting authorities with slight variations.

[2] Shareholders in 1965 were reported as Phillips Petroleum 37·34 per cent., Signal Oil and Gas 33·58 per cent., Ashland Oil 14·13 per cent., J. S. Abercrombie 7·07 per cent., and others 7·88 per cent.

[3] The Burgan and the Ratawi horizons in the Wafra field gave oil of 23·5 to 24·4 degrees A.P.I., the three Eocene horizons 16·5 to 17·5 degrees A.P.I. Production at Fuwaris, also from the Ratawi horizon, was of 33 degrees A.P.I.

In all, some 410 wells, of which nearly four-fifths were actual or potential though small-scale producers, were drilled in the Neutral Zone between 1949 and 1965. More than half of these were on pump by the end of the period; the remainder flowed.[1] It appeared more or less unlikely in the early months of 1966 that any substantial increase of production from the mainland of the Neutral Zone could be expected; it had by the end of 1965 produced a total of some 75 million tons since 1954.

The smaller of the two dependent refineries, that of the Getty Company at Mina Sa'ud within the Zone, was in 1964–5 substantially modernized to produce more varied products, including aviation gasoline: its throughput in 1964 was 9·6 million bbl. That of Aminoil, at Mina 'Abdullah in Kuwait territory, was in 1961–2 extended from a capacity of 2 million t/y to one of 5 million. A number of technical refinements were introduced, and additional pipeline, storage, and loading facilities were installed.

An administrative change made in the period mattered little to the two Companies. The governmental administration—of an almost uninhabited territory!—was by agreement between the two sovereigns altered in 1965 from one of undivided vagueness to one of clear bisection with one-power control in each of two halves; but the exploitation of mineral resources was to be unaffected by the change. The financial basis of Aminoil's concession was amended in 1961 so as to provide for tax-payment by the Company, after 1 January, at a rate of 57 per cent. of net profits calculated on actually realized prices, *or* of 50 per cent. based on posted prices, whichever should be the greater. This arrangement was to be retroactive also for the period 1955–60.

The Japanese-owned enterprise of the Arabian Oil Company, operating in the Neutral Zone Continental Shelf waters (pp. 311–12), generally confirmed the promise shown in the early months of 1960. The Company's fourth well in the Khafji field, a mile from the discovery well and on the same structure, gave at midsummer 1960 a potential of 6,000 b/d of similar sour crude of 26 degrees A.P.I.; and this was followed by the drilling of another eight wells in 1960, and fifteen more in 1961. These were drilled by American-Dutch and American-Lebanese contractors from one fixed and one

---

[1] In December 1965, in the Wafra field, there were 25 flowing and 19 pumping wells in the Burgan sands, 25 and 12 respectively in the Ratawi, and 57 and 210 in the Eocene. In the Fuwaris field there were 2 flowing and 5 pumping.

mobile drilling-platform. Late in 1961 the first dual-horizon well, no. 3, was brought in from two levels in the Bahrain sands. Further dual producers were completed in 1962, with yields upwards of 11,000 b/d. All the wells drilled, with rare exceptions, were or could be producers from an average depth of 5,000 feet; many were initially shut in, pending extended export facilities. Temporary equipment designed for the immediate storage, loading, and exporting of oil was quickly brought to the spot. The first shipment was made in April 1961, in which year a total of 1·25 million tons from the structure (which was early recognized as forming an extension of, or a single field with, the Safaniya field in Sa'udi Arabia) was dispatched to Japan.

Rapid all-round development continued, including not only outside surveys and development-drilling in Khafji field but also the construction of a land operational base and a comprehensive system of permanent export facilities—even though the period corresponded unhappily with a period of acute financial embarrassment in the Company itself. Both the host Governments, Kuwaiti and Sa'udi, hastened to take up the 10 per cent. shareholding provided in their concessions. Mutual goodwill was shown in the establishment, for bunkering and the sale of marine diesel oil, of a Japan Petroleum Trading Company, with 51 per cent. of its capital subscribed by the Kuwaiti public. The difficulty of breaking into the Japanese market (none other, except a small outlet to Italy, being available) proved persistent, and could not but limit the scale of production; indeed Arabian Oil found it wise to take shares itself in a number of refinery enterprises in Japan. Meanwhile, the Sa'udi Government insisted upon a modification of their 1957 agreement so as to conform with that of Kuwait (of 1958) as being slightly more favourable to the State; and both Governments reminded the Company of the obligation to build a refinery as soon as production could be maintained at 60,000 b/d or more for three months, a condition duly reached before the end of 1962. In fact a small 30,000 b/d plant at Khafji, designed mainly for bunkering, was envisaged, and work was put in hand in the middle months of 1965.

The continuous programme of well completion, maintained at a rate of more than a dozen wells a year, with remarkably homogeneous qualities, was kept up from 1962 through 1965. Production was mainly from the Bahrain sands, with lesser output from the slightly deeper Ratawi horizon and later, in 1964, from a shallower Middle Cretaceous level. A total of forty completed wells was available by the end of 1963, fifty by 1964, and fifty-four by 1965, almost all producers from one or two horizons except for the half-dozen observation wells.[1] Depths ranged from 4,500 to 7,550 feet. Production amounted to 3·5 million tons in 1962, 7·9 in 1963, 9·2 in 1964, and 9·5 million in 1965, the potential of the Khafji field being, however, well in excess of these qualities. The oil as produced belonged in respect of 10 per cent. each to the Sa'udi and Kuwaiti states, 80 per cent. to the Japanese operator. The export of almost the entirety of the oil was carried out, after mid-1962, by the now completed permanent facilities begun a year earlier at Khafji terminal on the mainland. These had cost some $70 million, and included twenty-five miles of submarine crude-oil line of 26-inch diameter, four flow stations of 75,000 b/d capacity each, a gathering-station and pump platform, a loading dock three miles offshore able to handle 100,000-ton tankers, storage tanks of some two million bbl capacity, a power plant, a fresh-water distillation plant, and much more. These works, with their throughput capacity of some 210,000 b/d, were all completed by June 1962. The temporary loading facilities were then dismantled, the stationary tankers dispatched elsewhere, and work on the permanent offices and domestic 'camp' was begun; this included all base buildings, a 400-foot causeway, and piers for small craft. The first loading from the offshore tanker-dock was carried out on 18 July 1962. A disastrous fire occurred at the loading dock in August 1965, reducing exports for that month; the tanker and much of A.O.C.'s loading platform were destroyed, but emergency offshore loading arrangements were rapidly improvised. In November 1965 these arrangements were extended.

The Khafji field, by this time one of already seven offshore producing fields in the Arabian Gulf, was now established, and important from many angles. The possibility existed, moreover, of other discoveries in adjacent waters within the Japanese concession. A first mid-sea wildcat was drilled some twelve miles offshore of Khor al-Mufatta in 1962. It proved dry, and no better fortune attended two more wildcats drilled in 1963: Zaur no. 1 was dry, and Hout no. 1, some thirty miles north of the Khafji

---

[1] At the end of 1965, A.O.C. had 48 producers, 2 standing wells, and 4 observation wells.

field, encountered fierce gas pressure and some light 35 degrees A.P.I. oil at 8,800 feet. Both the Hout discovery and the newly appreciated Ratawi horizon at Khafji seemed to be of significance, though Hout remained in fact shut in for the next two years.

The Japanese Company's marketing difficulties appeared to be lightened when in 1964 the important American independent, Cities Service, was willing to take 16¼ per cent. of Arabian Oil's output, for a 17½ year term, at cost price plus a small sum (possibly 10 cents) per barrel, in return for payment of an appropriate share of the Company's past and future expenditures. Difficulties were encountered from both Japanese and Sa'udi quarters but, after nearly two years of negotiation and delay, agreement was reached—subject to final ratification in Tokyo and Kuwait—in the spring of 1966, to an arrangement involving both Cities Service and Continental Oil. These Companies were to take 20 per cent. each of and from the Kuwait share of Arabian Oil's production, on payment as indicated above, an arrangement which would provide some 30,000 b/d to each of the purchasing Companies. If new fields were discovered within the concession area, the 17½-year period would run, in respect of each, from the date of such discovery.

Completion of the K.N.P.C.'s refinery at Shu'aiba was likely also to provide a market for Arabian Oil crude.

## CHAPTER XXIV

# EASTERN AND SOUTHERN ARABIA,
## 1960-6

I N this area of very small and politically and militarily powerless
dynastic units, even though in the case of Bahrain rich, and in
those of Qatar and abu Dhabi rich to excess, neither social nor
political progress was or could be rapid in our present period.
Socially, as a result of the intrusion of modern industry in all its
aspects, and of consequent sophistication which many would call
corruption, the old semi-static Islamic ways of life were increasingly threatened or eroded, with little satisfying substitute in sight;
politically, the incongruity, so striking as to make a comfortable
symbiosis impossible, between these oases of hitherto self-
sufficient but impoverished mediaevalism and the requirements
and dangers of twentieth-century international life, rendered their
permanence difficult to visualize, yet failed to provide any acceptable plan for their disposal. To most aspects of modernization,
other than those purely material, the rulers were almost without
exception totally opposed. They dreaded absorption into the
domains of a stronger neighbour—Sa'udi Arabia, Persia, or Egypt;
they refused to federate, accepted with reluctance the conception
even of pooled or shared public services, desired to keep their
money, if any, strictly to themselves, and seemed indifferent to the
embarrassing problems they were presenting to the *de facto* paramount power in the area, Her Majesty's Government; the latter,
inheriting from the nineteenth century a score of expressed or
implied obligations for the external defence of the shaikhdoms
(though none for their internal government), would most gladly
have been rid of them, provided that itself was not replaced by
an acquisitive Power disliked by the statelets themselves and
hostile to the West. In fact, an uneasy and unsatisfactory *status quo*
was maintained, strongly criticized as 'imperialist' by Arab
nationalists everywhere, and notably by the small but ever-growing
local intelligentsia. The dream of the latter was, most naturally,
of some sort of 'independence' which would exclude all foreign
interference and all patriarchal or shaikhly privilege, but would
include power, position, and progress for themselves.

These problems, half forgotten in some years and some territories but all too visible in others, differed slightly from one shaikhdom or sultanate to another. No solution appeared during our present period; but they offered, on the whole, an unhappy and unconfident background for the development of a great modern industry with sufficient problems of its own.

### I. BAHRAIN

During the six years following midsummer 1960 the oil history of Bahrain Island—still an independent Arab principality, still persistently claimed by Iran—was uneventful. Its features were the quiet continuance of crude production from the single field of 'Awali; the vain search by land and sea for other structures within Bapco's concession area; and the operation of the highly important refinery on the Island (dating from 1937) for the treatment of both Bahraini and Sa'udi crude (pp. 219, 313). In the government of the Island when Shaikh 'Isa succeeded his father Shaikh Salman al-Khalifa in 1961, the strictly patriarchal form was maintained, while modern public services and amenities continued to develop. Oil revenues, according to the Island's 1965-6 budget, were to be responsible for over 70 per cent. of the State's total receipts: that is, for £4·4 million out of £6·2 million.

Annual oil-production from the mid-island field did not vary sensationally from former levels. It has risen in 1953-60 from 1·5 million t/y of 33 degrees A.P.I. crude to 2·25 million; in 1960-3 inclusive it was unchanged; in 1964 it was 2·4 and in 1965 2·8 million tons. This persistent increase was due to further development-drilling at rates of six to eight completed wells per year, an improved pattern of withdrawal, more gas injection, and increased pumping. Late in 1965 a rate of 60,000 b/d was reached, giving promise of record production in 1966. Every well, be it a single, dual, or treble-zone producer, was the subject of careful maintenance and servicing, the reservoir being constantly studied and possible extensions explored. The total of completed wells, including some twenty finally abandoned, rose from 190 in 1960 to 223 in 1964 and 229 (including 35 shut-in) in 1965. The latter figure included a great majority (186) of oil producers, five gas producers, a dozen 'standing' or under servicing, and half a dozen gas-injection wells. By the end of 1965 a total of 45 million tons had been withdrawn from the 'Awali structure, the remaining accessible reserves in which were reckoned at 35 million tons. Off the structure a comprehensive stratigraphic survey was carried out in 1961–2, both seismic and gravity surveys were completed in hopeful or not-hopeless areas, and shallow structure drilling was conducted to locate possible faults which could accommodate reservoirs. But results were everywhere negative. Full-scale exploratory wells, which proved dry, were drilled in 1960–1 from a platform at the Fasht al-Jarim reefs, fourteen miles north of Manama, and in 1961–2 on Hawar Island close to the coast of Qatar (p. 218). In 1964–5 further geological work was carried out, and four structure-holes were bored in Buri area; in 1965 a well, Salt Marsh no. 1, was drilled on the west flank of the Island, and by 1966 the conviction was not far off that Bahrain had revealed, more than thirty years earlier, its only secret. Meanwhile, however, the Island's government would gain something considerable from the expected production of Aramco's abu Sa'fa field, which was discovered in 1964 in the sea area which had been determined in 1958 as one of equally shared Sa'udi-Bahraini interest. Abu Sa'fa was expected to yield 30,000 b/d. Bapco's proved reserves were of the order of 33 million tons.

The great refinery (p. 313) was in this period the subject of minor enlargement, of further improvement in many technical respects, and of modifications to suit changing market requirements: for instance, in increased output of asphalt, improved drum-making plant, laboratory refinements, and added tankage. The quantity of crude run to stills in 1960 was 76 million bbl, of which 58·5 million were of Sa'udi origin; in 1965 it was 71·7 million bbl, 48·9 million being Sa'udi. Crude exported from Bahrain as such was insignificant: exported cargoes were almost entirely of refined products—gasoline, naphtha, kerosene, aviation turbine fuel, power kerosene, diesel and fuel oil, and asphalt. Considerable improvements and modernizations were carried out at the Sitra loading terminal. A two-berth 'island wharf' was completed in 1960–1, designed to take tankers of up to 45,000 tons draught. This was followed by rehabilitation of the main T-head wharf, with its four berths. The deep-water channel leading into Sitra was in regular use. A new small-craft wharf was completed in 1962 and work on the loading manifold and sea-lines was carried out in 1963–4.

Bapco, as an exemplary employer, continued its policy of providing a full and beneficent range of advantages and amenities for its employees: impeccable fire and safety services, full medical care, a new club, adult education, and comprehensive technical training and apprenticeships to enable Bahrainis to achieve ever more responsible positions.[1] The policy of obtaining a maximum range of goods and services from the Island itself was pursued, and important contracts were allocated locally. The consumption of petroleum products on the Island rose year by year.

A new element entered the world of Bahrain oil in the summer of 1965 with the granting to Continental Oil of a forty-five-year concession for 2,500 square kilometres (relinquished by Bapco) of its offshore territory north-east of the Island, adjoining the area already granted to that company by the Qatar authorities. The terms of Continental's grant resembled those agreed in the Iranian offshore grants. The Company proceeded at once to a campaign of seismic survey.

## II. QATAR

The Qatar peninsula and shaikhdom continued during 1960-6 to be, or was increasingly, a highly fortunate oil territory with the steady exploitation of its Dukhan field and the discovery and development also of valuable sea-bed resources.

The State itself developed from a purely personal autocracy to a somewhat more evolved and specialized administration, with an (Egyptian) Chief Minister, a (Palestinian) Director of Oil, and other State officials. Shaikh Ahmad succeeded his father, Shaikh 'Ali bin 'Abdullah al Thani, who abdicated in October 1960. Public security and satisfactory labour relations were maintained. The spending of the country's sudden and almost overwhelming riches continued to be on the whole for the material benefit of its public (p. 314). Towards this goal the operating Company, Qatar Petroleum, was able to help substantially by its highly organized educational and technical training programmes, its assistance to

---

[1] Progress in the number and scope of these promotions of newly trained Bahrainis was very marked by 1966. In the Company's employees as a whole Bahrainis in 1965 represented almost 80 per cent. of the total, with United Kingdom citizens providing 9·3, the British Commonwealth 6·8, Gulf Arabs and others 4, and Americans 0·3 per cent. The Senior Local Executive of Bapco in the first half of this period was H. H. Arnold, in the second half, R. L. Lay.

the Government in road and harbour building, medical organization, the supply of natural gas to State enterprises of power production and water distillation, and collaboration with the State's officials in the field of industrial relations. Qatar's direct revenues derived from Q.P.C. varied in the period 1961–5 from £19·5 million to £23 million per year. The Agreements between the Company and the Shaikh remained unmodified, with the important reservation that in December 1961 the Company relinquished one-third (or 1,737 square miles) of its total concession area of some 4,200 square miles, and a further 1,237 square miles in mid-1963, thus keeping only one-quarter of the original area. In August 1965 yet another 1,104 square miles was given up, nothing but the Dukhan structure—an area of some fifty by eight miles—being retained. The relinquished lands, offered by the Government to other bidders on unspecified terms, were in 1963 taken up by the Continental Oil Company, which assumed the local identity and name of Continental Oil of Qatar (p. 417); its scope of operation was extended by the further grant to it of the marine areas relinquished by Shell of Qatar.

The efforts of Q.P.C. to locate a second oilfield to supplement Dukhan were still, and by now finally, unavailing. Outside drilling, following geophysical examination, was carried out at Fuwairat (p. 315), which in 1960–1 was abandoned at 7,000 feet; at Busaiyir in the centre of the peninsula in 1961–2, to be abandoned as dry at 6,220 feet; and at Musaimir, twelve miles north of Umm Sa'id, in 1963–4, abandoned at over 12,000 feet. In 1966, moreover, it seemed improbable that the existing sole structure, that of Dukhan, could do more than maintain for some years its present scale of production. The offtake from the field was, year by year from 1960 to 1965 (in millions of tons) 8·08, 8·25, 8·67, 8·95, 8·80, and 9. The figures for Q.P.C. crude exported from the territory were, in the absence of any but minimal local use, only marginally less than these totals. By far the greatest part of Qatar production derived from the no. 4 Limestone horizon. By the end of 1965 forty-four producing wells, all flowing, were available, and twenty-one shut-in wells.

Of the routine operation of the field, its collecting stations, pipeline system, topping plant, storage and loading facilities, nothing of substance need be added to previous pages (314–17). A miscible gas injection scheme, to maintain pressure, was completed in March 1964, and after some initial difficulties was brought into operation. The total cessation of outside drilling and geo-physical work led, especially in 1964, to a substantial reduction of the labour force as well as of plant and buildings in use; total employed personnel dropped steadily from 3,460 in 1960 to 1,470 in 1964 and 1,499 in 1965.[1] Nevertheless Q.P.C. remained a vigorous and persistent enterprise—and the supreme benefactor, in material terms, of this desolate and resourceless territory. That such enterprises and that of the transport of oil by sea were not without their physical risks was grievously recalled in mid-August 1966 by a serious (and mysterious) engine-room explosion and fire on board a British-owned tanker off Doha; it cost nineteen lives and left many injured, and the vessel was totally destroyed.

The I.P.C. Group's Chief Representative and General Manager in Qatar in this period was G. J. R. Tod until March 1962, and thereafter W. J. S. D. Cole.

The operations of the Shell Company of Qatar[2] in their 10,000-square-mile sea-bed area of the Qatar shaikhdom were, as we have already seen (pp. 316-17), still of uncertain issue in 1960. The second of the first three wells—Id al-Sharqi nos. 1 and 2, and a wild-cat at Hadat Shabib—had shown the presence of oil in some quantity and in more than one horizon, but on a doubtfully commercial scale. In early 1961 Id al-Sharqi no. 3, fifty miles north-east of Doha, showed some oil but the information derivable from it was inconclusive. No. 4 proved dry. Further drilling, however, gave promising results which were synchronized with exhaustive tests, and for these the necessary mid-sea facilities were installed while the drilling of the Id al-Sharqi structure proceeded. At the same time exploratory drilling, but with results wholly negative, was pursued in the 'North Qatar Marine area'; here six wells were drilled, of which the designations and depths need not here be recorded. The failure of all these led to the relinquishment of that part of the concession area.

By the end of 1962 more than £16 million had already been spent in the concession, but by this time close examination of the

[1] Of the 1965 total, 961 were Qataris, the remainder being nationals of other Arab countries, with some Indians and Pakistanis and a few Europeans and Americans.

[2] The General Manager from October 1959 to July 1964 was M. W. Godfrey, and thereafter A. O. Twigg till January 1965, next R. A. B. Clough till September 1966, next A. O. Twigg from September 1966.

Id al-Sharqi structure had shown hopeful or good results. Another half-dozen wells were completed, including producers of some 7–8,000 b/d, and the field was at last accepted as commercially exploitable. The crude flowed at this stage, in and after 1964, into a moored tanker, to be trans-shipped thence at sea to export vessels; loading was by way of a single-point mooring buoy, no shore base being used. Shell's export thus achieved amounted to 1·5 million tons in 1964, and 1·8 million in 1965.

Exploration and test-drilling outside the Id al-Sharqi field continued, and, while four more dry holes were completed, an accumulation of commercial value was located in 1963 at Maidan Mazham, twelve miles north-east of the former field and in deeper water. Development drilling there proceeded continuously, with the aid later of a second floating drilling vessel which had been brought early in 1965 from Shell's Borneo fields. The Maidan Mazham field appeared indeed at one time to have a greater potential than that of Id al-Sharqi, with wells flowing at 10–15,000 b/d. (Two exploratory wells in the area north of Halul proved dry and were abandoned.) The Company reached the decision to install permanent facilities for the combined fields, at a probable cost of some £8 million, with the intention of assuring an initial offtake of around 150,000 b/d, or 7·5 million t/y. A terminal was completed early in 1966 at Halul Island, a tiny uninhabited salt-plug, declared—after unsuccessful claims by abu Dhabi—to be a Qatar possession. Crude, after passing by way of two multi-well production platforms operating unattended, was stored in four 335,000 bbl tanks. From Halul the crude was loaded from a mooring buoy into tankers. The works carried out on the Island included those of water distillation, an equipped dock and harbour, and domestic buildings for a hundred men. Export operations on these lines at Halul started in December 1965, with an initial offtake equivalent to some 4·5 million t/y from the combined fields. The blended crude was of 36–37 degrees A.P.I. The export facilities provided for 190,000 b/d.

Shell Company of Qatar in 1963 relinquished to the Government some 2,125 square miles of its maritime concession, and later in the same year a further 2,900, the two areas together amounting to some 60 per cent. of its original grant. The Company's fields under present exploitation, with a surrounding area, were retained, but nothing south of Doha was included, and

nothing due north of the peninsula. Oil-rights over these relinquished areas, together with those given up by Q.P.C. on land
(p. 418), and a hitherto unallocated strip of some 340 square miles
in the extreme south of the peninsula, were in the autumn of 1963
bestowed on Continental Oil of Qatar (p. 418), whose total grant
from the Doha authorities thus amounted to some 9,000 square
miles. These included Halul Island itself and its territorial waters.
Continental initiated seismic work on land, and this, with similar
work offshore, continued throughout 1965. Qatar's combined
'proved reserves' were assessed early in 1966 as some 400 million
tons.

### III. ABU DHABI

The slow progress in the abu Dhabi shaikhdom of concessionairing, oil search and test-drilling, which had led by 1960 only to
some hopeful indications on the mainland (p. 319) of the 26,000-
square-mile territory, and to the stage of imminent oil production
from the marine area (p. 320), has been described in earlier pages;
these have indicated the quite separate identity of the two enterprises—those respectively of the Abu Dhabi Petroleum Company
(A.D.P.C.)[1] by land, and Abu Dhabi Marine Areas (A.D.M.A.)
by sea—operating under agreements with Shaikh Shakhbut bin
Sultan. If the difficulties and hazards of mid-sea exploration and
production need no repeated emphasis, those on such terrain as
that of the abu Dhabi principality can hardly be overstressed; it is
a land of maximum desolate emptiness, with a climate of extreme
severity, almost no potable water, minimal vegetation, endless high
and ever-encroaching sand dunes, and wide grim flats of salt-
marsh. These, with a total lack of all the physical or human infra-
structure of modern industry, were the conditions in which oil
development was pursued.

The search by A.D.P.C. had by mid-1960 narrowed down, at
least temporarily, to the promising Murban structure (p. 319),
some sixty miles south-west of abu Dhabi village. Here Well no. 3
declared itself in that year a producer, with a test of some 5,000
b/d. Another half-dozen wells in 1960–1 were sufficient to indicate
the limits of the structure (known thereafter as the Bab Dome) and
to confirm its value, and as many more indicated a potential of,

[1] The name was adopted by the I.P.C. interests in lieu of P.D. (Trucial
Coast) Limited, in 1962.

initially, at least 6–7 million t/y of production. The field, in which production was from Cretaceous Limestone at an average depth of 8,700 feet, showed good pressure and porosity, with light oil of 40–42 degrees A.P.I. Plans for its immediate development, at an estimated cost of at least £15 million, were initiated late in 1962. Drilling, with a wide spacing of wells, continued; for this function, as indeed to an unusual extent for almost the whole of oilfield operations, A.D.P.C. employed foreign and, as far as possible, local contractors. Away from Murban, geophysical parties continued to explore the territory, and half a dozen exploration wells in widely spread localities were drilled in the period 1961–5. The latter included dry holes at Ruwais and Umm al-Ishtan.

The drilling of Murban no. 12, at a point some twenty-five miles south-west of the centre of the Bab Dome, revealed what was at first thought to be an extension of the same structure but soon came to be recognized as a separate formation, the Bu Hasa Dome. A series of subsequent wells drilled, following seismic guidance, in the vicinity of no. 12 were all completed as full-scale producers from the Lower Cretaceous, with productivity of some 12,000 to 15,000 b/d per well, exceeding that of the Bab.

By mid-1964 some thirty wells, including twenty-four producers, had been completed on the Bab structure, and a dozen, all producers, on Bu Hasa. Gas and water observation wells were suitably sited in both fields. A passable track, though constantly threatened by sand encroachment, was opened between the two structures, and another between Habshan and the A.D.P.C. local headquarters—at that period—at Tarif on the coast,[1] and farther eastward to the lighter-unloading beach at Ras Zubaya, and to abu Dhabi itself. While these works proceeded, the installation of field production facilities, first on the Bab and a year later on the Bu Hasa Domes, was pressed forward. On the former the 'remote station' at Shamis collected and partially treated oil received by 6-inch flow-lines from seven wells and passed it on by a 16-inch line to Habshan, after which it was pumped to a slightly elevated 78,000 bbl tank, in readiness for its further journey for export. At Habshan also was situated the distillation plant for treating the local brackish water, and other necessary installations—hutments, store sheds, dwelling quarters, pumps, power-plant—on the

---

[1] The Company moved its headquarters to abu Dhabi town in 1965–6 but Tarif remained an important centre.

smallest practicable scale. The producing wells at Bu Hasa delivered to a single gathering station of some 150,000 b/d capacity in the centre of the structure. This station was entirely unmanned, with provision for a wholly automatic shutdown in case of trouble; no construction was carried out or was necessary for living quarters, power supply, or potable water. Degassing was in three stages, following which the treated oil passed into a 24-inch spur line completed and opened in mid-1965. This joined the main Bab–Habshan to Jabal Dhanna 24-inch trunk line some fifty miles from the sea. This development raised the present export potential of the abu Dhabi mainland to some 12 million t/y.

The first export of abu Dhabi oil took place in December 1963, though the formal opening of the system, to which the rank and fashion of the territory and the industry were bidden, was postponed until March 1964. The terminal, designed for an export throughput of 6 million t/y at the beginning, was situated on the coast at Jabal Dhanna. The site had been chosen, after prolonged marine surveys of this extremely unfavourable coast, as the only spot capable of providing deep water near the shore; it had the further advantages of shelter from Sir Bani Yas Island and of sufficient elevation to allow loading by gravity. Here, therefore, A.D.P.C. erected its store-sheds, tank farm (210 feet up), distillation plant, communications centre, airstrip, and metering station; and here the oil finally flowed into the holds of waiting tankers by way of two 36-inch concrete-coated sea lines, two submarine tanker berths in fifty-seven feet of water three miles from shore, and four 12-inch flexible hoses. A third tanker berth was to be added later. A small-boat harbour and causeway were constructed for the easier handling of materials. Pilots for the incoming tankers were taken on at Ghasha, seventeen miles out at sea.

Export of crude from the Murban field including Bu Hasa amounted to 5·9 million tons in 1964, and 8·9 million in 1965, carried in 250 tankers to many destinations. At mid-1966 export was proceeding at an average rate of 250,000 b/d (12·5 million t/y). It was probable that this figure would within very few years be doubled, trebled, or more.

Besides continuous development-drilling on the productive structures, exploration outside the Bab and Bu Hasa areas was continued by seismic parties throughout and after 1964. Further but unsuccessful exploration wells were drilled at Qamara and at

Mushash in the deep south of the area, Bida Hamama in the extreme east, Salabikh in the central area, and Asab. A trial well at abu Jidu, south-west of Murban, however, spudded in in November 1964, found oil in January 1965 in a major anticline and aroused some hopes of an interesting discovery; the next four wells, however, were unproductive of oil.

In October 1965 the Company relinquished to the Shaikh three areas, with a total surface of 5,000 square miles, of its countrywide concession, and faced the prospect of further surrenders in the future. The relinquished area, now available for other grantees, included also abu Dhabi town and island. It was reported in mid-1966 that inquiries were being made by half a dozen American independents, and by French, Italian, and German interests.

The future of abu Dhabi shaikhdom as a crude exporting area thus appeared in mid-1966 to be fully established. Meanwhile its ruler, Shaikh Shakhbut, showed himself more cautious than his similarly enriched fellow rulers on the Gulf Coast in the headlong plunge into modernity and expenditure that was forced upon them.[1] He consulted experts on urban and other development and permitted, but with little enthusiasm, the fairly rapid transformation of abu Dhabi from a squalid village to a growing urban centre with a new piped water supply from a hinterland source, a power-station, an improved causeway across the abu Dhabi creek, a hospital, two schools, and (provided by private enterprise) banks, offices, shops, and dwelling houses—including those intended for A.D.P.C. personnel. No 'company town', such as those of Doha or Ahmadi or Dhahran was here constructed. The social effects of the sudden influx of wealth to the shaikhdom, with a total population estimated in 1965 as some 18,000, must be awaited. The Shaikh in September 1965 agreed to modify his original agreement so as to enjoy, instead, the far more advantageous fifty-fifty principle prevalent elsewhere.[2] He received from A.D.P.C. in 1963 the equivalent of some £5·6 million, in 1964 £13 million, and in 1965 £20 million.

The Company's Chief Representative and General Manager in

[1] Shaikh Shakhbut gave way, as ruler of the territory, to his younger brother Zaid in July 1966, and a less hesitant approach to the territory's problems of modernization immediately appeared.

[2] The old rate was Rs 3¼ per ton (or roughly 5s.); the new at 50 per cent. of (locally accruing) profit based on posted prices, gave about Rs 25, or roughly £2 per ton.

abu Dhabi during these years was J. J. Page from June 1961 until February 1965, and thereafter R. Milne.

At sea, sixty miles from the abu Dhabi coastline, the Anglo-French A.D.M.A. had been pursuing its search for oil since 1954, and since 1959 had been concentrating on the early development of the seemingly considerable productive submarine structure which it had discovered, known as Umm Shaif. The timetable planned in early 1960 was faithfully observed, and the works referred to on an earlier page (p. 320) were by great efforts, and at a cost which brought total expenditure on the enterprise to more than £20 million, accomplished by July 1962, when the first cargo left Das Island. Nine wells, drawing their oil from an average depth of 9,000 feet, had by that time been completed, six of which were connected by their gathering lines to a central collecting platform and thence dispatched to Das for degassing and loading. In 1962 export of crude amounted to 800,000 tons. The oil was of 37·5 degrees A.P.I., with a sulphur content of only 0·015 per cent.

Drilling continued; by late 1963 a score of wells had been completed and output was running at a rate of 3 million t/y, soon to be increased. Exploration drilling in adjacent waters revealed the presence of Lower Cretaceous oil in the fall of 1963, in the first well drilled at Zakhum, forty miles south-east of Umm Shaif, and by mid-1965 subsequent wells had confirmed the structure as potentially one of importance. Steps were taken early in 1966 to bring Zakhum into production before the end of 1967, to an extent of perhaps 10 million t/y, rising to 16 million. The prospect involved further tankage, some processing, additional pipelines, and a second jetty, all at Das Island. In 1965 other outside drilling some twenty miles south-east of Das revealed light oil at al-Bunduq, a discovery followed up by a second well which (September 1965) proved dry, as did a further exploration well on another structure, Bu'l Hanin, sixteen miles north-north-west of Das. In mid-1966 it remained to confirm whether Bunduq was an exploitable oilfield or not. Two marine rigs were in action throughout the year in A.D.M.A. waters.

The terms of the concession were at the end of 1965 still unaltered, payment being on the basis of a fixed sum per ton. A.D.M.A. was in 1966 expected to reach an export total of 13 million t/y within the next eighteen months. Meanwhile, offtake from their concession area amounted in 1963 to 2·25 million tons, in 1964 to 3·04 million, in 1965 to 4·5 million. Six more wells were to be connected for production in 1966, bringing capacity to 120,000 b/d. Payments to the Shaikh were of the order of £5 million in 1963, £6·8 million in 1964, and £10 million in 1965.[1] How far these figures, already well surpassed by those of mainland production, would increase in later years could not be foreseen. Meanwhile total production from the land and sea of the Shaikhdom had been 2·25 million tons in 1963, 8·9 million in 1964, and 13·4 million in 1965; and a total export of 600,000 b/d, or 30 million t/y as early as 1968–9 could reasonably be foreseen. The shaikhdom's direct annual receipts on account of its oil in the years 1963–4 and 1965 were of the order of £10 million, £20 million and £30 million. The territory's reserves were provisionally assessed at this time as 1·35 billion tons.

In 1964–6, the absence of abu Dhabi from the ranks of O.P.E.C. was considered by its friends a point of weakness in that organization, or even a threat to it. Adherence to it was impossible as long as Shaikh Shakhbut ruled, his suspicion of all outside factors or persons being extreme; but ultimate membership was probable, and the bringing of pressure to bear in that sense on the incoming Shaikh was reported.

General Managers of A.D.M.A. from its inception were: P. Wainwright (1957–9), E. R. Babb (1959–60), H. C. Cannon (1960–1), J. Haines (1961–3), R. E. Linton (1963–5), and P. A. Mann (1965– ).

### IV. THE TRUCIAL COAST

The oil history of the shaikhdoms of the Coast, other than fortunate abu Dhabi, is after 1959 one of the hungry eagerness of the shaikhs, the willing abandonment of their rights by the 'Iraq Petroleum Company Group as here represented, the assumption of these by other, non-major, concessionaires hitherto strange to the region, and the vigorous initial field-work of the latter. Not until midsummer 1966, however, did some success at Dubai and, not yet certainly, at Sharja, crown the efforts made over two decades.

The ruler of Ras al-Khaima called for bids for his hopefully

[1] Abu Dhabi was in 1966 using the Bahrain dinar, equal to Rs 10 or 15s. Qatar and the Trucial Shaikhdoms used the Sa'udi riyal of which 4½ equal $1.00. Oman used the Indian rupee at its pre-devaluation value of Rs 13·33 to £1 sterling.

imagined oil-wealth, by land and sea, as soon as Petroleum Development (Trucial Coast) had abandoned its rights in 1960; but it was not until early in 1964 that he was able to find applicants to whom to issue a grant. These were two American independents, Union Oil of California (with an 80 per cent. interest) and Southern Natural Gas (with 20 per cent.). These, as the Ras al-Khaima Oil Company, busied themselves with field geology for some weeks in 1965. The yet smaller shaikhdoms of 'Ajman and Umm al-Qaiwain shared the fortunes of Sharja; concessions for oil in the land and waters of each of these territories were granted by their respective rulers in 1961-2 to another newcomer, the John W. Mecom Company of Texas, which was simultaneously trying its hand elsewhere in Arabia (pp. 429, 432). It was reported in the summer of 1963 that the Pure Oil Company of Ohio had taken a share in the Mecom enterprise. The latter, after suitable surveys, sited and spudded in an offshore well, in Sharja waters, thirty-five miles from shore. The well, begun in October 1963, was abandoned as dry at 5,350 feet after a few weeks' work. This was followed by Sharja no. 2 and Umm al-Qaiwain no. 1, each taken to over 8,000 feet but abandoned. In the hot weather of 1966, however, the Mecom Company, in their fourth well, Juwaisa no. 2, inland, found good quality oil but in quantities not immediately hailed as commercial.

It was reported almost simultaneously that the tiny shaikhdom of Fujaira (which faces the Gulf of Oman) had bestowed its oil-development rights on the German Company, Bomin Bochumer Mineralölgesellschaft.

The Shaikh of Dubai, busiest and perhaps most progressive of the Coast village-capitals, called on P.D.(T.C.) in midsummer 1961 to amend his 1937 concessionary terms so as to conform to the fifty-fifty principle now prevalent elsewhere; his wish was gratified, but a few months later the Company saw fit to abandon the territory (in which it had drilled a single well ten years earlier). The rights were re-granted in the spring of 1963 to the Continental Oil Company which, agreeing *inter alia* to pay an initial bonus and to observe the fifty-fifty principle, formed forthwith a Dubai Petroleum Company for local operation, and hastened to undertake active geophysical survey work. Later in the year Continental acquired a half interest in the offshore concession given by the Shaikh in 1954 to the *ad hoc* Anglo-French formation, Dubai

Marine Areas (p. 320), and, inheriting the results of the latter's offshore geological and seismic work, agreed to become operator for that company as well as for Dubai Petroleum. The attractive power of the tiny Dubai territory was, however, not yet exhausted: in May 1964 it was reported that Deutsche Erdöl A.G. (known as D.E.A.) and Sun Oil Company had each taken a 22½ per cent. share in Dubai Petroleum and shares also in the Marine Areas, so as to leave the shareholding in the latter thereafter as B.P. 33¾ per cent., C.F.P. 16½, Continental Oil 35, D.E.A. 10, and Sun Oil 5 per cent.

Two wells within the combined Dubai areas—Faʻiz no. 1 at sea and Qamr no. 1 on land—were spudded in in the autumn of 1964, but by the year's end both had been abandoned, by reason, it was announced, of drilling difficulties. A second well on land, at Rimah, was undertaken in October 1964, but was abandoned in May 1965 at 10,200 feet. The moment of discovery was now at hand for Dubai. In the offshore waters, some sixty miles seaward and north-westward from the Dubai coast—and close to abu Dhabi waters—from a floating drilling-vessel, the *Glomar Tasman*, oil of 31 degrees A.P.I. was located in the early summer of 1966 in well Fatih no. 1 at 8,500 feet, with the promise initially of some 6,000 b/d production. The discovery—the first to the credit of Continental, D.E.A., or Sun in the Middle East—could be accepted as commercial, and early development was awaited.

### V. OMAN

In this long isolated, independent, and still socially and administratively mediaeval Sultanate of Muscat and Oman, fortune, after resolutely refusing her favours since oil interest was first aroused in the nineteen-thirties (pp. 155–6)—or indeed in 1920 (p. 101)—was to relent at last; by mid-1966 important oil had been discovered, and necessary facilities for processing, transport, and storage were being constructed.

None of this occurred, however, in the detached Dhofar province where, after one disappointment had succeeded another in the forties and fifties, Cities Service and Richfield, the current concessionaires of the 30,000-square-mile territory, had by the end of 1960 come near to abandoning hope (p. 318). The oil-rights were at this juncture, in the summer of 1962, given up by these Companies in favour of the Sultan's next grantee, the John W.

Mecom Company, with which the Pure Oil Company joined forces (with a half share) in the summer of 1963. A small number of dry holes in the Marmul area were drilled in 1962-3 by Mecom and by the joint Company, followed, however, in 1964 by Mecom's effective withdrawal, equipment and all, from the Dhofar province. In 1965 Continental took over a one-third share in the Mecom and Pure enterprise, and proceeded to fresh, including seismic, exploration.

In the main part of the Sultan's dominions, a period of comparative public disorder, organized and financed from abroad (that is, from Egypt and Sa'udi Arabia), was followed by one of improved security, and the hopes of Petroleum Development (Oman), under its new control (p. 319), could be renewed. The Company, now under Shell management,[1] soon (1961) put seismic parties into the field and collected fresh data. They could thus, early in 1962, select a drilling site and they spudded in Yibal no. 1 and no. 2, thirty miles south-west of the Jabal Fahud, at the end of March. Here and at Natih, in the same general area of mid-hinterland Oman, shows of oil were found at moderate depths, whereby further drilling and testing were encouraged. The same was true of a third location at Fahud itself. Field-work continued, with commercial production still doubtfully justifiable, throughout 1963 and early 1964. A number of wells were drilled at Yibal, Natih, Fahud, al-Ghubar, Umm al-Samin, and Lakhwair, with varying results. Seismic parties still ranged the territory, and drilling continued at the three first-mentioned of these sites and elsewhere.

By late 1964 sufficient positive evidence was in hand from the good results at Natih, Fahud, and Yibal, and extensive further geophysical work in 1965 to justify forward action, and the quality of the local crude (30 degrees A.P.I. and low in sulphur) aided a favourable decision. Average potential per well from the Natih and Fahud fields was reported as some 7,000 b/d. It was announced that a multi-million pound programme of field development, with a system of flow lines and gathering stations, gas separation, storage, etc., all operated from Fahud, was to be installed, and a 30-36-inch pipeline was to run north-eastwards across the mountains by the Sumail Gap (altitude 2,000 feet). A terminal was

---

[1] Shell took over control of P.D. (Oman) operations in the field from the appointment of R. A. B. Clough as Chief Representative in September 1961; he was succeeded by F. Hughes in January 1965.

located at Saih al-Malih immediately west of Muscat–Matra on the Gulf of Oman. The pipeline would be 156 miles long, with completion planned for late 1967. It would pass close to the hitherto little-known towns of Izki and al-Gaila. Gravity would serve to carry the oil, in quantities estimated at initially 6–7 million t/y, from the crest of the mountains into the holds of tankers; the provision of deep-water quays close to the shore, and a loading procedure *via* a single-buoy mooring, would present no difficulty. The Saih al-Malih tank-farm would have capacity for 1½ million bbl. Meanwhile, drilling with two rigs proceeded and tireless seismic and gravity-meter parties continued to explore the territory in the confident hope of further discoveries.[1] Work on the pipeline and the terminal projects was in full swing throughout 1965–6. Shell, frustrated in the Kuwaiti waters, had found a new and much-desired source of crude; and a more prosperous future for the Sultan, Sayid Sa'id, and his country seemed at long last to be assured. Oil reserves could be guessed at possibly 150 million tons.

The West German Company, Wintershall A.G., was reported in 1966 as having acquired from the Sultan (but through an American middleman) rights over 4,600 square miles offshore from the north-east coast of the Sultanate. Marine surveys were contemplated to permit location of a drilling-site. Other German interests might later participate.

## VI. SOUTHERN ARABIA

We turn now to deal with the territory long known as the Colony and Protectorate of Aden, but now, unless all goes awry, in process of becoming the Federation of South Arabia and destined to be born as an independent State in 1968: a conversion or promotion attended, however, by all too visible internal difficulties due to Egyptian and Yemeni hostility, to the disagreements of its own politicians, and to the refusal of membership by some of the rulers.

The refinery built by B.P. at Little Aden within the Colony (pp. 321–2),[2] was substantially enlarged and perfected during this period. Its capacity had been raised by 1961 to 6·8 million t/y, and by April 1966 to 8·3 million. The capacities of the catalytic

[1] Drilling in the area in 1965 included 4 wells at Fahud, 3 at Yibal, 5 at Natih, and 1 each at Sunaina (taken to 10,000 feet) and Maradi.

[2] B.P. here took the form of Aden Petroleum Refinery Limited, later (1956), B.P. Refinery (Aden) Limited.

reformer and the $SO_2$ extraction unit were, by the latter date, respectively 14,000 and 10,000 b/d. The local distribution, and on a far greater scale the export, of refined products, and the supply of piped gas to the Aden Electricity Authority, continued with normal increases of scale.

The development of the refinery company's housing estates, training programmes, medical services, and sports and other amenities was further expanded. More than two thousand men were kept in regular employment, nearly 90 per cent. of these being Arabs. The supply of bunkering fuels—fuel oil, diesel, and gas oils—to the installations and tank-farm of B.P. (Aden) Limited at Aden Harbour, to furnish the 425 ocean-going ships per month which required them, was the subject of a twenty-four-hour service with increased facilities. The Company maintained eight terminals served by submarine lines from shore tanks, two of these being dolphin berths, each capable of supplying 1,500 tons an hour; the other six supplied bunkers by floating line barges. Aden could now claim to possess the largest bunkering installation of the 300 which operated in the B.P. international service.

In the ex-Aden Protectorate, now the South Arabian Federation, we left matters, as in mid-1960, in an inanimate condition; the I.P.C. had withdrawn from their long-drawn attempts to find structures of oil-bearing interest, and no new 'takers' had appeared (p. 323). Nevertheless, the two major rulers of the Eastern Protectorate, the Sultans of the Qu'aiti and Kathiri States, managed late in 1961 to attract the American International Oil Company[1] (a subsidiary of Standard of Indiana) to take up a concession over 45,000 square miles of their territory, extending from the sea to the Empty Quarter. An *ad hoc* company, Pan American Hadhramaut Oil Company, was formed. The two States were entitled under the agreement to take either 55 per cent. of net profits or a 20 per cent. participation in the Companies' enterprise and 50 per cent. of profits. As between the two rulers, the division of profits was to be two-thirds to the Qu'aiti State, and one-third to the Kathiri. Ten years, extendable to fifteen, were allowed for exploration and thirty years for the exploitation of any field discovered. A refinery—surely, in such a territory, the most absurd of projects—was to be built locally as soon as commercial supplies

[1] The name was changed from Pan American International Oil Corporation in July 1962.

of crude were assured. The two sultans were later reported to be discussing the establishment of a joint Petroleum Authority. The Company proceeded actively to survey work, and thence in 1964 to structure drilling; by 1966 extensive geophysical surveys had been carried out, and a small number of test-wells had been drilled in inland areas, but without discovering oil. In the summer of 1966 the Company decided to abandon the territory and its concession.

In November 1961, still in the Eastern Protectorate, the ruler of the spacious but primitive Mahra Sultanate of Qishn and Sokotra (Suqutra) granted a concession to American International, which again formed a local company, Pan American Mahra Oil. The terms were similar to those agreed for the Qu'aiti–Kathiri country. The concession included 77,000 square miles of territory, of which 2,000 were the Island of Sokotra. The Company carried out considerable geophysical work in the territory and drilled four dry holes. But success was again denied; it was reported in June 1966 that the Company had decided to relinquish its Mahra as well as its Hadhramaut concession, after so large an unproductive expenditure. The three sultans prepared now to look for other foreign clients—who might well prove hesitant.

No news affecting oil exploration or discovery came during this period from the western part of the Federation.

### VII. THE YEMEN

In the troubled Yemen, torn by civil war and foreign (Egyptian) military occupation from 1962 to the time of writing (late 1966), there could be little hope of successful, or indeed of any, oil enterprise. Before the death of the Imam Ahmad, however, in September 1962, a concession had been granted to the John W. Mecom Company over a 10,000-square-mile area situated in the coastal plain of the Tihama and its nearby waters. The agreement provided for a five-year exploration and a thirty-year development period. The Company showed more activity than its predecessor in the territory (p. 321); it drilled, without success, three or four wells to medium depths at Salif, Zaidiya, and near Hudaida. Its efforts, however, were brought to an end by the outbreak of civil war, and the Yemen remains an oil-less country.

In mid-1964 the formation was reported of a Yemen Fuel Company to conduct miscellaneous operations connected with oil.

The Republican Government, by now some eighteen precarious months old, was to enjoy a minority status in the enterprise, of which 51 per cent. of the shares would belong to the Government of the U.A.R., through its General Petroleum Authority. No activities of this body have been reported.

## CHAPTER XXV

# TURKEY, THE LEVANT STATES, AND EGYPT, 1960–6

## I. TURKEY

THE oil history of Turkey from 1960 to 1965 was one of alternating hope and frustration; of some progress in the discovery of oil-sources, though on a scale far below the prevailing Middle Eastern standard of profuseness; of the transformation of the refining industry from almost nothing to a capacity exceeding the country's needs, but also ill-balanced and not easily supplied; of major and minor foreign companies abandoning their efforts to play a part on the oil-stage of Turkey, only to be replaced, if never fully, by other aspirants; of rapidly rising popular demand for oil products, but still on a scale which represented a remarkably low *per capita* consumption.

In 1959 the total output of the oilfields of Turkey was some 365,000 tons, in 1960 slightly less. The whole production came from the Raman Dagh–Garzan–Germik group of small fields discovered and developed by the Turkish Petroleum Corporation (T.P.A.O.—p. 327); no other deposits, in spite of all efforts and formidable expenditure on survey and test-drilling by a score of foreign companies (pp. 326–7), had been located by the summer of 1960,[1] and already a number of the hopeful licence-holders, including Jersey Standard, had given up and departed, to be followed by more in 1960–1.[2] Nevertheless, late in 1960 and in 1961 some successes appeared. In August 1960 Mobil discovered sulphur-free oil of 36 degrees A.P.I. at Bulgurdagh, thirty miles east of Mersin; their first well produced 250 b/d from 4,760 feet, and in

[1] The hope-inspiring well no. 1 at Kuleli in Thrace which, drilled by Deilmann and Shell (p. 326), found some oil in July 1960, proved non-commercial.

[2] Among departing companies were, by early 1962: Jersey Standard, Tidewater, Atlantic Refining, Gilliland, Feldman (who passed their rights to Gulf), Marmara Petroleum (Husky), Bolsa Chica, Deutsche Erdöl, Deilmann Montan, and the Istanbul Gas Company. The main foreign Companies remaining in the field were, therefore, Caltex, Mobil, Shell, and Gulf, and these had given up a proportion of their licences. With them were Amoseas, Panley, and others. Licences frequently changed hands. New entrants included Petropar (French, drilling in Districts V and VI), Clark, Panoil, San Jacinto, Aladdin, Perkins, and Landa.

later tests showed 1,000 b/d. This was the first discovery in the Adana Basin; but a year later the field was proved to be of sadly limited capacity, not exceeding 1,100 b/d in all, and further drilling in the vicinity, in which a number of licence-holding companies took part, found nothing. In October 1960 Shell, in their second well at Kayakoy, twenty-five miles north of Diyarbakr and fifty miles west of the Raman group, found light oil at a depth of 5,800 feet in a well planned to reach 10,000 feet: oil which could have no other outlet than by train or tank-lorry to Mersin. Later wells drilled by Shell nearby showed that the field was small, incapable of more than a 1,000–1,200 b/d production. In 1961 T.P.A.O. found three more small productive structures in the Raman district and therefore available for refining at Batman. These were: Magrip, yielding at first 500 b/d of 21 degrees A.P.I. crude, increased by later drilling to 1,100 b/d; Kurtalan, giving, after a better start, a mere 200 b/d of excellent 33 degrees A.P.I. oil; and Bati Raman, twelve miles east of Raman itself, which could by pumping give, from 4,500 feet, a few hundred barrels a day of heavy 14 degrees A.P.I. crude. Finally, still in this 1960–1 period, Amoseas (that is, Caltex) discovered a barely commercial field at Kahta near Gaziantep, half-way between Mersin and Raman, with a production of a few hundred b/d of thick asphaltic oil, rated at 11 degrees A.P.I. This field was later (1963) sold by Caltex to a local Group, Ersan Petroleum Industrial Company, which intended to produce from it for local purposes.

Amid a wealth of further test-drilling in various districts of Turkey, there were other minor successes in the period 1962–6, besides the steady but too often disappointing development of the fields already mentioned. The potential of Shell's Kayakoy field was confirmed as slight, and it could not be fully exploited for lack of outlets; the field, partly flowing and partly pumped, produced in 1964 about 60,000 tons of its unusually light oil and 70,000 in 1965. Two more small producers in the Kayakoy neighbourhood, Kurkan and later Beykan, after considerable drilling together yield about 100,000 t/y of 31 degrees A.P.I. oil. Mobil's Bulgurdagh field showed signs of rather rapid depletion, and after a year or two produced less than Kayakoy; but the Company was able to report in 1963–4 the discovery of two more productive structures elsewhere. The first of these was a small field at Silivanka, which, in spite of production from more than one horizon, offered a very modest (pumped) contribution of some 25,000 t/y of 20 degrees A.P.I. oil; the other, much more considerable, was at Şelmo. Both were immediately north of the Garzan–Germik fields. The oil at Şelmo, which was hailed in 1964 as, by Turkish standards, a discovery of major importance, was of 34 degrees A.P.I. By the end of that year six producing wells there had been completed, five of which lay in a concession shared as to 80 per cent. by Mobil, and 20 per cent. by Panoil of Dallas; the sixth was wholly Mobil-owned. Production from Şelmo began in October 1964 at some 5,500 b/d (a rate sustained in 1965), and enabled Mobil's production to surpass that of Shell.

T.P.A.O., the largest producer but, in spite of its Batman refinery, cramped as always in its production by limited ways of disposal, added two small discoveries in these years. Çelikli, north of its Kurtalan field, was found in 1963 and could produce about 120 b/d; Bada, north-east of Garzan, was not yet equipped for production. Both had small quantities of light 33 degrees A.P.I. oil.

Production in Turkey amounted in 1964, therefore, pending the completion of a pipeline system, to less than one million tons a year, and well over half of this derived from T.P.A.O. fields in which (unlike the arrangement in Iran) no foreign partner had been admitted: the figure was 746,000 tons in 1963, 921,000 tons in 1964.[1] Producing wells numbered in all some 170, production per well (nearly all on pumping) being extremely small. Almost all production, except Mobil's at Bulgurdagh and Şelmo, was still in Si'irt and Diyarbakr, District V of the nine districts into which the country was divided for oil-exploration purposes. A lesser effort of exploration continued in 1964 in District VI (Gaziantep) and District VII (Adana), while some persisted, unrewarded, in Districts VII (Black Sea coast) and I (Thrace).

The year 1965 was one of successful activity. Exploration— largely because it was the last chance for some licence-holders to fulfil their obligations—was on as wide a scale as ever before, stimulated in part also by the Şelmo discovery. As before, the main interest was in District V but drilling was also reported from Districts VI and I. The only successes, and these of negligible value, were in a T.P.A.O. wildcat at Başur, with a small show of

---

[1] This was made up of T.P.A.O. 631,580, Shell 101,000, Mobil 158,000, Ersan 30,000 tons.

light oil, and a still smaller show in a Petropar[1] well at Malahermo, another at Hazro, and a trace of gas in T.P.A.O.'s well at Dodan. Mobil's drilling at Kara Ali yielded a trace of oil, and its well at Çorlu (in District I) gave a slight show of gas.

The year's list of exploration or wildcat wells, all except three in District V, is formidably long. It includes, at a variety of locations not easily identifiable, wells drilled by Aladdin, Clark, Landa, Mesopotamian Petroleum, Mobil Exploration, Panoil, Perkins, Petropar, Shell, and T.P.A.O., in District V; Mobil and T.P.A.O. in District I; and Shell in District VI. The total of wildcat drilling for the year in Turkey is recorded at 184,000 feet. Development-drilling was carried out by Ersan Petroleum (three wells at Kahta in District VI), by Mobil-Panoil (five wells at Şelmo, District V), Mobil (three at Silivanka, District V), Shell (three at Beykan, three at Kurkan, District V), and T.P.A.O. (three at Raman, eighteen at Bati Raman, nine at Garzan, two at Germik, three at Çelikli, one at Dodan, all in District V). It is safe, in summary, to say that the year witnessed a very serious, costly, and widespread effort to find new sources of oil, and to develop those already discovered. In 1966 the traffic in licences and activity in fulfilling their obligations seemed somewhat diminished but still persistent. The German Company, Gewerkschaft Elwerath, entered the field, and with partners planned an offshore well—the first in Turkey—in the Adana region; the well was spudded in early in 1966, with the help of an offshore rig acquired while *en route* for the Persian Gulf. The Italian A.G.I.P. also seemed interested in exploration of Turkey.

The total Turkish production in 1965 was not far from double that of 1964, reaching over 1·5 million tons,[2] against the 1964 total of 920,000. The increase was due, as we know, to production from Bati Raman, Bulgurdagh, and Magrip, each producing nearly twice as much as a year earlier; from Kurkan, with production increased from an average of 580 b/d to one of 2,750; and above all from Şelmo with a daily average of almost 5,000 bbl, exceeded only by Bati Raman's 6,750 b/d. For the Şelmo field and reservoir

[1] Société de Participations Pétrolières.
[2] The total, 1,534,000 tons, was made up of 701,275 from T.P.A.O., 366,000 from N.V. Turkse Shell, 303,000 from Mobil, and 74,750 from Ersan Petroleum. Shell's production was from Kurkan, Kayakoy, and Beykan; Mobil's from Bulgurdagh, Şelmo, and Silivanka; T.P.A.O.'s from Raman and Bati Raman, Garzan–Germik and Magrip.

high hopes were entertained: a production of 30,000–40,000 b/d was anticipated as soon as outlets were available. A rough estimate of Turkey's 'proved' reserves in 1965 was some 450 million tons, but the figure could, at the present stage of exploration, have little value.

Even in the absence of new discoveries, production in Turkey seemed in 1966 likely to increase materially as soon as the long-expected pipeline from the fields in District V to the Mediterranean could be completed. The 18-inch line finally projected, and to be built at a cost of some $35 million by French and Japanese contractors, would have an initial capacity of 37,000 b/d, a later one of 70,000 b/d, and a length of 350 miles or slightly less. It would run, with three pump-stations, from the Batman area (serving the T.P.A.O., Shell, and Mobil fields) to Dortyöl at the head of the Gulf of Iskenderun. It was intended that crude should be dispatched to the Mersin refinery from Dortyöl by tanker.

The refining industry in Turkey made good progress. In mid-1960 (p. 327) there was no refinery operating in the territory, except the small plant at Batman in the heart of T.P.A.O.'s first-discovered fields; this, with a throughput at that time of some 7,000 b/d, was by 1962 raised to 13,000, and by 1966 to 15,000, but local outlets still did not enable it to work at full capacity. During 1966 a small reforming plant was added. The I.P.R.A.S. (Istanbul Petroleum Refinery Company) refinery near Izmit, with T.P.A.O. holding 51 per cent. and Caltex 49 per cent. of the shares, came on stream in the fall of 1961, with operating and output arrangements as planned (p. 328); its designed throughput was of 28,000 b/d, with cracking and reforming plant; early application was made to the Government (but not granted) for permission to enlarge capacity to 44,000 b/d. The projected refinery to be sited at Büyük Çekmece near Istanbul, and to be locally financed, never came into existence. However, that of the foreign-owned[1] Anatolian Refining Company (A.T.A.S.) at Mersin (p. 327) was begun early in 1961 and completed in October 1962, with a capacity of 65,000 b/d, or 3·25 million t/y. This was by Turkish standards an important industrial asset, and a major saver of foreign exchange; it brought Turkish refining capacity to well above their current domestic needs of over 2 million t/y,[2] though the refinery did not

---

[1] Mobil 56 per cent., Shell 27 per cent., B.P. 17 per cent. (p. 327).

[2] These needs increased from some 1·6 million tons of products in 1959 to 2·25 million tons in 1962, and near to 3 million in 1965.

initially operate at full capacity. Efforts were made from the beginning to train Turkish personnel to operate the plant, which employed 350 to 400 men. The refinery was supplied with some of its crude by road and rail from the Si'irt fields and with far more, some 90 per cent., by tanker from overseas; this awkwardness and expense must continue until the projected pipeline can be completed. The port of Mersin could accommodate two 50,000-ton tankers at a time.

Foreign exchange considerations, mixed with some of a political nature, had in the refining and marketing spheres some effects adverse to the foreign Companies.[1] The Caltex-T.P.A.O. plant at Izmit was enabled, by the priority it enjoyed in Government contracts, to maintain its throughput at full capacity; that of A.T.A.S. at Mersin, foreign-owned, was forced to run at a lower level. Resulting also from the imbalance between the pattern of local demand and the actual refinery output, the export of unneeded light products was particularly difficult in the already oversupplied Mediterranean area. The Mersin plant of which, on export anticipations, the owners proposed in 1965 to increase the capacity from 3·25 to 4·5 million t/y, met delays in obtaining such authorization; but a T.P.A.O. project to build a 3 million t/y plant at Ismir, as part of a wide industrial agreement with Russia, was favourably regarded, though in mid-1964 no final or detailed decisions had been made. It would cost some $30 million, for completion late in 1968. If Turkish consumption were indeed to double by 1970, as some expected, there would be room for all;[2] meanwhile there was heavy pressure on foreign companies, who imported crude from their parent concerns, to reduce their import prices to levels which they felt to be unreal, but which were offered by the Russian competitor or might be obtained from other sources eager to dispose of crude.

## II. CYPRUS

The Forest Oil Corporation whose licence, covering nearly the whole island and its waters, had been issued in 1957 (p. 328), was

---

[1] This, since Caltex handed its refined products in bulk to the Government's Petrol Ofisi, meant in fact Mobil, Shell, and B.P., the owners of the Mersin plant.

[2] By late 1965, of the Turkish demand for products (nearly 3 million t/y), one-third was being met by Petrol Ofisi, two-thirds by the foreign marketers. Consumption was rising annually by some 14 per cent.

wholly inactive in the field throughout 1960 and 1961, while prolonged negotiations regarding its status were in progress between
it and the Government. In the fall of 1962 terms for its operations
were at last agreed: they included the fifty-fifty principle, an early
drilling obligation, a 12½ per cent. royalty payable to the Government (in kind if so demanded), annual rentals, a minimum expenditure by the Company on its operations, and relinquishment of
proportions of the territory at stated times. The term was forty
years. A resident geologist-manager was installed on the Island,
and survey operations planned. These led, however, to no more
than minor operations of exploration in 1963, and in 1964
and 1965, by reason of the disturbances in the Island, to even
less.

An exploration licence for the Limassol district, issued in 1962
to a Cypriot resident, P. S. Kyriakides, did not result in any visible
field-work.

A project to build a refinery on the south coast of the Island was
submitted to the Government in 1962 and, largely by reason of
counter-claims by private Cypriots, remained pending until the
fall of 1965. The consortium of Shell, Mobil, and Esso, which had
applied, was then authorized by the Cypriot Parliament to erect
the proposed 10,000 b/d plant at Larnaca; a second and smaller
Cypriot-owned refinery at the same place was envisaged. Owing
to conditions on the Island, however, no work had begun on either
project by October 1966.

### III. THE LEBANON

The Compagnie Libanaise, with the majority interest held by
the (German) Gewerkschaft Elwerath Erdölwerke, continued in
1960 both its seismic exploration work and its drilling of well
Qa'a no. 1 in the Beka'a (p. 328). The latter having been abandoned
as dry at a depth of 2,560 metres, another location was chosen
between Sur (Tyre) and Sidon, and well 'Adlun no. 1 was spudded
in, only to be abandoned in turn at 2,150 metres in February 1961.
The German interests thereupon withdrew, and the Compagnie
Libanaise became for the moment wholly Lebanese-owned, 85
per cent. privately and 14 per cent. governmentally. So ended the
third attempt by drilling to find the ever-elusive—or almost
certainly non-existent—Lebanese oil; the previous efforts (p. 241)

had been those of I.P.C. in 1947–8, and of Pacific Western and the Compagnie Libanaise in 1953.

No field-work was carried out in 1962, but hope was not yet dead. It was announced in March 1963 that Ausonia Mineraria (a member of the Italian Edison group of companies) was to drill two more wells on behalf of the Compagnie, payment to be made from oil discovered. A well was in fact drilled at Suhmur in the southern Beka'a, and another at Tel Zanub at its northern end. Both proved dry, in spite of a minor gas-show at Suhmur; and this failure put an end, it seemed, to drilling in the Lebanon, since licences for acreage elsewhere in the country, held by eminent Lebanese— Messrs Eddé, Alfred Tabet, Abdeni, Shahin, K. Foury, and Bis-hara—did not lead to any field-work in 1964–6. Ausonia Mineraria withdrew and a replacement as foreign financier-backer was sought in vain.

The Lebanon, with two ocean terminals at Tripoli and Sidon fed by trans-desert trunk pipelines, remained an obviously vital transit territory. Aramco's Tapline system was never used to its 24 million t/y capacity, though annual throughput rose in this period from 15·3 million tons in 1961 to 21·95 million in 1965. These massive deliveries of oil were, except for those to be refined at the Medreco refinery (with capacity of 16,500 b/d), duly loaded into tankers at Zahrani (Sidon—p. 245). Minor works of main-tenance and improvement at this terminal were carried out during the period. A matter of importance and long vexation, that of the transit-dues owed to Government in respect of Aramco oil crossing the Lebanon (p. 330)—a distance of forty-one miles—was settled at last in the summer of 1962. Tapline was to pay, retrospectively to November 1961, 0·465 U.S. cent per barrel for transit, with 2 cents per barrel more on all oil loaded at Zahrani, the latter fee to be divided with Syria; and in addition, a 0·47 cent per barrel loading charge. For crude oil delivered to Medreco (some 650,000 t/y) the transit fee would be 0·457 cent a barrel only, but Tapline was to pay $500,000 per annum in lieu of supplying cheaper crude for refining for local consumption. The dues for 'security' and payments to local townships were raised to $161,000 and $60,000 per annum, and other payments, unchanged, amounted to more than $600,000 a year. A lump sum payment of $11·6 million was to cover all previous and outstanding claims by the Government. All this represented, for a throughput of some 20 million t/y, an increase from $1·2 million per annum to over $5·28 million. The terms thus agreed correspond fairly closely to those concluded with Syria in February 1962 (p. 446).

'Iraq Petroleum, whose own transit arrangement with Lebanon had been concluded in 1959 (p. 329), substantially increased its throughput between 1960 (7·5 million tons), 1963 (14·5 million), and 1965 (14·5 million). This advance became possible through completion in 1960 of the looping of the Company's 'Iraq–Syria–Lebanon trunk line (p. 361) and particularly the spur from it leading from mile 494 into Tripoli terminal. At the same time terminal tankage was augmented, the capacity of the sea-loading lines was increased by larger-dimension pipe, and three berths for tankers were extended into deeper water.

The Medreco refinery (that is, Mediterranean Refining Company, jointly owned by Caltex and Mobil) at Zahrani (Sidon) continued to operate on its small scale (p. 330) of some 12,500 b/d, well below its capacity. An agreement between the Company and the Lebanese Government was announced late in 1965, amending the basis of payments due to the latter. The older refinery of the I.P.C. at Tripoli, originally of French war-time construction (p. 140), was in 1960 capable of processing some 550,000 t/y of crude. Plans were made during 1962 for the modernization and some extension of the plant, at a cost exceeding £2·3 million; among other features a catalytic reformer would be built, and high-octane gasoline and aviation jet-fuel would be produced. The Lebanese Government, which was faced with a rising public demand for products (some 650,000 t/y in 1962), guaranteed the Company a profit of 7½ per cent. on its outlay, and was itself to receive a lump sum of £200,000 in return for certain modifications in the existing agreements. An increased and more profitable output for the refinery was anticipated: it processed in 1962 only 190,000 tons of crude (from I.P.C. and M.P.C.), but in 1964 it processed 550,000 and in 1965, 740,000 tons. Steps were being taken in 1965–6 substantially to increase this volume.

## IV. SYRIA

Syrian progress towards securing its own crude-oil supplies from wells within the country was in this period slow and ill-organized; to foreign observers indeed it appeared that an integrated international company with assured working capital and markets could have served the Republic far more effectively, and brought it before 1966 into the ranks of producer-exporter States. But local political conditions and emotions precluded this elsewhere successful method of handling a national resource.

At the close of 1960 the German Company, Concordia, had found oil in the Suwaidiya area of extreme north-eastern Syria, and could show already two productive wells (p. 337).[1] In that year the Company had had to relinquish much of its territory and it retained now little but the Suwaidiya district. In the Qarachauq field—once a Syria Petroleum (S.P.C.) interest, later of Minhall, finally of the (Syrian) General Petroleum Authority—nine wells had been drilled, seven of these being capable of modest production; the field was officially considered commercial.

The following five years saw some progress. In the Qarachauq the direction of affairs was assumed late in 1961, after the constitutional union with Egypt had been dissolved, by the Syrian Petroleum Authority, a semi-independent body under the Ministry of Industry; and this (after a half-hearted invitation to the outside world to undertake development had failed to arouse any but a slight Japanese and/or Italian interest) formed an *ad hoc* company, the Jazira Oil Company, with 70 per cent. governmental shareholding. Two more wells, K9 and K10, were completed as producers in 1961, while Russian geophysicists and drillers explored neighbouring areas—Hasaja, Rumailan, and districts close to Qarachauq itself—for other and better structures. The heaviness (21 degrees A.P.I.) and high sulphur-content (4·2 per cent.) of Qarachauq oil for a time discouraged pipelining to the coast or to the Homs refinery, 600 and 500 kilometres away respectively; in other respects output and estimated reserves were thought to justify such a project. In 1962 three more producing wells were completed, assuring another 5,000 b/d from the field; and the G.P.A., aided by their Russian friends, announced three, perhaps four discoveries of new fields. These finds were at Tel Rumailan, where the first two wells, some twelve miles south-west of Qarachauq, gave interesting production of 23–24 degrees A.P.I. oil from the Upper Cretaceous; and later three wells were reported as yielding about 2,000 b/d each: at Hamza, in the same area but nearer Qarachauq; at Kirba, fifteen miles south of Rumailan; and

---

[1] Varying shares in Deutsche Erdöl's Concordia Company were held by Ausonia Mineraria, Clark Oil, and Atlantic Refining.

at 'Ulaiyan, but probably on a non-commercial scale. Russian-conducted exploration continued, and four of their rigs were working in 1963–4. In the latter year, the last under the current Syro-Russian agreement, a well at the promising Rumailan field showed light oil and gas-condensate in an Upper Triassic stratum —the first pre-Cretaceous oil to be found in Syria. The Qara-chauq wells, now eighteen in number, included twelve potential producers. The finds at Kirba and 'Ulaiyan were on further tests disappointing. Early in 1965 a further agreement with Russia was made under which Technoexport would supply three rigs to operate under G.P.A. direction.

The Concordia Company's field or fields showed minimal pro-gress between 1960 and 1962, and nothing came of negotiations for the supersession or reconstruction of the present consortium by a joint Syrian-and-foreign company. In the field, three more wells capable of production from the Upper Cretaceous, Suwaidiya nos. 3, 4, and 5, with average depths of 5,000 feet, were drilled, with but a single rig in operation; again, the heaviness of the 22 degrees A.P.I. crude was discouraging, though it suggested the possibility of blending with lighter ('Iraqi) crudes, to help in the supply of Homs refinery. Suwaidiya reserves were at this stage assessed at some 35 million tons. Late in 1962, when the field was thought capable of a sustained production of 12,000 b/d, field operations were suspended, pending some agreed form of con-cession or licence for further Concordia operations. This was not forthcoming and, after a single deep test-well had been drilled in 1963, the Concordia enterprise and rights were listed in the fol-lowing year (December 1964), among the innumerable properties in the country to be nationalized—that is, taken over in exchange for long-term bonds by the Russian-aided G.P.A. which could now organize as it pleased and arrange outlets for all the oil in north-east Syria. In 1965 a seismic and gravity-meter exploration programme was carried out in Palmyra, Dair al-Zor, and Nebek areas; production wells were drilled in the Qarachauq and Tel Rumailan fields (and one wildcat elsewhere) as part of the current drilling contract with Technoexport, the Czech contractors, which came into force in July 1965. In early 1966, five miles from Malikiya village and nine miles from the nearest Qarachauq well, an exploration well found seemingly commercial oil at 6,670 feet, in a massive Cretaceous limestone: a discovery which awaited later assessment. The total wells completed by this time were twenty-three at Qarachauq, five at Suwaidiya, and five at Rumailan; and more wildcats were planned. Government was calling also for tenders for a fifty-well development project additional to that of Technoexport.

In mid-1965 agreement was reported between the Syrian authority concerned and a group of British engineers and pipe-manufacturers, for the construction of a pipeline from the combined oilfields in the Bec de Canard area to the coast at Tartus, via Homs. British banks would provide £13·76 million against an expected total of £18–20 million. Pipe was to be of 18-, 20-, and 22-inch diameter, completion by 1968, and throughput capacity 5 million t/y. In July 1966, however, for whatever political or economic reasons, these arrangements were cancelled and the contract awarded, it was understood, to a company of the E.N.I. group.

As a transit country for other people's oil Syria maintained and quantitatively increased its important rôle. The I.P.C. trunk-lines had been augmented and in some measure replanned (p. 339), giving a throughput capacity in Syria, by the end of 1960, of some 35 million t/y. These works were practically completed in 1961 and included the comprehensive modernization of the three main pumping-stations on Syrian soil, with the introduction of un-manned automation at T2 and T4 and the use of natural gas piped from Kirkuk for driving the gas turbines. The I.P.C. trans-Syria system passed in 1962 a total of 37·4 million tons, in 1964, 41·5 million; in 1965 almost the same. A connected operation was the increase in the capacity of the Banias loading-terminal;[1] this was achieved by further internal pipeline capacity, increased tankage, and other development.

As to the transit-dues payable by I.P.C. to Syria as negotiated and finally agreed and signed in 1955 (p. 339), in the late summer of 1966 the terms suddenly ceased to be acceptable to the Government and the claim for a major increase, possibly a doubling, of payments was announced, accompanied by an aggressive Press campaign. Talks between Government and Company spokesmen began in September.

The Tapline system, which had first operated late in 1950 (p.

[1] Loadings at Banias were of 23·5 million tons in 1962, 25·9 million in 1964, and 26·2 million in 1965.

208), had called for only a limited mileage, and no pump-station, in Syria. Its throughput, always below its designed capacity of 24 million t/y for economic reasons—low ocean freight-rates and the new prevalence of larger tankers—increased during the period from 15 to 21·9 million t/y, all of which passed westward into the Lebanon for loading or for local refining. Up to 1960 no firm agreement had been reached between the Syrian Government and Tapline as to transit-dues payable (p. 340) and considerable ill-feeling had resulted. This was corrected by an agreement reached early in 1962 whereunder annual sums payable to the Damascus authorities would be nearly trebled, to reach approximately $2·8 million per annum, while a single lump sum of $10 million would be payable to cover outstanding claims. The transit-fee was to be 1·423 U.S. cents per barrel, equivalent to $1·80 per 100 bbl per mile for the seventy-nine miles of Syrian territory traversed. In addition, Syria was to take a share (to be agreed with Beirut, which had recently (p. 441) made its own corresponding agreement with Tapline) of the loading-fees collected at Zahrani. If greater amounts than 175 million bbl were ever to make the transit in a year, an increase in the dues payable would be discussed. Combined I.P.C. and Tapline payments to the Syrian Government on account of transit for 1964 amounted to some $30·8 millions or £11 million.

The Czech-built, government-owned refinery at Homs, operating with a throughput of 750,000 t/y since 1959 under direct governmental management and I.P.C. crude-supply (p. 237),[1] received additions to its plant in 1959–60—an l.p.g. unit and a bitumen plant, soon to be followed by a lubricating-oil installation, as well as a system of 6-inch product-lines to Damascus, Aleppo, and Lattakiya which came into operation early in 1964; and plans were made for the linking of the refinery to a new Russian-directed petrochemical industry. As output was gradually increased, first to 850,000 tons in 1961, later to 1 million t/y, some surplus gasoline became available for export, while certain products (notably gas- and diesel-oil and aviation spirit) had still to be imported; the arrangements for these exchanges were made with Russia and Rumania. Local demand for products rose to some 1·3 million t/y during the period. This led in 1964 to plans for the extension of

[1] Quantities thus delivered by I.P.C. rose from 775,000 tons in 1962 to 1 million tons in 1965.

the refinery by the Czechs to a capacity of 1·75 million t/y in 1966, and by stages to 2·5 million by 1968, with modifications of the plant, also, to take Syrian crude. Plans existed, moreover, for the construction of a small secondary refinery in the Bec de Canard district of north-east Syria. Distribution of all products was early in 1965 taken out of the hands of the long-established companies (Esso, Mobil, Shell, and half a dozen Syrian independents) and undertaken by the Government, as part of the now almost total nationalization of industry and commerce in the country.

## V. JORDAN

The search for oil resources, the lack of which seemed to Jordanians a monstrous injustice, continued to be carried out in the kingdom during these years, though discontinuously. The Phillips Company showed its energetic goodwill by two years of seismic exploration and the drilling of four dry wells (p. 334), of which the last, at al-Lisan on the Dead Sea, was abandoned late in 1960 at 12,050 feet. The Company then quit its operations and its concession, having spent, it was said, more than $5 million. In 1961 and 1962 no further field-work was in progress, in spite of the efforts of the authorities at 'Amman to interest foreign (probably including Russian) concerns.

A geological survey and report, carried out by German experts in 1962-3, was, however, handed to Government during the latter year, and indicated the north-western shores of the Dead Sea as the most hopeful area; but discussions with the Elwerath concern and with Preussag reached no hopeful conclusion. In the spring of 1964 the John W. Mecom Company (pp. 427-9) kept matters alive by taking a concession for the whole of Jordan's territory. The term was to extend to forty years provided that oil be found in the first five, with provision for a 50 per cent. relinquishment after two years and thereafter 20 per cent. every five years; drilling must not fall below a rate of 20,000 feet a year; profits would be divided on a half-and-half basis. The Mecom drillers lost no time; first they deepened the Phillips well at Halhul (abandoned at 6,000 feet in 1958), then in December 1964 spudded in another, Mar Saba' no. 1, near Bethlehem. This was abandoned at 4,600 feet, as were later wells at 'Azzun (at 1,840 feet), near Jericho (at 5,400), and north-west of Nablus. Mecom abandoned the enterprise in the spring of 1966. It was then announced that the Jordan

Government was forming a Mineral Resources Authority. This body initiated a geological survey. Government at the same time awaited proposals from abroad for exploration licences or concessions.

The 12-inch and 16-inch pipelines of the 'Iraq Petroleum Company remained inoperative and deteriorating. The former ceased its functions in 1947 (pp. 334–5), the latter had never come into use. In the summer of 1961 the Jordan Government acquired the use of these pipelines from the Company. The pipe was to be used in the Government's water development campaign to combat drought, for the transit of crude oil to the refinery at Zerka, and for the transport of refined products within Jordan. The I.P.C. transit concession itself was surrendered in September 1963, all employments were terminated and offices closed. Pumping stations H4 and H5 were taken over by Government; H5 was used as a guest-house.

With the owners of Tapline, whose transit of Jordan covered 110 miles, an agreement was reached by the Jordan Government early in 1962 on lines strictly similar to those affecting Syria (p. 446). Payment was to be at a rate of 1·976 U.S. cents per barrel (or $1.80 per 100 bbl per mile) for the distance traversed, and a lump sum of $10 million was to settle all retrospective claims. There was no Tapline pumping station in Jordan and no terminal.

The Kingdom's first and only refinery at Zerka (Zarqa), twenty-four miles north of 'Amman, was finished according to plan (p. 335) with an initial throughput of 180,000 t/y (about half its designed capacity), sufficient for almost the whole of Jordan's demand; output was later raised to about 325,000 t/y. The local need for bitumen and for liquid petroleum gas was catered for, but the import of some other products—gas- and diesel-oils, lubricants, aviation spirit—was still necessary. The refinery, paid for by the sale of shares in the Jordan Petroleum Refining Company throughout the Arab world, and to a lesser extent by the Government, was an immediate relief and asset to the Kingdom.

## VI. ISRAEL

The progress of discovery and development of oil and natural gas in Israel in these years, if 'as good as could be expected' in a narrow land of low hydrocarbon promise, was by international standards unimpressive.

In search of greater local production much effort continued to be spent on the exiguous but useful Heletz field (p. 332) which, with Bror-Hayil, had in 1959 produced 145,000 tons of oil, from reserves estimated at some 5 million. Wells nos. 25 and 26 brought a useful addition in 1960: Israel could in that year feel that its home-grown petroleum was supplying not far from 10 per cent. of its needs, which then amounted to 1·9 million tons a year, approximately half of this being fuel-oil. Later in the same year the companies jointly developing Heletz-Bror found small-scale oil in their third well, at Negba three miles away, and in the spring of 1962 Heletz no. 28 showed further useful oil and gas. Later in 1962 Lapidoth found a small yield of oil at Kokhav, north of and close to Heletz, and pressed ahead with more drilling: a majority of these wells were producers, and the field, especially after the testing of nos. 10 and 11, showed a modestly useful potential; it was the best discovery since Heletz itself.

Multiple completions at some of the Kokhav wells helped to bring the country's total output in 1965 to 201,000 tons (as against 134,000 in each of 1961 and 1962, 151,000 in 1963, and 198,000 in 1964), from twenty-two producing wells at Heletz-Bror and eleven at Kokhav. It was decided in 1964 that a wider use of secondary recovery methods should be applied to many of these wells. Also in that year a minor discovery was made, this time with a one-fifth participation of the State-controlled National Oil Company, at Nir-Am where a number of hopeful development wells were drilled. In 1965 some decrease in production from the Bror field, from 2,600 down to 1,995 b/d, was compensated by a rise at Kokhav from 1,100 to 1,855 b/d. Moreover, an extension of the Kokhav field was revealed in 1965 by a well drilled beyond its known limits.

Exploration, survey, and test-drilling continued indeed in all parts: in a typical year, 1963-4, the total exploration effort was represented by seismic programmes both offshore and in various parts of the country, and by a dozen exploratory wells in the northern and central Negev and the coastal plain. Earlier, in 1962, the authorities had issued the first offshore licence to a Canadian company, Petrocana, an *ad hoc* subsidiary of Sancana. This enterprise undertook a submarine geophysical survey, which was shortly followed by another, conducted by the Asher Oil Company of Delaware offshore of Haifa; but, when survey led on to drilling, only dry holes resulted. Early in 1966 the arrangement with Petro-cana gave place to one with Livingstone Oil of the U.S.A., who were to drill offshore. The same outcome awaited tests on dry land drilled in 1963–4 by Naphtha and Lapidoth—the latter, in which private and statal, foreign and Israeli capital was all repre-sented, being the owner of all the producing fields in the country. Late in 1965 an Israeli-American company based in the U.S.A. began gravimetric surveys in an area south of the Dead Sea. Lapi-doth Israel drilled in 1965 some 160,000 feet, about equally divided between development (including five producing wells) and outside exploration—jointly, in some cases, with other companies—which achieved ten dry holes. The programme for and in 1966 was not less active: it would include Naphtha Israel Petroleum (presently producing gas in the Negev) drilling in the Dead Sea area.

Discovered supplies of natural gas did something to supplement liquid fuel. Such were encountered in 1959–60 at Zohar and Kidod in the Negev (p. 332), and were soon conveyed by pipeline to industrial sites. Further drilling for gas was begun in 1960 at Daya, twelve miles from Zohar, by the Naphtha Corporation, and at Raman Gat, south of Tel Aviv, by the Israeli-American Oil Corporation. In late 1961 a further limited gas-supply was dis-covered by the Naphtha enterprise at Kana'im, north-east of Zohar. As at Zohar it consisted almost entirely of methane, and was piped to the Negev industrial settlements.

It remained, as this period closed, not improbable that further, but almost certainly not large-scale, discoveries of both oil and gas would be made in Israel: sufficient, possibly, to justify the high cost of search. In the meantime the quest continued; though many aspirants had given up, enough with, it seemed, adequate capital, domestic or foreign, still remained in the field. These, doubtless in part for political reasons, did not include any of the international majors, all heavily committed to the Arab countries. The number of applicants was, however, not notably increased by changes made during 1963–4 in the terms of the basic 1952 Petroleum Law: changes which were all in the direction of en-abling greater areas than before to be granted to single licence-holders, and of less insistence on premature drilling too hastily located. The amendments were made on the advice of distinguished foreign advisers brought in by the Israeli Government.

The period was one of much activity in other branches of the industry, less central to our theme of discovery and development. In the field of refining, the important plant at Haifa had passed in 1959 (p. 332) into possession of the Government-controlled group now renamed Haifa Refineries Limited. This concern proceeded between 1963 and 1965 to a costly campaign of modernization of the plant, which was now more than twenty years old. Throughput was raised by the first stage of this operation from 1·75 million t/y to about 3 million (a third of this being exportable), and by the second stage, completed in 1965, was brought to 4·7 million tons. Hundred-octane gasoline was among the improved products now available. A further programme was planned in 1964 to increase the quantity and perfect the quality of products by greater distillation capacity and specialized units for, among other purposes, sulphur recovery. Funds for a part of these works were provided by the U.S. Export-Import Bank. Construction of a small 250,000 t/y refinery at Eilat, mainly for bunkering, was begun in the autumn of 1965 as a joint project of Haifa Refineries and Sonol, Paz, and Delek, the leading marketing companies; it was intended to produce middle distillates and fuel-oil for use locally and in the Negev, and for bunkering. Partly processed gasoline would be transmitted from the refinery to Haifa. It was due to be completed late in 1966.[1]

The 235-mile Eilat–Ashdod Yam–Haifa 16-inch crude pipeline (p. 333), essential to supply the Haifa refinery, was in 1963-4 increased in throughput capacity from under 3 million t/y to over 3·6 million by the addition of a new pumping station. It was further raised, by yet another pump-station, to 4·9 million t/y at the end of 1965. At Eilat itself facilities were improved and tankers of 50,000 tons could now be accommodated. The Israeli tanker-fleet was developed in these years to a total tonnage exceeding 200,000. Provision for shipping and unloading crude and products at the port of Haifa was also improved, and a 32-inch submarine loading-line to serve tankers of up to 80,000 tons was installed.

Consumption of petroleum products in Israel rose during 1960-5 from 1·9 million tons in 1960 to 2·34 million in 1963, and 2·9 million in 1965. Distribution was in the hands of three all-Israeli marketing companies—Paz, Delek, and Sonol—who controlled 250 or more filling stations.

[1] It was announced late in 1966, however, that 'on grounds of amenity' construction had been delayed.

An interesting result of petroleum development in Israel, though its scale could scarcely interest the outside world, was the establishment by Israel International Enterprises (itself a combination of interested companies and the Government) of a promising petrochemical industry, based both on refinery products and on the natural gas which had become available. The more important plants were located at or near Haifa, where, in 1962, a formidable complex began to come into existence. Other factories in the same general field, using petroleum products both as feed-stock and as fuel, were established in other parts of the country.

### VII. EGYPT (THE UNITED ARAB REPUBLIC)

The period 1960–6 was, in the career of Egyptian oil, one of gratifying progress in the discovery and production of crude, and of high hopes for further progress in those activities. It was a period of interesting new grants of exploration and production rights to foreign companies, on terms securing great advantages to the Government; of development in the field of refining; of increasingly strict governmental control over all enterprises connected with oil—to the point of the nationalization even of veteran foreign firms who had long served Egypt; and, finally, of improvements to the country's unique artificial water-highway, the Canal, to respond to the increasing oil-traffic which afforded by far its greatest source of revenue. Egypt's own requirements in petroleum products steadily increased, but continued to be matched very imperfectly with products derivable from the local refineries. There was in these years no important physical interruption of the operations of the industry, such as there had been in 1956–7 (p. 346); it was, on the contrary, since it supplied some 90 per cent. of the country's energy, unusually favoured by the Government of the U.A.R. In the 1960–5 Economic Plan £E.120 million was to be invested in it, £E.64 million in refining and petrochemicals, £E.40 million on exploration and oilfield development, and £E.11 million on pipelines, storage, and terminals. Similarly, in the 1965–70 Five Year Plan provision was made for a petrochemical complex to be sited near Alexandria, to cost £E.46 million. It may indeed be said that Egyptian oil, so long meagre in amount and poor in quality by all Middle Eastern standards, had by mid-1966 reached a greatly improved position.

In the production of crude, the year 1960 (partly reported on earlier pages (343-5)) showed but a slight improvement on previous years; the total reached only 3·35 million tons, against 3·16 million in 1959. The increase came substantially from the new (1955), and by Egyptian standards important, Balayim field of the Compagnie Orientale (C.O.P.E.), a concern of which E.N.I. secured control in 1961 by acquiring Petrofina's 40 per cent. holding in International Egyptian, which controlled C.O.P.E. (p. 344). C.O.P.E.'s smaller fields at Firan, abu Rudeis, and Sidri contributed small quantities, although much effort in survey and drilling was expended on them, as well as on exploration elsewhere in C.O.P.E.'s licensed areas. Anglo-Egyptian Oilfields (A.E.O.) in the same year witnessed the continued decline in the production of its fields at Ras Gharib and Hurghada, and at those in Sinai—Sudr, Ras Matarma, and 'Asl—which A.E.O. shared with Mobil. Production by the Group fell from 1·5 million tons in 1955 to 1·2 million in 1960, and the Company, because foreign, was still debarred from further exploration. The wholly State-owned General Petroleum Company contributed small quantities of crude from its fields at Bakr and Karim, at the former of which a vigorous drilling campaign was carried out, with fair results: it gave 175,000 tons in 1960, individual well yields were exiguous. A discovery, destined never to produce, was made at Rahmi, thirty miles north of Bakr. General Petroleum conducted wide exploration in the Eastern Desert in this year. The Société Coopérative des Pétroles drilled a wildcat, without success, at Ras Shukhair. The General Petroleum Authority offered licences during the year for or in the Western Desert, on terms of 50 per cent. profit-sharing, with an explicit preference for companies which would accept Egyptian participation; but no agreements were concluded for another three years.

In the years 1961-5 total Egyptian production in millions of tons amounted successively to: 3·76, 4·3, 5·60, 6·35, and 6·4. Towards these totals, A.E.O. from its above-mentioned fields made an annually decreasing contribution of the order of 1 million t/y,[1] and not only was it given by Government no chance to discover more, but in the summer of 1961 the State constrained the main foreign shareholders (Shell and B.P.) to halve their holdings

[1] Of the A.E.O. fields, Hurghada, with 145 wells, in 1965 gave 168,000 bbl; Gharib, with 187 wells, 2·9 million (a drop of 0·9 million since 1964); Sudr, with 40 wells, 822,000; 'Asl, with 29 wells, 771,000; Matarma, with 7 wells, 100,000 bbl.

(from 30·9 per cent. each to 15·5 per cent.) in favour of the State, thus surrendering control: the consideration was to be in the form of Government bonds. This action was but a minor part of the wholehearted campaign of nationalization in progress in the Egypt of President Gamal 'Abdul Nasir; and the process was in this case completed by the renaming of the whole A.E.O. enterprise as al-Nasr Oilfields. The production part of al-Nasr was linked to the statal General Petroleum, and continued its sad decline. In 1964 the remaining foreign-owned shares were taken over by the Government; al-Nasr became a wholly statal property, by now yielding some 15 per cent. of total Egyptian production. Mobil retained an un-nationalized share in the Sinai fields of ex-A.E.O.

The General Petroleum Company (pp. 342 ff.), whose Bakr field alone was of importance for production,[1] claimed a discovery in 1961 at Jabal Zait, south-east of Ras Gharib, from which, however, little resulted; and the same was true of the Company's wide-ranging surveys elsewhere. It did, however, in 1965 find a more interesting quantity of offshore oil at Ras Amir, twenty-five miles north of Ras Gharib, where the first well, drilled from an artificial island, yielded 600 b/d of 22·5 degrees A.P.I. oil from a depth of some 2,900 feet. Early development of this 'find' was expected, up to at least 10,000 b/d. And the G.P.C. was to enjoy one more stroke of good fortune; in October 1966 it was announced that a discovery at Shukhair on the west coast of the Gulf of Suez, twenty-three miles south of Ras Gharib, at 2,400 feet of depth, had shown light oil of 35 degrees A.P.I. in quantities indicated by two tests as 1,000 or 3,000 b/d. This would certainly be brought as early as possible to production; terminal facilities would be close to those in preparation by Pan American for their Murgan field. The Société Coopérative (pp. 254, 344) drilled more than one wildcat to considerable depths, but no production resulted.

Better fortune attended C.O.P.E. (pp. 344 f.) which now stepped into the primacy among Egyptian producers once held by A.E.O. The major discovery at Balayim Marine, nine miles out to sea, was at first assumed to be an extension of the Balayim field on land, but was in fact a separate structure and a provider of lighter oil (31·3 degrees and 29·7 degrees A.P.I., from two producing

[1] Production rose from 1,134,000 bbl in 1960 by annual increases to 5·5 million bbl in 1965. The Karim field reached 810,000 bbl in the latter year. Rahmi produced nothing.

horizons, against Balayim's 22 degrees). Eager steps were taken to develop the new field which produced over 1·1 million bbl in 1962, 6·1 million in 1963, 14·1 million in 1964, and 13·9 million in 1965, thus rapidly overtaking the mainland structure.[1] A well drilled at Balayim Marine in midsummer 1964 revealed a third producing horizon, giving oil of 33 degrees A.P.I., and a month later a fourth horizon was found, with good production. The equipment and much of the management of C.O.P.E. was provided by E.N.I. which enjoyed the high favour of the G.P.A.[2] A second offshore drilling platform was brought to site in 1962, and was available for use; it was also used at Ba'ba and abu Suwair, other sites under licence to C.O.P.E.; and C.O.P.E.'s lesser fields at Firan, abu Rudais, and Sidri continued in minor production.[3] In October 1964 a further offshore discovery was claimed at Ghara in the Gulf of Suez, fifty miles south of the Balayim fields: it gave 31 degrees A.P.I. oil at 2,500 b/d, from 7,220 feet. The end of such discovery had certainly not yet been reached. A full programme of exploration and drilling was carried out in 1965 and continued into 1966.[4] Completed producing wells drilled in 1965 were at abu Rudais (1), Balayim (4), Balayim Marine (5), Amir (1), Karim (1), al-Murgan (4), Ras Bakr (4), and Ras Gharib (3): Total, 23 wells.

New agreements by Government with foreign firms, sought without definite result since 1960, were announced in the fall of 1963; they were likely, with reasonable good fortune, substantially to expand the country's oil industry. International Egyptian, now almost wholly owned by E.N.I. and itself controlling C.O.P.E.,

[1] This gave, in 1960-5 inclusive, in millions of bbl, 10·6, 14·07, 19·8, 21·3, 18·3, 17·7.

[2] An agreement was made in November 1961 between the Government and E.N.I. under which the latter gave a credit of $50 million repayable from oil to be produced later by C.O.P.E. E.N.I. was also to become grantee of concessions in the north-east of the country and the Red Sea coast (p. 456). Later (1965-6) further negotiations between E.N.I. and the Government delayed full development of the sea-bed field which could thereafter hope to increase output well above the mid-1966 level of some 50,000 b/d. (The E.N.I.-Government dispute was concerned with the latter's obstruction to the Company's right to repatriate its Egyptian-made profits.)

[3] These in 1965 yielded: Firan (6 wells), 130,000 bbl; abu Rudais (7 wells), 932,000; Sidri (6 wells), 477,000.

[4] Marine seismic work was carried out by all the Companies; field geology, gravity-meter, and/or land seismic work by some or most. G.P.C. drilled 7 wildcats, Pan American 3 (which included Murgan), Phillips 2 (in the Western Desert).

was granted two areas: the first, of 24,000 square kilometres between the Canal and the Rashid branch of the Nile; the second,
of 2,000 square kilometres on the Red Sea coast between Hurghada
and Jabal Zait. At the same time an important newcomer to Egypt,
Phillips Petroleum, was granted most of the Delta and the Western
Desert to the Libyan frontier—the eastern border, that is, of a
newly and fantastically successful oil territory. The area covered
was 96,000 square kilometres. Shortly afterwards, Pan American
(or, the Pan American U.A.R. Oil Company), a subsidiary of
Standard of Indiana, similarly agreed with the Egyptian Government to explore 28,000 square miles of the Western Desert (including the Fayum area) southwards from Cairo. To this grant
was added, three weeks later (February 1964), another which
covered all parts of the Gulf of Suez coast not already under
licence to anyone else. The terms of these grants varied but little.
In each case a large sum must be spent on exploration: by I.E.P.C.
(that is, E.N.I.) $20 million, by Phillips $30 million, by Pan
American $17 and $27·5 million. In all cases there would be an
equal partnership between the foreign company and the Egyptian
General Petroleum Corporation (the G.P.A. renamed), each bearing half the costs—with the statal partner, however, being spared
this burden until after the foreigner had spent the amounts prescribed above. The period was thirty years, with a fifteen-year
extension envisaged. Periodic relinquishment of territory would
be enforced. The Government as such would take 50 per cent. of
profits as calculated on posted prices, and as equal partner would
claim half the remainder. This followed the model established in
Iran. Each partner would hold and handle half the total oil
recovered. Locally made equipment was to enjoy priority.

The foreign companies concerned early initiated exploration
activities, mainly seismic and magnetometric, and within a few
months (the obligation being one year) prepared to drill. Pan
American commenced an offshore well in the Gulf of Suez, East
Bakr no. 1, seven miles from the coast, using the floating drilling-
vessel *Discovery*; but the well proved dry. In March 1965, however, a major success was announced—the discovery known as the
al-Murgan field. This was located by a well drilled, in ninety feet
of water, eleven miles west of al-Tor and forty miles south-east
of Balayim. It showed three production zones in the Eocene, and
yielded on test more than 12,000 b/d of 24·7 degrees to 30·9

degrees A.P.I. crude. By September 1965 three wells had been completed, with a probable production rate of 8,000 b/d each. Plans were made for drilling in 1966 with a new type of mobile drilling equipment, by which ten wells could be drilled directionally in water of depth up to over two hundred feet: the drilling platform could serve also as a permanent drilling and production platform. Operations thus conducted gave excellent results in early and mid-1966, further good producing wells being brought in. It was arranged to convey the oil by submarine pipeline to Ras Shukhair on the west side of the Gulf of Suez, where construction of the necessary jetty, loading lines, houses, workshops, and landing-ground was put in hand. A new jointly-held producing company, as between Pan American and the General Petroleum Corporation, was registered after some delay as the Gulf Petroleum Company or G.U.P.C.O. An initial production of 50,000 b/d in 1966 was at first expected to be increased later to 100,000, but the date of production had subsequently to be postponed until 1967;[1] it would in any case mark a day of prime importance to the Egyptian economy. Pan American, with further mid-sea drilling, discovered in the spring of 1966 a second and separate structure ten miles south of al-Murgan and likely to be of equal value.

Pan American had at the same time spudded in a deep test-well in their section of the Western Desert, at Mubarak, north-west of Fayum. Phillips also, after similar prolonged seismic survey, were in December 1965 drilling at 'Alamain, and making their own arrangements for clearing the still dangerous minefields of wartime. A depth of 15,000 feet was the objective. E.N.I. (or Independent Egyptian) decided in the spring of 1965 to site the first well in its Delta concession in the Daqaliya district. No success was reported from any of these locations.

A Russo-Egyptian agreement signed in February 1966 visualized increased aid from the U.S.S.R. in the country's oil search and production; some £E.16 million was to be devoted to the supply of equipment and the services of Russian experts. This formed part of Egypt's 1965–70 Industrialization Plan.

In the field of refining, the small 250,000 b/y plant at Alexandria,

---

[1] Some time was spent in further bargaining between the Government and Pan American regarding taxation; the Company suspended all field operations for some months.

originally owned by the Société Égyptienne pour la Raffinage et le Commerce du Pétrole (S.E.R.C.O.P.—p. 345),[1] was during 1961–2 enlarged to a capacity of 1·25 million t/y, and in 1966 a further extension of 23,000 b/d capacity was a firm proposal; this would probably be completed in 1967. The long-established State-owned refinery at Suez was, thanks to distillation units imported from Czechoslovakia, increased to a capacity of 70,000 b/d or 3·5 million t/y. The range of products from these installations was also extended, distribution being facilitated by products pipelines.[2] The Anglo-Egyptian Oilfields plant at Suez had by 1960 attained a level of 3·25 million t/y; the crude, however, was only in part that from A.E.O.'s own production, the remainder being processed, for a fixed fee, on behalf of the General Petroleum Authority.

Both S.E.R.C.O.P. and A.E.O. fell victims in July 1961 to the current Egyptian enthusiasm for nationalization. This in the case of A.E.O. involved (as we have seen) a surrender by the foreign part-owners of half of their holdings, while S.E.R.C.O.P. also was forced to admit a predominant Government share. In the summer of 1964, when the whole of A.E.O. was nationalized, the Company's refinery activities were continued in the guise of the Nasr Petroleum Company; an extension of capacity by 24,000 b/d or 1·25 million t/y, was approaching completion in 1966. Thus by the end of 1965 Egyptian refineries, now all State-owned, had a present capacity of 165,000 b/d or 8·25 million t/y; an addition of 24,000 b/d or 1·2 million t/y or more was under construction; and further extensions at all three of the plants were under study or preparation. The current Five-Year Plan visualized an ultimate increase of capacity up to about 300,000 b/d or 15 million t/y.

The consumption of petroleum products in Egypt, which had increased but slowly in recent years, amounted to some 4·75 million t/y in 1960, in which year no less than 0·75 million tons represented demand for kerosene, almost as much for gas-diesel oils, and remarkably little (250,000 tons) for motor gasoline. Total demand had risen by 1965 to some 7 million tons, of which more than 5 million was internally consumed; but the demand, which

[1] Shareholders included Caltex, Swiss and Egyptian private subscribers, and the Government's Economic Development Corporation. By 1966, as the Alexandria Petroleum Corporation it was 97 per cent. owned by the Egyptian General Petroleum Corporation.

[2] The products lines from Suez were to Cairo and Helwan; from Mex (Alexandria) to Mahallat al Kubra and Tantah.

increased notably for fuel-oil and kerosene but very little for gasoline, remained awkwardly constituted. The failure of the local refineries to yield products in the proportion demanded led necessarily to the import of kerosene and gas-diesel oils, and to a surplus of gasoline which was available for export. In fact, the peculiarities of nearly all Egyptian crude (except for that of Balayim Marine) called for a considerable import of other-type foreign crudes, which in turn led to export of home-produced crude (largely to Italy) and of locally unusable products. Crude oil imported into Egypt came mainly from the U.S.S.R., or from Shell or Caltex. In 1965, out of 8·4 million tons processed in Egyptian refineries, 4·5 million were local crude, 3·4 million imported. Exports amounted to 1·8 million tons of crude, and 2·1 million tons of products, mainly fuel-oil. These included an arrangement, renewed late in 1966, whereunder the Spanish authorities were to take some 200,000 tons of Egyptian crude per year. Although refinery extensions completed in and after 1962 improved the position, Egypt appeared likely (unless Murgan radically changed the situation) to remain a simultaneous importer and exporter on a considerable scale, with some loss of foreign exchange. The whole of the resulting trade was handled by the Egyptian General Petroleum Corporation, through the international companies locally represented and the Russians.

Changes occurred in these years in the marketing sphere. In 1960 the retail market was divided between a governmental section, composed of the Société Coopérative (about 40 per cent.), and a larger private section. In the latter the Shell Company of Egypt, Mobil of Egypt, Esso (New Jersey), and Caltex (for lubricants, and bunker and aviation fuels only) each had a part in this highly competitive market. The three last-mentioned retained a probably diminishing share till the end of the period, having somehow escaped (as did E.N.I.) the zeal of the nationalizers; but Shell, whose production and refining company (A.E.O.) was taken over by stages in 1961 and 1964, suffered also the nationalization of its marketing company in the latter years.[1] Its network, which had been supplying rather more than 25 per cent. of Egypt's internal

[1] The law presented in 1966 to the U.A.R. National Assembly, covering compensation for the three Shell companies concerned (A.E.O., Shell Company of Egypt, and Shell Chemicals Distributing Company), provided for payments of £E.10 million (or £8·3 million) in interest-free instalments spread over eight years.

needs, was now merged with the statal marketing companies, under the name of Misr Petroleum.

Northbound shipments of oil through the Suez Canal, which represented from 50 to 70 per cent. of total Canal tonnage, amounted in 1961 to 114 million tons, a figure little changed since 1960; approximately nine-tenths represented crude oil, the rest products. Southbound oil shipments, mainly Russian, were some 6·3 million tons, double the 1960 figure. By 1963 the northbound total figure had reached 133 million (120 million being crude); southbound had fallen to 5 million tons of which two-thirds were products. The corresponding figures for 1965 were 155 million northbound (143 million being crude) and 7·9 million southbound. The main suppliers of northbound cargoes were, consistently, Kuwait, Iran, and Sa'udi Arabia; the main destinations were the United Kingdom, Italy, France, the Netherlands, West Germany, Belgium, and the U.S.A. Southbound cargoes (mainly products) were in general destined for Japan, India, Ceylon, China, with the first-named taking more than half the total.

The average size of tankers making the passage continued to rise. The maximum permitted draught, which during 1961 had been increased by stages from 35 to 37 feet, was raised to 38 feet in February 1964, in which year Canal dues, collected by the well-administered Canal Authority, amounted to £E.77 million or £64 million sterling. (Figures for the previous two years were £E.71 and £E.52 million.) The desirability of deepening and widening the Canal to permit the passage of bigger, and the biggest, tankers was obvious; but a one-foot deepening throughout its length would cost, it was stated, £10 million sterling, which must have presented a difficult problem for the planners and prophets. The next stage in improving Canal facilities, after reaching the 38-foot limit, was to be an increase to 41 feet: a boon, obviously, to the owners of the larger-sized vessels at present forced to use the Cape route, even though a 41- or even a 42-foot depth would still be insufficient for vessels over 60,000 tons, of which the numbers were constantly increasing. In July 1964 Canal dues, which had long stood at 6s. 3d. per ton of oil carried for the round trip, northward and southward, were increased by a surcharge of 1 per cent., and it was further provided that vessels with a draught exceeding 37 feet, or a width exceeding 104 feet, should pay an extra 1 per cent. for each additional foot or part of a foot of draught, and/or for each additional 6 feet of width. These additions could amount to an extra 3*d.* to add to an existing transport cost of some 39*s.* 9*d.* per ton of oil passing, for example, from Kuwait to the United Kingdom. Kuwait itself, from its own abundant revenues, made in 1964 a loan of some £E.10 million for improvements to the Canal. The Canal Authority had already borrowed £E.20 million from the World Bank; it inspired confidence not only by its day-to-day administration and its enlargement of the waterway, but also by its expansion of the dredger fleet, improved dry-dock facilities, provision for maintenance, and new works at Port Said to lessen navigational difficulties.

## VIII. THE SUDAN

In the Sudan there was some not very intensive exploration for oil, and some shallow test-drilling, by E.N.I. in the period following 1959, in accordance with their agreement of that year with the Sudan Government (p. 348); the Shell group also carried out some prospecting. No hopeful news resulted from either of these enterprises, which were discontinued. Of the same two groups, who in 1959 were both competitors for permission to erect the Sudan's first refinery (p. 348), Shell proved the more convincing, and a refinery of 1 million t/y throughput was entrusted to that Company jointly with B.P., in the guise of Shell and B.P. (Sudan) Limited. Work began in 1962 and was completed in late 1964. The country's consumption of petroleum products entered the sixties with a rate of some half-million t/y, and increased annually and substantially thereafter.

## CHAPTER XXVI

# MIDDLE EAST OIL IN 1966:
# FACTS AND COMMENTS

## I. PRODUCTION, EXPORTS, RESERVES

THE reader of these pages must by this stage be fully satisfied that in this latest period here under review, 1960–6, the progress of our region in oil discovery and production was far from halting or slowing down. He will recall, from earlier pages, a number of discoveries of productive structures hitherto unknown (including the rare case of a gas-field which turned oil-producer), and the important and always upward reassessments made of known but incompletely explored reservoirs and horizons. He will have noted the recent bringing into effective production of structures already known as oil-containing but not, by 1960, yet harnessed as contributors and in some cases not yet proved as fully commercial deposits; and he will be aware that, within a year or little more from the present time of writing (autumn 1966), at least two more Middle Eastern territories, Oman and Syria, will have joined the ranks of producing countries.

The 'Big Four' among the exporting States have all, in the last six years since 1959, greatly increased their output: Kuwait from 68 million tons in 1959 to 107 in 1965, Sa'udi Arabia from 53 to 100 million, Iran from 45 to 93 million, 'Iraq from 41 to 63 million. Among these the primacy in new discovery rests no doubt with Iran, where both land and sea were seen to be offering new sources of oil, to new enterprises as well as to those long established; and discovery in Sa'udi Arabia was little inferior. The contribution made to production by these four States (even ignoring, as these figures do, the contribution of the Neutral Zone to two of them) is dominant to an extent of some 87 per cent. in the whole region.

These countries are more likely to be joined soon in their front-rank position by abu Dhabi than by any other competitor. If today in the second rank, the last-mentioned shaikhdom, with its important production since 1962 by land and sea, will certainly see this greatly and rapidly increased unless the Murban structures strangely disappoint. Qatar, perhaps incapable of serious increases by land, was already in 1966 exporting oil from two sea-bed fields. The Neutral Zone, whose field on land is clearly in decline, has large potential supplies in the marine Khafji field, available as soon as facilities (and demand) are suitably increased; its total output trebled between 1959 and 1965. Egypt, in spite of an over-all doubling of production in the last six years, has been kept to relatively humble figures, rising to 6·3 million t/y in 1965, but the development of recent more massive discoveries must greatly change this; the year 1970 may show an Egyptian production of 20 million t/y.

In spite of widespread effort and some recent discoveries of moderate interest, Turkey remains in 1966 a small producing country with little hope of a radical change for the better; but at least local self-sufficiency is near or achieved. Bahrain Island does rather better than hold its own in production and is henceforth to benefit, half-and-half, from a Sa'udi marine discovery. Oman is on the threshold of production as at least a medium-scale new supplier, with a hopeful future. Syria can, it seems, scarcely hope to find major resources, but, after strange delays, should soon be producing and exporting modest quantities of crude. Dubai, offshore, has imminent possibilities. Israel is not quite oil-less. No oil has yet been discovered in Cyprus, Jordan, the Sudan, the Yemen, or South Arabia.

Among free-world oil regions established as such for some years (which excludes those of North Africa) the Middle East region still shows the highest percentage annual increase in production; that of the U.S.A. has been 2½ per cent. per annum, of North America as a whole 3 per cent., for the period 1960–5; of the Caribbean it has been 4 per cent., of South East Asia 3·5 per cent., of Western Europe 7·5 per cent. That of the Middle East is 9·5 per cent., while the U.S.S.R. claims 10·5 per cent. The total off-take from Middle Eastern fields (including Egypt) in 1965 was 415 million tons, in a world total of 1,550 million: that is, nearly 27 per cent. of world supplies. This quantity (admittedly the product of a number of separate States) is less than that of the U.S.A. (427 million tons, including 51 million of natural gas liquids); more than double that of Venezuela; 70 per cent. greater than the U.S.S.R., and leaves all other areas out of sight.

In the matter of proved reserves (see Appendix III) the region holds unshakeably its dominating position. With its assessed total of 29 billion tons, it possesses more than 60 per cent. of the world's discovered and available stocks (excluding shale and tar-sand oil), as against the share of the U.S.A. calculated as 10·6 per cent., the Communist bloc with 9·4 per cent., Africa with 6·3 per cent., and the Caribbean with 5·7 per cent. (It should be added that these 'western' estimates, good as may be their authority, would be totally rejected by Soviet experts, who claim the greatest reserves in the world.) It is in any case notable that, in a mere five years (1960–5), the accepted estimates of the world's proved reserves rose from 41·5 billion tons to 48 billion, while those of the Middle East increased from 24 to 29 billion tons—reserves which in 1950 were reckoned for this region at 5·57 billion tons, and in 1955 as 16·8 billion.

The ratio between reserves and annual offtake in the Middle East is clearly unique in the world and, foreseeably, will long remain so. Moreover, local consumption of petroleum products being relatively low in the region,[1] the offtake is 85 per cent. available for export to the oil-demanding world. This, if we take the Middle Eastern countries concerned as a single group, gives the region the position of easily the leading exporter of oil into the world's markets: exporter, that is, from one of the Syrian or Lebanese ports (Banias, Tripoli, Sidon), or from a Persian (Arabian) Gulf port (Fao, Khor al-Amaya, Abadan, Bandar Mashhur, Kharg, Ahmadi, offshore Neutral Zone, Ras Tanura, Bahrain, Umm Sa'id and offshore Qatar, Jabal Dhanna and offshore abu Dhabi). Without here distinguishing between these, or between crude and products, and without including Egypt's small contribution, the picture was in 1965 one of some 205 million tons a year of Middle Eastern oil carried to Western Europe, 72 million to Japan, over 20 million to Africa, 17 million to the U.S.A., and 19 million to other Western Hemisphere destinations. Total exports in that year exceeded 372 million tons. The contribution to Western European needs (376 million tons in 1965) was thus of the order of 55 per cent.; it remained to be seen how far North African supplies, which would soon exceed 100 million t/y, would affect this predominance in coming years.

[1] About 37 million tons, including bunkers, in 1965, out of a free-world usage of 1,294 million, of which 544 million in the U.S.A. and 376 million in Western Europe.

The share of refined products[1] in the figures given above as Middle Eastern production or exports is a relatively small one, since the nearly 90 million tons of refined products (including Egyptian) manufactured in the region in 1965 represented little more than one-fifth of total production, 415 million tons. The corresponding figure had been about 62 million tons in 1960, subsequently increased by some 5·5 per cent. per year. Although, largely for reasons of national *amour propre* and to save foreign exchange, almost every territory except the unhappy Yemen and the south-east Arabian statelets had in 1966, on some scale, its own refining industry, it was likely that the latter will grow less rapidly than will crude production. It is certain that both local consumption and local bunkering will increase, and that governments will continue to favour the local establishment of industries and to press operating oil companies accordingly; but the foreign Companies which, in most though not all cases,[2] must find the capital, prefer to erect their plants near to or in the major products-consuming areas, except in so far as bunkering considerations are important. Apart from broad economic reasons which favour consumer-country refineries, the prevailing though not universal Middle Eastern attitude to conspicuous foreign installations in their countries is scarcely one to inspire confidence in a future of trouble-free operation; many companies would prefer to minimize rather than augment the capital which their operations compel them to tie up in these lands of restless and emotional nationalism.

## II. THE PRESENT AND THE FUTURE

Previous pages have shown the extent to which the great integrated foreign companies, American and British, played by far the greatest part in the discovery and development of Middle Eastern oil. To the question: Could this have been otherwise? Would it not have been better to let national (governmental or public) agencies carry out the work, and thus avoid the blow to local *amour propre* caused by this too-successful foreign enterprise?

---

[1] Rough figures for refinery capacity, per country, are (in millions of t/y) for 1965: Iran 25, Kuwait 16, Sa'udi Arabia 13, Bahrain 9, Egypt 8, Aden 7, and the rest ('Iraq, Syria, Lebanon, Turkey, Jordan) 11. For details, see previous pages and Appendix IV.

[2] Refining enterprises are governmental in all cases in Egypt, Syria, and 'Iraq, and in some cases in Turkey and Iran.

the answer seemed clear: foreign agencies (in effect, foreign oil companies, possessing the money, knowledge, technology, willingness to accept great risks, world-wide contacts, and, above all, access to markets) offered a means of development which was indispensable in territories where all of these qualities and advantages were (and largely still are) lacking. No public or private concern in the Middle East could imaginably have handled these great works of highly specialized and immensely demanding industrial enterprise, nor did they at any time offer themselves to do so. They were fortunate indeed that all the risks were run for them, and outstanding success achieved on their behalf by friendly foreign concerns of high probity and goodwill acting under freely negotiated (and frequently revised) agreements between Company and Government. Nor, in spite of immense progress since 1910 in technology, and in modernity of outlook, among the publics and rulers, did it appear in 1966 that the time had come, or was near, when the essential present functions of the great Companies could, by whatever procedures, be handed *en bloc* to local hands without great and immediate damage to the countries concerned. This was, however, far from meaning that local enterprise need be for ever debarred from entering the field of oil operation; quite the contrary was the case.

The great Companies referred to, and their wide-reaching concessions, were those so often mentioned in these pages. In Persia the part of developer was played by a single British company, the Anglo-Persian (later Anglo-Iranian) Oil Company, from 1901 to 1951, to be succeeded in 1954 by a no less foreign consortium of British, American, Anglo-Dutch, and French companies acting as a single concern; further agencies of development in Iran appeared partly with the operations of the National Iranian Oil Company and partly with the highly interesting joint companies formed by N.I.O.C., in the late fifties and again in 1964, with important, though mostly non-major, foreign concerns—American, Italian, Anglo-Dutch, French, German, and, to a very minor extent, Indian and Spanish. In 'Iraq the task fell to an international group: the Turkish (later the 'Iraq) Petroleum Company, and its sister companies, formed by British, Anglo-Dutch, French, and American interests—that is, Anglo-Iranian (B.P.), Shell, the Compagnie Française, Near East Development (New Jersey and Mobil), and the 5 per cent. Gulbenkian interest; a single small area of

'Iraq, the Transferred Territories, was handled by A.P.O.C. (A.I.O.C., B.P.) until 1952, and thereafter by the 'Iraq Government. In Kuwait the sole developing authority since 1938 has been the Kuwait Oil Company, equally shared between a British and an American partner—Anglo-Iranian and the Gulf Oil Corporation; here, however, the K.N.P.C., in association with foreign companies, was in 1966 likely to try its hand at oil finding, and rights in Kuwait's offshore waters had been granted to the Shell group in 1961. In the Kuwait-Sa'udi Neutral Zone two American concerns, Getty and Aminoil (which includes non-major participants) have operated together since 1949, and the offshore waters were granted by the two sovereigns in 1957 to a Japanese consortium. In Bahrain a company equally linking two American concerns has been responsible for production since the earliest days of 1932; Bapco remained the sole grantee until 1965, when Continental Oil acquired rights for most of Bahrain's sea areas. In Sa'udi Arabia an American vast-scale concessionaire dating from 1933 developed in 1947 into a powerful all-American group —California, Texas, New Jersey, and Mobil; and only by 1966 was the Government, through its new national company, Petromin, looking elsewhere for foreign partners or grantees for the wide areas of Aramco-relinquished territory.

In south-eastern Arabia the earliest grantees and operators were companies of the I.P.C. group formed *ad hoc*, territory by territory. These, which had covered Qatar, the Trucial Coast, and Oman, survived in 1966 only in a small part of Qatar (mainland) and less than the whole of abu Dhabi (ditto). A Shell company had appeared offshore of Qatar in the early fifties, followed by an American newcomer as successor in part of the same waters in 1963, while B.P. and French interests had taken the offshore rights for abu Dhabi and Dubai, though Continental Oil and others came on the scene in 1963 as concessionaires of Dubai land and waters, and a variety of non-major Americans had appeared in the other Trucial Coast territories both by land and sea. Oil-search in Oman had been handed in 1960 to Shell, with a Gulbenkian minority interest. In southern and south-western Arabia a number of non-major American concerns intermittently tried their luck— in vain; and the French were due in 1966 to appear in the Hijaz. In Egypt important American and Italian concerns were, as we have seen, allowed to participate with the Government in certain areas, while the latter was itself the operator in others; both there and in Syria State activity and operation were paramount, foreign enterprises or elements were to be used only as might appear immediately helpful. Jordan and Lebanon were both for a time part of the I.P.C. area of rights and oil-search, but the group later abandoned both territories, in 1954 and 1958 respectively; thereafter lesser investigators and operators, American and Lebanese, tried to locate oil resources, always without success. In Turkey exploration attracted enterprises of American, German, Anglo-Dutch, French, and Turkish origin; but ill-success had considerably reduced their numbers by 1966.

If the decade 1955–65 was, as we see, one of fragmentation of the original areas granted by licence or concession, and the multiplication of ambitious foreign grantees, it seemed likely in 1966 that the ensuing decade would follow, perhaps more intensively, a similar pattern. The desire and policy of host governments would be, no doubt, to grant minimum rights over defined and diminished areas, no longer for periods of seventy-five or ninety-nine years, but rather of twenty-five or thirty, with provision for restricted renewals and for early relinquishment of much or most of the area granted. And, within the limits of their financial and industrial competence, the Governments would wish themselves to participate in as much as possible of major productive as well as refining and distributing operations. For this purpose the series of National Oil Companies had been formed: a natural and hopeful development which, however, did little to solve the problem of effectively entering the world's highly competitive markets for oil products, already overcrowded with would-be sellers. Nor did it solve the evident dilemma which seemed to be curiously ignored in many emotionally reiterated government demands: that is, the dilemma between the States' insistence on high prices for their exported oil and an equal insistence on an ever-increased volume of such exports—even though these must, by flooding the market, inevitably decrease the likelihood of such prices.

As we have seen, the stage following that of extensive loose long-term 'blanket' concession has been and will be that of tighter, shorter, more restricted and restrictive grants of rights, often in the pattern of Company–Government partnership which made great progress in the period 1954–64: a pattern which in 1966 seemed to commend itself to many of the statal authorities for psychological as well as practical and financial reasons. But a further stage could be envisaged, following precedents established in other parts of the world (South America, Indonesia) and indeed in the Middle East itself (already adumbrated): that is, the stage wherein the foreign Company, with its paramount contribution of capital, 'know-how', and access to markets, will be employed as a simple contractor by the local Government, on terms which may well be very variable but must succeed in attracting willing and fully competent operators. The adaptation of some such plan to Company–Government relations in the Middle Eastern oil world has, it seems, still a long way to go before an acceptable, if not a more or less standardized, formula can be evolved; nor would it remove some of the major difficulties in the inter-relationship. The chief of these are, as we know, the xenophobia too commonly directed at the foreign concern; the not infrequent ignoring of actually valid economic considerations; and the destruction of the foreign capitalists' confidence which cannot but follow the threats of damaging and blatantly illegal unilateral action against the Companies' interests—and, one may add, the actions seen more than once in fact to follow such threats, actions which, however suicidal, are always sure of rapturous local applause. Indeed serious statesmen and writers in the most advanced of the Middle Eastern countries did not and do not hesitate to proclaim the moral and legal rightness and the patriotic duty of tearing up existing legally ratified agreements made after long and often arduous periods of negotiation and bargaining, their excuse being that times have changed (even in half a dozen years), that the previous bargainers on behalf of the nation must have been stupid or unpatriotic or corrupt, that 'the Company' had bullied or deceived them or misused its great-power status, and that anyhow today the 'rights' of the local citizenry were paramount. To question such views, which in fact are demonstrably erroneous, was the hallmark of a traitor or imperialist.

These considerations, added to what previous pages of this book have recorded, are sufficient to show that the political background in most Middle Eastern territories is, for the large-scale foreign industrial concern, one of precarious security, with the generalized or sometimes focused spirit of adverse criticism or active ill will as a powerful disincentive.

In fact, the uneasy background, at times the foreground, of some of the main concession-holding companies' operations has led directly to the question 'Since foreign-company agency there must needs be, how can this anti-company attitude be so corrected or mitigated as to ensure continuity of fruitful operation in everybody's interest?' The answer can be no single or simple one. The blanket or semi-blanket concessionaire companies will not, unless under extreme compulsion, consent to hand over blocks of their shares, or majorities on their Boards, or control of their essential functions, or the reasonable interest of their shareholders. Nor can one expect that the basic political conditions of the times will foreseeably change: for example, the strong and emerging position of 'small nations' in the world's debates, the practical impossibility of invoking force, the well-known difficulty in securing enforcement of a contract made by a company, of whatever nationality, with a sovereign State. These are facts which must, in the circumstances of 1966, be recognized. Nor does it, nor will it, prove enough for a foreign company thus situated to be intelligent, just, and imaginative in matters of recruiting, local purchase, labour relations, amenities, training, and all the functions of a good employer and a benevolent resident of the country. Such steps as these, on the lines most likely to be acceptable to local critics, are already habitual with the concessionaire companies, who, moreover, in their own self-defending interest, do the utmost that seems reasonable towards meeting demands made upon them, outside as well as within the terms of concessions, for the gratification of local feeling and governmental demand.

The way of wisdom for the great near-monopolist concerns seems rather to be the minimization, as far as feasible, of the scope of their monopoly and its bad psychological effects. They should view with equanimity the installation of other concessionaires in relinquished or never-allotted parts of their own country of operation. If Government wishes itself to administer some non-basic services, a *modus vivendi* should not be too difficult to find, and a measure of efficiency may have to be sacrificed with a good grace. The Government should no doubt be encouraged rather than discouraged in its own ventures (to which many Middle Eastern governments have already shown themselves inclined) in various branches of the oil industry: that is, in producing operations, directly as a government department or in the form of a statal company or in partnership with a foreign concern; in refining; in distribution; in tanker-owning; in the petrochemical industry; or in the oil trade. Such activities by the local Government can do no harm or at worst little harm to a major concessionaire, and can preserve or restore the self-respect of Government as an active participant in the handling of its own resources. They can, moreover, be helpfully educative.

With all this, the commonly expressed fear that Middle Eastern governments or O.P.E.C. may one day arbitrarily withhold oil supplies from the West, under pressure of militant nationalism (or of the U.S.S.R.),[1] though not to be lightly dismissed, may be to some degree exaggerated. The oil-wealthy States have come to rely heavily on these revenues for their development projects and often for their daily administration, and for major infusions of wealth by the Companies into the community. Cessation of company operations must entail immediate cessation of all these blessings; nor, as Persia in 1951–4 made clear, can the machinery of wealth production once stopped be quickly restarted. The Company, it is clear, especially when (as is usual) possessed of alternative sources of crude, would no doubt be less fatally afflicted by such a stoppage than would the Government and public. A withholding of supplies would be truly effective as a nationalist gesture only if adopted simultaneously by all Middle Eastern producers, an event almost impossible to envisage: Persia is non-Arab, and the Arab States are quite unlikely to achieve so self-destructive a form of unity.

Previous pages of this book have referred to the immense importance of governmental oil-derived revenues to the Treasuries of producing (and, in their degree, transit) countries,[2] as well as that of local oil-company expenditure among the public on pay, salaries, purchases, and contracts. It will therefore suffice here to indicate, as part of the general picture of the industry, the extent to which, amid a society awakened, enlivened, and enriched by

---

[1] It is, however, to be observed that the U.S.S.R. is now a competitor against Middle Eastern supplies in the world's oil markets: and much as the Russians might wish to damage Western interests in the Middle East, such damage by oil denial to the West would evidently be equally or more disastrous to the producing countries.

[2] The following table shows *in millions of dollars* the annual receipts of the Treasuries of the four greatest producing countries, year by year, from 1960 through 1965. A figure is added representing a total for the lesser recipients. These figures show both the scale and the continuous increase of these oil-derived revenues. It has been emphasized elsewhere that they do not include

this sudden access of wealth, governments can improve their social services, their schools and colleges, hospitals and dispensaries and preventive services, town-planning and improvement, water-supply and power and light; their country-wide administration and armed services, by better selection, training, upkeep standards, and scale; their communications by road, railway, telegraph, post, port, and harbour and airport, by new construction and better servicing; their industry, by pilot plants, assisted enterprises and, as an effect of increased purchasing power, their commerce also, by using newly opened lines of commercial contact and to satisfy new needs; their agriculture, by research, experiment and instruction, by new cultures, plant types and desalination—and by improved storage, transport, packing, marketing of agricultural produce. These potential features, of which no one country offered the entirety but of which none was absent in one or other of the fortunate States, exemplify rather than exhaust the ways in which oil-wealth could and did open the door to higher standards of living. With varying procedures, but usually under some European advice, the new riches have in fact been on the whole wisely spent in the beneficiary States—'Iraq, Persia, Kuwait, Qatar, Bahrain; less wisely at first, and with a negligible impact on the public, in Sa'udi Arabia, where, however, there have been, since the advent of King Faisal to the throne or even before that, clear signs of improvement. In the transit States (Jordan, Egypt, Syria, Lebanon) the payments made by the Companies for their pipelines and their shipping are a substantial part of the national revenues.

That these blessings, the degree of benefit from which must depend evidently on the use made of them by their recipients—and this in turn upon their own degree of wisdom and character, which the paying companies are powerless to influence—could be

amounts of money, and foreign exchange, distributed directly to the Companies' employees and the general public as salaries, wages, local purchases, contracts, etc.

| Year | Kuwait | Sa'udi Arabia | Iran | 'Iraq | Other M.E. States | Total |
|------|--------|---------------|------|-------|-------------------|-------|
| 1960 | 465 | 355 | 285 | 266 | 70 | 1,442 |
| 1961 | 464 | 396 | 301 | 266 | 70 | 1,497 |
| 1962 | 526 | 446 | 334 | 267 | 75 | 1,648 |
| 1963 | 555 | 489 | 398 | 308 | 83 | 1,833 |
| 1964 | 624 | 552 | 474 | 353 | 95 | 2,099 |
| 1965 | 636 | 639 | 532 | 368 | 120 | 2,295 |

in part counterbalanced by dangers, was obvious to observers, and has already been suggested. So abrupt a change from poverty to affluence, so sudden an irruption of Western or modern ways of life—by no means always at their best, and too uncritically received —could lead disastrously to demoralization, irreligion, and loss of traditional loyalties and certainties without the acquisition of new. It could lead to the loss of social freedom and equalities and Islamic graciousness, and replace these by the regimented drabness of industrial life. It could lead to added rather than diminished ferment in the political field, with keener competition and greater prizes, and to more open discontent with traditional (perhaps anachronistic) forms of government. Such considerations as these, more obvious perhaps to Western observers than to the public most concerned—or even to their political leaders—were familiar to the more enlightened personnel of the operating oil companies, and were, in their manner, doubtless more significant in the contemporary history of Western Asia than many current events and personalities far more publicized. The impact of the oil industry on the Middle East and the immediate and indirect results of its rapid production of great wealth in territories long impoverished are matters worthy of close and sympathetic study; but in the present pages they cannot be more than thus rapidly indicated. Nor does it seem appropriate here to describe the inter-statal jealousies or even menaces—and, more rarely, attractions—actual or possible, between Middle Eastern countries themselves by reason of the oil resources of some.

Could the further triumphant progress of the oil industry in the Middle East, which the above considerations take for granted, be checked by any probable set of events? Could one of these be a general recession in world trade, or industry, or power demand? This is highly unlikely; any broad yet critical view of the future of the world's requirements in energy-production cannot but show constantly increasing and multiplying figures of such demand, in the existing developed and industrialized countries and, even more, in the great population masses (China, India, and Africa) whose need for mechanical power and heat and transport has yet scarcely begun.

Could then a lesser or static demand for Middle Eastern oil be due to more specific factors? Such factors could imaginably be any of three. The first such possibilities could be an outbreak of

disorder or an extreme phase of anti-Western feeling in the producing countries, leading to general denial of oil supplies; the
second could be a major displacement of oil as a producer of
energy for the world's requirements by some other power or heat-
producing fuel or agency; the third could be the substitution of
oil from other sources for that of the Middle East in the world's
markets.

The first of these possibilities has already been sufficiently
covered, and was found to be not impossible but improbable. The
second, if we ignore the non-commercial fuels and also sources of
power (tides, winds, solar or outer-space radiation, etc.) not yet
in use, involves an estimate of the future competitive availability
of coal, natural gas, hydro-electricity, and atomic power. Of these,
coal will not be a serious rival—indeed, is already struggling to
keep its place; natural gas is a most important source of power,
especially in the Western Hemisphere, but by its nature can never
attain a place widely competitive with liquid petroleum in international trade. Hydro-electricity, however vigorously developed,
is unlikely to keep its present proportion, some 8 per cent., in the
world's energy supply. Atomic power, with unquestionably a very
great future in human civilization, is unlikely by reason of its high
cost and only gradual availability, to be a serious competitor with
oil for some decades to come, and will never be such in many
spheres of oil's utilization. In the vast and growing field of the
energy supply of the future, petroleum is assured of an extremely
important or indeed a dominant part.

If so, will the share of Middle Eastern oil in this task suffice to
permit the full expected development of its potential? There
appears, beyond reasonable doubt, the strongest probability of this.
On all present indications the Western Hemisphere, even with its
current over-supply and temporarily shut-in resources in some
territories, notably the United States and Canada, will be fortunate
to continue its present hemispheric self-sufficiency; indeed, imports from the Eastern Hemisphere will almost certainly be a
feature of North American oil supply within a few years, unless
new discovery reaches (which is improbable) a quite surprising
scale; and the South American surplus, if any, will be used for the
supply of the North. In the Old World, immense demands for oil
are clearly foreseeable within the next half-century, and, with all
generous allowance for the influx of Algerian and Libyan (and

Nigerian and perhaps other yet undiscovered African) sources of oil, it seems unlikely that any area of supply other than those of the Middle East will be capable of supplying these demands. Any probable exportable surplus from the U.S.S.R. can scarcely be so capable, other than locally or temporarily, in view of its own immense needs and projects, even though, admittedly, Russian exports have by 1966 assumed major importance; and no other part of the world seems, on present indications, to possess resources on any adequate scale.

The main task of providing the world with the next century's demand for energy—that is, for fuel—seems therefore ineluctably to belong to the Middle Eastern oilfields. It is one to which, unless malignant political crises supervene or the oilfields are prevented in some unforeseeable manner from performing their functions, they will be entirely adequate. In spite of remoteness from markets, industrial and technological backwardness, severity of climate, an uneasy political atmosphere, and limited natural and constructional resources, the region and its great oilfields are accessible, civilized, and not unhealthy; labour is abundant, intelligence high, skill fast improving. Proved oil reserves are by far the greatest in the world, oil-containing structures extraordinarily large and productive, individual and average production per well remarkably high. The main tasks and enterprises have been handled by concerns of the highest status and greatest resources, in the forefront of world industry in science and research, technology, organization, management, and ability to transport, refine, and market. Many or most of the problems of the industry in the region have been met and solved; others (such as the profitable use of natural gas) are under study and already partial solution. New methods and techniques are constantly under trial. And the desire of the great Companies, who have created the industry, to be of genuine service to the rulers and people of the oil-bearing territories is as certainly sincere as is their conviction that real community of interest exists between both—or all—parties in the continued progress and stability of the industry.

# COUNTRIES OF THE MIDDLE EAST

| Country | Area (000 sq. m.) | Population (000) | Capital | Currency (Note (A)) | Form of Government |
|---|---|---|---|---|---|
| Persia (Iran) | 635 | 22,000 | Teheran | Riyal (B) | Constitutional monarchy |
| 'Iraq | 170 | 8,260 | Baghdad | Dinar (D) | Republic (D) |
| Kuwait | 1·9 | 465 | Kuwait | Dinar (C) | Constitutional Principality |
| Neutral Zone | 1·9 | Nil | — | — | Sovereignty divided, Kuwait/S. Arabia |
| Bahrain | 0·23 | 182 | Manama | Dinar (E) | Absolute rule (Shaikh) |
| Qatar | 8·0 | 35 | Doha | Riyal (F) | Absolute rule (Shaikh) |
| abu Dhabi | 25·0 | 20 | abu Dhabi | See (E) | Absolute rule (Shaikh) |
| Trucial Coast States | 7·0 | 90 | Various (G) | See (E) | Absolute rule (Shaikh) |
| Oman | 114 | 735 | Muscat | See (H) | Absolute rule (Shaikh) |
| Aden territories (J) | 112 | 800 | Aden: al-Ittihad | Dinar (C) | See (J) below |
| Yemen | 75 | 4,000 | San'a | Silver riyal (K) | Civil war; under Egyptian military occupation |
| Sa'udi Arabia | 620 | 6,000 | Riyadh | S.A. riyal (L) | Absolute monarchy |
| Sudan | 970 | 13,500 | Khartum | £Sudan (C) | Republic (D) |
| Egypt (U.A.R.) | 386 | 29,000 | Cairo | £E=16s. | Republic (D) |
| Jordan | 37 | 2,000 | 'Amman | Dinar (C) | Constitutional monarchy |
| Israel | 8 | 2,560 | Jerusalem | £Is=2s. 4d. | Republic |
| Lebanon | 3·4 | 2,152 | Beirut | £L=2s. 4d. | Republic |
| Syria | 71 | 5,400 | Damascus | £Syr=1s. 10½d. | Republic (D) |
| Turkey | 301 | 32,000 | Ankara | £T=2s. 2½d. | Republic |
| Cyprus | 3·57 | 500 | Nicosia | £ sterling | Republic, internally disturbed |

NOTES:   (A)  In relation to sterling and/or U.S. dollars.
            (B)  75 riyals = $1.00; 210 = £1 sterling.
            (C)  Equals £1 sterling.
            (D)  No effective democratic machinery.
            (E)  Equals 10 rupees or £0 15s. 0d.
            (F)  Riyal 6 per cent. less than Sa'udi riyal (see p. 426, footnote 1).
            (G)  Various: Dubai, Sharja, 'Ajman, Umm al-Qaiwain, Ras al-Khaima, Fujaira.
            (H)  Pre-devaluation Indian rupee: Rs 13·3 = £1.
            (J)  Federation of South Arabia (including ex-Aden Colony) and Eastern Aden Protectorate (Qu'aiti, Kathiri, Mahri Sultanates).
            (K)  Equals about 90 cents; various other currencies exist.
            (L)  20–22 cents.

477

## MIDDLE EASTERN OIL PRODUCTION BY COUNTRIES, 1934–65

(in millions of long tons)

| Year | Egypt | Persia | 'Iraq | Bahrain | Sa'udi Arabia | Kuwait | Qatar | Turkey | Neutral Zone | Israel | abu Dhabi | Middle East | World |
|---|---|---|---|---|---|---|---|---|---|---|---|---|---|
| 1934 | 0·21 | 7·54 | 1·06 | 0·04 | — | — | — | — | — | — | — | 8·85 | 207 |
| 1935 | 0·17 | 7·49 | 3·66 | 0·17 | — | — | — | — | — | — | — | 11·49 | 225 |
| 1936 | 0·17 | 8·20 | 4·02 | 0·62 | — | — | — | — | — | — | — | 13·03 | 244 |
| 1937 | 0·17 | 10·19 | 4·29 | 1·52 | — | — | — | — | — | — | — | 14·76 | 278 |
| 1938 | 0·23 | 10·16 | 4·32 | 1·11 | — | — | — | — | — | — | — | 14·85 | 270 |
| 1939 | 0·65 | 9·58 | 4·04 | 1·01 | 0·53 | — | — | — | — | — | — | 15·81 | 278 |
| 1940 | 0·91 | 8·62 | 2·65 | 0·94 | 0·68 | — | — | — | — | — | — | 13·90 | 289 |
| 1941 | 1·19 | 6·60 | 1·61 | 0·91 | 0·57 | — | — | — | — | — | — | 10·88 | 300 |
| 1942 | 1·14 | 9·40 | 3·25 | 0·84 | 0·59 | — | — | — | — | — | — | 15·54 | 282 |
| 1943 | 1·26 | 9·71 | 3·78 | 0·90 | 0·64 | — | — | — | — | — | — | 16·29 | 313 |
| 1944 | 1·32 | 13·27 | 4·25 | 0·91 | 1·05 | — | — | — | — | — | — | 20·80 | 348 |
| 1945 | 1·30 | 16·84 | 4·62 | 0·95 | 2·84 | — | — | — | — | — | — | 26·55 | 356 |
| 1946 | 1·27 | 19·19 | 4·60 | 1·10 | 7·99 | 0·80 | — | — | — | — | — | 34·95 | 371 |
| 1947 | 1·32 | 20·19 | 4·65 | 1·25 | 12·15 | 2·20 | — | — | — | — | — | 41·76 | 415 |
| 1948 | 1·89 | 24·87 | 3·40 | 1·50 | 18·95 | 6·30 | — | — | — | — | — | 56·91 | 465 |
| 1949 | 2·31 | 26·81 | 4·10 | 1·51 | 23·10 | 12·20 | 0·01 | 0·01 | — | — | — | 70·15 | 465 |
| 1950 | 2·31 | 31·75 | 6·50 | 1·51 | 25·90 | 17·00 | 1·62 | 0·01 | — | — | — | 86·60 | 518 |
| 1951 | 2·30 | 16·72 | 8·55 | 1·50 | 36·90 | 27·80 | 2·30 | 0·02 | — | — | — | 96·19 | 582 |
| 1952 | 2·37 | 0·75? | 18·45 | 1·50 | 41·00 | 37·10 | 3·25 | 0·02 | — | — | — | 104·44 | 605 |
| 1953 | 2·32 | 0·75? | 27·65 | 1·50 | 40·88 | 42·60 | 3·99 | 0·03 | — | — | — | 119·50 | 650 |
| 1954 | 1·95 | 3·00 | 30·08 | 1·50 | 46·13 | 46·90 | 4·70 | 0·06 | 0·83 | — | — | 135·10 | 679 |
| 1955 | 1·76 | 15·95 | 33·11 | 1·50 | 46·78 | 53·90 | 5·36 | 0·20 | 1·34 | — | — | 159·80 | 763 |
| 1956 | 1·42 | 26·05 | 30·82 | 1·50 | 47·93 | 54·10 | 5·78 | 0·29 | 1·58 | 0·03 | — | 169·50 | 830 |
| 1957 | 2·24 | 34·95 | 21·56 | 1·54 | 48·32 | 56·37 | 6·50 | 0·30 | 3·30 | 0·07 | — | 175·10 | 875 |
| 1958 | 3·15 | 39·95 | 35·15 | 2·00 | 49·35 | 69·10 | 8·09 | 0·30 | 4·20 | 0·09 | — | 211·60 | 900 |
| 1959 | 3·60 | 44·85 | 41·10 | 2·22 | 52·80 | 68·40 | 7·87 | 0·37 | 5·90 | 0·13 | — | 227·20 | 964 |
| 1960 | 3·23 | 51·8 | 46·7 | 2·22 | 61·1 | 80·6 | 8·1 | 0·36 | 7·2 | 0·13 | — | 261·0 | 1,079 |

APPENDIX II—*continued*

| Year | Egypt | Persia | 'Iraq | Bahrain | Sa'udi Arabia | Kuwait | Qatar | Turkey | Neutral Zone | Israel | abu Dhabi | Middle East | World |
|------|-------|--------|-------|---------|---------------|--------|-------|--------|--------------|--------|-----------|-------------|-------|
| 1961 | 3·72 | 58·5 | 48·2 | 2·22 | 68·1 | 81·4 | 8·2 | 0·41 | 9·3 | 0·13 | — | 279·7 | 1,150 |
| 1962 | 4·25 | 65·0 | 48·4 | 2·22 | 74·6 | 90·7 | 8·7 | 0·53 | 12·8 | 0·13 | 0·8 | 307·9 | 1,246 |
| 1963 | 5·51 | 72·6 | 55·8 | 2·22 | 79·8 | 95·7 | 9·0 | 0·72 | 16·2 | 0·15 | 2·44 | 339·7 | 1,340 |
| 1964 | 6·3 | 83·5 | 60·6 | 2·43 | 85·0 | 105·0 | 10·0 | 0·87 | 19·1 | 0·2 | 9·00 | 380·7 | 1,447 |
| 1965 | 6·3 | 93·3 | 63·4 | 2·76 | 99·2 | 107·3 | 10·8 | 1·48 | 18·8 | 0·2 | 13·3 | 415·2 | 1,549 |

NOTES: Production before 1934 was:

(1) In Egypt, 1911–33 inclusive: 0·003, 0·03, 0·01, 0·1, 0·03, 0·06, 0·14, 0·27, 0·23, 0·16, 0·18, 0·17, 0·15, 0·16, 0·18, 0·17, 0·18, 0·26, 0·27, 0·28, 0·28, 0·26, 0·23.

(2) In Persia (Iran), 1912–33 inclusive: 0·04, 0·08, 0·27, 0·38, 0·45, 0·65, 0·89, 1·11, 1·38, 1·74, 2·32, 2·96, 3·71, 4·33, 4·56, 4·83, 5·36, 5·46, 5·94, 5·73, 6·45, 7·08.

(3) In 'Iraq, 1927–33 inclusive: 0·11, 0·11, 0·11, 0·12, 0·11, 0·10, 0·10.

*N.B.*: Many similar tables of Middle East production do not include Egypt, which can lead to an apparent discrepancy.

479

# APPENDIX III

## PROVED RESERVES, 1965[1]

| Country | Reserves | |
|---|---|---|
| | Million tons | Million bbl |
| abu Dhabi | 1,350 | 10,000 |
| Bahrain | 32 | 230 |
| Egypt (U.A.R.) | 290 | 2,000 |
| Iran | 5,335 | 40,000 |
| 'Iraq | 3,300 | 25,000 |
| Israel | 4 | 30 |
| Kuwait | 8,480 | 62,500 |
| Neutral Zone | 1,780 | 12,400 |
| Oman | 150 | 1,050 |
| Qatar | 380 | 3,000 |
| Sa'udi Arabia | 8,045 | 60,000 |
| Syria | 170 | 1,200 |
| Turkey | 70 | 500 |
| TOTAL MIDDLE EAST | 29,280 | 217,850 |
| *For comparison* | | |
| U.S.A. | 5,100 | 39,400 |
| Total Western Hemisphere | 9,600 | 72,300 |
| W. Europe | 400 | 2,600 |
| Africa | 3,000 | 23,000 |
| U.S.S.R. and Group | 4,500 | 33,500 |
| Free World | 43,400 | 323,800 |
| World | 47,900 | 357,300 |

Thus Middle East reserves of crude oil are some 61 per cent. of the world total.

[1] 'Proved Reserves' are the amounts of oil discovered in well-delineated reservoirs that can be recovered by presently available techniques at present costs and prices.

APPENDIX IV

## REFINERIES IN THE MIDDLE EAST, EARLY 1966

| Country | Location | Owners | Date | Extensions | Capacity in 1966 (in b/d) | Remarks |
|---|---|---|---|---|---|---|
| 'Iraq | Alwand | 'Iraq Govt. | 1927 | 1930 etc. | 12,500 | Formerly Khanaqin Oil Co. (p. 265). |
| | Daura | 'Iraq Govt. | 1955 | 1957–9 etc. | 50,000 | Major (Government) refinery near Basra planned in 1963–5 for 1967–8. |
| | Muftiya | 'Iraq Govt. | 1952 | | 4,250 | Formerly B.O.D./M.P.C. Not operating 1966. |
| | Qaiyara | 'Iraq Govt. | 1955 | Various | 2,250 | Handed over to Govt. by I.P.C. |
| | Haditha (K3) | 'Iraq Govt. | 1962 | Various | 6,000 | Company's topping plant. |
| | Kirkuk (K1) | I.P.C. | 1935 | | 3,000 | |
| Iran (Persia) | Abadan | Consortium | 1913 | | 420,000 | Originally A.P.O.C. (A.I.O.C.) now Iranian Oil Refining Co. (App. V). |
| | Masjid-i-Sulaiman | Consortium | 1955 | Various | 75,000 | As above, but now Iranian Oil Exploration and Producing Co. (App. V). |
| | Kirmanshah | N.I.O.C. | 1935 | | 4,000 | (A major refinery, 100,000 b/d, owned by N.I.O.C., near Teheran, was under construction 1966.) |
| | Naft-i-Shah | N.I.O.C. | 1930 | | 5,250 | |
| | Alborz | N.I.O.C. | 1950 | | 10,000 | |
| Sa'udi Arabia | Ras Tanura | Aramco | 1945 | Various | 255,000 | For Aramco, see App. V. The near-statal Sa'udi Refinery Co. (Sarco) planned a small refinery in the Hijaz (see p. 388). |
| Kuwait | Ahmadi | K.O.C. | 1949 | Various | 250,000 | |
| | Mina 'Abdullah | Aminoil | 1958 | Various | 100,000 | For Aminoil see App. V. Neutral Zone crude. |
| | Shaiba | K.N.P.C. | ?1968 | | 100,000 | K.N.P.C. project under construction 1966. |
| Neutral Zone | Mina Sa'ud | Getty Oil Co. | 1958 | | 50,000 | Under enlargement 1966. |
| | Khafji | Arabian Oil Co. | ?1968 | | 30,000 | Under construction from mid-1965. |
| Bahrain | 'Awali | Bapco | 1937 | Various | 205,000 | For Bapco see App. V. |
| Qatar | Umm Sa'id | Q.P.C. | 1955 | | 600 | Company topping plant. |
| Aden | Little Aden | B.P. Ltd. | 1954 | Various | 150,000 | B.P. Refinery (Aden) Ltd. (Name adopted 1956.) |

APPENDIX IV—*continued*

| Country | Location | Owners | Date | Extensions | Capacity in 1966 (in b/d) | Remarks |
|---|---|---|---|---|---|---|
| Egypt (United Arab Republic) | Alexandria (Mex) | Alexandria Petroleum Co. | 1956 | Various | 30,000 | Now mainly State-owned, via the Egyptian General Petroleum Corporation (p. 458). Under extension 1966. |
| | Suez | Nasr Oil Co. | 1913 | Various | 80,000 | Ex-Anglo-Egyptian Oilfields (see p. 458). Now Egyptian Govt. Major extension begun 1966. |
| | Suez | Suez Oil Processing Co. | 1921 | Various | 55,000 | Egyptian Govt. Extension in hand 1966. |
| Israel | Haifa | Haifa Refineries Ltd. | 1939 | | 95,000 | Govt.-controlled. Formerly Consolidated Refineries, until 1958. (See pp. 332–3.) |
| | Eilat | Sonol Industries Ltd. | ?1967 | | 5,000 | For ownership, see p. 451 and App. V. Sonol is a subsidiary of Sonneborn Associates Corporation, N.Y. |
| Jordan | Zarqa | Jordan Petroleum Refin. Co. | 1960 | | 7,500 | Some Government participation (p. 335). |
| Lebanon | Tripoli | I.P.C. | 1940 | Various | 30,000 | Extension made 1966. For origins, see p. 140. |
| | Sidon | Mediterranean Refin. Co. | 1955 | | 16,500 | See App. V. for Medreco. |
| Syria | Homs | Gen. Petroleum Authority | 1959 | | 25,000 | Syrian Govt. Authority. To be extended. |
| Turkey | Mersin | Anatolian Refining Co. (A.T.A.S.) | 1961 | | 65,000 | See App. V, and pp. 327, 438. |
| | Batman | T.P.A.O. | 1955 | 1962 and 1965–6 | 15,000 | Turkish Govt. Authority. |
| | Izmit | Istanbul Petroleum Refin. Co. | 1961 | | 32,000 | I.P.R.A.S.: see App. V, and pp. 328, 438. |

## OWNERSHIP OF SOME COMPOSITE COMPANIES

| Name of Company | Abbreviation | Nationality | Constituent Elements | Remarks |
|---|---|---|---|---|
| Abu Dhabi Petroleum Co. Ltd. | A.D.P.C. | Brit. | As I.P.C., q.v. (Named Petroleum Development, Trucial Coast, until July 1962.) | |
| Abu Dhabi Marine Areas Ltd. | A.D.M.A. | Brit. | B.P. Exploration Co. Ltd. $\frac{2}{3}$; Compagnie Française des Pétroles (CFP) $\frac{1}{3}$. | French interests and Caltex until 1962. |
| Alexandria Petroleum Co. | | | All except 3 per cent. belongs to Government (of the U.A.R.), through Egyptian General Petroleum Corp. | |
| American Independent Oil Co. | Aminoil | U.S.A. | Phillips Petroleum 37·34 per cent., Signal Oil and Gas Co. 33·57, Ashland Oil and Refining 14·13; J. S. Abercrombie Mineral Co. 7·07, Globe Oil and Refining 1·77, Sunray DX Oil Co. 2·94, Pauley Petroleum Inc. 1·41, Lario Oil and Gas Co. 1·77. | Through a subsidiary holds a 0·32 per cent. interest in Iran Consortium. |
| Anadolu Tasfiyehanesi A.S. | A.T.A.S. | Turk. | B.P. 17 per cent., Mobil Oil Corpn. 56, Shell 27. | Mersin refinery. |
| Anglo-Egyptian Oilfields | A.E.O. | | Until 1956 majority share equally to A.I.O.C. and Shell, lesser shares to Egyptian Government and public. Nationalized July 1961 and subsequently. | |
| Arabian Oil Co. | | Japan | 80 per cent. to a consortium of Japanese companies, 10 per cent. each to Governments of Kuwait and Sa'udi Arabia. | |
| Arabian-American Oil Co. | Aramco | U.S.A. | 30 per cent. each to Standard of California, Standard (New Jersey), Texaco Inc, 10 per cent. to Mobil Oil Corpn. | |
| Atlantic Richfield Co. | | U.S.A. | Merger of Atlantic Refining Co. and Richfield Oil Corpn. | |
| Bahrain Petroleum Co. | Bapco | U.S.A. | Half each to Standard of California and Texaco, now united (1946) as California Texas Oil Corpn. (Caltex). | |
| Basrah Petroleum Co. | B.P.C. | Brit. | As I.P.C., q.v. | |
| B.O.D. Ltd. | | Brit. | For original composition, see pp. 75 and 120. Now succeeded by Mosul Petroleum Co., q.v. | |
| California Texas Oil Corpn. | Caltex | U.S.A. | See above, Bahrain Petroleum Co. | |

483

APPENDIX V—*continued*

| Name of Company | Abbreviation | Nationality | Constituent Elements | Remarks |
|---|---|---|---|---|
| California Arabian Standard Oil Co. | Casoc | U.S.A. | Half California Standard, half Texas Corpn. | Superseded by Aramco. |
| Compagnie Orientale des Pétroles d'Egypte | C.O.P.E. | Egypt | 1,250,000 shares to International Egyptian, q.v., 750,000 to Egyptian General, 500,000 to Société Coopérative des Pétroles. | |
| Consolidated Petroleum Co. Consolidated Refineries Ltd. | | Brit. | Both 50 per cent. Shell, 50 per cent. A.I.O.C. (B.P.) | Holding company for Shell/B.P. companies in Asia-Africa. |
| Consortium, the Iranian | | Iran | See Iranian Oil Participants Ltd. | |
| Dashtestan Offshore Petroleum Co. | D.O.P.C.O. | Iran | Half N.I.O.C., half Shell. | |
| Dubai Marine Areas | | Brit. | B.P. 33⅓ per cent., C.F.P. 16⅔, Continental Oil 35, Deutsche Erdöl 10, Sun Oil 5 per cent. | |
| Dubai Petroleum Co. | | U.S.A. | Continental Oil 55 per cent., Sun Oil Co. and Deutsche Erdöl each 22½ per cent. | |
| Farsi Petroleum Co. | | Iran | Half N.I.O.C., half Société Française des Pétroles d'Iran, which is itself composed of three French companies. | 'Sofiran' is 45 per cent. E.R.A.P., 35 Auxirap, 20 Aquitaine. |
| International Egyptian Oil Co. | I.E.O.C. | Ital. | Almost wholly owned by E.N.I. Owns half C.O.P.E. | |
| Iranian Offshore Petroleum Co. | I.R.O.P.C.O. | Iran | Half N.I.O.C., half in equal shares to Cities Service, Kerr-McGee, Atlantic Richfield, Skelly, Sunray DX, Superior, and Tidewater. | |
| Iranian Oil Exploration and Producing Co. Iranian Oil Refining Co. | | Dutch | Consortium's operating companies, H.Q. Tehran. See Iranian Oil Participants Ltd. | |
| Iranian Oil Participants Ltd. | | Brit. | Holding Co. for 'the Consortium', i.e. the above two (Dutch) Companies. Shares—105,000 to each of Esso (New Jersey), Gulf, California, Texaco, Mobil; 90,000 to (French) C.F.P., 210,000 to Royal Dutch-Shell, 600,000 to B.P., 75,000 to participants in Iricon Agency (q.v.). | Total 3,000,000 shares of 6s. 8d. each. |

APPENDIX V—*continued*

| Name of Company | Abbreviation | Nation-ality | Constituent Elements | Remarks |
|---|---|---|---|---|
| Iran Marine International Oil Co. | I.M.I.N.O.C.O. | Iran | Half N.I.O.C., half between A.G.I.P., Phillips Petroleum, and Hydro-Carbon (India) Ltd. | |
| Iran Pan American Oil Co. | I.P.A.C. | Iran | Half N.I.O.C., half Pan American International Petroleum Corpn. (Standard of Indiana). | |
| 'Iraq Petroleum Co. Ltd. | I.P.C. | Brit. | $23\frac{3}{4}$ per cent. each to Shell, B.P., C.F.P., N.E.D.C., 5 per cent to Participations and Explorations Corpn. (Gulbenkian) | So, throughout I.P.C. Group. |
| Iricon Agency Ltd. | | | Holds 5 per cent. in Iranian Oil Participants (Consortium), divided as to 2/12 each to American Independent (Aminoil), Signal Oil and Gas; 1/12 each to Getty, Continental, Standard of Ohio, Tidewater; 4/12 to Atlantic Richfield. | Note changes since 1954 (p. 279, footnote). |
| Istanbul Petrol Rafinerisi A.S. | I.P.R.A.S. | Turk. | 51 per cent. Turkish Petroleum Corpn. shareholding, 49 per cent. Caltex. | Refinery at Istanbul. |
| Kuwait Oil Co. | K.O.C. | Brit. | Half B.P., half Gulf Kuwait Co. | |
| Lavan Petroleum Co. | L.A.P.C.O. | Iran | Half N.I.O.C., half between Atlantic Exploration, Murphy, Sun, and Union (each $12\frac{1}{2}$ per cent). | |
| Mediterranean Refining Co. | Medreco | U.S.A. | Half each to Caltex and Mobil | Refinery near Sidon. |
| Near East Development Corpn. | N.E.D.C. | U.S.A. | Co. holding the American $23\frac{3}{4}$ per cent. share in 'Iraq Petroleum Co. Group. Half each to Mobil and New Jersey (thus, each $11\frac{7}{8}$ in I.P.C. etc.). | |
| Persian Gulf Petroleum Co. | P.E.G.U.P.C.O. | Iran | Half N.I.O.C., half between Wintershall, Deutsche Schachtbau, Gelsenkirchener, Elwerath, Scholven Chemie, Deutsche Erdöl, Preussag. | |
| Petroleum Development (—) Ltd. | P.D.(—) | Brit. | Companies (from 1936) of I.P.C. Group (q.v.). | |
| Petroleum Development (Oman) Ltd. | P.D. (O.) | Brit. | Shell 85 per cent., Gulbenkian (through Partex) 15 per cent. | I.P.C. Group until 1961. |
| Qatar Petroleum Co. | Q.P.C. | Brit. | I.P.C. Group, q.v. | |
| Ras al-Khaima Oil Co. | | U.S.A. | 80 per cent. Union Oil, 20 per cent. Southern Natural Gas. | |

485

APPENDIX V—*continued*

| Name of Company | Abbreviation | Nation-ality | Constituent Elements | Remarks |
|---|---|---|---|---|
| Shell Group | Shell | Brit. | Everywhere and always, since 1907, all Royal Dutch-Shell Companies are 60 per cent. Dutch, 40 per cent. British. British holding company is 'Shell' Transport and Trading Co. Main holding/operating companies in the Group are Bataafse Petroleum Maatschappij N.V., and Shell Petroleum Co. Ltd. | |
| Société Iran-Italienne des Pétroles | S.I.R.I.P. | Iran | Half N.I.O.C., half A.G.I.P. Mineraria S.p.A. (an E.N.I. subsidiary). | |
| Syria Petroleum Co. Ltd. | S.P.C. | Brit. | I.P.C. Group, q.v. | |
| Trans-Arabian Pipeline Co. | Tapline | U.S.A. | As for Arabian-American Oil Co. (Aramco), q.v. | Not in operation since 1952. |

# APPENDIX VI

## CONVERSION TABLE (tons, barrels)
## AND QUALITY OF
## SOME MIDDLE EASTERN CRUDES

for

(1) *Specific Gravity to A.P.I. Gravity*

(2) *Long Tons to Barrels*

(3) *Barrels to Long Tons*

(4) *Barrels per day (b/d) to Tons per year (t/y)*

| Specific Gravity (60°F.) | A.P.I. Gravity | Multiplication factor | | |
|---|---|---|---|---|
| | | Long Tons to Barrels | Barrels to Long Tons | b/d to t/y |
| 0·820 | 41·06 | 7·812 | 0·1280 | 46·72 |
| 0·825 | 40·02 | 7·764 | 0·1288 | 47·01 |
| 0·830 | 38·90 | 7·717 | 0·1296 | 47·30 |
| 0·835 | 37·96 | 7·671 | 0·1304 | 47·58 |
| 0·840 | 36·95 | 7·635 | 0·1311 | 47·87 |
| 0·845 | 35·96 | 7·580 | 0·1319 | 48·15 |
| 0·850 | 34·57 | 7·536 | 0·1327 | 48·44 |
| 0·855 | 34·00 | 7·491 | 0·1335 | 48·72 |
| 0·860 | 33·03 | 7·448 | 0·1343 | 49·01 |
| 0·865 | 32·08 | 7·405 | 0·1351 | 49·29 |
| 0·870 | 31·14 | 7·362 | 0·1358 | 49·58 |
| 0·875 | 30·21 | 7·320 | 0·1366 | 49·86 |
| 0·880 | 29·30 | 7·278 | 0·1374 | 50·15 |
| 0·885 | 28·39 | 7·237 | 0·1382 | 50·44 |
| 0·890 | 27·49 | 7·196 | 0·1390 | 50·72 |
| 0·895 | 26·60 | 7·156 | 0·1397 | 51·01 |
| 0·900 | 25·72 | 7·116 | 0·1405 | 51·29 |
| 0·905 | 24·85 | 7·077 | 0·1413 | 51·57 |
| 0·910 | 23·99 | 7·038 | 0·1421 | 51·86 |
| 0·915 | 23·14 | 7·000 | 0·1429 | 52·15 |
| 0·920 | 22·30 | 6·961 | 0·1437 | 52·43 |
| 0·925 | 21·47 | 6·924 | 0·1444 | 52·72 |
| 0·930 | 20·65 | 6·887 | 0·1452 | 53·00 |
| 0·935 | 19·84 | 6·850 | 0·1460 | 53·29 |
| 0·940 | 19·03 | 6·813 | 0·1468 | 53·57 |
| 0·945 | 18·24 | 6·777 | 0·1476 | 53·86 |
| 0·950 | 17·45 | 6·741 | 0·1483 | 54·14 |
| 0·955 | 16·67 | 6·746 | 0·1491 | 54·43 |
| 0·960 | 15·90 | 6·671 | 0·1499 | 54·71 |

A.P.I. rating of some Middle Eastern crudes:
'IRAQ: Kirkuk 36–36·9, Rumaila 35–35·9. QATAR: Dukhan 41–41·9, Shell 36–37. ABU DHABI: Murban 39–41, Umm Shaif 37·5. SA'UDI ARABIA: Safaniya 27–27·9, Khursaniya 31–31·9, Ghawar 34–34·9. IRAN: Darius 29, Kharg 29, Gach Saran 31–31·9, Agha Jari 34–34·9, Bahrgansar 34–34·9. KUWAIT: Burgan 31–31·9. NEUTRAL ZONE: Wafra 16·5–17·4 (Eocene), 23·5–24·4 (Ratawi and Burgan). BAHRAIN 33·4.

# MAPS

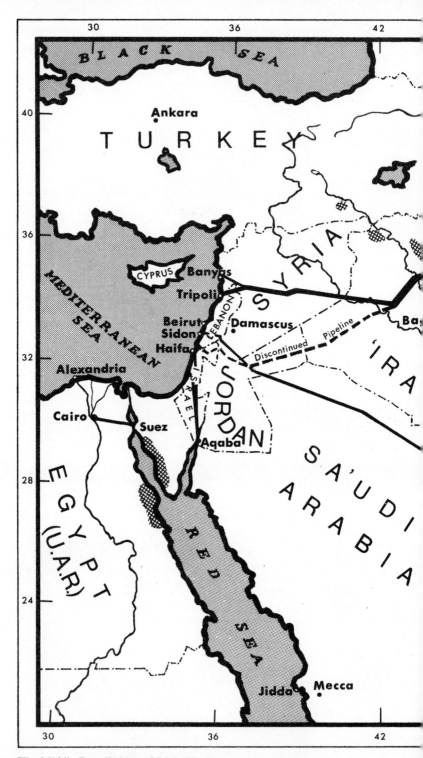

The Middle East, Fields and Main Pipelines

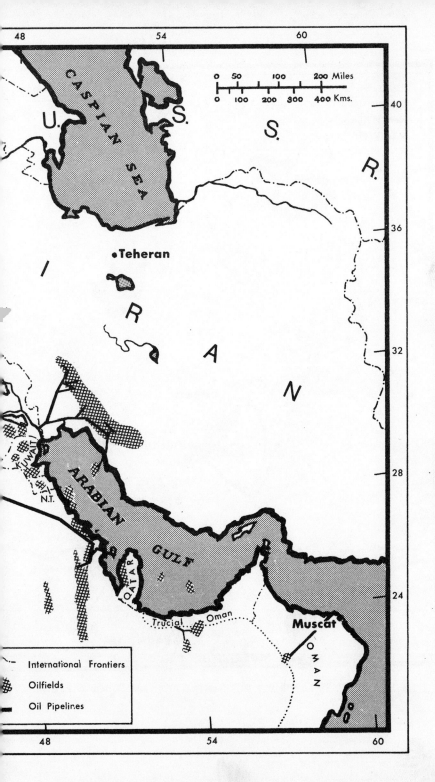

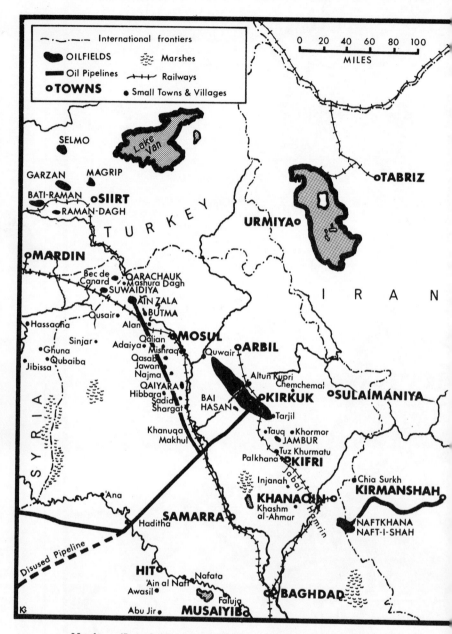

Northern 'Iraq (with part of Southern Turkey and Eastern Syria)

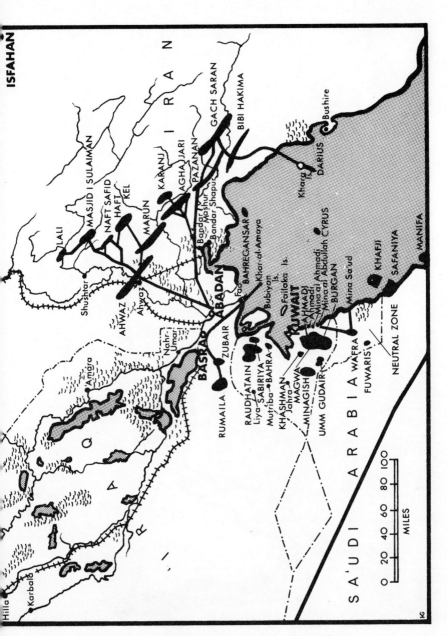

Southern 'Iraq, part of Iran, Kuwait and the Neutral Zone

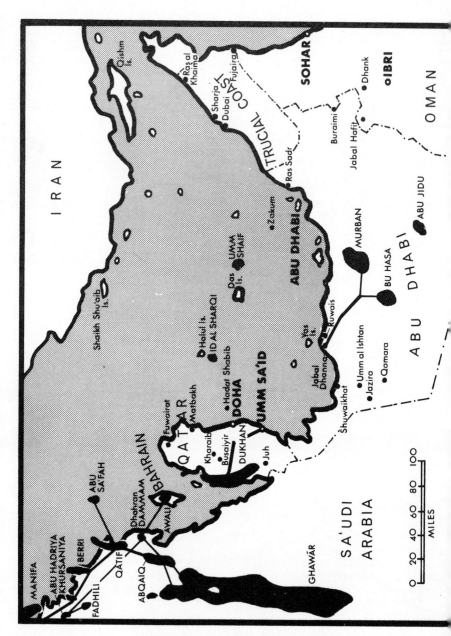

Arabian (Persian) Gulf, Southern Shore

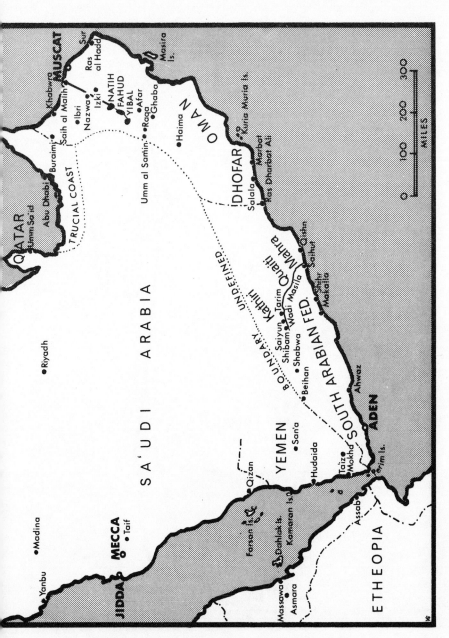

Southern Arabia—Oman, Aden Federation and Yemen

495

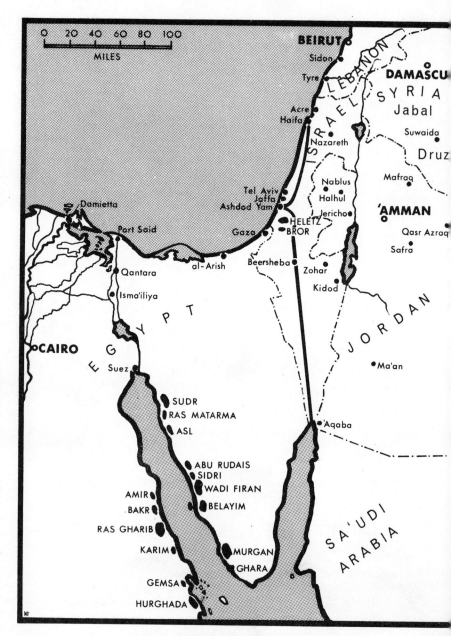

U.A.R. (Egypt) and Israel

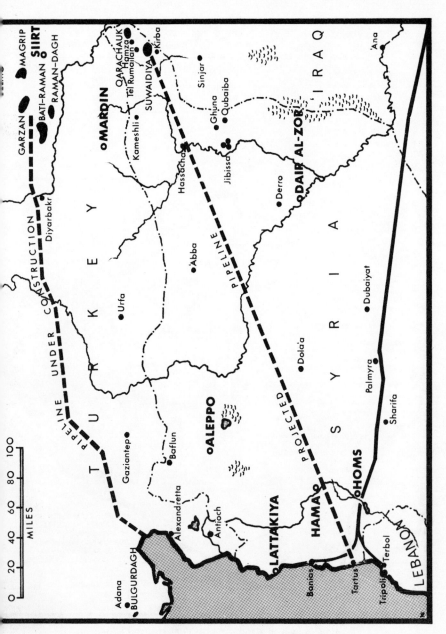

Syria–Lebanon, and part of Southern Turkey

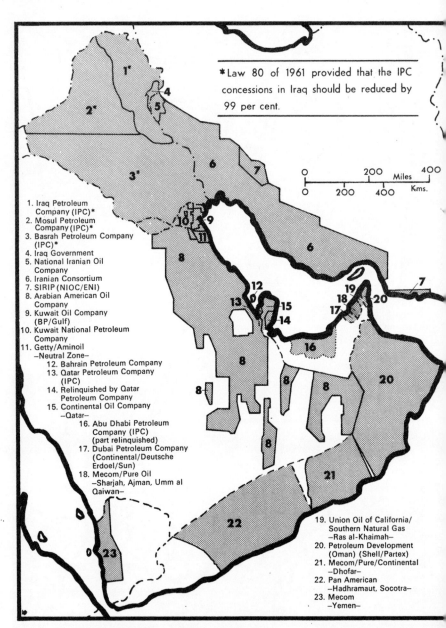

* Law 80 of 1961 provided that the IPC concessions in Iraq should be reduced by 99 per cent.

1. Iraq Petroleum Company (IPC)*
2. Mosul Petroleum Company (IPC)*
3. Basrah Petroleum Company (IPC)*
4. Iraq Government
5. National Iranian Oil Company
6. Iranian Consortium
7. SIRIP (NIOC/ENI)
8. Arabian American Oil Company
9. Kuwait Oil Company (BP/Gulf)
10. Kuwait National Petroleum Company
11. Getty/Aminoil
   –Neutral Zone–
12. Bahrain Petroleum Company
13. Qatar Petroleum Company (IPC)
14. Relinquished by Qatar Petroleum Company
15. Continental Oil Company –Qatar–
16. Abu Dhabi Petroleum Company (IPC) (part relinquished)
17. Dubai Petroleum Company (Continental/Deutsche Erdoel/Sun)
18. Mecom/Pure Oil –Sharjah, Ajman, Umm al Qaiwan–

19. Union Oil of California/ Southern Natural Gas –Ras al-Khaimah–
20. Petroleum Development (Oman) (Shell/Partex)
21. Mecom/Pure/Continental –Dhofar–
22. Pan American –Hadhramaut, Socotra–
23. Mecom –Yemen–

Concessions on Land, Arabian Gulf area and hinterland

498

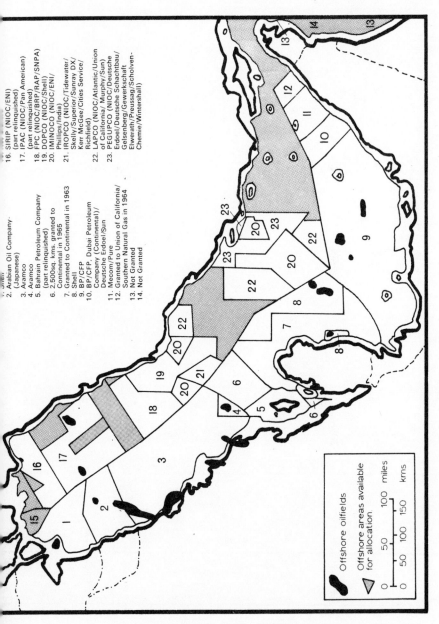

1. Shell
2. Arabian Oil Company.
   (Japanese)
3. Aramco
4. Aramco
5. Bahrain Petroleum Company
   (part relinquished)
6. 2,500sq. kms. granted to
   Continental in 1965
7. Granted to Continental in 1963
8. Shell
9. BP/CFP
10. BP/CFP, Dubai Petroleum
    Company (Continental)/
    Deutsche Erdoel/Sun
11. Mecom/Pure
12. Granted to Union of California/
    Southern Natural Gas in 1964
13. Not Granted
14. Not Granted

16. SIRIP (NIOC/ENI)
    (part relinquished)
17. IPAC (NIOC/Pan American)
    (part relinquished)
18. FPC (NIOC/BRP/RAP/SNPA)
19. DOPCO (NIOC/Shell)
20. IMINOCO (NIOC/ENI/
    Phillips/India)
21. IROPCO (NIOC/Tidewater/
    Skelly/Superior/Sunray DX/
    Kerr McGee/Cities Service/
    Richfield)
22. LAPCO (NIOC/Atlantic/Union
    of California/ Murphy/Sun)
23. PEGUPCO (NIOC/Deutsche
    Erdoel/Deutsche Schachtbau/
    Gelsenberg/Gewerkschaft
    Elwerath/Preussag/Scholven-
    Chemie/Wintershall)

Offshore oilfields

Offshore areas available
for allocation.

0    50    100 miles
0  50  100  150 kms

Concessions (Marine), Arabian Gulf area

499

# INDEX

(For main branches of the subject and principal projects, see Contents, p. v. References to the Appendixes are not here given, since the latter are largely self-indexed.)